Discovering Geometry
An Investigative Approach

Solutions Manual

DISCOVERING

MATHEMATICS™

Key Curriculum Press
Innovators in Mathematics Education

Teacher's Materials Project Editor: Elizabeth DeCarli

Editor: Kendra Lockman

Project Administrator: Brady Golden

Writers: Abby Tanenbaum, Stacey Miceli

Accuracy Checker: Dudley Brooks

Production Editor: Holly Rudelitsch

Copyeditor: Jill Pellarin

Editorial Production Manager: Christine Osborne

Production Supervisor: Ann Rothenbuhler

Production Coordinator: Jennifer Young

Text Designers: Jenny Somerville, Garry Harman

Composition, Technical Art, Prepress: ICC Macmillan Inc.

Cover Designer: Jill Kongabel, Marilyn Perry, Jensen Barnes

Printer: Data Reproductions

Textbook Product Manager: James Ryan

Executive Editor: Casey FitzSimons

Publisher: Steven Rasmussen

Key Curriculum Press
1150 65th Street
Emeryville, CA 94608
510-595-7000
editorial@keypress.com
www.keypress.com

Printed in the United States of America
10 9 8 7 6 5 4 3 2   12 11 10 09 08   ISBN 978-1-55953-890-9

Contents

Introduction vii

Chapter 0–Geometric Art

Lesson 0.1: Geometry in Nature and in Art 1

Lesson 0.2: Line Designs 1

Lesson 0.3: Circle Designs 2

Lesson 0.4: Op Art 4

Lesson 0.5: Knot Designs 5

Lesson 0.6: Islamic Tile Designs 6

Chapter 0 Review 6

Chapter 1–Introducing Geometry

Lesson 1.1: Building Blocks of Geometry 7

Using Your Algebra Skills 1: Midpoint 9

Lesson 1.2: Poolroom Math 9

Lesson 1.3: What's a Widget? 12

Lesson 1.4: Polygons 14

Lesson 1.5: Triangles 16

Lesson 1.6: Special Quadrilaterals 18

Lesson 1.7: Circles 20

Lesson 1.8: Space Geometry 22

Lesson 1.9: A Picture Is Worth a Thousand Words 24

Chapter 1 Review 26

Chapter 2–Reasoning in Geometry

Lesson 2.1: Inductive Reasoning 28

Lesson 2.2: Finding the *n*th Term 30

Lesson 2.3: Mathematical Modeling 32

Lesson 2.4: Deductive Reasoning 34

Lesson 2.5: Angle Relationships 35

Lesson 2.6: Special Angles on Parallel Lines 37

Using Your Algebra Skills 2: Slope 40

Chapter 2 Review 40

Chapter 3–Using Tools of Geometry

Lesson 3.1: Duplicating Segments and Angles 42

Lesson 3.2: Constructing Perpendicular Bisectors 44

Lesson 3.3: Constructing Perpendiculars to a Line 46

Lesson 3.4: Constructing Angle Bisectors 48

Lesson 3.5: Constructing Parallel Lines 50

Using Your Algebra Skills 3: Slopes of Parallel
and Perpendicular Lines 52

Lesson 3.6: Construction Problems 53
Exploration: Perspective Drawing 55
Lesson 3.7: Constructing Points of Concurrency 55
Lesson 3.8: The Centroid 59
Exploration: The Euler Line 60
Chapter 3 Review 60

Chapter 4–Discovering and Proving Triangle Properties

Lesson 4.1: Triangle Sum Conjecture 62
Lesson 4.2: Properties of Isosceles Triangles 65
Using Your Algebra Skills 4: Solving Equations 68
Lesson 4.3: Triangle Inequalities 70
Lesson 4.4: Are There Congruence Shortcuts? 72
Lesson 4.5: Are There Other Congruence Shortcuts? 74
Lesson 4.6: Corresponding Parts of Congruent Triangles 76
Lesson 4.7: Flowchart Thinking 77
Lesson 4.8: Proving Special Triangle Conjectures 78
Exploration: Napoleon's Theorem 80
Chapter 4 Review 80
Take Another Look 83

Chapter 5–Discovering and Proving Polygon Properties

Lesson 5.1: Polygon Sum Conjecture 84
Lesson 5.2: Exterior Angles of a Polygon 86
Lesson 5.3: Kite and Trapezoid Properties 88
Lesson 5.4: Properties of Midsegments 90
Lesson 5.5: Properties of Parallelograms 92
Using Your Algebra Skills 5: Writing Linear Equations 95
Lesson 5.6: Properties of Special Parallelograms 97
Lesson 5.7: Proving Quadrilateral Properties 100
Chapter 5 Review 102
Take Another Look 105

Chapter 6–Discovering and Proving Circle Properties

Lesson 6.1: Tangent Properties 106
Lesson 6.2: Chord Properties 108
Lesson 6.3: Arcs and Angles 111
Lesson 6.4: Proving Circle Conjectures 114
Lesson 6.5: The Circumference/Diameter Ratio 117
Lesson 6.6: Around the World 119
Using Your Algebra Skills 6: Solving Systems of Linear Equations . . 120
Lesson 6.7: Arc Length 125
Chapter 6 Review 128
Take Another Look 132

Chapter 7–Transformations and Tesselations

Lesson 7.1: Transformations and Symmetry 133

Lesson 7.2: Properties of Isometries 134

Lesson 7.3: Compositions of Transformations 137

Lesson 7.4: Tessellations with Regular Polygons 140

Lesson 7.5: Tessellations with Nonregular Polygons 141

Lesson 7.6: Tessellations Using Only Translations 142

Lesson 7.7: Tessellations That Use Rotations 143

Lesson 7.8: Tessellations That Use Glide Reflections 144

Using Your Algebra Skills 7: Finding Points of Concurrency 145

Chapter 7 Review 147

Take Another Look 148

Chapter 8–Area

Lesson 8.1: Areas of Rectangles and Parallelograms 150

Lesson 8.2: Areas of Triangles, Trapezoids, and Kites 153

Lesson 8.3: Area Problems 157

Using Your Algebra Skills 8: Products, Factors, and
    Quadratic Equations 158

Lesson 8.4: Areas of Regular Polygons 162

Lesson 8.5: Areas of Circles 165

Lesson 8.6: Any Way You Slice It 166

Exploration: Geometric Probability II 168

Lesson 8.7: Surface Area 168

Exploration: Alternative Area Formulas 170

Chapter 8 Review 170

Take Another Look 174

Chapter 9–The Pythagorean Theorem

Lesson 9.1: The Theorem of Pythagoras 175

Lesson 9.2: The Converse of the Pythagorean Theorem 178

Using Your Algebra Skills 9: Radical Expressions 180

Lesson 9.3: Two Special Right Triangles 181

Lesson 9.4: Story Problems 185

Lesson 9.5: Distance in Coordinate Geometry 188

Lesson 9.6: Circles and the Pythagorean Theorem 192

Chapter 9 Review 196

Take Another Look 202

Chapter 10–Volume

Lesson 10.1: The Geometry of Solids 203

Lesson 10.2: Volume of Prisms and Cylinders 204

Lesson 10.3: Volume of Pyramids and Cones 207

Lesson 10.4: Volume Problems 210

Lesson 10.5: Displacement and Density 213

Lesson 10.6: Volume of a Sphere 216
Lesson 10.7: Surface Area of a Sphere 219
Using Your Algebra Skills 10: Solving for Any Variable 221
Chapter 10 Review 223
Take Another Look 226

Chapter 11–Similarity

Using Your Algebra Skills 11: Proportion and Reasoning 227
Lesson 11.1: Similar Polygons 230
Lesson 11.2: Similar Triangles 232
Lesson 11.3: Indirect Measurement with Similar Triangles 236
Lesson 11.4: Corresponding Parts of Similar Triangles 239
Lesson 11.5: Proportions with Area 242
Lesson 11.6: Proportions with Volume 245
Lesson 11.7: Proportional Segments Between Parallel Lines 248
Exploration: Two More Forms of Valid Reasoning 251
Chapter 11 Review 251
Take Another Look 254

Chapter 12–Trigonometry

Lesson 12.1: Trigonometric Ratios 255
Lesson 12.2: Problem Solving with Right Triangles 256
Exploration: Indirect Measurement 259
Lesson 12.3: The Law of Sines 259
Lesson 12.4: The Law of Cosines 262
Lesson 12.5: Problem Solving with Trigonometry 266
Exploration: Trigonometric Ratios and the Unit Circle 270
Using Your Algebra Skills 12: Transforming Functions 270
Chapter 12 Review 271
Take Another Look 278

Chapter 13–Review

Lesson 13.1: The Premises of Geometry 279
Lesson 13.2: Planning a Geometry Proof 281
Lesson 13.3: Triangle Proofs 285
Lesson 13.4: Quadrilateral Proofs 292
Exploration: Proof as Challenge and Discovery 299
Lesson 13.5: Indirect Proof 299
Lesson 13.6: Circle Proofs 301
Lesson 13.7: Similarity Proofs 306
Using Your Algebra Skills 13: Coordinate Proof 314
Chapter 13 Review 319

Introduction

The *Solutions Manual* for *Discovering Geometry: An Investigative Approach* contains solutions to the exercises at the end of each lesson and to the Extensions, Using Your Algebra Skills, Improving Your Reasoning Skills, Improving Your Visual Thinking Skills, Improving Your Algebra Skills, Projects, and Take Another Look activities. You can find solutions for the Investigations and Explorations in the *Teacher's Edition*.

The solutions in this *Solutions Manual* are more complete than those offered as annotations in the *Teacher's Edition*. Although complete solutions for the problems are provided here, keep in mind that often there is more than one method students might use to solve a particular problem. Also, the answers will vary for some problems, depending on assumptions that students make. For problems that could have many different answers, a sample solution is given.

In order to save space, the size of constructions has been reduced in the *Solutions Manual*. Keep this in mind as you check student constructions.

Refer to these solutions when your students have difficulty solving a problem and need some assistance in determining a possible approach toward solving it. You might also want to provide a copy of certain solutions for students who have been absent for an extended period of time.

CHAPTER 0

LESSON 0.1

EXERCISES

1. Possible answers: snowflakes and crystals; flowers and starfish

2. Possible answers: to create shapes and patterns, to show perspective and proportions, to create optical illusions

3. Possible answers: a butterfly, a valentine heart, a person; bilateral symmetry

4. A, B, C, and F

5. A, B, D, and E

6. 4 of diamonds; none

7. The line of symmetry is a line along the surface of the lake.

8. There is a vertical line of symmetry through the middle of the Taj Mahal, and a horizontal line of symmetry between the Taj Mahal and the reflecting pool. The pool reflects the building, giving the scene more reflectional symmetry than the building itself has.

9. Designs will vary, but all should have 2-fold rotational symmetry. It is impossible to have two intersecting lines of reflectional symmetry without rotational symmetry.

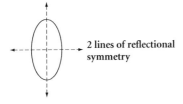

2 lines of reflectional symmetry

10. Answers will vary.

11. Answers will vary.

IMPROVING YOUR VISUAL THINKING SKILLS

Stick *j* is on top, so visually remove it. Then determine which stick is next. It appears to be stick *f*. Visually remove that stick and figure out which stick is next. Continue this process until all the sticks have been "removed." The order of removal is *j, f, g, b, i, k, h, c, e, a, d.*

EXTENSIONS

A. Possible answer: If you set an apple, a pear, or an orange on its "bottom" on a table, then cross sections parallel to the table are circular (and therefore have both reflectional and rotational

symmetry). Cross sections perpendicular to the table are fairly round for an orange, but not for an apple or a pear. For all three fruits, these perpendicular cross sections have approximate reflectional symmetry, but only the orange has rotational symmetry. You can slice a banana to get a round cross section that has both reflectional and rotational symmetry. You can also slice it to create a long, skinny cross section that may or may not have reflectional symmetry, depending on the shape of the banana.

B. Possible answer: Bilateral symmetry gives humans balance, which allows them to make smooth, even movements. Symmetry also makes it easier to lift and catch objects.

LESSON 0.2

EXERCISES

1. Compass and straightedge

2. Answer will be the Astrid or 8-Pointed Star, possibly with variations.

3. Answer will be a design from among the three choices.

Steps for creating the first design:

Draw a 12-by-12 frame. Then draw half an Astrid (see the instructions on page 8 of the student book) on the left side of the frame. Draw three more half-Astrids, on the top, right, and bottom of the frame.

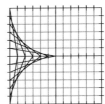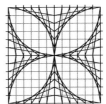

Steps for creating the second design:

Draw a triangle. Mark and connect the midpoints of the sides. Then mark and connect the midpoints of the sides of the three outer triangles. Then mark and connect the midpoints of the sides of the three *smaller* outer triangles of each of the three *large* outer triangles. Finally, color the smallest "point-up" triangles to create the final design.

Steps for creating the third design:

Draw a regular hexagon. Move clockwise around the hexagon. On each side, mark the point one-third of the way from the first endpoint to the second endpoint. Connect the points in the order you mark them. Then follow the procedure described in the previous step with the new, inside hexagon. Repeat the process several more times, each time marking points on the innermost hexagon, until the design looks like the one in the student book. Then color the design.

4. The first design has 4-fold rotational symmetry and four lines of reflectional symmetry (the horizontal line through the center, the vertical line through the center, and the two diagonals of the square).

The second design has 3-fold rotational symmetry and three lines of reflectional symmetry (from each vertex of the large triangle to the midpoint of the opposite side).

The third design has 6-fold rotational symmetry if you ignore color and 2-fold rotational symmetry if you don't.

5. Answers will vary. The given design may be placed in any corner. Once that design is in place, the rest of the pattern is determined by the symmetry. Here are two possible answers:

2 lines of reflectional symmetry

6. Possible answer:

7.

3 lines of reflectional symmetry

3-fold rotational symmetry: rotated 120°, 240°, 360°

$a = 20$, $b = 36$, $c = 24$, $d = 17$. The easiest way to find the solution is to write and solve systems of equations. For example, using the information in the pyramid, you can write these equations:

$a + b = 56$

$a + d = 37$

Subtracting the second equation from the first gives $b - d = 19$.

From the pyramid, you also know that $b + d = 53$. So, to find the value of b, you can add these equations:

$b - d = 19$

$b + d = 53$

The sum of the equations is $2b = 72$, or $b = 36$. Once you know the value of b, you can easily find the other values: $b + c = 60$, so $c = 24$; $b + d = 53$, so $d = 17$; $b + a = 56$, so $a = 20$.

EXTENSIONS

A. Answers will vary.

B. Sample designs:

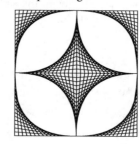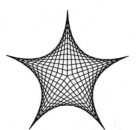

LESSON 0.3

EXERCISES

1. Create the grid of circles by using the technique described on page 10 of the student book. The grid should look like the one shown below. The way the grid is colored will vary, but the final design should have reflectional symmetry.

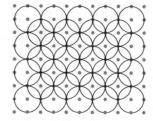

2. Using compass and straightedge: Draw an equilateral equiangular hexagon with side length 2. Each vertex will be the center of a circle with radius 1. Fit the seventh small circle inside the other six.

The large circle has the same center as the seventh circle and has radius 3.

Using isometric dot paper: Start by drawing a circle centered at one of the dots and passing through the surrounding six dots. Then draw a circle of the same radius centered at each of the six dots surrounding the original circle. Draw the large surrounding circle and color the result. The result should look like the design below. The way the design is colored will vary, but it should have rotational symmetry.

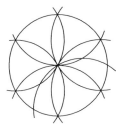

3. Create the daisy by using the technique described on page 11 of the student book. The way the daisy is colored will vary. The final design should have rotational symmetry, but *not* reflectional symmetry. Possible answer:

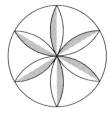

4. To create the 12-petal daisy, first draw a 6-petal daisy using the technique described on page 11 of the student book. Then, without changing the compass setting, make an arc centered on the outer circle, halfway between two of the petals.

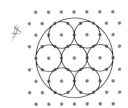

Next, make arcs centered at the two points where this arc intersects the circle. Continue this process until the daisy is complete. The shape of the final daisy should look like the one below. The way the daisy is colored may vary; the result should have reflectional symmetry, but *not* rotational symmetry. Possible answer:

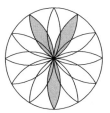

5. To create the central hexagon, use a technique similar to the one described on page 11 of the student book, but draw entire circles instead of arcs.

Then, without changing the compass setting, draw circles centered at the intersection points of the outer circles. (Each of these new circles should intersect the endpoints of one of the hexagon's sides.)

Use the technique described on page 11 to create a hexagon inside each of these new circles.

IMPROVING YOUR ALGEBRA SKILLS

The diagonal from the lower left corner to the upper right corner is complete, so add the numbers. The sum is 90, so the numbers in each row, column, and diagonal must add to 90.

The four numbers in the other diagonal have sum 73, so the fifth number must be $90 - 73$, or 17.

20			8	14
	19	25	26	
	12	18		30
29	10	11	17	
22			15	16

Once that number is filled in, you can find the last number in the fourth row (23) and the third number in the fourth column (24). Continue looking for rows or columns with a single blank and filling in that blank. When you have done all you can, the magic square should look like this.

20			8	14
13	19	25	26	7
6	12	18	24	30
29	10	11	17	23
22			15	16

The three numbers in the first row have sum 42, so the numbers in the two blank squares must have sum $90 - 42$, or 48. The only two numbers on the list with sum 48 are 21 and 27. Try putting 21 in the first blank square and 27 in the second.

20	21	27	8	14
13	19	25	26	7
6	12	18	24	30
29	10	11	17	23
22			15	16

The four numbers in the second column have sum 62. So, the fifth number must be $90 - 62$, or 28. The four numbers in the third column have sum 81. So, the fifth number must be 9. As a check, add the numbers in the fifth row. The sum is 90, which is what it should be.

20	21	27	8	14
13	19	25	26	7
6	12	18	24	30
29	10	11	17	23
22	28	9	15	16

LESSON 0.4

EXERCISES

1. Possible answer: The designs appear to go in and out of the page (appear to be three-dimensional). The squares appear to spiral (although there are no curves in the drawing). The spiral appears to go down as if into a hole. Lines where curves meet look wavy. Bigger squares appear to bulge out.

2. Possible answer: When zebras group together, their stripes make it hard for predators to see individual zebras. (*Note:* Lions, which are the main predators of zebras, are color-blind, so color differences wouldn't matter.)

3. Designs will vary.

4. Designs will vary, but should have reflectional symmetry and not rotational symmetry.

5. Possible answers: Two-dimensional: rectangle, triangle, trapezoid; three-dimensional: cylinder, cone, prism. The palace facade has one line of reflectional symmetry (bilateral symmetry).

IMPROVING YOUR REASONING SKILLS

Here is one way to reason through Game 1: Clue 1 indicates that the digits 1, 2, and 3 are *not* digits of the number. Clue 2 indicates that the number includes *one* of the three digits 4, 5, and 6. Clue 3 indicates that it includes *one* of the three digits 7, 8, and 9. The third digit must be 0 because it is the only digit left. In Clue 4, there are two correct digits. You know one of the correct digits must be 0, so the other must be either 7 or 5. Clue 5 contains only one correct digit, which must be 0. Therefore, the number cannot contain 7 or 8. Combining Clues 5 and 4, you can conclude that the number contains 5, and combining Clues 3 and 5, you can conclude that the number contains 9. So, the three digits are 0, 5, and 9. Clue 5 indicates that 0 cannot be the first digit. Combining this information with Clue 4, you can conclude that 5 is the last digit. Therefore, 0 must be the second digit, so the number is 905.

Here is one way to reason through Game 2: Clue 1 indicates that 9, 0, and 8 are *not* digits of the number. Clue 3 indicates that two of the digits 3, 8, and 7 are digits of the number. Because 8 was eliminated in Clue 1, 3 and 7 must be digits of the number. Therefore, in Clue 2, the one correct digit must be 3, so 1 and 4 are eliminated as possible digits. In Clue 3, either 3 or 7 must be in the correct position. Using Clue 5, we can conclude that 3 is in the correct position. Because 7 cannot be in the third or first position (3 is in the first position), it must be in the second position. Thus, the number is of the form 37_. In Clue 4, the digit in the correct position must be 6, so the number is 376.

LESSON 0.5

EXERCISES

1. Possible answers: Scotland, Nigeria

2. Possible answer:

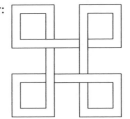

3. Possible answer:

4. Possible answer: (You would cut open the middle ring.)

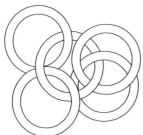

5.

6. Answer will be a *lusona* from among the three choices.

7. It means to solve a problem boldly and decisively or in a creative way not considered by others.

8. The square knot has reflectional symmetry across a horizontal line. The less secure granny knot has 2-fold rotational symmetry.

9. The result is a regular pentagon.

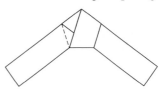

PROJECT

Project should satisfy the following criteria:

- Descriptions of the events depicted are tied to the etching.

- Geometric shapes mentioned include triangles and rectangles.

- Student story is clearly tied to his or her art.

Extra credit

- Paragraph about etching includes how the shapes are related and mentions that rectangles and triangles are not exact because of perspective and because they are bent or broken.

EXTENSIONS

A. Encourage students to experiment with shapes that can be deformed into a circle. Remind them that any one ring must be completely above or completely below any other ring. This is a difficult problem, but students can find plenty of material on the Internet. The Borromean Rings are an example of *Brunnian links,* which are configurations of any number of rings that are linked but cease to be linked if any one of them is removed. Solutions for four and five rings are shown.

4 rings

5 rings

B. Research results will vary.

LESSON 0.6

EXERCISES

1. Possible answers: Morocco, Iran, Spain, Malaysia

2. The Alhambra

3. The shortest translation is a vertical or horizontal slide of 2.1 cm.

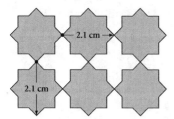

4. The tiles will match up 4 times around some points, and 2 times around others. In terms of the original square tile: 4-fold symmetry in the center (center of orange) or corner (center of white); 2-fold symmetry in the midpoint of the edge of the tile (where two orange shapes meet)

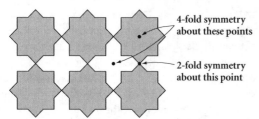

4-fold symmetry about these points

2-fold symmetry about this point

5. To create the Petronas Towers design, first construct the 8-Pointed Star using the instructions on page 21 of the student book, but don't erase the interior lines of the squares. Then make arcs centered at the dents in the star and just touching the large circle.

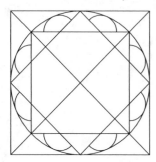

6. Designs will vary.

7. Designs will vary, but should contain a regular hexagon.

8. Tessellations will vary.

PROJECT

Project should satisfy the following criteria:

- Includes photographs with captions or a videotape with commentary.

- The captions or the commentary mentions geometry terms from this chapter.

- The use of terms is accurate.

Extra credit

- Students find a wide variety of designs and give thoughtful descriptions.

EXTENSION

Research results will vary.

CHAPTER 0 REVIEW

EXERCISES

1. Possible answers: Islamic, Hindu, Celtic, Japanese, American

2. Depending on how you look at them, the large hexagons can appear as blocks with a corner removed or as corners with small cubes nestled in them.

3. Compass: A geometry tool used to construct circles.

Straightedge: A geometry tool used to construct straight lines.

4. To create the 12-petal daisy, first draw a 6-petal daisy using the technique described on page 11 of the student book. Then, without changing the compass setting, make an arc centered on the outer circle, halfway between two of the petals. Next, make arcs centered at the two points where this arc intersects the circle. Continue this process until the daisy is complete. The shape of the final daisy should look like the one below.

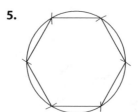

5.

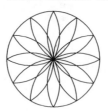

6. Possible answers: hexagon: honeycomb, snowflake; pentagon: starfish, flower

7. Answers will vary but should be some form of an interweaving design.

8. Wheel A has four lines of reflectional symmetry, and Wheel C has five lines of reflectional symmetry. Wheels B and D do not have reflectional symmetry.

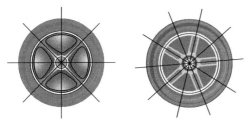

9. Wheels B and D have only rotational symmetry. Wheel B has 4-fold rotational symmetry, and Wheel D has 3-fold rotational symmetry. Wheels A and C have both reflectional and rotational symmetry (A: 4-fold; C: 5-fold).

10. Designs will vary but should contain concentric circles and symmetry in some of the rings.

11. Designs will vary but should contain concentric circles and symmetry in some of the rings.

12. Designs will vary but should use techniques from Islamic art, be a knot design, and have optical effects.

13. a. The flag of Puerto Rico is not symmetric because of the star and the colors.

Puerto Rico

b. The flag of Kenya does not have rotational symmetry because of the colors and the spearheads.

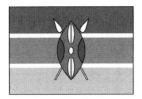

Kenya

c. Possible answers:

Japan

Nigeria

CHAPTER 1

LESSON 1.1

EXERCISES

1. Possible answers: point: balls, where lines cross; segment: lines of the parachute, court markings; collinear: points along a line of the court structure; coplanar: each boy's hand, navel, and kneecap, points along two strings

2. $\overrightarrow{PT}$, $\overrightarrow{TP}$

3. The name can have any two of the point names—A, R, or T—in either order. So, the correct answer can be any two of the following: $\overleftrightarrow{AR}$, $\overleftrightarrow{RA}$, $\overleftrightarrow{AT}$, $\overleftrightarrow{TA}$, $\overleftrightarrow{RT}$, $\overleftrightarrow{TR}$.

4. Any two of the following: $\overrightarrow{MA}$, $\overrightarrow{MS}$, $\overrightarrow{AS}$, $\overrightarrow{AM}$, $\overrightarrow{SA}$, $\overrightarrow{SM}$

5.
  A   B

6.
  K   L

7.

8. $\overline{AC}$ or $\overline{CA}$

9. $\overline{PQ}$ or $\overline{QP}$

10. $\overline{TR}$ or $\overline{RT}$, $\overline{RI}$ or $\overline{IR}$, and $\overline{TI}$ or $\overline{IT}$

11. •——————•
  A   B

12.

13. $m\overline{AB} = 14.3$ cm   **14.** $m\overline{CD} = 6.7$ cm

15–17. Check the length of each segment to see if it is correct. Refer to each exercise for the correct measurements.

18. R is the midpoint of $\overline{PQ}$. X is the midpoint of $\overline{WY}$. Y is the midpoint of $\overline{XZ}$. No midpoints are shown in △ABC. (*Note:* Even though $\overline{AD}$ and $\overline{DC}$ appear to be the same length, you cannot assume they are congruent without the markings.)

19. Possible answers:

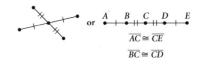

$\overline{AC} \cong \overline{CE}$
$\overline{BC} \cong \overline{CD}$

20. First, draw a segment $\overline{ST}$ with midpoint M. Add congruence marks.

Next, add point P so that $SP = PT$. Draw $\overline{SP}$ and $\overline{PT}$ and add congruence marks.

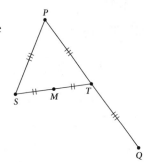

Finally, extend $\overline{PT}$ to twice its length. Mark the endpoint Q. Because $PT = TQ$, mark $\overline{TQ}$ with the same congruence mark used for $\overline{PT}$.

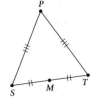

21. The first point listed must be the endpoint, A; the other point can be either B or C. So, the two names are $\overrightarrow{AB}$ and $\overrightarrow{AC}$.

22. $\overrightarrow{PM}$, $\overrightarrow{PN}$

23. $\overrightarrow{XY}$, $\overrightarrow{XZ}$

24. The first point listed must be the endpoint of the ray.

25.

26.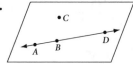

27.

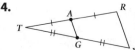

28. 10. First, list all the segments with endpoint A: $\overline{AB}$, $\overline{AC}$, $\overline{AD}$, $\overline{AE}$. Next, list the segments with endpoint B, but don't include $\overline{AB}$ because you already listed it: $\overline{BC}$, $\overline{BD}$, $\overline{BE}$. Next, list all the segments with endpoint C, but don't include $\overline{AC}$ or $\overline{BC}$ because you already listed them: $\overline{CD}$, $\overline{CE}$. The only segment with endpoint D that hasn't been listed yet is $\overline{DE}$. All the segments with endpoint E have been listed. In all, there are 10 possible segments: $\overline{AB}$, $\overline{AC}$, $\overline{AD}$, $\overline{AE}$, $\overline{BC}$, $\overline{BD}$, $\overline{BE}$, $\overline{CD}$, $\overline{CE}$, $\overline{DE}$.

29–31.

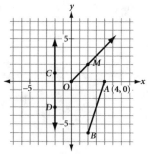

32. Yes. Change the signs of the coordinates to get $P'(6, 2)$, $Q'(5, -2)$, $R'(4, -6)$.

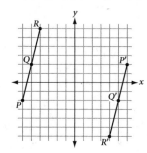

Because the slope $\left(\frac{\text{rise}}{\text{run}}\right)$ between any two points is $\frac{4}{1}$, the points are collinear.

33. Plot point N. It will be easiest to determine the lengths if you draw a horizontal or vertical segment. To locate P and Q, mark points the same number of units above and below (or to the left and the right of) point N.

Possible answer:

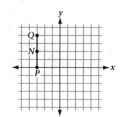

34.

35. Possible answer: use the ruler to draw $\overline{AB}$ of length 8 cm. Then, use the ruler to draw any segment $\overline{BC}$ of length 11 cm for which A, B, and C are not collinear. Connect points A and C to form $\overline{AC}$, which becomes the third side of $\triangle ABC$.

For the second triangle, use the same procedure to draw $\triangle DEF$, but change the size of the opening between the two sides with lengths 8 cm and 11 cm.

Discovering Geometry Solutions Manual
©2008 Key Curriculum Press

Project should satisfy the following criteria:

- Student uses concentric circles whose radii increase by a constant amount and segments that divide the circles into equal sectors.

- The decoration of the design emphasizes the spirals.

Extra credit

- Student creates clockwise and counterclockwise spirals in one design.

USING YOUR ALGEBRA SKILLS 1

EXERCISES

1. $x = \frac{x_1 + x_2}{2} = \frac{12 + (-6)}{2} = 3$ and $y = \frac{y_1 + y_2}{2}$
$= \frac{-7 + 15}{2} = 4$, so the midpoint is $(3, 4)$.

2. $x = \frac{x_1 + x_2}{2} = \frac{-17 + (-1)}{2} = -9$ and $y = \frac{y_1 + y_2}{2}$
$= \frac{-8 + 11}{2} = 1.5$, so the midpoint is $(-9, 1.5)$.

3. $x = \frac{x_1 + x_2}{2} = \frac{14 + (-3)}{2} = 5.5$ and $y = \frac{y_1 + y_2}{2}$
$= \frac{(-7) + 18}{2} = 5.5$, so the midpoint is $(5.5, 5.5)$.

4. Let (x, y) represent the other endpoint; then
$3 = \frac{12 + x}{2}$ and $18 = \frac{-8 + y}{2}$. Here are the
step-by-step solutions to these equations:

$$3 = \frac{12 + x}{2}$$

$6 = 12 + x$ Multiply both sides by 2.

$-6 = x$ Subtract 12 from both sides.

$$18 = \frac{-8 + y}{2}$$

$36 = -8 + y$ Multiply both sides by 2.

$44 = y$ Add 8 to both sides.

The endpoint is $(-6, 44)$.

5. Yes. The coordinates of the midpoint of a segment with endpoints (a, b) and (c, d) are found by taking the average of the x-coordinates, $\frac{a + c}{2}$, and the average of the y-coordinates, $\frac{b + d}{2}$. Thus, the midpoint is $\left(\frac{a + c}{2}, \frac{b + d}{2}\right)$.

6. $(3, 2)$ and $(6, 4)$. To get the first point of trisection, add the coordinates of points A and B to get $(9, 6)$, then multiply those coordinates by $\frac{1}{3}$ to get $(3, 2)$. To get the second point of trisection, add the coordinates of points A and B to get $(9, 6)$, then multiply those coordinates by $\frac{2}{3}$ to get $(6, 4)$. This only works because the coordinates of one of the points are $(0, 0)$.

7. Possible method: Find the midpoint of the segment, and then find the midpoint of each half of the segment.

8. a. For Figure 1, both midpoints are $(5.5, 6.5)$. For Figure 2, both midpoints are $(16, 6.75)$. For Figure 3, both midpoints are $(29.75, 5.5)$.

   b. For these figures, the midpoints of the two diagonals are the same point. This means the diagonals intersect each other at their midpoints.

LESSON 1.2

EXERCISES

1. When three letters are used to name an angle, the middle letter must be the vertex. Also, a single letter can name an angle only if there is no confusion about which angle it is referring to. For example, there is only one angle with vertex E, so it can be named $\angle E$. However, there are two angles with vertex O, so the name $\angle O$ is ambiguous. $\angle TEN$, $\angle NET$, $\angle E$; $\angle FOU$, $\angle UOF$, $\angle 1$; $\angle ROU$, $\angle UOR$, $\angle 2$.

In Exercises 2–4, the angles may be any size, but the vertex labels should be the same as those in the answers below.

2.    **3.**

4.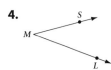

5. In the first figure, $\angle S$, $\angle P$, $\angle R$, $\angle Q$. The other angles all have the same vertex, T, so none of them can be described with just one letter. In the second figure, all the angles have the same vertex, D, so none of them can be described with just one letter.

6. Possible answer:

7. 90°

8. Side $\overrightarrow{QC}$ passes through 60° on one scale and 120° on the other. Because $\angle AQC$ is larger than a 90° angle, 120° must be the correct measure.

9. 45°   **10.** 135°   **11.** 45°   **12.** 135°

13. One way to find $m\angle CQB$ is to find $m\angle AQC$ and $m\angle AQB$ and subtract. $m\angle AQC = 120°$ and $m\angle AQB = 90°$, so $m\angle CQB = 30°$.

14. To find $m\angle XQY$, find $m\angle AQY$ and $m\angle AQX$ and subtract. $m\angle AQY = 135°$ and $m\angle AQX = 45°$, so $m\angle XQY = 90°$.

15. Yes. $m\angle XQA + m\angle XQY = 45° + 90° = 135°$, which equals $m\angle AQY$.

16. 69°. Place the center mark of the protractor on point A. Rotate the zero-edge of the protractor to line up with side $\overrightarrow{AC}$. $\overrightarrow{AM}$ passes through 69° on one scale and 111° on another. Because $\angle MAC$ is smaller than a 90° angle, $m\angle MAC = 69°$.

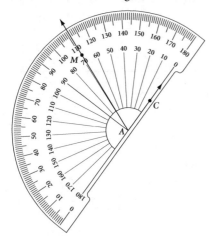

17. 110°   **18.** 40°   **19.** 125°   **20.** 55°

21. $\angle SML$ has the greater measure because $m\angle SML \approx 30°$ and $m\angle BIG \approx 20°$. The measure of an angle is the amount of rotation from one side to the other. It has nothing to do with the lengths of the angle's sides.

22. Draw a ray with endpoint A.   A•————————▸

Place the center mark of the protractor on point A and line up the zero-edge with the ray.

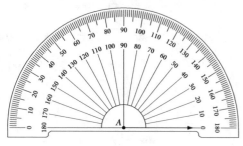

Mark a point next to the 44° mark of the protractor. (Use the scale that will give you an angle smaller than 90°.)

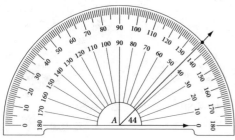

Remove the protractor, and draw a ray from point A through the point you marked.

23.

24.

25. Align your protractor as if you were going to measure $\angle A$. Mark a point at the 22° mark (half the measure of $\angle A$). Remove the protractor, and draw a ray from point A through the point you marked. Add markings to show that the two angles formed are congruent.

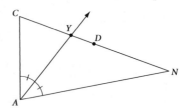

26. D and Y are not the same point.

27. Don't forget that at half past the hour, the hour hand will be halfway between 3 and 4.

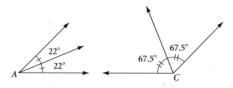

28.

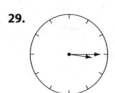

29.

30. Possible answer: 4:00

31.

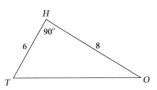

32.

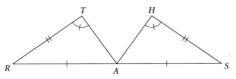

33.

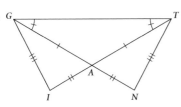

34.

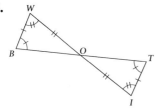

35. $\overline{MI}$ and $\overline{MY}$ have the same congruence markings, so they are the same length. That is, $MI = MY$. $\overline{IC}$ and $\overline{CK}$ have the same markings, so $IC = CK$. $\angle M$ and $\angle I$ have the same markings, so $m\angle M = m\angle I$.

36. $\angle SEU$; $\angle EUO$; MO

37. A quarter of a rotation is 90°. So,
$x = 90° - (15° + 21°) = 54°$.

38. Half of a rotation is 180°. So,
$y = 180° - (41° + 37°) = 102°$.

39. A full rotation has measure 360°. Both angles marked as congruent have measure z, so
$2z = 360° - (87° + 135° + 74°) = 64°$. Therefore, $z = 32°$.

40. 288°. First, measure $\angle ACU$ with a protractor to find $m\angle ACU = 72°$. Because a complete rotation around a point is 360°, the reflex measure of $\angle ACU$ is $360° - 72° = 288°$.

41. 242°. First, measure $\angle QUA$ with a protractor to find $m\angle QUA = 118°$. Because a complete rotation around a point is 360°, the reflex measure of $\angle QUA$ is $360° - 118° = 242°$.

42. They add to 360° because a complete rotation around a point is 360°.

43. The incoming angle has measure 50°. Draw an outgoing angle of measure 50°. The side of the angle does not pass through the pocket, so the ball will not go in.

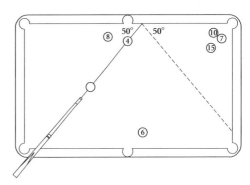

44. You will miss the target because the incoming angle is too big.

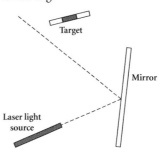

45. 180 km. The diagram shows the relative positions of the three towns.

Because P, S, and G are collinear (the towns lie along a straight highway) and Smallville is between Podunkville and Gotham City, segment addition applies: $PG = PS + SG = 70 + 110 = 180$, that is, Podunkville and Gotham City are 180 km apart.

46.

47. The wire has length 4.36 cm. The center of gravity is the midpoint of the wire, which is 4.36 divided by 2, or 2.18 cm from the end of the wire.

48. Possible answer: $MS = DG$ means that the distance between M and S equals the distance between D and G. $\overline{MS} \cong \overline{DG}$ means that segment MS is congruent to segment DG. The first statement equates two numbers. The second statement concerns the congruence between two geometric figures. However, both statements convey the same information and are marked the same way on a diagram.

49. Possible answer: Using the ruler, draw $\overline{AB}$ of length 4 cm. (Any length can be used for $\overline{AB}$.) Using the protractor, draw an angle with vertex A so that $m\angle A = 40°$ and $\overline{AB}$ lies along one of the sides of $\angle A$. Using the protractor, now draw an angle with vertex B so that $m\angle B = 70°$ and $\overline{AB}$ also lies along one of the sides of ∠B. If necessary, extend the two rays of each angle that do not contain $\overline{AB}$ until they intersect. Label their point of intersection as C. Then △ABC will meet all of the requirements.

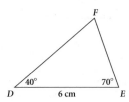

You can draw a different triangle with these two angle measures, but any two such triangles will be similar (look alike). Triangle DEF with DE = 6 cm is one such triangle.

IMPROVING YOUR VISUAL THINKING SKILLS

In problems of this kind, it's a good strategy to move the coins so that the middle ones form an alternating sequence. Note that due to the symmetry of the problems, switching the P's and D's is also a solution.

Possible solution: The steps are shown below. (Read across the rows rather than down the columns.)

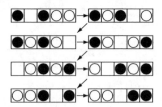

LESSON 1.3

EXERCISES

1. Possible answer:

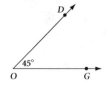

2. Possible answer:

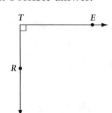

3. Possible answer:

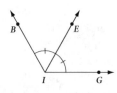

4. Note that $\overline{DG}$ must be a segment and $\overleftrightarrow{MS}$ must be a line.

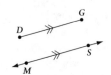

5. Note that $\overline{PE}$ must be a segment and $\overrightarrow{AR}$ must be a ray.

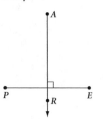

6.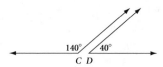

7. ∠A and ∠B are complementary, so their measures must add to 90°. Because $m\angle A = 40°$, $m\angle B = 50°$.

8. ∠C and ∠D are supplementary, so their measures must add to 180°. Because $m\angle D = 40°$, $m\angle C = 140°$.

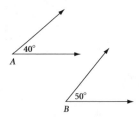

9. B is a Zoid. A Zoid is a creature whose interior contains a small triangle surrounding a black dot.

10. A good definition places an object in a class and also differentiates it from other objects in that class. A good definition has no counterexamples.

11. The sum of the measures of two complementary angles is 90°, whereas the sum of the measures of two supplementary angles is 180°.

12. No. Supplementary angles can be unconnected, but a linear pair must share a vertex and a common side. In the figure, ∠A and ∠B are supplementary because $m\angle A + m\angle B = 180°$, but they are not a linear pair. Note that they neither share a common vertex nor a common side, both of which are required for a pair of angles to be a linear pair.

13. a. an angle; measures less than 90°

b. angles; have measures that add to 90°

c. a point; divides a segment into two congruent segments

d. a geometry tool; is used to measure the size of angles in degrees

14. If *P* is not between *A* and *B* or not between *C* and *D*, then the definition is not true. Here is a counterexample:

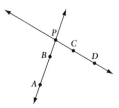

The following is a correct definition: If $\overleftrightarrow{AB}$ and $\overleftrightarrow{CD}$ intersect at point *P* so that *P* is between *A* and *B* and *P* is between *C* and *D*, then $\angle APC$ and $\angle BPD$ are a pair of vertical angles.

15. True

16. True

17. True

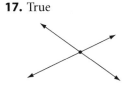

18. False

19. False. Think in three dimensions. There are an infinite number of planes that contain the given line, and each one contains a line perpendicular through the given point.

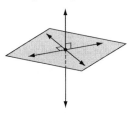

20. False. Possible counterexample:

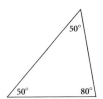

21. True. (Parallel lines must be in the same plane.)

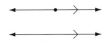

22. False. Possible counterexample:

23. False. Possible counterexample:

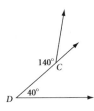

24. False. Possible counterexample:

25. Point *P* must be on the line through *T* and *S*. The slope of $\overleftrightarrow{TS}$ is $\frac{6}{9}$, or $\frac{2}{3}$. One way to find another point on the line is to start at point *T* and move up 2 units and right 3 units. This would give you point $(-3, 0)$. You can continue moving up and over to find more possible points. Possible answers: $(-3, 0)$, $(0, 2)$, or $(6, 6)$.

26. For $\overleftrightarrow{QR} \parallel \overleftrightarrow{TS}$, the lines must have the same slope. The slope of $\overleftrightarrow{TS}$ is $\frac{6}{9}$, or $\frac{2}{3}$. One way to find point *Q* so that the slope of $\overleftrightarrow{QR}$ is $\frac{2}{3}$ is to start at point *R* and move up 2 units and right 3 units. You will be at point $(2, -3)$. You can continue moving up and over to find more possible points. Possible answers: $(2, -3)$ or $(5, -1)$.

27. Just as in pool, the measure of the incoming angle is equal to the measure of the outgoing angle. The incoming angle has measure 46°, so draw an outgoing angle with measure 46°.

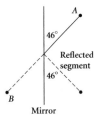

You should find that the reflected ray and the ray that passes through (called the "refracted" ray) are mirror images of each other. They form congruent angles with the mirror.

28. This problem is best solved by trial and error. Here is a possible method. Point C has to lie on $\overleftrightarrow{TR}$, so choose that point first. Put it far enough to the left of point S so that you have room for points A and B. Because $\angle BAC$ will be a right angle, you know points A and B will be on a segment perpendicular to $\overline{AC}$. Because $\angle ABS$ will be obtuse, B needs to be to the right of A and to the left of S. $\angle BAT$ needs to be an acute angle, so place segment AB somewhere such that $\angle ABS$ is obtuse and $\angle BAT$ is acute. Possible answer: $A(-8, 8)$, $B(-4.5, 6.5)$, $C(-11, 1)$.

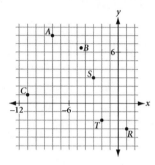

29. Make a sketch showing the given information. Because D is the midpoint of $\overline{AC}$, $AC = 6$ cm. Because C is the midpoint of $\overline{AB}$, $AB = 12$ cm.

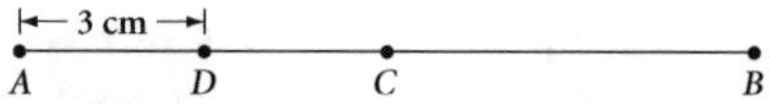

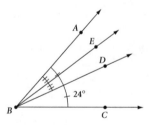

30. Make a sketch showing the given information. Because $\overrightarrow{BD}$ is the bisector of $\angle ABC$, $m\angle ABD = 24°$. Because $\overrightarrow{BE}$ is the bisector of $\angle ABD$, $m\angle EBD = 12°$. Therefore, $m\angle EBC = 12° + 24°$, or $36°$.

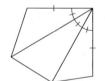

31. Possible answer:

32.

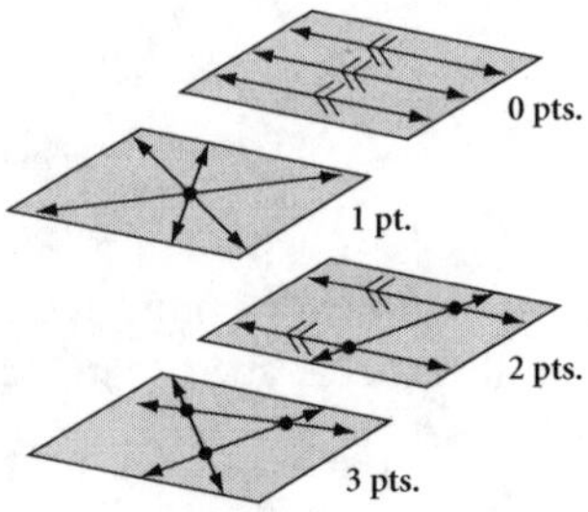

33.

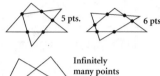
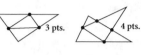

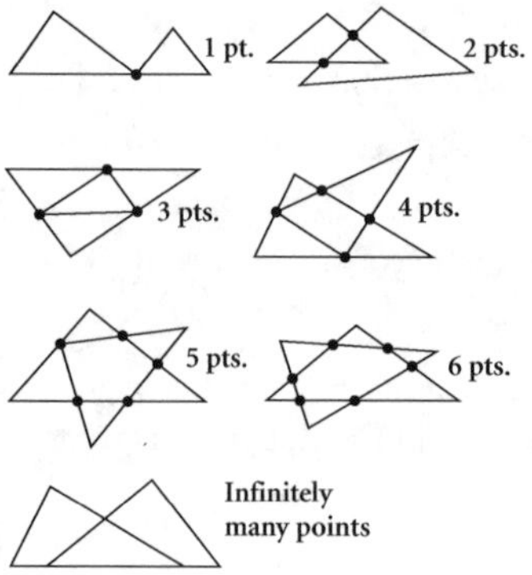

34. a. $\frac{120°}{360°}$, or $\frac{1}{3}$ is missing, so $\frac{2}{3}$ is left.

b. $\frac{60°}{360°}$, or $\frac{1}{6}$ is missing.

c. $\frac{360°}{9} = 40°$

IMPROVING YOUR VISUAL THINKING SKILLS

The other four tetrominoes:

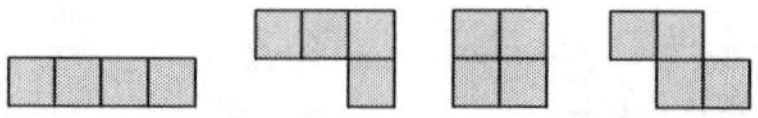

Note that if two tetrominoes are congruent, they are considered to be the same. For example, these tetrominoes are all the same:

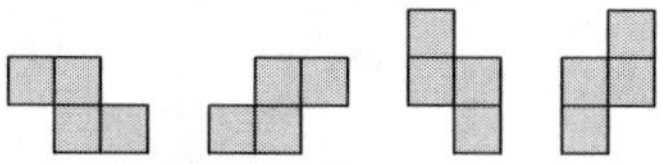

LESSON 1.4

EXERCISES

1. Possible answer:

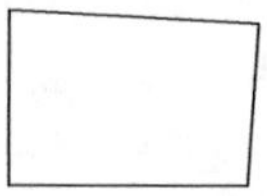

2. Possible answer:

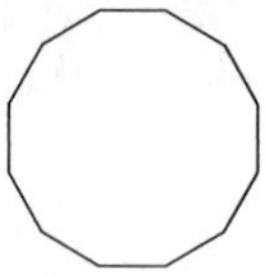

3. Possible answer:

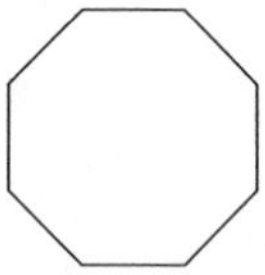

4. The polygon has eight sides so it is an octagon.

5. The polygon has six sides so it is a hexagon.

6. The polygon has seven sides so it is a heptagon.

7. The polygon has five sides so it is a pentagon.

8. To name the figure, start with any vertex, and list the letters in order as you move clockwise or counterclockwise around the figure. A few possible names are *FIVER, VERFI, REVIF, IVERF*.

9. Possible name: quadrilateral *FOUR*

10. Possible name: equilateral quadrilateral *BLOC*

11. a. a polygon; has eight sides

   b. a polygon; has at least one diagonal outside the polygon

   c. a polygon; has 20 sides

   d. a polygon; has all sides of equal length

12. Consecutive angles are angles whose vertices are endpoints of the same side. For example, ∠*C* and ∠*Y* are consecutive angles. Consecutive sides are sides that share a vertex. For example, $\overline{CY}$ and $\overline{YN}$ are consecutive sides.

13. Nine. A concave hexagon is a hexagon with at least one diagonal outside the polygon. The hexagon on the left below is a convex hexagon. On the right, the hexagon's nine diagonals have been drawn.

14. Make a sketch. The diagonals are $\overline{AC}$, $\overline{AD}$, $\overline{BD}$, $\overline{BE}$, and $\overline{CE}$.

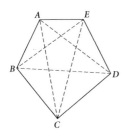

15. When stating that two triangles are congruent, you need to list the vertices in the order that shows the correspondences. Because *T* corresponds to *E*, *I* corresponds to *A*, and *N* corresponds to *R*, △*EAR* ≅ △*TIN*.

16. △*OLD* ≅ △*WEN*

17. a. *a* = 44; *b* = 58; *c* = 34. Match up corresponding sides of the two congruent pentagons, and apply the part of the definition of congruent polygons that says that corresponding sides of congruent polygons are congruent:

   $\overline{OW}$ corresponds to $\overline{HI}$, so *a* = 44.

   $\overline{ER}$ corresponds to $\overline{NK}$, so *b* = 58.

   $\overline{PR}$ corresponds to $\overline{TK}$, so *c* = 34.

   b. Because ∠*P* and ∠*T* correspond, *m*∠*T* = *m*∠*P* = 87°. Because ∠*W* and ∠*I* correspond, *m*∠*I* = *m*∠*W* = 165°.

18. $\overline{PA}$ ≅ $\overline{FI}$ and ∠*IVE* ≅ ∠*ANC*.

19. Many hexagons can be drawn that satisfy the requirements. The figure shows one such hexagon.

20. An equilateral concave polygon has five sides of equal length and at least one diagonal outside the pentagon. The figure shows one such pentagon.

An equiangular convex polygon has five angles of equal measure. The figure shows one such pentagon.

21. 84 in. A regular dodecagon has 12 congruent sides. If the length of each side is 7 in., the perimeter will be (12)(7 in.) = 84 in.

22. 5.25 cm. An equilateral octagon has eight congruent sides. If the perimeter is 42 cm, the length of each side will be $\frac{42\ cm}{8}$ = 5.25 cm.

23. *AB* = 14 m, *CD* = 25 m. Use the information given in the figure to write an equation. Notice from the figure markings that *AB* = *BC*, so *AB* = *x* − 3; and *CD* = *AE*, so *CD* = *x* + 8. The perimeter of pentagon *ABCDE* is 94 m, so 2(*x* − 3) + 2(*x* + 8) + 16 = 94. Solve this equation to find the value of *x*.

2(*x* − 3) + 2(*x* + 8) + 16 = 94	The original equation.
2*x* − 6 + 2*x* + 16 + 16 = 94	Distributive property.
4*x* + 26 = 94	Combine like terms.
4*x* = 68	Subtract 26 from both sides.
x = 17	Divide both sides by 4.

If *x* = 17, then *x* − 3 = 14 and *x* + 8 = 25. Therefore, *AB* = 14 m and *CD* = 25 m.

24. Complementary angles: ∠*AOS* and ∠*SOC*; vertical angles: ∠*OCT* and ∠*ECR*, or ∠*TCE* and ∠*RCO*

25.

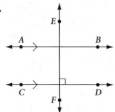

26. Possible answer:

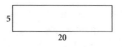

27. All are possible except two points.

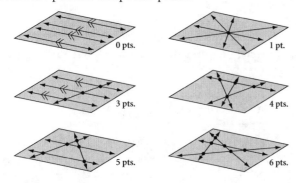

IMPROVING YOUR VISUAL THINKING SKILLS

Possible solution: PDDPPPDDDPPPDDP

LESSON 1.5

EXERCISES

1. Figure D. An equilateral triangle has three sides of equal length.

2. Figure A. A scalene right triangle has three sides of different lengths and one right angle.

3. Figure C. An isosceles right triangle has two sides of the same length and one right angle.

4. Figure B. An isosceles obtuse triangle has two sides of the same length and one obtuse angle.

5.

6.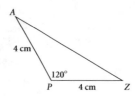

7.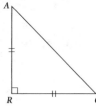

8. Possible answer:

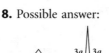

9. Possible answer:

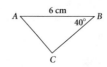 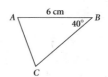

10. Possible answer: Use the ruler to draw $\overline{AB}$ of any length. (In the figure, the length of $\overline{AB}$ is 4 cm.) Then draw $\overline{BC}$ so that $BC = AB$, and A, B, and C are not collinear. (Any angle measure can be used for $\angle B$. In the figure, an 80° angle was used.) Connect points A and C to form the third side of △ABC. Notice that because $\overline{AB}$ and $\overline{BC}$ are the congruent sides of this isosceles triangle, $\overline{AC}$ is the base, as required.

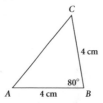

11. Possible answer: Use the protractor to draw any obtuse angle, and label its vertex as P. (In the figure, this angle measure was chosen to be 120°.) Along the rays of $\angle P$, measure equal distances to form $\overline{PA}$ and $\overline{PZ}$. (Any length can be used for these sides, as long as the two segments have the same length. In the figure, this length was chosen to be 4 cm.) Connect points A and Z to form the third side of the triangle. Notice that because $\overline{PA}$ and $\overline{PZ}$ are the two congruent sides of isosceles triangle ZAP, the base angles are $\angle A$ and $\angle Z$, as required.

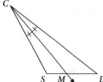

12. There is an infinite number of possible answers. Here are a few possibilities: $(-1, -1)$, $(-1, 0)$, $(-4, 3)$.

13. There are six possible answers: $(3, -3)$, $(3, 4)$, $(-11, 4)$, $(-11, -3)$, $(-0.5, 0.5)$, or $(-7.5, 0.5)$. The triangle must have one right angle and two congruent sides. To find the third vertex of an isosceles right triangle with right angle at vertex M, draw a horizontal line through M. Because $\overline{ME}$ is 7 units long, count over 7 units in either direction to locate point *O*. You will get (3, 4) or (−11, 4).

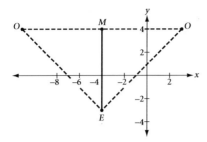

You can use a similar method to find the third vertex if the right angle is at *E*. You will get (3, −3) or (−11, −3).

If the right angle is at *O*, then $\overline{MO}$ and $\overline{EO}$ will be the congruent sides. Visually, you can see that vertex *O* must be located on the horizontal line $y = 0.5$ (that is, the horizontal line through the midpoint of $\overline{ME}$). For *O* to be a right angle, the slopes of $\overline{MO}$ and $\overline{EO}$ must be opposite reciprocals. The two points that satisfy these criteria are (−0.5, 0.5) or (−7.5, 0.5).

14. Possible answers: (−3, 1), (−1, −9), (2, 2), (4, −8), (0, −1), or (1, −6). If the right angle is at *C*, then the slope of $\overline{CR}$ will be −5, the opposite reciprocal of the slope of $\overline{CL}$. Draw a line through point *C* with slope −5 and locate point *R* so that *CR* = *CL*. You can use similar reasoning to locate point *R* if the right angle is at *L*. If the right angle is at *R*, the problem is a little trickier. You can see that in order for *RC* to equal *RL*, point *R* will have to be on the perpendicular line through the midpoint of $\overline{CL}$. The midpoint of $\overline{CL}$ is (0.5, −3.5). Draw a line with slope −5 through this point. Then try to locate a point *R* so that the slopes of $\overline{RC}$ and $\overline{RL}$ are opposite reciprocals.

15. Possible answer: Use your ruler to draw line segment $\overline{AB}$ of length 9 cm. Use your protractor to draw an angle with vertex *A* so that $m\angle A = 45°$ and $\overline{AB}$ lies along one of the sides of $\angle A$. Pick any point on the other side of $\angle A$, and label it *C*. Finally, draw segments $\overline{AC}$ and $\overline{BC}$. The triangle will be different depending on which point you choose for *C*. Two sample triangles are shown.

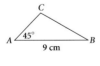

16. Possible answer: Use your ruler to draw line segment $\overline{AB}$ of length 10 cm. On a sheet of patty paper, use

your protractor to draw an angle with vertex *C* so that $m\angle C = 40°$, and extend sides of the angle. Move the patty paper with $\angle C$ over the drawing of $\overline{AB}$ until the points *A* and *B* touch the sides of $\angle C$. Trace over $\overline{AB}$ to create the triangle on the patty paper. The triangle will be different depending on where *A* and *B* touch the sides of $\angle C$. Two sample triangles are shown.

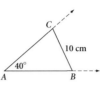

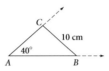

17. True   **18.** True

19. False. A diagonal connects *nonconsecutive* vertices.

20. False. An angle bisector divides an angle into two *congruent* angles.

21. True

22. (−4, 1) → (−3, −2); (1, 1) → (2, −2); (2, 4) → (3, 1); (−3, 5) → (−2, 2). Yes, the quadrilaterals are congruent.

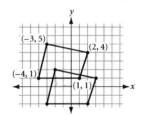

23. Find the midpoint of each rod. All the midpoints lie on the same line; place the edge of a ruler under this line.

24. Possible answer: **25.** Possible answer:

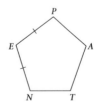   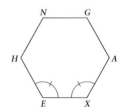

26. Possible answer:

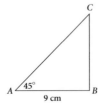

IMPROVING YOUR VISUAL THINKING SKILLS

Here is one way to organize your work to make sure you have found all the possibilities. Keep in mind that congruent pentominoes are considered to be the same.

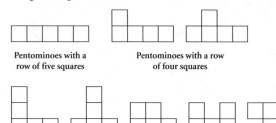

Pentominoes with a   Pentominoes with a row
row of five squares   of four squares

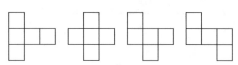

Pentominoes with a row of three squares and both other
squares on the same side of that row

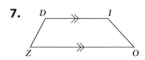

Pentominoes with a row of three squares and the other
squares on opposite sides of that row

LESSON 1.6

EXERCISES

1. First figure: $\overline{AD} \cong \overline{BC}$ and $\angle D$ is a right angle.

   Second figure: $\overline{EH} \cong \overline{HG}$ and $\overline{EF} \cong \overline{FG}$, or $EFGH$ is a kite. (*Note: EFGH is drawn so that it doesn't look like a kite, but the markings indicate it is a kite.*)

   Third figure: $\angle I$ and $\angle J$ are right angles.

   Fourth figure: $\overline{QP} \parallel \overline{MN}$ and $\overline{QM} \parallel \overline{PN}$, or $MNPQ$ is a parallelogram.

2. Figure B. A trapezoid is a quadrilateral with exactly one pair of parallel sides.

3. Figure D. A rhombus is a quadrilateral with four congruent sides.

4. Figure F. A rectangle is a parallelogram with four congruent angles.

5. Figure C. A kite is a quadrilateral with two distinct pairs of consecutive congruent sides.

6. Figures A, D, and F. A parallelogram is a quadrilateral with two pairs of parallel sides.

7.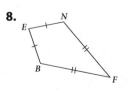

8.

9.

10.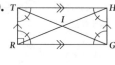

11. To have two outside diagonals, the hexagon must be concave with two "dents."

12. A regular quadrilateral has four congruent sides and four congruent angles. It is a square.

    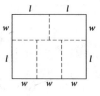

13. There are three possibilities for the other two vertices: (2, 6) and (−2, 4); (6, −2) and (2, −4); (3, −1) and (1, 3). In two cases, the given vertices are the endpoints of a side. In the third case, they are the endpoints of a diagonal.

    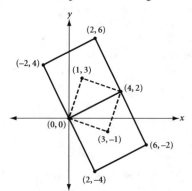

14. 90 cm. Let l and w represent the length and the width of one of the small rectangles. Then, as the diagram at right illustrates, the perimeter of the large rectangle is $4l + 5w$. So, $4l + 5w = 198$. You can also see from the diagram that $2l = 3w$.

    Now do a little algebra.

    $4l + 5w = 198$ The equation for the perimeter of the large rectangle.

    $2(2l) + 5w = 198$ Rewrite $4l$ as $2(2l)$.

    $2(3w) + 5w = 198$ Substitute $3w$ for $2l$.

    $11w = 198$ Simplify.

    $w = 18$ Solve for w.

To find *l*, go back to the equation $2l = 3w$.

$$2l = 3w$$

$2l = 3(18)$ Substitute 18 for *w*.

$2l = 54$ Multiply.

$l = 27$ Solve for *l*.

So, each small rectangle has length 27 cm and width 18 cm. Therefore, the perimeter of a small rectangle is $2(27 + 18) = 90$ cm.

15. (5, 6). Here is one way to reason through this problem: Point *P* is 5 units right of point *C* and 1 unit up. Point *E* is 5 units right of point *A* and 1 unit up. So, point *T* could be 5 units right and 1 unit up from point *R*. Counting squares, this gives one possibility for *T* as (5, 6).

16. *S*(9, 0), *I*(4, −2). Use reasoning similar to that described in the solution to Exercise 15.

17. *S*(−3, 0), *I*(−1, −5)

18. *A*(7, 6), *N*(5, 9) or *A*(−5, −2), *N*(−7, 1)

19. a. To form a kite, arrange the two triangles so that there are two pairs of congruent consecutive sides. The common side of the two triangles will be a diagonal of the kite.

b. To form a parallelogram, arrange the two triangles so that there are two pairs of opposite congruent sides. The common side of the two triangles will be a diagonal of the parallelogram.

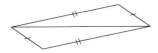

20. There are three possibilities. If the bases of the isosceles triangles are placed so that they coincide and become a diagonal of the quadrilateral, you will get a rhombus.

If one of the two congruent sides of one triangle and one of the two congruent sides of the other triangle are placed so that they coincide and become a diagonal of the quadrilateral, you will get either a concave kite or a parallelogram.

  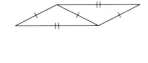

21. a. Right triangles. Two congruent right triangles must be used in order to get right angles for the rectangle. The right triangles are joined by their hypotenuses, and the common side becomes a diagonal of the rectangle.

b. Isosceles right triangles. Two congruent isosceles right triangles must be used in order to get right angles and four congruent sides for the square. The isosceles right triangles are joined by their hypotenuses, and the common side becomes a diagonal of the square.

22. Possible answer:

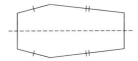

23. Possible answer:

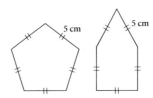

24. Use your compass to draw a circle. Because a regular pentagon has five equal sides, you want to divide the circle into five equal pieces. Draw five 72° angles (360° ÷ 5 = 72°) with vertices at the center of the circle as shown below. Then connect the points where the sides of the angles intersect the circle.

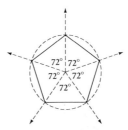

25. Possible answer: draw two sides of the octagon by connecting *A*, *B*, and *C*. Get two more sides by reflecting these sides over the *x*-axis. Get the remaining sides by reflecting those four sides over the *y*-axis. The octagon is not regular because its angles are not all the same size.

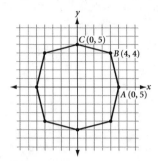

The octagon may be shaped very differently, for example by replacing the vertex at $(-4, 4)$ with one at $(-1, 1)$.

PROJECT

Project should satisfy the following criteria:

- Both of the given "impossible" objects are reproduced.
- Students created their own "impossible" object.

Extra credit

- The objects are drawn in creative ways that accentuate their impossibility.
- Students include analyses of Escher's *Waterfall* and *Belvedere*.

EXTENSION

Answers will vary.

LESSON 1.7

EXERCISES

1. Answers will vary. Sample answers: The green area on the irrigation photo is a circle, and the water is a radius. A path on the far side of the circle appears to be tangent to the circle. The wood bridge is an arc of a circle, and the horizontal support beam under the bridge is a chord.

2. Three of the following: $\overline{AB}$, $\overline{BD}$, $\overline{EC}$, $\overline{EF}$

3. $\overline{EC}$

4. $\overline{AP}$, $\overline{EP}$, $\overline{FP}$, $\overline{BP}$, $\overline{CP}$

5. Five of the following: $\overline{EF}$, $\overline{AE}$, $\overline{AB}$, $\overline{BC}$, $\overline{CD}$, $\overline{DF}$, $\overline{EB}$, $\overline{ED}$, $\overline{FC}$, $\overline{AC}$, $\overline{DB}$, $\overline{AF}$, $\overline{AD}$, $\overline{BF}$

6. $\overline{EDC}$ (or $\overline{EFC}$) and $\overline{EBC}$ (or $\overline{EAC}$)

7. Two of the following: $\overline{ECD}$, $\overline{ECF}$, $\overline{EDB}$, $\overline{EDA}$, $\overline{CBF}$, $\overline{CBD}$, $\overline{CDA}$, $\overline{CDB}$, $\overline{FED}$, $\overline{FCA}$, $\overline{BCA}$. Each of the above can be named in several other ways. For example, $\overline{ECD}$ can also be called $\overline{DCE}$, $\overline{EAD}$, $\overline{DAE}$, $\overline{EBD}$, or $\overline{DBE}$.

8. $\overleftrightarrow{FG}$, $\overleftrightarrow{HB}$

9. Either F or B

10. Possible answers: cars, trains, motorcycles; washing machines, dishwashers, vacuum cleaners; compact disc players, record players, car racing, Ferris wheel

11. $m\overset{\frown}{PQ}$ is the measure of the central angle whose sides pass through points P and Q. So, $m\overset{\frown}{PQ} = 110°$. Because $\overset{\frown}{PQ}$ and $\overset{\frown}{PRQ}$ make up a full circle, and a full circle has measure 360°, $m\overset{\frown}{PRQ} = 360° - 110°$, or 250°.

12. To make the 65° arc, first draw a circle. Then draw a 65° angle with its vertex at the center of the circle. The minor arc with endpoints at the intersection points has measure 65°. To make the 215° arc, first draw a circle. Then draw a 145° angle with its vertex at the center of the circle. The major arc with endpoints at the intersection points has measure 360° − 145°, or 215°.

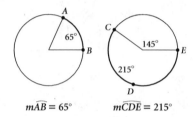

$m\overset{\frown}{AB} = 65°$ $m\overset{\frown}{CDE} = 215°$

13. Possible answers: concentric rings on cross sections of trees (annual rings), bull's-eye or target, ripples from a rock falling into a pond

14.

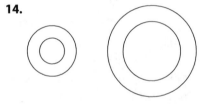

15.

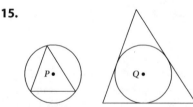

16. Equilateral quadrilateral (The figure is actually a rhombus, but students have not yet learned the properties needed to conclude that the sides are parallel.)

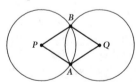

17. From the way the hexagon was constructed, you know that the length of each side is *s*, the same as the radius of the circle. Therefore, the triangles are equilateral. The perimeter of the hexagon is 6*s* and

Discovering Geometry Solutions Manual
©2008 Key Curriculum Press

the diameter of the circle is 2*s*, so the ratio is 6*s* to 2*s*, or 3 to 1.

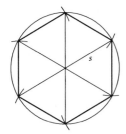

18.

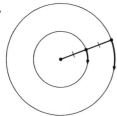

19. Yes; yes   **20.** Yes; no

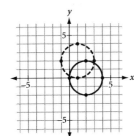 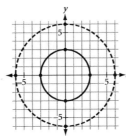

21. No; no

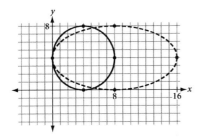

22. 80°. Let *x* = the degree measure of the central angle of the pizza slice that will be left for your friend.

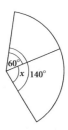

Angle addition applies here because the central angle for the piece that is to be shared is made up of the adjacent central angles of the two parts. Using angle addition, 60° + *x* = 140°, so *x* = 140° − 60° = 80°.

23.

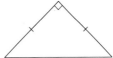

24. A scalene triangle has no congruent sides and an isosceles triangle has at least two congruent sides. Therefore, it is not possible to draw a triangle that is both isosceles and scalene.

25. Possible answer:

26. Possible answer:

27. About 0.986°. Divide 360° by 365.25 days: $\frac{360°}{365.25 \text{ days}} \approx 0.986°$ per day.

28. 15°. Divide 360° by 24 hours: $\frac{360°}{24 \text{ hours}} = 15°$ per hour.

29. Possible answer: **30.** Possible answer:

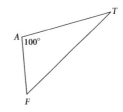 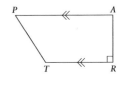

31. Possible answer:

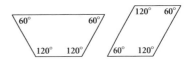

32. An equilateral triangle has three equal sides and three equal angles, so it cannot have one right angle. Therefore, it is not possible to draw a triangle that is both equilateral and right.

33. Possible answer:

34. Each side must have length $\frac{12a + 6b}{3}$, or 4*a* + 2*b*.

35. Possible answer: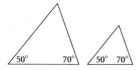

36. Possible answer: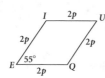

37. Possible answer: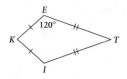

IMPROVING YOUR REASONING SKILLS

In both solutions, the third steps must be third, but the first two steps can be interchanged.

1. B1 to B3, A1 to A3, A3 to C3; or A2 to C2, A1 to C1, C1 to C3

2. A4 to C4, A3 to C3, C4 to C2, A1 to C1, C1 to C3, A2 to C2, C3 to C1

LESSON 1.8

EXERCISES

1.

2.

3.

4.

5.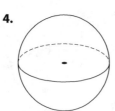

6.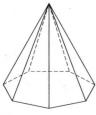

7. Possible answer: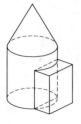

8. Follow Steps 1–4 below. The 3 m-by-4 m face is biggest, so it should be on the "bottom."

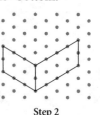

Step 1   Step 2

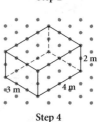

Step 3   Step 4

9. There are 3 · 4, or 12, boxes in the base layer, and there are 5 layers, so there are 12 · 5, or 60, boxes.

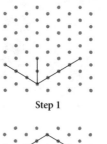

10.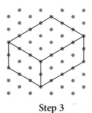

11.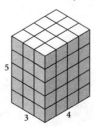

12.

13. B, D. Net A, when folded, would have too many sides; in net C the two top squares would coincide; net E would be missing a side; and net F would have too many sides in the horizontal direction and would be missing one in the vertical direction. Only nets B and D would fold into a cube.

14. B   **15.** C

16. D   **17.** A

18. To visualize the section, imagine slicing an orange. What shape is revealed?

19.

20. True

21. True

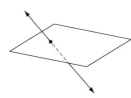

22. False. The two lines are not necessarily in the same plane, so they might be skew.

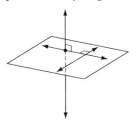

23. True

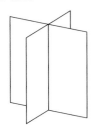

24. True

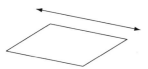

25. True

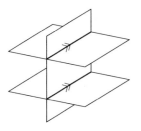

26. False. They divide space into seven or eight parts— seven if the three lines of intersection are parallel, eight otherwise.

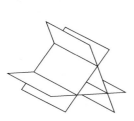

27. True

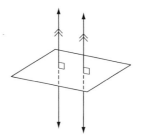

28. $(-3, 1)$

29. Perimeter = 20.5 cm; m(largest angle) = 100°.

30.

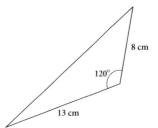

IMPROVING YOUR VISUAL THINKING SKILLS

First, draw A, B, and C. Because $AB = BC = AC$, points A, B, and C are vertices of an equilateral triangle.

Now, where does point D go? If it is in the same plane as A, B, and C, then it can be the same distance from any two points, but not from all three points. Try thinking in three dimensions. Imagine placing D above your paper so that $\triangle ABD$, $\triangle BCD$, and $\triangle ACD$ are equilateral triangles. If you could connect all four points, you would get a *tetrahedron*, a three-dimensional figure with four faces that are equilateral triangles. So, A, B, C, and D are vertices of a tetrahedron.

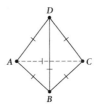

EXTENSIONS

A. Here is one way to divide the solids.

Solids with all straight edges: prism, pyramid

Solids with curved or no edges: cylinder, cone, sphere, hemisphere

B. To draw a cube truncated to edge midpoints, first draw a cube. Then mark the midpoints of each side and connect the midpoints surrounding each face to make triangular wedges at each corner. Finally, erase the corners of the cube (you will erase all the cube's lines) to make the truncated cube. This is also called a *cuboctahedron*.

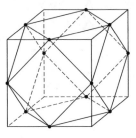 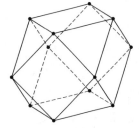

Draw the truncated tetrahedron in a similar way. A tetrahedron truncated to edge midpoints is an octahedron.

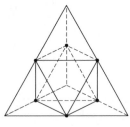

C. Answers will vary.   **D.** Results will vary.

LESSON 1.9

EXERCISES

1. Sample answer: Furniture movers might visualize how to rotate a couch to get it up a narrow staircase.

2. Yes. Draw a diagram. S Street is a lettered street, so it runs north-south. Because S is not a vowel, S Street must be a two-way street. Because it is an even-numbered street, 14th Street must run one-way east. The finished diagram indicates that a car traveling south on S Street could make a legal left turn onto 14th.

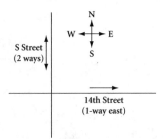

3. Make a number line on which each tick mark represents 10 meters. Mark the given information on the number line. The final diagram will show that Nadine is ahead.

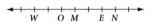

4. Draw a diagram. She will need 28 posts.

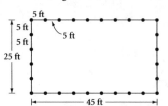

5. 28 days. You can draw a vertical number line representing the well. Mark the number line to show Freddie's location at the end of each day (D1, D2, and so on) and the end of each night (N1, N2, and so on). After marking the results for several days, you should begin to see a pattern: At the end of Day n, Freddie is $n + 2$ feet from the bottom of the well; at the end of Night n, he is n feet from the bottom of the well. So, Freddie will first reach the top of the 30-foot well on Day 28.

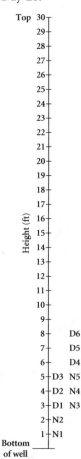

6. 0 feet. When the cable hangs, it is bent in half, with each half measuring 15 feet. However, the vertical distance from the lowest point on the cable to the horizontal line level with the top of the poles is also 15 feet. Therefore, the cable must be hanging vertically. For this to happen, the poles must be

touching. That is, the distance between the poles must be 0 feet.

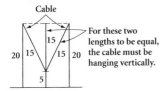

7. The locus of all points in the plane that are equally distant from A and B is the line that passes through the midpoint of $\overline{AB}$ and is perpendicular to $\overline{AB}$. The locus of all points in space that are equally distant from points A and B is the plane that passes through the midpoint of $\overline{AB}$ and is perpendicular to $\overline{AB}$.

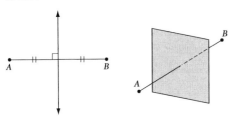

8. The locus of all points that are the same distance from the two sides of $\angle A$ is the bisector of $\angle A$.

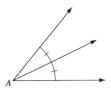

9. The locus of all points in the plane that are 3 cm from $\overleftrightarrow{AB}$ is two lines, one on either side of $\overleftrightarrow{AB}$, each 3 cm from $\overleftrightarrow{AB}$. The locus of all points in space that are 3 cm from $\overleftrightarrow{AB}$ is a cylinder of radius 3 cm with axis $\overleftrightarrow{AB}$.

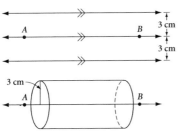

10.

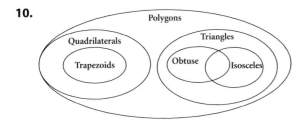

11. No. The diagram below shows Beth's route. The interval between two dots represents 1 km. The time is labeled every 4 km. The diagram shows that Beth will not reach Birnam Woods Road until 8:00, which is not before sunset.

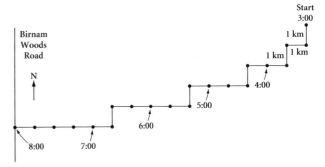

12. $A'(0, 0)$, $B'(0, 5)$, $C'(-2, 3)$, $D'(-2, 1)$. First, rotate the horizontal segment $\overline{AB}$. The rotated segment will be vertical with point A at $(0, 0)$ and point B at $(0, 5)$. Once you draw $\overline{AB}$, you can locate the other vertices relative to points A and B. (You could also copy trapezoid $ABCD$ onto patty paper or tracing paper, and then rotate the tracing paper 90°, or a $\frac{1}{4}$ turn, counterclockwise.)

13. $C'(3, -1)$, $Y'(-4, 1)$, $N'(0, 3)$; If $\triangle CYN$ were reflected over the y-axis, the y-coordinates would stay the same, but the x-coordinates would be the opposite of what they are now (the points would be the same distance from the y-axis, but on the opposite side).

14. $ABCD$ was slid right 3 units and up 2 units. So, the rule is $(x, y) \rightarrow (x + 3, y + 2)$.

15. $\overleftrightarrow{AB} \perp \overleftrightarrow{CP}$, $\overleftrightarrow{EF} \parallel \overleftrightarrow{GH}$; $i \perp k$, $j \perp k$ (Just because two lines *look* parallel or perpendicular, you cannot assume that they *are* parallel or perpendicular.) It can also be deduced that $i \parallel j$, but students are not expected to know that.

16. The perimeter of the first figure is 6, and then the perimeter increases by 4 with each subsequent figure. So, the perimeter of the second figure is $6 + 4(1)$, the perimeter of the third figure is $6 + 4(2)$, and the perimeter of the fourth figure is $6 + 4(3)$. Continuing this pattern, the perimeter of the eighth figure would be $6 + 4(7)$, or 34 cm.

17. Left photo: Three points determine a plane.

Middle photo: Two intersecting lines determine a plane.

Right photo: A line and a point not on the line determine a plane.

18. Pyramid with hexagonal base

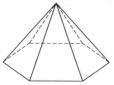

19. Prism with hexagonal base

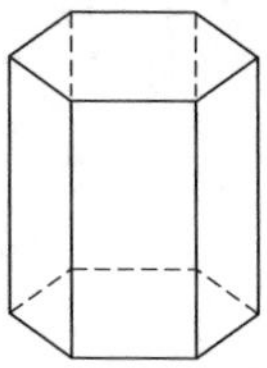

20. Pyramid with square base

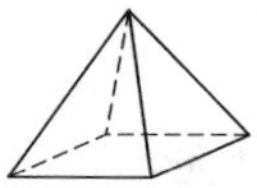

21. Below are sketches of the top and front views. From the top view, you can see that $17 + x + 13 = 45$, so $x = 15$. From the front view, you can see that $y + 18 = 45$, so $y = 27$.

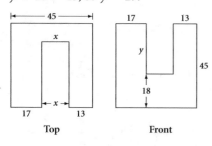

22. From this sketch of the front view, you can see that $x = 3 + 7 + 2$, so $x = 12$. You can also see that $y + 2 + 2 = 8$, so $y = 4$.

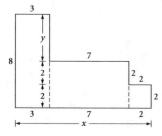

23. To visualize the solid, cut out a rectangle and tape it to your pencil. Rotate your pencil to see what shape the rotating rectangle forms.

24.

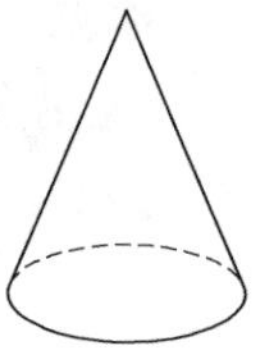

25. point, line, plane

26. $\overleftrightarrow{AB}$

27. $\overset{\frown}{AB}$

28. vertex

29. $\overrightarrow{AB}$

30. $\overleftrightarrow{AB} \parallel \overline{CD}$

31. protractor

32. $\angle ABC$

33. $\overline{AB} \perp \overleftrightarrow{CD}$

34. congruent to

35. The distance is two times the radius.

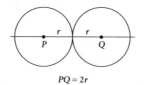

$PQ = 2r$

36. They bisect each other and are perpendicular.

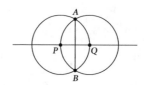

IMPROVING YOUR VISUAL THINKING SKILLS

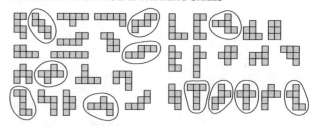

EXTENSIONS

Answers will vary.

CHAPTER 1 REVIEW

EXERCISES

1. True

2. False. It is written as $\overrightarrow{QP}$.

3. True

4. False. The vertex is point D.

5. True

6. True

7. False. The measure of an acute angle is less than 90°.

8. False. Here are two possible counterexamples:

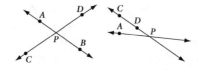

$\angle APD$ and $\angle APC$ are a linear pair.

$\angle APD$ and $\angle APC$ are the same angle.

9. True   **10.** True

11. False. They are supplementary.

12. True   **13.** True   **14.** True

15. False. A pentagon has five diagonals.

16. True   **17.** F   **18.** G   **19.** L

20. J   **21.** C   **22.** I   **23.** No match

24. A   **25.** No match

26.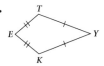

27.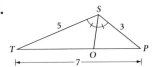

28. 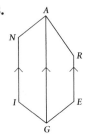   **29.**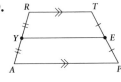

30. 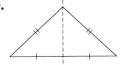   **31.**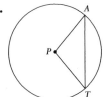

32. 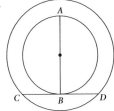   **33.**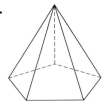

34. 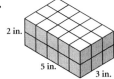   **35.**

36.

37. Here is one possible method. Draw a circle and one diameter. Draw another diameter perpendicular to the first. Draw two more diameters so that eight 45° angles are formed. Draw the regular octagon formed by connecting the endpoints of the diameters.

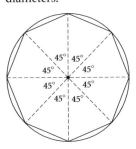

38. 114°   **39.** $x = 2$, $y = 1$

40. $x = 12$, $y = 4$ **41.** $x = 4$, $y = 2.5$

42. Find y first. $y + 12 = 20$, so $y = 8$. $x + 8 = 18$, so $x = 10$.

43. The diagram below illustrates the given information. $3z = 12$, so $z = 4$ cm. Therefore, $AB = 4z = 16$ cm.

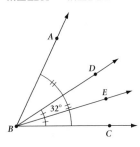

44. The diagram below illustrates the given information. Because $\overrightarrow{BE}$ is the bisector of $\angle DBC$, $m\angle DBC = 64°$. Because $\overrightarrow{BD}$ is the bisector of $\angle ABC$, $m\angle ABD = 64°$. So, $m\angle EBA = m\angle DBE + m\angle ABD = 32° + 64° = 96°$.

45. Drawing radii from each hour mark to the center of a clock forms 12 central angles, each with measure $\frac{360°}{12}$, or 30°. The angle formed by the hands at 2:30 includes $3\frac{1}{2}$ of those central angles. (At 2:30, the hour hand will be halfway between 2 and 3.) So, the angle has measure 3.5(30°), or 105°.

46. $\frac{360°}{12} = 30°$

47.

48. The top and the bottom each need one 9-inch strip and one 14-inch strip. The four sides each need one 5-inch strip. So, the total length needed is 2(9 + 14) + 4(5) = 66 inches.

49. Draw a number line on which each tick mark represents 3 feet. Label the line to show each boy's position. The completed diagram shows that Paul was 3 feet ahead of George.

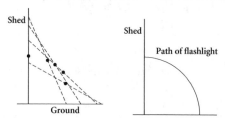

50. The dashed segments in the following diagram represent the ladder in various positions as it slides down the wall. The midpoint of each segment is marked. The path traced by the midpoint is an arc of a circle or a quarter-circle if the ladder slides all the way from the vertical to the horizontal.

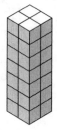

51. He will get home at 5:46 (assuming he goes inside before he gets blown back again).

52. If the triangle is rotated 90° clockwise, $\overline{AB}$ will be a vertical segment. Point *B* will have the same location as it does now, and point *A* will be at (2, 3).

53.

54.

55.

56.

57.

CHAPTER 2

LESSON 2.1

EXERCISES

1. "All rocks sink." Stony needs to find one rock that will not sink.

2. Possible conjecture: If two angles are formed by drawing a ray from a line, then their measures add up to 180°.

3. 10,000, 100,000. Each term is 10 times the previous term.

4. $\frac{5}{6}$, 1. Written with the common denominator 6, the sequence becomes $\frac{1}{6}, \frac{2}{6}, \frac{3}{6}, \frac{4}{6}, \frac{5}{6}, \frac{6}{6}, \cdots$

5. −17, −21. Four is subtracted from each term to get the next term.

6. 28, 36. To get from term to term, you add 2, then add 3, then add 4, and so on.

7. 21, 34. To find each term, you add the two previous terms.

8. 49, 64. The terms are the squares of consecutive whole numbers: $1^2, 2^2, 3^2, 4^2, 5^2, 6^2, \ldots$ The next two terms are $7^2 = 49$ and $8^2 = 64$.

9. −10, −24. To get from term to term, you subtract 2, then subtract 4, then subtract 6, and so on.

10. 64, 128. Each term is double the previous term.

11. Each figure has one more point than the previous figure. Each point in a figure is connected to each of the other points.

12. To get the next figure, increase the number of rows by 2 and the number of columns by 1.

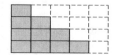

13. To get the next figure, add one row to the bottom and one column to the right of the previous figure, and then shade all the rectangles in the bottom row but the rightmost one.

14. To create each figure, add two branches to each of the new branches from the previous figure.

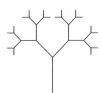

15. To create each figure, connect the midpoints of the sides of each shaded triangle of the previous figure, dividing it into four triangles, and then color the middle triangles white.

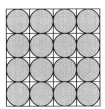

16. The *n*th figure is an *n*-by-*n* grid of squares with a shaded circle inscribed in each square.

17. The first term is $3(1) - 2$, the second term is $3(2) - 2$, the third term is $3(3) - 2$, and so on. So, the first five terms are 1, 4, 7, 10, 13.

18. The fifth term is $\frac{5(5 + 1)}{2}$, the sixth term is $\frac{6(6 + 1)}{2}$, and so on. So, the next five terms are 15, 21, 28, 36, 45.

19. Sample answer: 1, −2, 4, −8, 16, ... Each term is −2 times the previous term.

20. Sample answers: 3, 6, 12, 24, 48, . . . and 4, 8, 12, 16, 20, ...

21. Sample answer: I learned by trial and error that you turn wood screws clockwise to screw them into wood and counterclockwise to remove them. This is inductive reasoning because it involves making generalizations from patterns.

22. 7th term: 56; 10th term: 110; 25th term: 650. Look for a pattern in the arrangements of dots. Notice that in each figure, the number of columns of dots is one greater than the number of rows. Also notice that the number of rows is the same as the term number. Thus, the *n*th figure has *n* rows and $(n + 1)$ columns, so it contains $n(n + 1)$ dots. To find the 7th term, let $n = 7$. $7(7 + 1) = 7(8) = 56$. Likewise, the 10th term is $10(11) = 110$, and the 25th term is $25(26) = 650$.

23. The conjecture is false. Sample counterexample: $14^2 = 196$ but $41^2 = 1681$.

24. In each case, the middle digit in the product is the number of 1's in each factor. The digits to the left of the middle digit are consecutive integers, from 1 up to the middle digit. The digits to the right of the middle digit are the same as the digits on the left, but in reverse order. So

$11{,}111 \cdot 11{,}111 = 123{,}454{,}321$

$111{,}111 \cdot 111{,}111 = 12{,}345{,}654{,}321$

However, in the tenth line, 1,111,111,111 is multiplied by itself. The digits can't go up to 10, so, carrying the 1, you get

$1{,}111{,}111{,}111 \cdot 1{,}111{,}111{,}111$
$= 1{,}234{,}567{,}900{,}987{,}654{,}321$

25.

26.

27.

28.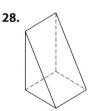

29. Turn your book so that the red line is vertical. Imagine rotating the figure so that you can see faces on both sides of the red line. Possible answers:

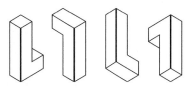

30. Sample answer:

31. collinear

32. isosceles

33. dodecagon

34. parallel

35. protractor

36. radius

37. diagonal

38. regular

39. 90°

40. perpendicular

41. Sample answer:

42. Sample answer:

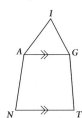

43. Sample answer:

44. Possible answer:

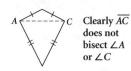

Clearly $\overline{AC}$ does not bisect $\angle A$ or $\angle C$

45. Possible answer: Draw $\overline{AB}$ with length 9 cm. Using A as the vertex, draw a 40° angle with $\overline{AB}$ along one side. Then, using B as the vertex, draw a 60° angle that also has $\overline{AB}$ along one side. Extend the sides of the two angles until they intersect. Their point of intersection, C, will be the third vertex of the triangle.

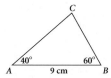

No. It is not possible to draw a second different triangle with the same two angle measures and side length between them. A second triangle drawn with these given measures would be congruent to the first one.

IMPROVING YOUR REASONING SKILLS

1. 9. The sequence is the perfect squares, in reverse order, written backward. That is, the first term is 9^2, or 81, written backward; the second term is 8^2, or 64, written backward; and so on. Because the last term listed is 4^2, or 16, written backward, the next term must be 3^2, or 9, written backward. But 9 written backward is just 9, so the next term is 9.

2. T. The terms are the first letters in the words *One, Two, Three, Four,* and so on. The last term listed is the first letter in *Nine,* so the next term must be T, the first letter in *Ten.*

3. 64. The sequence can be rewritten as 1, 2^2, 3, 4^2, 5, 6^2, 7. The next term must be 8^2, or 64.

4. 8671. To find each term, you double the previous term and then write the digits in the reverse order. To find the next term, double 884 to get 1768 and then reverse the digits to get 8671.

5. 18. The numbers added to or subtracted from each term to get the next term are consecutive primes. The pattern alternates between addition and subtraction. The next term is $1 + 17$, or 18.

6   8   5   10   3   14   1
+2   −3   +5   −7   +11   −13

6. 2. Each number is the number of "open ends" on the previous letter. The letter **G** has two open ends.

7. 2. The steps below show how the sequence is generated. To get the third term, multiply the first two

terms, 2 and 3, and write the product, 6, at the end of the list. To generate the next term, multiply the 3 (the second term you used to find the previous product) and the next term, 6. Write the digits of the product, 1 and 8, as separate terms at the end of the list. To get the next term, multiply the 6 (the second term you used to find the previous product) by the next term, 1, and write the product's digits (in this case, just 6) at the end of the list. Continue this process to get the remaining terms.

$\underline{2}, \underline{3} \rightarrow 2 \cdot 3 = 6 \rightarrow 2, 3, 6$

$2, \underline{3}, \underline{6} \rightarrow 3 \cdot 6 = 18 \rightarrow 2, 3, 6, 1, 8$

$2, 3, \underline{6}, \underline{1}, 8 \rightarrow 6 \cdot 1 = 6 \rightarrow 2, 3, 6, 1, 8, 6$

$2, 3, 6, \underline{1}, \underline{8}, 6 \rightarrow 1 \cdot 8 = 8 \rightarrow 2, 3, 6, 1, 8, 6, 8$

$2, 3, 6, 1, \underline{8}, \underline{6}, 8 \rightarrow 8 \cdot 6 = 48 \rightarrow 2, 3, 6, 1, 8, 6, 8, 4, 8$

$2, 3, 6, 1, 8, \underline{6}, \underline{8}, 4, 8 \rightarrow 6 \cdot 8 = 48 \rightarrow 2, 3, 6, 1, 8, 6, 8, 4, 8, 4, 8$

$2, 3, 6, 1, 8, 6, \underline{8}, \underline{4}, 8 \rightarrow 8 \cdot 4 = 32 \rightarrow 2, 3, 6, 1, 8, 6, 8, 4, 8, 4, 8, 3, 2$

$2, 3, 6, 1, 8, 6, 8, \underline{4}, \underline{8}, 4, 8, 3, 2 \rightarrow 4 \cdot 8 = 32 \rightarrow 2, 3, 6, 1, 8, 6, 8, 4, 8, 4, 8, 3, 2, 3, 2$

$2, 3, 6, 1, 8, 6, 8, 4, \underline{8}, \underline{4}, 8, 3, 2, 3, 2 \rightarrow 8 \cdot 4 = 32 \rightarrow 2, 3, 6, 1, 8, 6, 8, 4, 8, 4, 8, 3, 2, 3, 2, 3, 2$

8. The letters in the top row are formed from straight segments only. The letters in the bottom row have curves. Because X, Y, and Z have only straight segments, they belong in the top row.

EXTENSION

Discussions will vary.

LESSON 2.2

EXERCISES

1. $6n - 3$; 117. Possible method: The difference between terms is always 6, so the rule is $6n +$ "something." Let c stand for the unknown "something." The first term, $f(1)$, is 3, so $6(1) + c = 3$. Solving this equation gives $c = -3$. So, the rule is $f(n) = 6n - 3$. To find the 20th term, substitute 20 for n: $f(20) = 6(20) - 3 = 120 - 3 = 117$.

2. $-3n + 4$; -56. Possible method: The difference between the terms is always -3, so the rule is $-3n + c$ for some number c. To find c, use the fact that the value of the first term, $f(1)$, is 1. So, $-3(1) + c = 1$. Solving this equation gives $c = 4$, so the rule is $f(n) = -3n + 4$. To find the 20th term, substitute 20 for n: $f(20) = -3(20) + 4 = -56$.

3. $8n - 12$; 148

4. 33

Number of sides	3	4	5	6	n	35
Number of triangles formed	1	2	3	4	$n - 2$	33

5. $8n$; 1600. Possible method: Fill in the table for the first four terms. The difference is always 8. Continue this pattern for terms 5 and 6. The rule is $8n + c$ for some number c. Because the first term is 8, $8(1) + c = 8$, and so $c = 0$. Thus, the rule is $8n$. The number of tiles in the 200th figure must be $8(200)$, or 1600.

Figure number	1	2	3	4	5	6	n	200
Number of tiles	8	16	24	32	40	48	$8n$	1600

6. $4n - 3$; 797. Possible method: Fill in the table for the first four terms. The difference is always 4. Continue this pattern for terms 5 and 6. The rule is $4n + c$ for some number c. Because the first term is 1, $4(1) + c = 1$, and so $c = -3$. Thus, the rule is $4n - 3$. The number of tiles in the 200th figure must be $4(200) - 3$, or 797.

Figure number	1	2	3	4	5	6	n	200
Number of tiles	1	5	9	13	17	21	$4n - 3$	797

7. Number of matchsticks: $4n + 1$; 801. Possible method: Fill in the table for the first four terms. The difference of the numbers in the "number of matchsticks" row is always 4. Use the pattern to fill in the table for Figures 5 and 6. The rule is in the form $4n + c$. Using the first term, $4(1) + c = 5$. Therefore, $c = 1$, so the rule for the number of matchsticks is $4n + 1$. The 200th figure has $4(200) + 1$, or 801, matchsticks.

Matchsticks in perimeter: $3n + 2$; 602. Possible method: The difference of the numbers in the "number of matchsticks in perimeter of figure" row is always 3. Use this fact to fill in the numbers for Figures 5 and 6. The rule is in the form $3n + c$. Using the first term, $3(1) + c = 5$. Therefore, $c = 2$, so the rule for the number of matchsticks in the perimeter is $3n + 2$. The 200th figure has $3(200) + 2$, or 602, matchsticks in its perimeter.

Figure number	1	2	3	4	5	6	n	200
Number of matchsticks	5	9	13	17	21	25	$4n + 1$	801
Number of matchsticks in perimeter of figure	5	8	11	14	17	20	$3n + 2$	602

8. The points for $8n$ (Exercise 5) lie on the steepest line. The coefficient of n gives a measure of the steepness. (It is the slope of the line.)

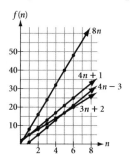

9. C_2H_{2n+2}. Each carbon atom has one hydrogen atom above it and one hydrogen below it, plus there is always one hydrogen atom on each end of the chain. So, if there are n carbon atoms, there are $2n + 2$ hydrogen atoms.

$$H - C - C - C - C - C - C - C - C - H$$

Octane (C_8H_{18})

10. $y = \frac{3}{2}x + 3$. Possible reasoning: The slope of the line through the points is $\frac{9 - 6}{4 - 2}$, or $\frac{3}{2}$, and the y-intercept is 3. So the equation is $y = \frac{3}{2}x + 3$.

x	-4	-2	0	2	4
y	-3	0	3	6	9

11.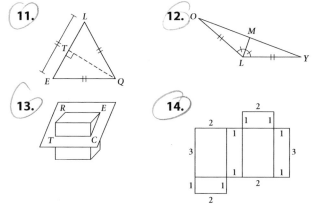

12.

13.

14.

15. Possible answer: Márisol should point out that although all the triangles José drew were isosceles, it is possible to draw a triangle with no two sides congruent. She should then show José such a counterexample.

16. Possible answer: Use the ruler to draw $\overline{AB}$ of length 8 cm. Use the protractor to draw a 45° angle with point A as its vertex. Use the ruler to measure a distance 9 cm along the side of the angle that does not lie along $\overline{AB}$ to form $\overline{AC}$. Connect points B and C to form the third side of triangle ABC.

No. A second triangle drawn with these given measures would be congruent to the first one.

17. She could try eating one food at a time; inductive.

18. 2600. Look for a pattern in the arrangements of squares in the rectangular arrays. Notice that in each one, the number of columns of squares is two greater than the number of rows. Also notice that the number of rows is the same as the array number. Thus, the nth array has n rows and $(n + 2)$ columns, so it contains $n(n + 2)$ squares. To find the number of squares in the 50th array, let $n = 50$: $50(52) = 2600$, so the 50th array contains 2600 squares.

PROJECT

Project should satisfy the following criteria:

- Topic, relationship, data, and source are clearly presented.

- Accurate graph shows a line of best fit.

- Student includes two or more predictions and a summary of results.

Extra credit

- Student chooses one relationship where it is expected that the points will fall in a straight line, and another where there is some scatter.

- A geometric pattern is explored such as data on width and area of figures, or number of figures in a sequence and figure perimeter.

- A slider is used in Fathom to fit a curve to nonlinear data.

LESSON 2.3

EXERCISES

1. $2n$; 70. The diagrams below show the results for one line through four lines. Notice that the number of regions is always twice the number of lines. So, the function rule is $2n$, and 35 concurrent lines divide the plane into 70 regions.

| 1 line | 2 lines | 3 lines | 4 lines |
| 2 regions | 4 regions | 6 regions | 8 regions |

Lines	1	2	3	4	5	n	35
Regions	2	4	6	8	10	$2n$	70

2. $n + 1$; 36. The diagrams below show the results for one parallel line through four parallel lines. Notice that the number of regions is always one more than the number of lines. Therefore, the rule is $n + 1$, and 35 parallel lines divide the plane into 36 regions.

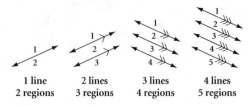

| 1 line | 2 lines | 3 lines | 4 lines |
| 2 regions | 3 regions | 4 regions | 5 regions |

Lines	1	2	3	4	5	n	35
Regions	2	3	4	5	6	$n + 1$	36

3. $n - 3$; 32. From each vertex, you can draw a diagonal to any vertex except the two adjacent vertices and the vertex itself. Therefore, if a polygon has n sides, you can draw $n - 3$ diagonals from each vertex. So, if a polygon has 35 sides, you can draw 32 diagonals.

Sides	3	4	5	6	7	n	35
Diagonals	0	1	2	3	4	$n - 3$	32

4. $\frac{n(n - 3)}{2}$; 560. For an n-sided polygon, you can draw $n - 3$ diagonals from each vertex (see Exercise 3) for a total of $n(n - 3)$ diagonals. However, this counts each diagonal twice. Therefore, the total number of diagonals for an n-sided polygon is $\frac{n(n - 3)}{2}$. So, if a polygon has 35 sides, you can draw $\frac{35(35 - 3)}{2}$, or 560, diagonals.

Sides	3	4	5	6	7	n	35
Diagonals	0	2	5	9	14	$\frac{n(n - 3)}{2}$	560

5. $\frac{n(n - 1)}{2}$; 595. This is essentially the same as the handshake problem in the investigation. If there are n points, you need to draw $n - 1$ segments (each point must be connected to each point but itself) for a total of $n(n - 1)$ segments. However, this counts each segment twice, so you must divide by 2. Therefore, for n points, you need to draw

$\frac{n(n-1)}{2}$ segments. So, for 35 points, you need to draw $\frac{35(35-1)}{2}$, or 595, segments.

Points	1	2	3	4	5	n	35
Segments	0	1	3	6	10	$\frac{n(n-1)}{2}$	595

6. $\frac{n(n-1)}{2}$; 595. If there are n lines, then each line intersects each of the other $n-1$ lines for a total of $n(n-1)$ intersection points. However, this counts each intersection point twice, so you must divide by 2. Therefore, for n lines, there are $\frac{n(n-1)}{2}$ intersection points. So, for 35 lines, there are $\frac{35(35-1)}{2}$, or 595, intersection points.

Lines	1	2	3	4	5	n	35
Intersections	0	1	3	6	10	$\frac{n(n-1)}{2}$	595

7. Visualize the points in Exercises 5 and 6 as vertices of a polygon, as in Exercise 4. The total number of segments connecting n random points is the number of diagonals of the n-sided polygon, $\frac{n(n-3)}{2}$, plus the number of sides, n. Thus, the total number of segments connecting n random points is

$$\frac{n(n-3)}{2} + \frac{2n}{2} = \frac{n(n-3)+2n}{2}$$
$$= \frac{n^2-3n+2n}{2} = \frac{n^2-n}{2}$$
$$= \frac{n(n-1)}{2}$$

8. 780. If each house must be connected to each of the other houses by a direct line, then this situation is similar to Exercise 5 (and to the handshake problem). The formula for n houses is $\frac{n(n-1)}{2}$. So, for 40 houses, 780 lines are needed. It is more practical to have a central hub with a line to each house, so that only 40 lines are needed. The diagrams show the direct-line solution and the practical solution for six houses.

9. 180 games are played. Possible model: First suppose each team plays each of the other teams *once*. Use points to represent the teams and segments to represent the games. This is the same model used in Exercise 5 (and the handshake problem). If n teams each play each other once, $\frac{n(n-1)}{2}$ games are played. If they play each other four times, $4 \cdot \frac{n(n-1)}{2}$, or $2n(n-1)$, games are played. For a ten-team league, $2(10)(10-1)$, or 180, games are played.

10. 12. If $\frac{n(n-1)}{2} = 66$, then $n(n-1) = 132$. Find two consecutive integers whose product is equal to 132. Because $12 \cdot 11 = 132$, n must be 12. Thus, there were 12 people at the party.

11. True

12. True

13. False. An isosceles right triangle has two congruent sides.

14. False. Here, $\angle AED$ and $\angle BED$ are not a linear pair.

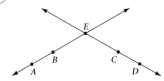

15. False. They are parallel.

16. True

17. False. A rectangle is a parallelogram with all of its angles congruent.

18. False. A diagonal connects any two *nonconsecutive* vertices.

19. True

20. 5049. In each figure, the number of rows of circles is one more than the figure number, while the number of columns is one less than twice the figure number. Thus, the nth figure will contain $(n+1)$ rows and $(2n-1)$ columns of circles, for a total of $(n+1)(2n-1)$ circles. This means that the nth term in the numbers pattern is $(n+1)(2n-1)$, so the 50th term will be $(50+1)(2 \cdot 50 - 1) = (51)(99) = 5049$.

IMPROVING YOUR VISUAL THINKING SKILLS

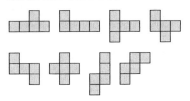

EXTENSION

Below are several examples of quadratic functions. In each case the constant second difference is twice the coefficient of the squared term.

$y = 3x^2 - 10$

x	1	2	3	4	5	6	7
y	−7	2	17	38	65	98	137

+9 +15 +21 +27 +33 +39

+6 +6 +6 +6 +6

$y = -x^2 + 2$

x	1	2	3	4	5	6	7
y	1	−2	−7	−14	−23	−34	−47

−3 −5 −7 −9 −11 −13

−2 −2 −2 −2 −2

$y = 2x^2 - 3x + 1$

x	1	2	3	4	5	6	7
y	0	3	10	21	36	55	78

+3 +7 +11 +15 +19 +23

+4 +4 +4 +4 +4

LESSON 2.4

EXERCISES

1. inductive; deductive

2. $m\angle B = 65°$. This problem is solved *deductively,* by subtracting 25° from 90°.

3. Each term includes a figure and a number. Each figure is a regular polygon with one more side than the previous polygon and contains two fewer dots than the number of sides. The numbers are squares of consecutive integers. The next two terms are shown below. This solution involves observing patterns and making generalizations, which is inductive reasoning.

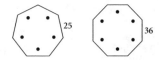

4. $DG = 258$ cm; deductive. $TD + DG + GT = 756$. Let x be the length of DG. Then x is also the length of TD. So, $x + x + 240 = 2x + 240 = 756$. Therefore, $2x = 516$, so $x = 258$ cm. This solution involves deductive reasoning because it uses a sequence of logical statements that are based on agreed-upon assumptions and proven facts.

5. $m\angle 1 = 20°$; $m\angle 2 = 32°$; $m\angle 3 = 37°$; $m\angle 4 = 27°$; $m\angle 5 = 64°$. The sum of these angle measures is 180°. If this pattern continues, the sum of the marked angles in star E will also be 180°. This solution involves inductive reasoning.

6. *LNDA* is a parallelogram. This conclusion involves deductive reasoning because it is based on agreed-upon assumptions.

7. Possible answer: Use the same figure that appears in Step 2 of the Overlapping Segments Investigation.

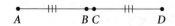

From the given information, $AB = CD$, so by the Addition Property of Equality, $AB + BC = CD + BC$. Using Segment Addition gives $AB + BC = AC$ and $CD + BC = BD$; so, by Substitution, $AC = BD$. By the Definition of Congruent Segments, $\overline{AC} \cong \overline{BD}$.

8. a. $CD = AB = 3$

   b. By the Overlapping Segments Property, $BD = AC = 10$.

   c. By the Overlapping Segments Property, $AC = BD = 4 + 3 = 7$.

9. Just over 45°. The smallest possible obtuse angle is just over 90°. So, the smallest possible acute angle formed when an obtuse angle is bisected is just over $\frac{1}{2}(90°)$, or 45°.

10. $m\angle CPB = 48°$; $m\angle APD = 17°$; $m\angle CPB = 62°$. Conjecture: If points C and D lie in the interior of $\angle APB$, and $m\angle APC = m\angle DPB$, then $m\angle APD = m\angle CPB$.

11. Possible answer: Refer to the figure for Exercise 10 in the textbook. From the given information, $m\angle APC = m\angle BPD$. Add the same measure to both sides to get $m\angle APC + m\angle CPD = m\angle BPD + m\angle CPD$. By Angle Addition, $m\angle APC + m\angle CPD = m\angle APD$, and $m\angle BPD + m\angle CPD = m\angle CPB$. By Substitution, $m\angle APD = m\angle CPB$.

12. Sample answer: I wanted to buy a CD that cost $15.89. I had $17, and I wasn't sure it would be enough. The sales tax is 5%. I know that 10% of $16 is $1.60, so 5% of $16 would be half of that, or $0.80. So, if the CD had cost $16, the total price would have been $16.80. Because the actual cost was $15.89, I knew the total price would have to be less than that. So, I figured out that I did have enough money. This is an example of deductive reasoning because it involves a series of logical steps, each of which is based on facts.

13. The pattern cannot be generalized because once the river is straight, it cannot get any shorter.

14. 900, 1080. Each term is 180 more than previous term.

15. 75, 91. Add 10, then add 11, then add 12, and so on.

16. $\frac{4}{5}$, 12. The terms alternate between fractions and integers. The integers are consecutive. The denominators of the fractions are consecutive integers, and each numerator is one less than its denominator.

17. The first term is one line, the second term is two intersecting lines, and the third term is three lines, each of which intersects the other two. So, the fourth term is four lines, each intersecting the other three.

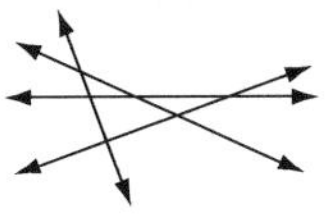

18. Each term has one more row and one more column than the previous term. The shading alternates between "top half shaded" and "left half shaded."

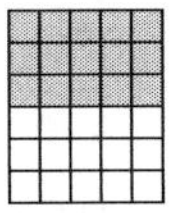

19. In the next term, the number of rows will increase by 2 and the number of columns will increase by 1. In each corner, a 3-by-3 square will be shaded.

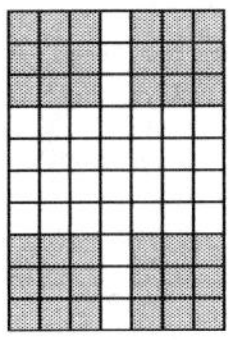

20. Each term contains polygons with one more side than the previous term, so the next term must be hexagons. In each term the midpoints of the outer polygon are connected, and then the midpoints of that polygon are connected to form a third polygon.

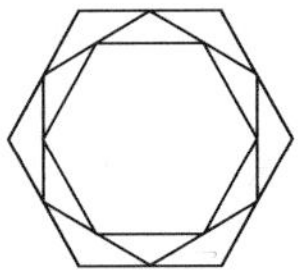

21. Sample answer: My friend is on the basketball team. She has taken two tests the day after a game and received A's on both of them. She concluded that she will get an A on any test given the day after a game. This is an incorrect use of inductive reasoning. The fact that the two A tests were taken the day after a game is probably just a coincidence. The A's also involved a lot of work and studying by my friend. Using her reasoning, you would conclude that no matter how much she studies for a test, even if she doesn't study at all, she will get an A. This is probably not true.

22. L (*Note:* K *looks* like a kite, but without information about the lengths of the other two sides, you cannot conclude that it *is* a kite.)

23. M

24. A (*Note:* O *looks* like a trapezoid, but without information about whether the sides are parallel, you cannot conclude that it *is* a trapezoid.)

25. B   **26.** E   **27.** C   **28.** G

29. D   **30.** H

31. I (*Note:* The segment in J *looks* like an angle bisector, but without information about whether the angles formed are congruent, you cannot conclude that it *is* an angle bisector.)

32. 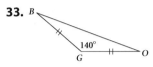   **33.**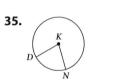

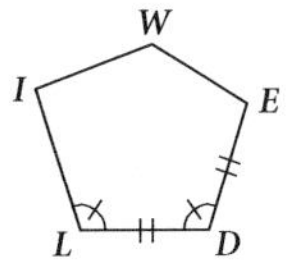

34. 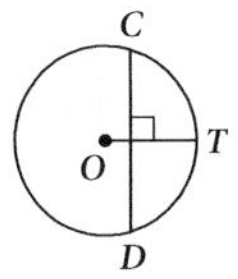   **35.**

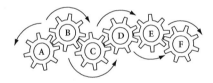

IMPROVING YOUR VISUAL THINKING SKILLS

Each gear will rotate in the opposite direction of the gear to its left. Gear E will rotate counterclockwise.

EXTENSION

Discussions will vary.

LESSON 2.5

EXERCISES

In Exercises 1–5, there is more than one way to find each answer. One possible method is described.

1. By the Vertical Angles Conjecture, $a = 60°$. By the Linear Pair Conjecture, $b = 120°$ and $c = 120°$.

2. By the Linear Pair Conjecture, $a = 90°$ and $b = 90°$. By the Vertical Angles Conjecture, $40° + c = 90°$, so $c = 50°$.

3. By the Linear Pair Conjecture, $51° + (a + 52°) = 180°$, so $a = 77°$. By the Vertical Angles Conjecture, $b = 52°$, $c = 77°$, and $d = 51°$.

4. By the Vertical Angles Conjecture, $a = 60°$. By the Linear Pair Conjecture, $b = 120°$ and $c = 120°$. Similar reasoning can be used to find the other angles: $d = 115°$, $e = 65°$, $f = 115°$, $g = 125°$, $h = 55°$, $i = 125°$.

5. By the Linear Pair Conjecture, $a = 90°$. By the Vertical Angles Conjecture, $b = 163°$. By the Linear Pair Conjecture, $c = 17°$. By the Linear Pair Conjecture, $d = 110°$ and $e = 70°$.

6. The measures of the linear pair of angles add to $170°$. They should add to $180°$.

7. The angles must be the same size and their measures must add to $90°$, so he should cut the ends at a $45°$ angle.

8. Greatest: $120°$; smallest: $60°$. Possible explanation: The tree is perpendicular to the horizontal. The angle of the hill measures $30°$. The smaller angle and the angle between the hill and the horizontal form a pair of complementary angles, so the measure of the smaller angle is $90° - 30°$, or $60°$. The smaller angle and the larger angle form a linear pair, so the measure of the larger angle is $180° - 60°$, or $120°$.

9. The converse is not true. Possible counterexample:

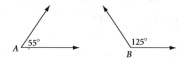

10. Each must be a right angle.

11. Let x be the measure of each of the congruent angles. The angles are supplementary, so $x + x = 180°$. Therefore $2x = 180°$, so $x = 90°$. Thus each angle is a right angle.

12. The ratio is always 1. The ratio does not change as long as the lines don't coincide. The demonstration may convince students that the Vertical Angles Conjecture is true, but it does not explain *why* it is true.

13.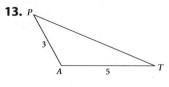

14.   **15.**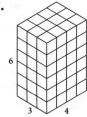

16.   **17.**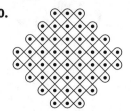

18. Possible answer: All the cards look exactly as they did, so it must be the 4 of diamonds because it has rotational symmetry, while the others do not.

19. $\dfrac{360°}{16} = 22.5°$ **20.**

21. C_nH_{2n}. The number of hydrogen atoms is always twice the number of carbon atoms. So, if there are n carbon atoms, there are $2n$ hydrogen atoms.

22. $4n + 6$; 806; $(n + 1)(n + 2)$; 40,602. Possible method for perimeter: Fill in the table for the fourth rectangle. Notice that the perimeter increases by 4 with each rectangle. Use this pattern to fill in the values for 5 and 6. The rule is in the form $4n + c$ for some number c. Using the data for case 1, $4(1) + c = 10$, so $c = 6$. Therefore, the rule is $4n + 6$. The perimeter of the 200th rectangle is $4(200) + 6$, or 806.

To find the rule for the number of squares, notice for the first few cases that the number of columns for the nth rectangle is $n + 1$, and the number of rows is one more than that, $n + 2$. Thus, the total number of 1×1 squares is $(n + 1)(n + 2)$. The number of squares in the 200th rectangle is $201 \cdot 202 = 40,602$.

Rectangle	1	2	3	4	5	6	n	200
Perimeter of rectangle	10	14	18	22	26	30	$4n + 6$	806
Number of squares	6	12	20	30	42	56	$(n + 1)(n + 2)$	40,602

23. 3160. Possible method: This is essentially the same as the handshake problem, so use the rule $\dfrac{n(n - 1)}{2}$. For 80 students, $\dfrac{80(79)}{2}$, or 3160, pieces of string are needed.

24. 3160. Possible method: If there are 80 lines, then each intersects 79 other lines, for a total of 80(79) intersections. However, this counts each intersection twice, so there are actually $\frac{80(79)}{2}$, or 3160, intersections.

25. 760. Possible method: There are 40 people and each shakes hands with 38 other people. However, simply multiplying 40 · 38 counts each handshake twice, so you must divide by 2. Therefore the number of handshakes is $\frac{40(38)}{2}$, or 760, handshakes.

26. 21; 252. Possible method: 21 diagonals can be drawn from each of the 24 vertices for a total of 21 · 24 diagonals. However, this counts each diagonal twice. So, the actual number of diagonals is $\frac{24(21)}{2}$, or 252.

27. 35. Possible method: Let n be the number of diagonals, then $\frac{n(n-3)}{2} = 560$. So, $n(n-3) = 1120$. You can solve this problem by guessing and checking or by rewriting the equation as $n^2 - 3n - 1120 = 0$ and then factoring or using the quadratic formula. The solution is $n = 35$, so the polygon has 35 diagonals.

28. M is the midpoint of $\overline{AY}$; deductive.

IMPROVING YOUR ALGEBRA SKILLS

1. The length of the first segment is $3(x-3) + 20$. The length of the second segment is $2(2x-23) + 30$. Because the segments are the same length, set these expressions equal and solve.

$3(x-3) + 20 = 2(2x-23) + 30$

$3x - 9 + 20 = 4x - 46 + 30$ Apply the distributive property.

$3x + 11 = 4x - 16$ Combine the constant terms.

$11 = x - 16$ Subtract $3x$ from both sides.

$27 = x$ Add 16 to both sides.

2.
$x+3$	$x+3$	14

$x-4$	$x-4$	$x-4$	11

LESSON 2.6

EXERCISES

1. By the Alternate Interior Angles Conjecture, $w = 63°$.

2. By the Corresponding Angles Conjecture, $x = 90°$.

3. No. By the Linear Pair Conjecture, the angle above the 122° angle has measure 58°. Because the corre-

sponding angles indicated below are not congruent, the lines are not parallel.

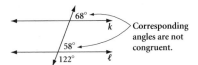

Corresponding angles are not congruent.

4. Extend $\overline{AN}$ to the left and label a point Q on the extension. Because $\overleftrightarrow{AN}$ and $\overleftrightarrow{TU}$ are parallel, the alternate interior angles $\angle T$ and $\angle QAT$ are congruent. Thus, $m\angle QAT = 57°$. Because $\overleftrightarrow{AT}$ and $\overleftrightarrow{NU}$ are parallel, the corresponding angles $\angle N$ and $\angle QAT$ are congruent. Thus, $y = m\angle N = 57°$.

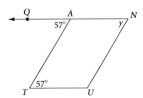

5. Yes. Extend $\overline{FI}$ to the left and label a point G on the extension. By the Linear Pair Conjecture, $m\angle HFG = 65.°$ Because the alternate interior angles $\angle SHF$ and $\angle HFG$ are congruent, $\overline{HS}$ and $\overline{FI}$ are parallel by the Converse of the Parallel Lines Conjecture. Because the corresponding angles $\angle HFG$ and $\angle I$ are congruent, the same conjecture tells us that $\overline{SI}$ and $\overline{HF}$ are parallel. Because quadrilateral $FISH$ has two pairs of parallel opposite sides, it is a parallelogram.

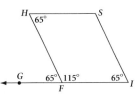

6. In the diagram below, some of the angles have been numbered. Because $m \parallel n$, $m\angle 1 = 67°$ by the Alternate Interior Angles Conjecture. Thus, $m\angle 2$ is also 67°. Because $\angle 2$ and $\angle 3$ are alternate interior angles, $m\angle 3 = 67°$. By the Linear Pair Conjecture, $z = 113°$.

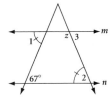

7. $a = 64°$, $b = 116°$, $c = 116°$, $d = 64°$, $e = 108°$, $f = 72°$, $g = 108°$, $h = 72°$, $i = 108°$, $j = 108°$, $k = 108°$, $m = 105°$, $n = 79°$, $p = 90°$, $q = 116°$, $s = 72°$, and $t = 119°$. $a = 64°$ by the Vertical Angles Conjecture, $d = 64°$ by the Alternate Exterior Angles Conjecture, $b = 116°$ by the Linear Pair Conjecture, $c = 116°$ by the Alternate Exterior Angles Conjecture, $e = 108°$ by the Alternate Interior Angles Conjecture,

$g = 108°$ by the Vertical Angles Conjecture, $i = 108°$ by the Corresponding Angles Conjecture, $j = 108°$ by the Vertical Angles Conjecture, $k = 108°$ by the Alternate Exterior Angles Conjecture, $f = 72°$ by the Linear Pair Conjecture, $h = 72°$ by the Alternate Exterior Angles Conjecture, $s = 72°$ by the Linear Pair Conjecture, $m = 105°$ by the Linear Pair Conjecture, $n = 79°$ by the Vertical Angles Conjecture, $p = 90°$ by the Linear Pair Conjecture, $q = 116°$ by the Corresponding Angles Conjecture, and $t = 119°$ by the Linear Pair Conjecture.

8. In the diagram, lines l and m are parallel and intersected by transversal k. By the Corresponding Angles Conjecture, $m\angle 1 = m\angle 2$. By the Vertical Angles Conjecture, $m\angle 2 = m\angle 3$. Substitute $m\angle 1$ for $m\angle 2$ in the last equation to get $m\angle 1 = m\angle 3$. The alternate exterior angles 1 and 3 are congruent. Therefore, if two parallel lines are cut by a transversal, then alternate exterior angles are congruent. (This is the Alternate Exterior Angles Conjecture.)

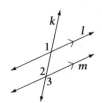

9. By the Linear Pair Conjecture, the angle labeled 1 at right has measure 124°. For the lines to be parallel, this angle would have to have measure 114°. Therefore, the lines are not really parallel.

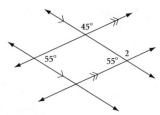

10. By the Linear Pair Conjecture, the angle labeled 2 below has measure 125°. For the lines marked with double arrowheads to be parallel, this angle would have to have measure 45°. Therefore, those lines are not really parallel. By a similar argument, the lines marked with single arrowheads are not parallel.

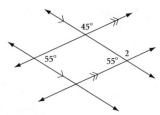

11. The incoming and outgoing angles measure 45°. The surfaces of the mirror are parallel. Possible explanation: The alternate interior angles are congruent and thus, by the Converse of the Parallel Lines Conjecture, the mirrors are parallel.

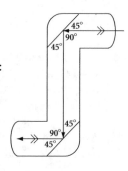

12. Explanations will vary. Sample explanation: I used the protractor to make corresponding angles congruent when I drew line PQ.

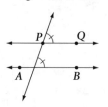

13. No. Tomorrow could be a holiday. Converse: "If tomorrow is a school day, then yesterday was part of the weekend." The converse is also false.

14. $x = 42°$. Look at the angle that forms a linear pair with the angle with measure x and is on the same side of the transversal. This angle and the angle with measure $4x - 30$ form a pair of corresponding angles, so they are congruent by the Corresponding Angles Conjecture. Therefore, the angle forming a linear pair with the angle with measure x must also have measure $4x - 30$. By the Linear Pair Conjecture, the two angles forming the linear pair are supplementary, giving the equation $x + (4x - 30) = 180$. Solve this equation to find the value of x.

$$x + (4x - 30) = 180$$

$x + 4x - 30 = 180$	Remove parentheses.
$5x - 30 = 180$	Combine like terms.
$5x = 210$	Add 30 to both sides.
$x = 42°$	Divide both sides by 5.

15. $y = 20°$. First look at the pair of corresponding angles with measures $3x + 16$ and $216 - 2x$. By the Corresponding Angles Conjecture, their measures are equal, which gives the equation $3x + 16 = 216 - 2x$. Solve this equation to find the value of x.

$3x + 16 = 216 - 2x$	
$5x + 16 = 216$	Add $2x$ to both sides.
$5x = 200$	Subtract 16 from both sides.
$x = 40°$	Divide both sides by 5.

Now look at the pair of angles with measures $7y - 4$ and $216 - 2x$. These are vertical angles, so their measures are equal, which gives the equation $7y - 4 = 216 - 2x$. Substitute 40 for x and then solve the resulting equation to find the value of y.

$7y - 4 = 216 - 2x$	
$7y - 4 = 216 - 2(40)$	Substitute 40 for x.
$7y - 4 = 216 - 80$	Multiply.
$7y - 4 = 136$	Subtract.
$7y = 140$	Add 4 to both sides.
$y = 20°$	Divide both sides by 7.

Discovering Geometry Solutions Manual
©2008 Key Curriculum Press

16. No. If $x = 12°$, then $4x - 2(6 - 3x) = 4(12) - 2(6 - 3 \cdot 12) = 48 - 2(6 - 36) = 48 - 2(-30) = 48 + 60 = 108$, so the measure of the lower exterior angle in the figure would be 108°. Now look at the angle directly above the lower exterior angle. It forms a linear pair with the angle whose measure we have found to be 108°, so its measure is $180° - 108° = 72°$. However, if the lines were parallel, its measure would have to be 80° by the Corresponding Angles Conjecture. Therefore, the lines are not parallel.

17. Isosceles triangles (which include equilateral triangles)

18. Parallelograms that are not rectangles, squares, or rhombuses

19. 18 cm

20. 39°

21. Each of the 84 phones is connected to 83 other phones, for a total of 83(84) lines. However, this counts each line twice, so the actual number of lines is $\frac{83(84)}{2}$, or 3486.

22. 30 squares (one 4-by-4, four 3-by-3, nine 2-by-2, and sixteen 1-by-1)

23. The triangle moved to the left one unit. The new triangle is congruent to the original.

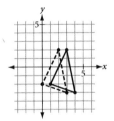

24. The quadrilateral was reflected across both axes, or rotated 180° about the origin. The new quadrilateral is congruent to the original.

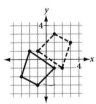

25. The pentagon was reflected across the line $y = x$. The new pentagon is congruent to the original.

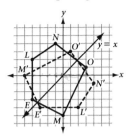

26. (See table at bottom of page.)

PROJECT

Project should satisfy the following criteria:

- Correct equations are given for the lines:
$y = -\frac{1}{7}x + 1$, $y = -\frac{2}{6}x + 2$, $y = -\frac{3}{5}x + 3$, $y = -\frac{4}{4}x + 4$, $y = -\frac{5}{3}x + 5$, $y = -\frac{6}{2}x + 6$, and $y = -7x + 7$.

- Student creates another line design and states equations that match the lines.

Extra credit

Student creates several unique line designs.

EXTENSIONS

A. Results will vary.

B. The angle properties of transversals crossing parallel lines are true on a cylinder, because the cylinder can be mapped without distortion onto the plane. To visualize this, draw long parallel lines and a transversal on a sheet of paper and wrap the paper into a cylinder, making the parallel lines become circles or helixes.

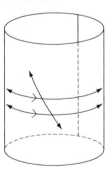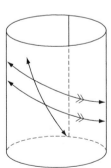

Lesson 2.6, Exercise 26

Figure number	1	2	3	4	5	6	n	35
Number of yellow squares	2	3	4	5	6	7	$n + 1$	36
Number of blue squares	3	5	7	9	11	13	$2n + 1$	71
Total number of squares	5	8	11	14	17	20	$3n + 2$	107

EXERCISES

1. $m = \dfrac{y_2 - y_1}{x_2 - x_1} = \dfrac{8 - 0}{12 - 16} = \dfrac{8}{-4} = -2$

2. $m = \dfrac{y_2 - y_1}{x_2 - x_1} = \dfrac{8 - (-4)}{-16 - (-3)} = -\dfrac{12}{13}$

3. $m = \dfrac{y_2 - y_1}{x_2 - x_1} = \dfrac{-1.5 - 8.2}{0.7 - 5.3} = \dfrac{-9.7}{-4.6} \approx 2.1$

4.

$\dfrac{y - 2}{2 - (-5)} = 3$	The slope of the line through $(-5, 2)$ and $(2, y)$ is 3.
$\dfrac{y - 2}{7} = 3$	Simplify the denominator.
$y - 2 = 21$	Multiply both sides by 7.
$y = 23$	Add 2 to both sides.

5.

$\dfrac{9 - 2}{7 - x} = \dfrac{7}{3}$	The slope of the line through $(x, 2)$ and 7, 9) is $\frac{7}{3}$.
$\dfrac{7}{7 - x} = \dfrac{7}{3}$	Simplify the numerator.
$7(3) = 7(7 - x)$	Multiply both sides by $3(7 - x)$.
$21 = 49 - 7x$	Use the distributive property.
$-28 = -7x$	Subtract 49 from both sides.
$4 = x$	Divide both sides by -7.

6. The slope of the line through $(0, 0)$ and $(3, -4)$ is $-\frac{4}{3}$. One way to locate another point on the line is to start at $(3, -4)$ and move down 4 units and right 3 units. This gives $(6, -8)$. To find other points, you can continue this pattern of moving down 4 units and right 3 units. Possible answers: $(6, -8)$, $(9, -12)$, and $(12, -16)$ (Any correct point will be of the form $(3p, -4p)$.)

7. The speed is the slope of the line. Using the points marked, $m = \frac{400 - 200}{6 - 3} = \frac{200}{3} \approx 66.7$ mi/h.

8. At 6 m/s, Skater 1 is 4 m/s faster than Skater 2 at 2 m/s.

9. A 100% grade has a slope of 1. It has an inclination of 45°, so you probably could not drive up it. You might be able to walk up it. Grades higher than 100% are possible, but the angle of inclination would be greater than 45°.

10. The slope of the adobe house flat roof is approximately 0. The Connecticut roof is steeper to shed the snow.

CHAPTER 2 REVIEW

EXERCISES

1. Diana is using poor inductive reasoning, but she was probably just joking.

2. Sample situation: One night my sister arrived home 15 minutes after her curfew and did not get in trouble. She concluded that she would never get punished as long as she wasn't more than 15 minutes late. A few days later, she got home 10 minutes late and was punished. My sister used poor inductive reasoning because she based her conclusion on only one observation.

3. Sample situation: When Leslie found out her party was on the same night as a home football game, she said, "Half the people I invited won't even show up!" Because she invited 20 people, her brother concluded that only 10 people would show up. On the night of the party, 18 guests arrived. This is incorrect deductive reasoning because it is based on a faulty assumption (that half the people would not show up).

4. 19, -30. Each term is the difference of the two previous terms. The next two terms are $8 - (-11)$, or 19, and $-11 - (19)$, or -30.

5. S, 36. The pattern alternates between numbers and letters. The letters start with A and skip 2 letters, then 3 letters, then 4 letters, and so on. The numbers are the squares of consecutive integers, starting with 2^2.

6. 2, 5, 10, 17, 26, 37. Here's how to calculate the first three terms:

$1^2 + 1 = 2$

$2^2 + 1 = 5$

$3^2 + 1 = 10$

7. 1, 2, 4, 8, 16, 32. Here's how to calculate the first three terms:

$2^{1-1} = 2^0 = 1$

$2^{2-1} = 2^1 = 2$

$2^{3-1} = 2^2 = 4$

8. Look at the pattern on each face separately. The top face appears to be rotating 90° with each term. On the left face, the shaded square alternates between the first and second row and moves down the columns. On the right face, the figures in the four squares seem to be rotating in a clockwise direction and alternating between a solid triangle and an outlined triangle.

9. The figures alternate between a net for a pyramid and a pyramid. The number of sides in the base increases by 1 with each term. Because the last figure shown is a pyramid with a hexagonal base, the next figure will be the net for a pyramid with a heptagonal base.

10. 900. Look for a pattern in the sums:

$$1 = 1 = 1^2 \quad \text{First 1 odd number}$$
$$1 + 3 = 4 = 2^2 \quad \text{First 2 odd numbers}$$
$$1 + 3 + 5 = 9 = 3^2 \quad \text{First 3 odd numbers}$$
$$1 + 3 + 5 + 7 = 16 = 4^2 \quad \text{First 4 odd numbers}$$
$$1 + 3 + 5 + 7 + 9 = 25 = 5^2 \quad \text{First 5 odd numbers}$$

Based on this pattern, the sum of the first 30 odd whole numbers is 30^2, or 900.

11. 930. Look for a pattern in the sums:

$$2 = 1(2) \quad \text{First 1 even number}$$
$$2 + 4 = 6 = 2(3) \quad \text{First 2 even numbers}$$
$$2 + 4 + 6 = 12 = 3(4) \quad \text{First 3 even numbers}$$
$$2 + 4 + 6 + 8 = 20 = 4(5) \quad \text{First 4 even numbers}$$
$$2 + 4 + 6 + 8 + 10 = 30 = 5(6) \quad \text{First 5 even numbers}$$

Based on this pattern, the sum of the first 30 even whole numbers is $30(31)$, or 930.

12. $-3n + 5$; -55. Possible method: The difference between $f(n)$ values is always -3, so the rule is in the form $-3n + c$ for some number c. Using the first term, $-3(1) + c = 2$, so $c = 5$. Therefore, the nth term is $-3n + 5$ and the 20th term is $-3(20) + 5 = -55$.

13. $\frac{n(n + 1)}{2}$, 210

14. n^2; 900. Possible method: The number of blocks in a stack n blocks high is the sum of the first n odd whole numbers. From Exercise 10, the sum is n^2. A stack 30 blocks high would require 30^2, or 900, blocks.

15. 5050. Possible method: The number of bricks in stacks like the one shown is always a triangular number, so it's determined by the formula $\frac{n(n + 1)}{2}$. A stack 100 bricks high would have $\frac{100(101)}{2}$, or 5050, bricks.

16. $\frac{n(n - 1)}{2} = 741$. Therefore, $n = 39$.

17. $\frac{n(n - 1)}{2} = 2926$. Therefore, $n = 77$.

18. 52. These diagrams show that for an n-sided polygon, you can draw $n - 3$ diagonals from each vertex, dividing the interior into $n - 2$ regions. So,

in a 54-sided polygon, the diagonals would divide the interior into 52 regions.

4 sides
1 diagonal
2 regions

5 sides
2 diagonals
3 regions

6 sides
3 diagonals
4 regions

7 sides
4 diagonals
5 regions

19. a. Sample answer: $\angle AFE$ and $\angle CFG$ (or $\angle CFH$)

b. Sample answer: $\angle AFE$ and $\angle CFE$

c. Sample answer: $\angle CFE$ and $\angle DGF$ (or $\angle DGE$)

d. Either of these pairs: $\angle AFG$ and $\angle DGF$, or $\angle CFG$ and $\angle BGF$

20. $\angle AFE \cong \angle CFG$ Vertical Angles Conjecture

$\angle AFE \cong \angle BGE$ Corresponding Angles Conjecture

$\angle AFE \cong \angle DGH$ Alternate Exterior Angles Conjecture

21. True. Converse: If the polygons have the same number of sides, they are congruent. The converse is false.

Possible counterexample:

22. Draw a ray and use a protractor to draw a 56° angle at the endpoint. Mark a point 7 cm from the endpoint, and use the protractor to draw another 56° angle to create congruent corresponding angles. Extend the side of each angle and mark a point 4.5 cm from the angle vertex. Connect these points. To check that the opposite sides are congruent, measure the corresponding angles and alternate interior angles shown to confirm that they measure 56°.

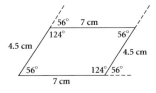

23. $\overrightarrow{PV} \parallel \overrightarrow{RX}$ and $\overrightarrow{SU} \parallel \overrightarrow{VX}$. Possible explanation: Look at points P, Q, R, S, and X. Each of these points is the vertex of four angles, one of which has a given angle measure. Using the Vertical Angles Conjecture and the Linear Pair Conjecture, find the measures of the other three angles at each of these vertices. At P and R, the angle measures are 132° and 48° (two angles with each measure at each vertex), while at S and X, the angle measures are 134° and 46°. By looking at the measures of corresponding angles and applying the Converse of the Parallel Lines Conjecture, $\overset{\leftrightarrow}{PV} \parallel \overset{\leftrightarrow}{RX}$ and $\overset{\leftrightarrow}{SU} \parallel \overset{\leftrightarrow}{VX}$.

24. Possible answer: Because the two lines cut by the transversal are parallel, the measure of the bisected angle must be 50° by the Alternate Interior Angles Conjecture. Then each half of the bisected angle must measure 25°. The angle bisector is also part of a transversal, so, again by the Alternate Interior Angles Conjecture, the measure of the other acute angle in the triangle must also be 25°. However, this angle and the 165° angle are a linear pair, so the sum of their measures must be 180°; but 165° + 25° = 190°, not 180°.

25. $a = 38°$, $b = 38°$, $c = 142°$, $d = 38°$, $e = 50°$, $f = 65°$, $g = 106°$, and $h = 74°$. $a = 38°$ by the Linear Pair Conjecture, $b = 38°$ by the Alternate Interior Angles Conjecture, $c = 142°$ because it forms a linear pair with the alternate interior angle of b, $d = 38°$ by the Alternate Exterior Angles Conjecture, $f = 65°$ because it is half of the angle corresponding to the 130° angle, $e = 50°$ by the Linear Pair Conjecture, $g = 106°$ by the Corresponding Angles Conjecture, and $h = 74°$ by the Linear Pair Conjecture.

CHAPTER 3

LESSON 3.1

EXERCISES

1. To duplicate $\overline{AB}$, draw a ray that is clearly longer than $\overline{AB}$. Label the endpoint A. Open your compass to the length of $\overline{AB}$ in the book. Then, without changing the compass opening, place the sharp end of your compass on point A of your ray and draw an arc that intersects the ray. Label the point of intersection B. Duplicate $\overline{CD}$ and $\overline{EF}$ in the same way.

2. Duplicate segment $\overline{AB}$ as described in the solution to Exercise 1. Then duplicate segment $\overline{CD}$ so that the left endpoint is the right endpoint of the previous segment.

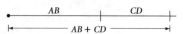

3. Draw a long ray and copy $\overline{AB}$.

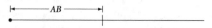

Copy $\overline{EF}$ twice so that the left endpoint of each segment is the right endpoint of the previous segment.

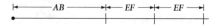

Copy $\overline{CD}$ so that its *right* endpoint is the right endpoint of the previous segment. (This essentially subtracts CD from the combined length of the previous segments.)

The segment from the left endpoint of the first segment copied to the left endpoint of the last segment copied has length $AB + 2EF - CD$.

4.

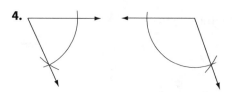

Follow these steps to duplicate each angle:

Step 1 Draw a ray.

Step 2 Go back to the angle in the book. Open your compass so that it reaches from the vertex of that angle to the arc.

Step 3 Without changing the opening of your compass, place the sharp end on the endpoint of the ray you drew, and draw a large arc.

Step 4 Go back to the angle in the book. Notice that the arc intersects the angle in two points. Open your compass so that it reaches from one intersection point to the other.

Step 5 Go back to your drawing. Without adjusting the compass, place the sharp end on the point where the arc intersects the ray, and draw a small arc that intersects the large arc.

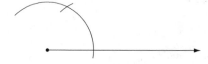

Discovering Geometry Solutions Manual
©2008 Key Curriculum Press

Step 6 Draw a ray from the endpoint of the original ray you drew through the point where the arcs intersect.

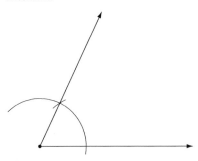

5. Possible answer:

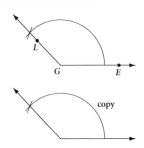

6. Possible answer:

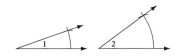

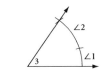

7. Possible answer:

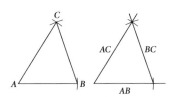

Follow these steps to duplicate △ABC:

Step 1 Duplicate ∠A.

Step 2 Duplicate $\overline{AB}$ on one side of ∠A, and duplicate $\overline{AC}$ on the other side.

Step 3 Connect the endpoints of the segments from the previous step. Use a compass to verify that the resulting segment is the same length as $\overline{BC}$.

8. Here are the steps for constructing the triangle.

Step 1 Duplicate the segment.

Step 2 From each endpoint of the duplicated segment, make an arc of the same length as the segment so that the arcs intersect above the segment.

Step 3 Connect the endpoints of the segment with the intersection point of the arcs to form a triangle.

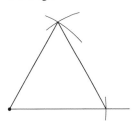

9. For Exercise 7, trace the triangle. For Exercise 8, trace the segment onto three separate pieces of patty paper. Lay them on top of each other, and slide them around until the segments join at the endpoints and form a triangle.

10. Quadrilaterals and methods will vary. Possible method: Draw $\overline{DU}$. Duplicate ∠Q and construct △COY ≅ △QUD. Duplicate ∠DUA at point O. Construct △OYP ≅ △DAU.

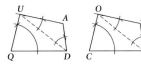

11. Possible method: Construct a daisy design using the Circle tool. Make sure the outer circles are connected to the center of the middle circle. Connect every other intersection point to form a triangle.

12. a = 50°, b = 130°, c = 50°, d = 130°, e = 50°, f = 50°, g = 130°, h = 130°, k = 155°, l = 90°, m = 115°, and n = 65°. a = c = 50° by the Linear Pair Conjecture, b = 130° by the Vertical Angles Conjecture, d = 130° by the Corresponding Angles Conjecture, e = 50° by the Linear Pair Conjecture, f = 50° by the Corresponding Angles Conjecture, g = 130° by the Linear Pair Conjecture, h = 130° by the Corresponding Angles Conjecture, k = 155° by the Linear Pair Conjecture, l = 90° by definition, m = 115° by the Corresponding Angles Conjecture, and n = 65° by the Linear Pair Conjecture.

13. West. Use the given information to make a sketch. The lettered streets are perpendicular to the numbered streets, which are all parallel, so the lettered streets must also be parallel. The fact that P is the northernmost street indicates that the lettered streets run west to east and are in reverse alphabetical order from north to south. Therefore, K is north of J. If Hyacinth is facing 24th Street with Avenue J to her left, she must be facing west.

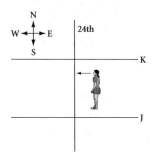

14. An isosceles triangle is a triangle that has at least one line of reflectional symmetry. Yes, all equilateral triangles are isosceles.

15.

16. New coordinates: $A'(0, 0)$, $Y'(4, 0)$, $D'(0, 2)$

17. Methods will vary. Students might draw two of the sides on tracing paper or patty paper, and arrange them over the third side to form a triangle.

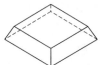

No. It is not possible to draw a different triangle with the same three side lengths. A second triangle drawn with the given side lengths would be congruent to the first one.

IMPROVING YOUR ALGEBRA SKILLS

$a = 32$, $b = 56$, $c = 46$, $d = 73$. Possible method: From the diagram, $b + d = 129$ and $b + c = 102$. Subtracting the second equation from the first gives $d - c = 27$. From the diagram, $d + c = 119$. Adding the equations $d - c = 27$ and $d + c = 119$ gives $2d = 146$, or $d = 73$. Once you know the value of d, it is easy to find the values of the other variables.

LESSON 3.2

EXERCISES

1. Draw $\overline{AB}$. Open your compass to more than half the length of $\overline{AB}$. With the sharp end of your compass on one endpoint of $\overline{AB}$, make arcs above and below the segment. Repeat for the other endpoint. Draw a line through the points where the arcs intersect.

2. Bisect $\overline{QD}$ and then bisect each half.

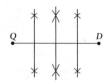

3. Use one compass setting to construct two intersecting arcs, one arc centered at each endpoint of the segment. Then repeat the process with a different compass setting. (All the arcs will be on the same side of the segment.) Draw a line that intersects the segment through the two intersection points.

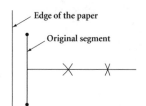

4. First, bisect $\overline{CD}$ to create two segments of length $\frac{1}{2}CD$. Second, construct a segment with length $2AB$. Then duplicate a segment with length $\frac{1}{2}CD$ so that the right endpoint of the segment is the right endpoint of the previous segment.

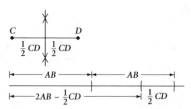

5. The average of two lengths is half the sum of the lengths. So, construct a segment of length $AB + CD$, and then bisect it.

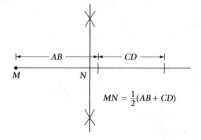

Discovering Geometry Solutions Manual
©2008 Key Curriculum Press

6. For Exercise 1:

This is the same as Investigation 1.

For Exercise 2:

Step 1 Draw a segment on patty paper. Label it $\overline{QD}$.

Step 2 Fold your patty paper so that endpoints Q and D coincide. Crease along the fold.

Step 3 Unfold and draw a line in the crease.

Step 4 Label the point of intersection A.

Step 5 Fold your patty paper so that endpoints Q and A coincide. Crease along the fold.

Step 6 Unfold and draw a line in the crease.

Step 7 Label the point of intersection B.

Step 8 Fold your patty paper so that endpoints A and D coincide. Crease along the fold.

Step 9 Unfold and draw a line in the crease.

Step 10 Label the point of intersection C.

For Exercise 3:

This is the same as Investigation 1.

For Exercise 4:

Step 1 Do Investigation 1 to get $\frac{1}{2}CD$.

Step 2 On a second piece of patty paper, trace $\overline{AB}$ two times so that the two segments form a segment of length $2AB$.

Step 3 Lay the first piece of patty paper on top of the second so that the endpoints coincide and the shorter segment is on top of the longer segment.

Step 4 Trace the rest of the longer segment with a different colored pen or pencil. That will be the answer.

For Exercise 5:

Step 1 Trace $\overline{AB}$ and $\overline{CD}$ so that the two segments form a segment of length $AB + CD$.

Step 2 Fold your patty paper so that points A and D coincide. Crease along the fold.

Step 3 Unfold and draw a line in the crease.

7. The perpendicular bisectors all intersect in one point.

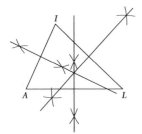

8. The medians all intersect in one point.

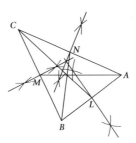

9. Possible answer: $\overline{GH}$ appears to be parallel to $\overline{EF}$, and its length is half the length of $\overline{EF}$.

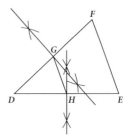

10. The quadrilateral appears to be a rhombus.

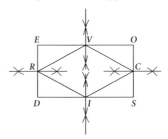

11. Any point on the perpendicular bisector would be equidistant from the two post offices. Therefore, any point on one side of the perpendicular bisector would be closer to the post office on that side.

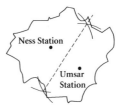

12. The quadrilateral appears to be a parallelogram.

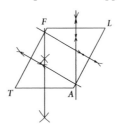

13. The triangles are not necessarily congruent, but their areas are equal. To balance a cardboard triangle on the edge of a ruler, line the ruler up with the median of the triangle.

14. One way to balance it is along the median. The two halves weigh the same. Sample figure:

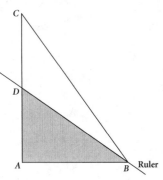

15. F   **16.** E

17. B   **18.** A

19. D   **20.** C

21. B, C, D, E, H, I, O, X (K is symmetric in some fonts, though not the one used).

22. Possible answer: Draw a 40° angle with vertex *A*. On a piece of patty paper, draw a 70° angle with vertex *B*. Line up one side of each angle and measure the distance from *A* to the intersection point of the other angle sides. Slide ∠*B* until the distance is 10 cm. Copy the triangle formed onto the patty paper, and label the intersection point *C*.

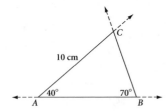

A second triangle drawn with these given measures would be congruent to the first one.

IMPROVING YOUR VISUAL THINKING SKILLS

  1. B   **2.** C   **3.** A

LESSON 3.3

EXERCISES

  1. The answer depends on the angle drawn and the placement of *P*. Possible construction:

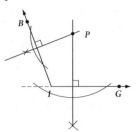

2. Construct a perpendicular from point *C* through $\overleftrightarrow{AB}$. Point *D* will be the intersection of the perpendicular and $\overleftrightarrow{AB}$. Possible construction:

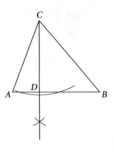

3. Extend $\overline{OT}$ and construct a perpendicular from point *B* to $\overleftrightarrow{OT}$. Point *U* will be the intersection point of the perpendicular with $\overleftrightarrow{OT}$. Possible construction:

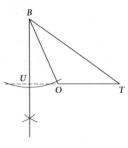

Two altitudes fall outside the triangle (the altitudes from the vertices with acute angles) and one falls inside.

4. From the point, swing arcs on the line to construct a segment whose midpoint is that point. Then construct the perpendicular bisector of the segment.

5. Construct perpendiculars to $\overleftrightarrow{QR}$ from points *Q* and *R*. Mark off $\overline{QS}$ and $\overline{RE}$ congruent to $\overline{QR}$. Connect points *S* and *E*.

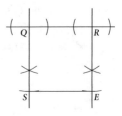

6. To construct the perpendicular through *Q*, fold the line onto itself so that *Q* is on the crease. If point *Q* is on the perpendicular through *P*, then the two folds will be the same. Otherwise, they will be parallel. The diagram at right shows the latter case.

7. Fold the patty paper through the point so that two perpendiculars coincide to see the side closest to the point. Fold again using the perpendicular of the side closest to the point and the third perpendicular; compare those sides.

8. To construct the triangle: Draw a line. Mark two points on it, and label them A and C. Construct a perpendicular at C. Mark off $\overline{CB}$ congruent to $\overline{CA}$. Connect points A and B.

To construct altitude $\overline{CD}$: Fold $\overline{AB}$ onto itself so that point C is on the crease. Label the point where the crease intersects $\overline{AB}$ point D. Draw $\overline{CD}$. The altitude $\overline{CD}$ is also the perpendicular bisector of $\overline{AB}$ (or, the altitude $\overline{CD}$ is also the median to side $\overline{AB}$).

9. Extend side $\overrightarrow{OT}$. Fold $\overrightarrow{OT}$ onto itself so that point B is on the crease. Label the point where the crease intersects $\overrightarrow{OT}$ point U. Draw $\overline{BU}$.

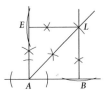

10. Draw a horizontal line and label a point on the line A. Construct the perpendicular to the line through point A. Draw an arc through $\angle A$. Put the sharp end of your compass on the points where the arc intersects the horizontal line of the angle, and make an arc to the upper right. Put the sharp end of the compass on the other place the arc intersects the angle, and make a small arc intersecting the last arc you made. Draw the line through this intersection and A. This will be the diagonal of your square. Copy $\overline{AL}$ onto the diagonal. Construct the perpendicular to the horizontal line through L. Label this point B. Construct the perpendicular to the vertical line through L and label this point E.

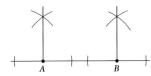

11. Draw $\overline{AB}$.

Construct perpendiculars at points A and B.

Bisect $\overline{AB}$. Label the midpoint M.

Duplicate $\overline{AM}$ on the perpendiculars to create $\overline{AD}$ and $\overline{BC}$. Connect points D and C.

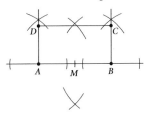

12. Duplicate $\angle A$. Then extend one side of $\angle A$ in the other direction. Construct the perpendicular to that side through point A.

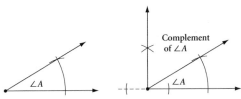

13. $(2n - 1)(n + 1)$; 2484 *(see table at bottom of page)*.

Possible method: In each term, the number of shaded triangles in each row is the same. So, the total number of triangles is the number of rows times the number of shaded triangles in each row.

Term 1	1 row of 2
Term 2	3 rows of 3
Term 3	5 rows of 4
Term 4	7 rows of 5

Look for a pattern. The number of rows in term n is $2n - 1$. The number of shaded triangles in each row of term n is $n + 1$. So, the nth term has $(2n - 1)(n + 1)$ shaded triangles. Therefore, the 35th term has 69(36), or 2484, shaded triangles.

14.

15.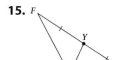

Lesson 3.3, Exercise 13

Rectangle	1	2	3	4	5	6	n	35
Number of shaded triangles	2	9	20	35	54	77	$(2n - 1)(n + 1)$	2484

16.

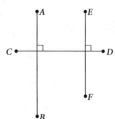

17. To draw the pentagon, start with a circle. Draw five central angles measuring $\frac{360°}{5}$, or 72°. Connect the points where the sides of the angle intersect the circle.

To construct the hexagon, start by drawing a circle. Without changing the setting on your compass, mark a point on the circle and copy the length of the radius five times around the circle. (This is similar to the daisy designs constructed in Chapter 0.) Then connect the points on the circle to form a hexagon, and draw three diagonals connecting alternating vertices to form an equilateral triangle. Connect the other three vertices to form another triangle.

18. The triangles are not congruent.

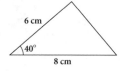 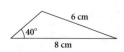

19. Possible answer: **20.** Possible answer:

 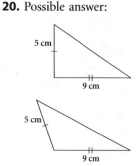

PROJECT

Sample construction:

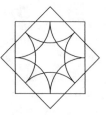

Project should satisfy the following criteria:

• Design is created with patty paper or a compass and straight-edge, and is based on an 8-pointed star.

• Design is filled in with color.

• Construction technique is shown clearly, both in a diagram and in a written description.

Extra credit

• Student creates a very elaborate design, like the sample design in the student text, and includes complete instructions for constructing it.

• Student makes several different designs and includes instructions for constructing each one.

EXTENSION

Put the straightedge on the line segment so that one end of the line segment touches one side of the straightedge and the other end touches the other side. Draw lines. Repeat with the sides touching opposite ends.

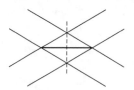

LESSON 3.4

EXERCISES

1. D   **2.** F   **3.** A   **4.** C

5. E

6. Construct a perpendicular at one endpoint of the segment. Put the sharp end of your compass on that endpoint and mark length z on the perpendicular. Connect the endpoints of the original segment and the perpendicular segment to form a triangle.

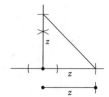

7. To construct the triangle: Duplicate $\overline{RP}$. Draw an arc with length RA centered at R. Draw an arc with length AP centered at P. The intersection point is vertex A. Connect points R and P to A to complete the triangle.

To construct median $\overline{PM}$: Construct the midpoint of $\overline{AR}$, and label it M. Connect points P and M. Construct angle bisector $\overline{RB}$ in the usual way.

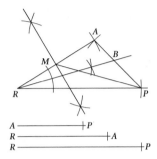

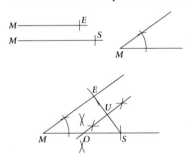

8. To construct the triangle: Duplicate $\angle M$. Duplicate $\overline{ME}$ on one side of $\angle M$ and $\overline{MS}$ on the other side. Connect the endpoints of these segments.

To construct $\overline{OU}$: Construct the midpoint of $\overline{MS}$, and label it O. Construct the midpoint of $\overline{SE}$, and label it U. Connect points O and U.

9. a., b. Constructing a perpendicular to a line creates two 90° angles. To create a 45° angle, bisect one of these angles.

   c. A 90° angle and a 45° angle combined form a 135° angle.

10.

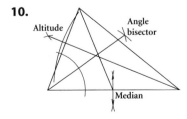

11. Preferences and explanations will vary.

12. The angle bisectors are perpendicular. Possible explanation: The sum of the angle measures of the linear pair is 180°. Therefore, the sum of half of each angle measure must be 90°.

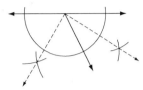

13. If a point is equally distant from the sides of an angle, then it is on the bisector of an angle. This is true for points in the plane of the angle. In three dimensions, these points lie in a plane through the angle bisector perpendicular to the plane of the angle. Opinions about the truth of this statement may vary. (See the note for Exercise 13 in the Helping with the Exercises section on page 161 of the Teacher's Edition.)

14. $y = 110$. Because the lines are parallel, by the Alternate Interior Angles Conjecture, $5x - 10 = 68 - x$. Solve this equation to find the value of x.

$$5x - 10 = 68 - x$$
$$6x - 10 = 68$$
$$6x = 78$$
$$x = 13$$

To find the measure of each of the alternate interior angles, substitute 13 for x in either $68 - x$ or $5x - 10$. Using $5(13) - 10 = 55$, each of these angles has a measure of 55°. Therefore, the measure of the bisected angle is $2(55°) = 110°$. Because the bisected angle and the angle with measure y are also a pair of alternate interior angles, their measures must be equal, so $y = 110$.

15. $m\angle R = 46°$. Because $\overrightarrow{AE}$ bisects $\angle CAR$ and $m\angle CAR = 84°$, $m\angle EAR = 42°$, so $4x + 18 = 42$. Solve this equation to find the value of x.

$$4x + 18 = 42$$
$$4x = 24$$
$$x = 6$$

Now substitute 6 for x in the expression $7x + 4$ to find $m\angle R$: $7(6) + 4 = 46$, so $m\angle R = 46°$.

16. ∠*A*. From the markings on the diagram, the two smaller angles with vertex *B* are $7x - 3 = 57 - 5x$. Solve this equation to find the value of *x*.

$$7x - 3 = 57 - 5x$$

$$12x - 3 = 57$$

$$12x = 60$$

$$x = 5$$

Substitute 5 for *x* to find the measures of each of the three angles of △*ABC*.

∠*A*: $6x + 36 = 6(5) + 36 = 66$, so $m\angle A = 66°$.
∠*B*: $(7x - 3) + (57 - 5x) = [7(5) - 3] + [57 - 5(5)] = 32 + 32 = 64$, so $m\angle B = 64°$. ∠*C*: $8x + 10 = 8(5) + 10 = 50$, so $m\angle C = 50°$. Therefore, ∠*A* is the largest.

17. Stop

18. Construct two perpendicular lines to form four 90° angles. Bisect each angle to form eight 45° angles. Construct a circle centered at the vertex of the angles. Connect the points where the angles intersect the circle.

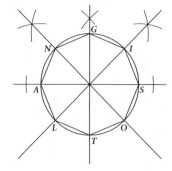

19.

20.

21. The triangles do not look congruent. To draw the first triangle, draw an 8 cm segment with a 40° angle on one end and a 60° angle on the other. Extend the angle sides until they meet to form a triangle. Drawing the second triangle is trickier. Draw a 40° angle and mark off 8 cm along one side. On a piece of patty paper, draw a 60° angle. Match up one side of the 60° angle with the unmarked side of the 40° angle, and slide it along that side until the other side of the 60° angle intersects the

8 cm mark. Copy the resulting triangle onto the patty paper.

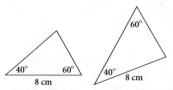

22.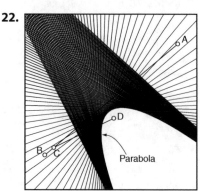

a. A web of lines fills most of the plane, except a U-shaped region and a V-shaped region. (The U-shaped region is actually bounded by a section of a parabola and straight lines. If $\overline{AB}$ were extended to $\overleftrightarrow{AB}$, the U would be a complete parabola.)

b. A line segment parallel to $\overline{AB}$ and half the length of $\overline{AB}$. (The segment is actually the midsegment of △*ABD*.)

IMPROVING YOUR VISUAL THINKING SKILLS

PDDPPPDDDDPPPPDDDDPPPDDP or
DPPDDDPPPPDDDDPPPPDDDPPD

EXTENSION

Align one edge of the straightedge with one side of the angle and draw a line along the other edge of the straightedge. Repeat this process with the other side of the angle. The point where the lines intersect is equidistant from the sides of the angle. The ray from the angle vertex through this intersection point is the angle bisector.

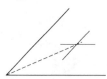

LESSON 3.5

EXERCISES

1. Draw a line intersecting the original line through the point. Duplicate the angle formed by the two lines to create a pair of congruent alternate interior angles, as shown below. Extend the side of the new angle to form a line.

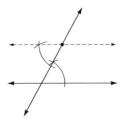

2. Draw a line intersecting the original line through the point. Duplicate the angle formed by the two lines to create a pair of congruent corresponding angles, as shown below. Extend the side of the new angle to form a line.

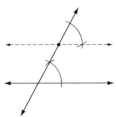

3. Construct a segment with length z. Bisect the segment to get a segment of length $\frac{z}{2}$. Bisect again to get a segment with length $\frac{z}{4}$. Construct a square with each side of length $\frac{z}{4}$.

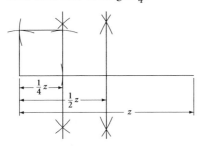

4. Duplicate $\angle A$. Mark off a segment of length x on each side of the angle. This creates two sides of the rhombus. From the endpoint of each of these sides, draw an arc of length x. The intersection point of these arcs is the fourth vertex of the rhombus.

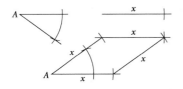

5. Trapezoids and construction methods will vary. The following method was used to construct the trapezoid below.

Step 1 Duplicate $\overline{TR}$.

Step 2 Draw a perpendicular to $\overleftrightarrow{TR}$ through R. Duplicate $\overline{AP}$ on the perpendicular, placing point P on point R. Label the other point A.

Step 3 Draw a perpendicular to $\overrightarrow{RA}$ through point A. (Note: This line and $\overleftrightarrow{TR}$ are both perpendicular to $\overrightarrow{RA}$, so they are parallel to each other.)

Step 4 Duplicate $\overline{AP}$ on the perpendicular drawn in the previous step.

Step 5 Connect points P and T.

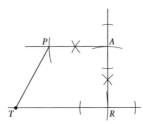

6. Draw a line and construct $\overline{ML}$ perpendicular to it. Swing an arc of length RA from M, and label the point where it intersects the line G. From point G, swing an arc to construct $\overline{RG}$. Finish the parallelogram by swinging an arc of length RA from R and swinging an arc of length GR from M. There is only one possible parallelogram.

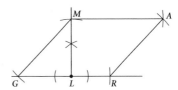

7. $\angle 1 \cong \angle S$ and $\angle 2 \cong \angle U$

8. $\angle 1 \cong \angle S$ and $\angle 2 \cong \angle U$ by the Alternate Interior Angles Conjecture.

9. The ratios appear to be the same.

10. $m\angle 1 \cong m\angle 3$ and $m\angle 2 \cong m\angle 4$ by the Corresponding Angles Conjecture.

11. A parallelogram.

12. In the diagram below, $\angle DAB \cong \angle ABC$. Therefore, by the Converse of the Parallel Lines Conjecture, $\overrightarrow{AD} \parallel \overrightarrow{BC}$. Because the quadrilateral has two pairs of parallel sides, it is a parallelogram.

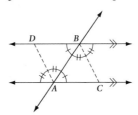

13. Construct the perpendicular bisector of each of the three segments connecting the fire stations.

Eliminate the rays beyond where the bisectors intersect. A point within any region will be closest to the fire station in that region.

14.

15.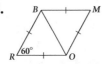

16.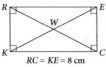

$RC = KE = 8$ cm

17. $a = 72°$, $b = 108°$, $c = 108°$, $d = 108°$, $e = 72°$, $f = 108°$, $g = 108°$, $h = 72°$, $j = 90°$, $k = 18°$, $l = 90°$, $m = 54°$, $n = 62°$, $p = 62°$, $q = 59°$, and $r = 118°$.
$a = 72°$ by the Linear Pair Conjecture, $b = 108°$ by the Vertical Angles Conjecture, $c = 108°$ by the Alternate Interior Angles Conjecture, $d = 108°$ by the Corresponding Angles Conjecture, $e = 72°$ by the Linear Pair Conjecture, $f = 108°$ by the Corresponding Angles Conjecture, $g = 108°$ by the Corresponding Angles Conjecture, $h = 72°$ by the Corresponding Angles Conjecture, $j = 90°$ by the Corresponding Angles Conjecture, $k = 18°$ by the Linear Pair Conjecture, $l = 90°$ by the Alternate Interior Angles Conjecture, $m = 54°$ by the Vertical Angles Conjecture, $n = 62°$ by the Linear Pair Conjecture, $p = 62°$ by the Corresponding Angles Conjecture, $q = 59°$ by the Linear Pair Conjecture, and $r = 118°$ by the Vertical Angles Conjecture.

IMPROVING YOUR VISUAL THINKING SKILLS

1. C   **2.** C   **3.** B

USING YOUR ALGEBRA SKILLS 3

EXERCISES

1. Slope of $\overleftrightarrow{AB} = \frac{4-2}{3-1} = \frac{2}{2} = 1$; slope of $\overleftrightarrow{BC} = \frac{2-4}{5-3} = \frac{-2}{2} = -1$. The slopes, 1 and -1, are opposite reciprocals of one another, so the lines are perpendicular.

2. Slope of $\overleftrightarrow{AB} = 1$; slope of $\overleftrightarrow{CD} = \frac{3-2}{8-5} = \frac{1}{3}$. The slopes, 1 and $\frac{1}{3}$, are neither equal nor opposite reciprocals of one another, so the lines are neither parallel nor perpendicular.

3. Perpendicular

4. Slope of $\overleftrightarrow{CD} = \frac{3-2}{8-5} = \frac{1}{3}$; slope of $\overleftrightarrow{EF} = \frac{5-8}{-6-3} = \frac{-3}{-9} = \frac{1}{3}$. The slopes are equal, so the lines are parallel.

5. Possible answer: $(-8, -7)$ and $(2, 5)$. The slope of $\overleftrightarrow{AB} = \frac{3-(-3)}{5-0} = \frac{6}{5}$. Let (x, y) represent the coordinates of point P. The slope of $\overrightarrow{PQ} = \frac{-1-y}{-3-x}$. The slopes of $\overrightarrow{PQ}$ and $\overleftrightarrow{AB}$ must be equal. That is, $\frac{-1-y}{-3-x} = \frac{6}{5}$. To find one possible solution, set the

denominators equal and set the numerators equal:

$$-3 - x = 5 \qquad -1 - y = 6$$
$$x = -8 \qquad y = -7$$

So, point P could be at $(-8, -7)$. To find another point, write $\frac{6}{5}$ in an equivalent form, say $\frac{-6}{-5}$. So, $\frac{-1-y}{-3-x} = \frac{-6}{-5}$. This gives two new equations:

$$-3 - x = -5 \qquad -1 - y = -6$$
$$x = 2 \qquad y = 5$$

So, P could also be at $(2, 5)$.

6. Possible answer: $(1, -5)$ and $(-2, -12)$. The slope of $\overleftrightarrow{CD} = \frac{-4-(-1)}{5-(-2)} = \frac{-3}{7}$. If (x, y) represents the coordinates of point P, then the slope of $\overrightarrow{PQ} = \frac{2-y}{4-x}$. The slopes of $\overrightarrow{PQ}$ must equal the opposite reciprocal of the slope of $\overleftrightarrow{CD}$, so $\frac{2-y}{4-x} = \frac{7}{3}$. To find one possible solution, set the denominators equal and set the numerators equal:

$$4 - x = 3 \qquad 2 - y = 7$$
$$x = 1 \qquad y = -5$$

So, point P could be at $(1, -5)$. To find another point, write $\frac{7}{3}$ in an equivalent form, say $\frac{14}{6}$. So, $\frac{2-y}{4-x} = \frac{14}{6}$. This gives two new equations:

$$4 - x = 6 \qquad 2 - y = 14$$
$$x = -2 \qquad y = -12$$

So, P could also be at $(-2, -12)$.

7. Slope $\overline{TE} = 1$, slope $\overline{IM} = \frac{4}{3}$, slope $\overline{TI} = -\frac{4}{5}$, slope $\overline{EM} = -1$; ordinary quadrilateral. No two sides have the same slope, so no sides are parallel (although $\overline{TE} \perp \overline{EM}$ because their slopes are opposite reciprocals).

8. Slope $\overline{TE} = \frac{1}{4}$, slope $\overline{AP} = \frac{3}{8}$, slope $\overline{TA} = -4$, slope $\overline{EP} = -\frac{7}{2}$; ordinary quadrilateral. No two sides have the same slope, so no two sides are parallel.

9. Slope $\overline{KC} = \frac{1}{3}$, slope $\overline{RO} = \frac{1}{3}$, slope $\overline{KR}$ is undefined, slope $\overline{CO} = -\frac{1}{3}$; trapezoid. $\overline{KC}$ and $\overline{RO}$ have the same slope, so they are parallel. $\overline{KR}$ and $\overline{CO}$ have different slopes, so they are not parallel. Because quadrilateral $KROC$ has exactly one pair of parallel sides, it is a trapezoid.

10. a. Slope $\overline{HA} = $ slope $\overline{ND} = \frac{1}{6}$; slope $HD = $ slope $NA = -6$. The opposite sides have the same slope, so they are parallel. The adjacent sides have slopes that are opposite reciprocals of one another, so they are perpendicular. Therefore, quadrilateral $HAND$ is a rectangle.

b. Midpoint $\overline{HN} = $ midpoint $\overline{AD} = \left(\frac{1}{2}, 3\right)$. The diagonals of a rectangle bisect each other.

11. a. Yes, the diagonals are perpendicular. Slope $\overline{OE} = 1$, slope $\overline{VR} = -1$.

b. Midpoint $\overline{VR}$ = midpoint $\overline{OE} = (-2, 4)$. The diagonals of *OVER* bisect each other.

c. *OVER* appears to be a rhombus. Slope $\overline{OV}$ = slope $\overline{RE} = -\frac{1}{5}$ and slope $\overline{OR}$ = slope $\overline{VE}$ = -5, so opposite sides are parallel. Also, all of the sides appear to have the same length.

12. a. Both slopes equal $\frac{1}{2}$.

b. The segments are not parallel because they are coincident.

c. Distinct

13. $(3, -6)$. Let (x, y) represent the coordinates of point *D*. Because $\overline{AB}$ and $\overline{CD}$ are parallel, their slopes are equal. That is, $\frac{y - (-3)}{x - 7} = \frac{3}{4}$. Using some algebra, you can rewrite this equation as $3x - 4y = 33$. Because $\overline{AB}$ and $\overline{AD}$ are perpendicular, the slope of $\overline{AD}$ is the opposite reciprocal of the slope of $\overline{AB}$. That is, $\frac{y - 2}{x - (-3)} = -\frac{4}{3}$. You can rewrite this as $4x + 3y = -6$. To find the values of *x* and *y*, solve the system

$$\begin{cases} 3x - 4y = 33 \\ 4x + 3y = -6 \end{cases}$$

To do this, multiply the first equation by 4 and the second equation by 3 and subtract:

$12x - 16y = 132$

$12x + 9y = -18$

$\overline{}$

$-25y = 150$

$y = -6$

Substitute -6 for *y* in either equation to get $x = 3$. So, point *D* has coordinates $(3, -6)$.

LESSON 3.6

EXERCISES

1. Sample description: Duplicate one of the segments, and mark arcs of the correct length from the endpoints. Draw sides to where those arcs meet.

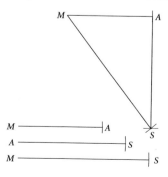

2. Sample description: Duplicate $\angle O$. Mark off distances *OD* and *OT* on the sides of the angle. Connect *D* and *T*.

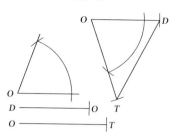

3. Sample description: Construct $\overline{IY}$. Duplicate $\angle I$ at point *I* and $\angle Y$ at point *Y*. Extend the sides of the angles until they intersect. The intersection point is point *G*.

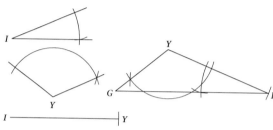

4. There are infinitely many triangles with the same three angles. Sample description: Draw one side with a different length than the lengths in the book. Copy one of the angles from the given triangle at one endpoint of the segment and another angle at the other endpoint. Extend the sides of the angles until they intersect. The intersection point is the third vertex of the triangle.

5. Sample description: Construct $\angle A$ and mark off the distance *AB* on one side of the angle. From *B* swing an arc of length *BC* that intersects the other side of $\angle A$ at two points. Each intersection point gives a different triangle.

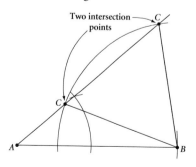

6. Sample description: The sum of the lengths of all the sides of the triangle is *y*. Duplicate the segment of length *y*. Mark off a segment of length *x* on the segment to account for the base of the triangle. The length of each of the other sides is half of the length that remains $\left(\text{that is, } \frac{y-x}{2}\right)$. Bisect the remaining length to find the length of each side. Now, copy the segment of length x. From each end of this segment, make an arc of length $\frac{y-x}{2}$. The point where the arcs intersect is the third vertex of the triangle.

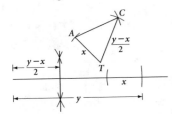

7. Sample description: Draw an angle and mark off congruent segments on the sides of the angle. Then use a different compass setting to draw intersecting arcs from the ends of those segments. The intersection is the fourth vertex of the kite.

8. Sample description: Draw an angle and mark off segments of different lengths on each side of the angle. At the other endpoint of the longer segment (the endpoint that is not the vertex of the angle), swing an arc with the same length as the shorter segment. From the other end of the shorter segment, swing an arc the length of the longer segment. Connect the endpoints of the segments to the intersection point of the arcs to form a quadrilateral.

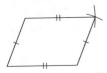

9. Sample description: Draw a segment and draw an angle with its vertex at an endpoint of the segment. Mark off a distance equal to the length of the original segment on the other side of the angle. Draw an angle at that point and mark off the same distance. Connect that point to the other end of the original segment.

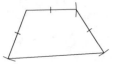

10. Sample description: Draw an angle and mark off equal segments on the two sides. From the other endpoint of each segment (the endpoint that is not the vertex of the angle), draw arcs with lengths equal to the length of the segments. Connect the endpoints of the segments to the intersection point of the arcs to form a quadrilateral.

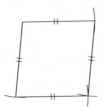

11. Answers will vary. The angle bisector lies between the median and the altitude. The order of the points is either M, R, S or S, R, M. One possible conjecture: In a scalene obtuse triangle, the angle bisector is always between the median and the altitude.

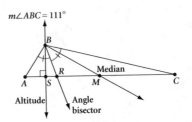

12. New coordinates: $E'(4, -6)$, $A'(7, 0)$, $T'(1, 2)$

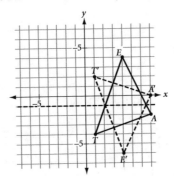

13.

Figure	Reflectional symmetries	Rotational symmetries
Trapezoid	0 or 1	0
Kite	1	0
Parallelogram	0	2
Rhombus	2	2
Rectangle	2	2

[*Note:* a trapezoid has one reflectional symmetry if it is isosceles and zero otherwise.]

14. Half a cylinder

15.
Use the formula from Exercise 3, Lesson 2.3:
diagonals = $n - 3$.
$n = 503$

16.
Draw $\overrightarrow{AC}$ with AC = 5.5 cm. Draw two corresponding 110° angles, one with vertex A and one with vertex C. Measure 3.2 cm along the side of $\angle C$, and label the point E. Draw a 110° angle with vertex E and one side on $\overrightarrow{CE}$ that corresponds to the 110° angle at C. Extend the side parallel to $\overline{AC}$ so that it intersects the side of $\angle A$. Label the intersection point R. By the Converse of the Parallel Lines Conjecture, $\overline{AR} \parallel \overline{CE}$ and $\overline{CA} \parallel \overline{ER}$, so $CARE$ is a parallelogram.

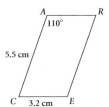

IMPROVING YOUR REASONING SKILLS

One way to solve this problem is to draw 13 blanks to represent the 13 facedown cards in the pile. The top card is represented by the blank on the left, and the bottom card by the blank on the right. To start, spell the word "ACE," moving one blank to the right each time you say a letter (moving to the right models moving the cards to the bottom of the pile). After you have finished spelling the name of the card, write "A" (for *ace*) in the next blank (in this case the fourth blank). Note that now the ace has been placed on the table, so it is no longer part of the deck.

$\underset{A}{\_\_}\ \underset{C}{\_\_}\ \underset{E}{\_\_}\ \overset{A}{\_\_}\ \_\_\ \_\_\ \_\_\ \_\_\ \_\_\ \_\_\ \_\_\ \_\_\ \_\_$

Now start with the next empty blank (which represents the card that is now at the top of the pile), and spell "TWO," moving one *empty* blank for each letter, and write "2" in the next empty blank.

$\_\_\ \_\_\ \_\_\ \overset{A}{\_\_}\ \underset{T}{\_\_}\ \underset{W}{\_\_}\ \underset{O}{\_\_}\ \overset{2}{\_\_}\ \_\_\ \_\_\ \_\_\ \_\_\ \_\_$

Continue this process being careful to *count the empty blanks only*. (Once a card has been turned over, it is no

longer part of the deck.) Here are the steps. The final step shows the way the cards should be ordered for the trick to work: 3, 8, 7, A, Q, 6, 4, 2, J, K, 10, 9, 5.

$\overset{3}{\_\_}\ \_\_\ \_\_\ \overset{A}{\_\_}\ \_\_\ \_\_\ \_\_\ \overset{2}{\_\_}\ \underset{T}{\_\_}\ \underset{H}{\_\_}\ \underset{R}{\_\_}\ \underset{E}{\_\_}\ \underset{E}{\_\_}$

$\overset{3}{\_\_}\ \underset{F}{\_\_}\ \underset{O}{\_\_}\ \overset{A}{\underset{U}{\_\_}}\ \underset{R}{\_\_}\ \_\_\ \overset{4}{\_\_}\ \overset{2}{\_\_}\ \_\_\ \_\_\ \_\_\ \_\_\ \_\_$

$\overset{3}{\_\_}\ \_\_\ \_\_\ \overset{A}{\_\_}\ \_\_\ \_\_\ \overset{4}{\_\_}\ \overset{2}{\_\_}\ \underset{F}{\_\_}\ \underset{I}{\_\_}\ \underset{V}{\_\_}\ \underset{E}{\_\_}\ \overset{5}{\_\_}$

$\overset{3}{\_\_}\ \underset{S}{\_\_}\ \underset{I}{\_\_}\ \overset{A}{\underset{X}{\_\_}}\ \_\_\ \overset{6}{\_\_}\ \overset{4}{\_\_}\ \overset{2}{\_\_}\ \_\_\ \_\_\ \_\_\ \_\_\ \overset{5}{\_\_}$

$\overset{3}{\_\_}\ \underset{N}{\_\_}\ \overset{7}{\_\_}\ \overset{A}{\_\_}\ \_\_\ \overset{6}{\_\_}\ \overset{4}{\_\_}\ \overset{2}{\_\_}\ \underset{S}{\_\_}\ \underset{E}{\_\_}\ \underset{V}{\_\_}\ \underset{E}{\_\_}\ \overset{5}{\_\_}$

$\overset{3}{\_\_}\ \overset{8}{\_\_}\ \overset{7}{\_\_}\ \overset{A}{\underset{E}{\_\_}}\ \_\_\ \overset{6}{\_\_}\ \overset{4}{\_\_}\ \overset{2}{\_\_}\ \underset{I}{\_\_}\ \underset{G}{\_\_}\ \underset{H}{\_\_}\ \underset{T}{\_\_}\ \overset{5}{\_\_}$

$\overset{3}{\_\_}\ \overset{8}{\_\_}\ \overset{7}{\_\_}\ \overset{A}{\_\_}\ \_\_\ \overset{6}{\_\_}\ \overset{4}{\_\_}\ \overset{2}{\underset{N}{\_\_}}\ \_\_\ \underset{I}{\_\_}\ \underset{N}{\_\_}\ \underset{E}{\_\_}\ \overset{9}{\_\_}\ \overset{5}{\_\_}$

$\overset{3}{\_\_}\ \overset{8}{\_\_}\ \overset{7}{\_\_}\ \overset{A}{\underset{T}{\_\_}}\ \_\_\ \overset{6}{\_\_}\ \overset{4}{\_\_}\ \overset{2}{\_\_}\ \_\_\ \underset{E}{\_\_}\ \underset{N}{\_\_}\ \overset{10}{\_\_}\ \overset{9}{\_\_}\ \overset{5}{\_\_}$

$\overset{3}{\_\_}\ \overset{8}{\_\_}\ \overset{7}{\_\_}\ \overset{A}{\_\_}\ \underset{J\atop K}{\_\_}\ \overset{6}{\_\_}\ \overset{4}{\_\_}\ \overset{2}{\_\_}\ \overset{J}{\underset{A\ C}{\_\_}}\ \_\_\ \overset{10}{\_\_}\ \overset{9}{\_\_}\ \overset{5}{\_\_}$

$\overset{3}{\_\_}\ \overset{8}{\_\_}\ \overset{7}{\_\_}\ \overset{A}{\_\_}\ \overset{Q}{\underset{U\atop E}{\_\_}}\ \overset{6}{\_\_}\ \overset{4}{\_\_}\ \overset{2}{\_\_}\ \overset{J}{\_\_}\ \underset{Q\atop E\atop N}{\_\_}\ \overset{10}{\_\_}\ \overset{9}{\_\_}\ \overset{5}{\_\_}$

$\overset{3}{\_\_}\ \overset{8}{\_\_}\ \overset{7}{\_\_}\ \overset{A}{\_\_}\ \overset{Q}{\_\_}\ \overset{6}{\_\_}\ \overset{4}{\_\_}\ \overset{2}{\_\_}\ \overset{J}{\_\_}\ \overset{K}{\_\_}\ \overset{10}{\_\_}\ \overset{9}{\_\_}\ \overset{5}{\_\_}$

EXPLORATION · PERSPECTIVE DRAWING

EXTENSIONS

A., B. Drawings will vary.

LESSON 3.7

EXERCISES

1. The first-aid center must be equidistant from the three bike paths, so it should be at the incenter of the triangle formed by the paths.

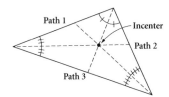

2. The circumcenter is the center of the circumscribed circle.

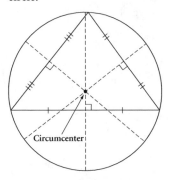

3. The largest circle that fits in a given triangle is the inscribed circle. The center of the inscribed circle is the incenter of the triangle.

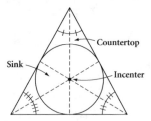

4. The refrigerator, stove, and sink are the vertices of a triangle. The point that is equidistant from these three items is the circumcenter of the triangle.

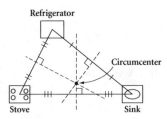

5. The table should be located at the circumcenter of the triangle with vertices at the three points where the classes are positioned. The planners should find the perpendicular bisectors of two of the sides of the triangle and locate the pie table where these two lines intersect.

6. Construct bisectors of two of the angles. The intersection of the bisectors is the incenter. Construct a perpendicular from the incenter to one of the sides of the triangle. Construct a circle centered at the incenter and with a radius equal to the length of the perpendicular from the incenter to the triangle's side.

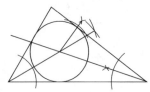

7. Construct perpendicular bisectors of two of the sides. The intersection point is the circumcenter.

Construct a circle centered at the circumcenter and passing through one of the vertices of the triangle.

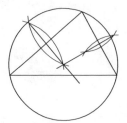

8. Yes. Any circle with a larger radius would not fit within the triangle. To get a circle with a larger radius tangent to two of the sides would force the circle to pass through the third side twice.

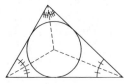

9. The circumscribed circle of an acute triangle does create the smallest circular region that contains the triangle. However, for an obtuse triangle, the circle with the largest side of the triangle as the diameter of the circle creates the smallest circular region that contains the triangle.

10. For an acute triangle, the circumcenter is inside the triangle; for an obtuse triangle the circumcenter is outside the triangle. The circumcenter of a right triangle lies on the midpoint of the hypotenuse.

11. For an acute triangle, the orthocenter is inside the triangle; for an obtuse triangle the orthocenter is outside the triangle. The orthocenter of a right triangle lies on the vertex of the right angle.

12. The midsegment appears to be parallel to, and half the length of, $\overline{MA}$.

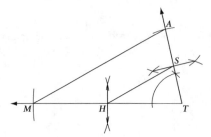

13. Duplicate $\overline{MT}$. Duplicate $\angle T$ at point T. Duplicate $\overline{AT}$ on the other side of $\angle T$. Construct a line parallel to $\overleftrightarrow{MT}$ through point A. Make an arc of length AT centered at point M. Label the point where the arc intersects the parallel line O. Complete trapezoid $MOAT$. The base angles of an isosceles trapezoid appear to be congruent.

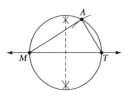

14. The measure of $\angle A$ is 90°. The angle inscribed in a semicircle appears to be a right angle.

15. The diagonals appear to be perpendicular bisectors of each other.

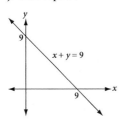

16. The points satisfy the equation $x + y = 9$, or $y = -x + 9$. This is a line with slope -1 and y-intercept 9.

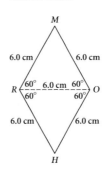

17. Construct the incenter by bisecting the two angles shown.

The incenter is one point on the bisector of the third angle. Now you need to find another point. From the incenter, make arcs of equal radius on the sides to the left and right of the incenter. These points are equidistant from the incenter.

Make arcs centered at each of the points you just constructed. The point where these arcs intersect

is equidistant from the two points, so it is on the angle bisector. To create the angle bisector, draw a line through this intersection point and the incenter.

18. Answers should describe the process of discovering that the midpoints of the altitudes are collinear for a right triangle.

19. A triangle

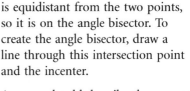

20. Methods for drawing the rhombus will vary. Students may use the fact that a rhombus has reflectional symmetry over its diagonals and draw two congruent equilateral triangles with a shared base.

M

6.0 cm · 6.0 cm

R ⟨60° 60° 6.0 cm 60° 60°⟩ O

6.0 cm · 6.0 cm

H

21. Methods for drawing the kite will vary. Students may use the fact that a kite has reflectional symmetry over one of its diagonals. Draw $\triangle KYE$ with $KY = 4.8$ cm, $m\angle KYE = 40°$, and $YE = 6.4$ cm. Then draw $\triangle TYE$ with $TY = 4.8$ cm and $m\angle TYE = 40$.

Y
40° | 40°
4.8 cm
6.4 cm
K   T
E

22.

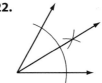

Construction of an angle bisector

23.

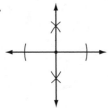

Construction of a perpendicular through a point on a line

24.

Construction of a line parallel to a given line through a given point not on the line

25.

Construction of an equilateral triangle

26.

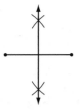

Construction of a perpendicular bisector

IMPROVING YOUR VISUAL THINKING SKILLS

There are several possible solutions. Here is one:

Coin	Placed on		Slid to
First	1	→	4
Second	2	→	7
Third	5	→	2
Fourth	6	→	1
Fifth	3	→	6
Sixth	8	→	3
Seventh	5	→	8
Eighth	5		

EXTENSIONS

A. The incenter of the original triangle is the ortho-center of the triangle formed by connecting the excenters, called the *excentral triangle.*

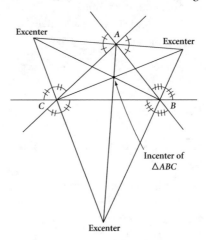

If you draw lines from each vertex of a triangle to the point of tangency of the opposite excircle, the three lines will be concurrent. The point of concurrency is the Nagel Point. Point *X* below is the Nagel Point.

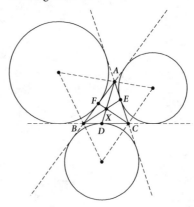

B. Other points of concurrency include the Gergonne Point and the Fermat Point. To construct the Gergonne Point of a triangle, inscribe a circle. Then, draw segments connecting each vertex with the point where the inscribed circle is tangent to the opposite side. The intersection of these segments is the Gergonne Point.

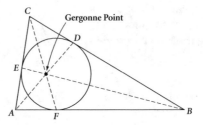

To construct the Fermat Point for $\triangle ABC$, construct equilateral $\triangle ABC'$ on $\overline{AB}$, equilateral $\triangle ACB'$ on $\overline{AC}$, and equilateral $\triangle BCA'$ on $\overline{BC}$. Then, connect A to A', B to B', and C to C'. The intersection of these segments is the Fermat Point.

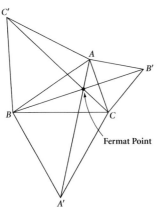

C. See the Teacher's Notes in *Discovering Geometry with The Geometer's Sketchpad* for more information.

LESSON 3.8

EXERCISES

1. The center of gravity is the centroid. She needs to locate the incenter to create the largest circle within the triangle.

2. $AM = 20$; $SM = 7$; $TM = 14$; $UM = 8$. By the Centroid Conjecture, $AM = 2(MO) = 2(10) = 20$. $SM + TM = TS = 21$. By the Centroid Conjecture, $TM = 2(SM)$. Therefore, $SM + 2(SM) = 3(SM) = 21$. So, $SM = 7$. $TM = 2(SM) = 14$. By the Centroid Conjecture, $CM = 2(UM)$. Because $CM = 16$, $UM = 8$.

3. $BG = 24$; $IG = 12$. $EG + GR = ER = 36$. By the Centroid Conjecture, $EG = 2(GR)$. So, $2(GR) + GR = 3(GR) = 36$. Therefore, $GR = 12$. It is given that $GN = GR$, so $GN = 12$. By the Centroid Conjecture, $BG = 2(GN) = 24$. It is given that $IG = GR$, so $IG = 12$.

4. $RH = 42$; $TE = 45$. By the Centroid Conjecture, $AZ = 2(CZ) = 28$. Because $RZ = AZ$, $RZ = 28$. By the Centroid Conjecture, $RZ = 2(HZ)$, so $HZ = 14$. $RH = RZ + HZ = 28 + 14 = 42$. By the Centroid Conjecture, $TZ = 30 = 2(EZ)$, so $EZ = 15$. Therefore, $TE = TZ + ZE = 30 + 15 = 45$.

5. The points of concurrency are the same point for equilateral triangles because the segments are the same.

6. The points of concurrency are collinear. The order is circum-center, centroid, incenter, orthocenter.

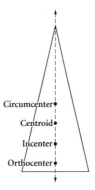

7. Orthocenter, incenter, centroid, circumcenter. The order changes when the triangle becomes equilateral, which is when the points become one.

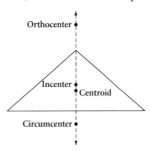

8. For a square, rectangle, and rhombus, the center of gravity is at the point where the diagonals intersect. To find the center of gravity for an ordinary quadrilateral, make a copy of the quadrilateral. Draw a diagonal on one copy, and draw a different diagonal on the other copy. On each copy, find the centroids of the two triangles formed by the diagonals, and construct a segment connecting those centroids. Place the two quadrilaterals on top of each other, matching the congruent segments and angles. The *centroid* of the quadrilateral is the point where the two segments connecting centroids of the triangles intersect.

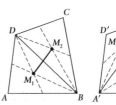

9. Circumcenter

10. The longest chord through P is the diameter through P. The shortest chord through P is a segment perpendicular to the diameter through P.

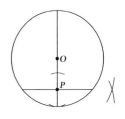

11.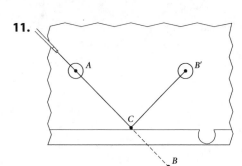

12. $2n - 2$. Possible method: The number of hydrogen atoms appears to increase by 2 each time the number of carbon atoms increases by 1, so the rule is in the form $2n + c$. Using the first term, $2(2) + c = 2$, so $c = -2$. Thus, the rule is $2n - 2$.

$$
\begin{array}{c}
HHH \qquad HHH \\
| | | \qquad | | | \\
H-C-C-C-C\equiv C-C-C-C-H \\
| | | \qquad | | | \\
HHH \qquad HHH
\end{array}
$$

13.

14. $a = 128°$, $b = 52°$, $c = 128°$, $d = 128°$, $e = 52°$, $f = 128°$, $g = 52°$, $h = 38°$, $k = 52°$, $m = 38°$, $n = 71°$, and $p = 38°$. $a = 128°$ by the Vertical Angles Conjecture, $b = 52°$ by the Corresponding Angles Conjecture and the Linear Pair Conjecture, $c = 128°$ by the Corresponding Angles Conjecture and the Linear Pair Conjecture, $d = 128°$ by the Corresponding Angles Conjecture, $e = 52°$ by the Linear Pair Conjecture, $f = 128°$ by the Corresponding Angles Conjecture and the Linear Pair Conjecture, $g = 52°$ by the Corresponding Angles Conjecture and the Linear Pair Conjecture, $h = 38°$ because g and h are complementary, $k = 52°$ by the Alternate Interior Angles Conjecture, $m = 38°$ by the Corresponding Angles Conjecture, $n = 71°$ by the Linear Pair Conjecture, and $p = 38°$ by the Vertical Angles Conjecture.

15. Construct altitudes from the two accessible vertices to locate the orthocenter. Through the orthocenter, construct a line perpendicular to the southern boundary of the property. This method will divide the property equally only if the southern boundary is the base of an isosceles triangle.

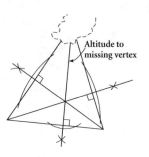

Altitude to missing vertex

16. 1580. There are $3 \cdot 20 = 60$ people at the open house, which gives a total of $\frac{60(59)}{2} = 1770$ greetings. However, you need to subtract all greetings that occur between dorm members. There are $\frac{20(19)}{2} = 190$ of these, so the total number of greetings possible is $1770 - 190 = 1580$.

IMPROVING YOUR REASONING SKILLS

Start dealing from the bottom of the deck in the opposite direction, starting with yourself, until all cards are dealt.

EXTENSION

Research results will vary. See the solutions to Extensions A and B in Lesson 3.7 for information about the Nagel Point and the Fermat Point.

EXPLORATION · THE EULER LINE

PROJECT

Project should satisfy the following criteria:

- The orthocenter of an acute triangle is inside the triangle, that of a right triangle is on the vertex of the right angle, and that of an obtuse triangle is outside the triangle.

- Given a triangle and its orthocenter, any triangle formed by the orthocenter and two vertices of the original triangle has as its orthocenter the third vertex of the original triangle.

Extra credit

- Conjecture: If in any given set of four points, one of the points is the orthocenter of the other three, then each of the four points is the orthocenter of the other three.

CHAPTER 3 REVIEW

EXERCISES

1. False. You use a straightedge and a compass.

2. False. A diagonal connects any two *nonconsecutive* vertices.

3. True

4. True

5. False. Possible counterexample:

6. False. The set of all points in the plane that are a given distance from the segment is a pair of *segments* parallel to the given segment and a pair of semicircles connecting them. The lines can't be a given distance from a segment because the segment has finite length and the lines are infinite.

7. False. Possible counterexample:

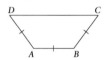

8. True   **9.** True

10. False. The orthocenter does not always lie inside the triangle.

11. A   **12.** B or K

13. I   **14.** H

15. G   **16.** D

17. J   **18.** C

19.   **20.**

21.   **22.**

 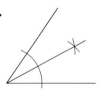

23. Construct a 90° angle and bisect it twice.

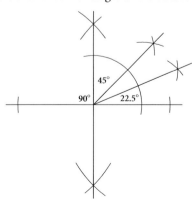

24.

25. Incenter

26. Dakota Davis should locate the circumcenter of the triangular region formed by the three stones, which is the location equidistant from the stones.

27.

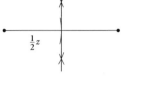

28.

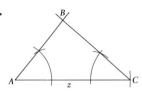

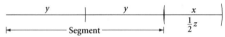

29.

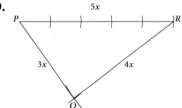

30. $m\angle A = m\angle D$. You must first find $\angle B$. $m\angle B = 180° - 2(m\angle A)$.

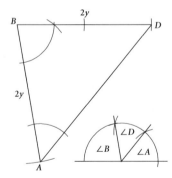

31.

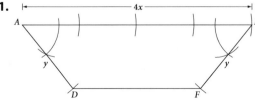

32.

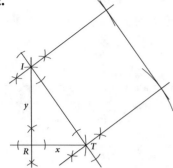

33. Rotational symmetry

34. Neither

35. Both

36. Reflectional symmetry

37. D

38. A

39. C

40. B

41. False. An isosceles triangle has two congruent sides.

42. True

43. False. Any non-acute triangle is a counterexample.

44. False. The orthocenter is the point of intersection of the three altitudes.

45. True

46. False. Any linear pair of angles is a counterexample.

47. False. Each side is adjacent to one congruent side and one noncongruent side, so two consecutive sides may not be congruent.

48. False. Possible counterexample:

49. False. The measure of an arc is equal to the measure of its central angle.

50. False. $TD = 2DR$.

51. False. A radius is not a chord.

52. True

53. False. Inductive reasoning is the process of observing data, recognizing patterns, and making generalizations about those patterns.

54. This is a paradox. If you answer true, you will make the answer false because there will then be four true statements in Exercises 41–54. If you answer false, then the statement will be true.

55. a. $\angle 2$ and $\angle 6$ or $\angle 3$ and $\angle 5$

   b. $\angle 1$ and $\angle 5$

   c. 138°

56. 55. To generate successive terms, you subtract 3, then you subtract 6, then 9, then 12, and so on.

57. Possible answer:

58. a. Yes

   b. If the month has 31 days, then the month is October.

   c. No

59.

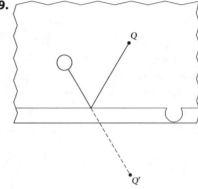

60. $f(n) = 3n - 4$; 56

61. $f(n) = n^2 - 1$; 399

62. $a = 38°$, $b = 38°$, $c = 142°$, $d = 38°$, $e = 50°$, $f = 65°$, $g = 106°$, and $h = 74°$. $a = 38°$ by the Linear Pair Conjecture, $b = 38°$ by the Alternate Interior Angles Conjecture, $c = 142°$ by the Corresponding Angle Conjecture and the Linear Pair Conjecture, $d = 38°$ by the Alternate Exterior Angles Conjecture, $f = 65°$ by the Corresponding Angles Conjecture, $e = 50°$ by the Linear Pair Conjecture, $g = 106°$ by the Corresponding Angles Conjecture, and $h = 74°$ by the Linear Pair Conjecture.

63. Triangles will vary. Check that the triangle is scalene and that at least two angle bisectors have been constructed.

64. $m\angle FAD = 30°$, so $m\angle ADC = 30°$, but its vertical angle has measure 26°. This is a contradiction.

65. Minimum: 101 regions by 100 parallel lines; maximum: 5051 regions by 100 intersecting, nonconcurrent lines.

CHAPTER 4

LESSON 4.1

EXERCISES

1. The angle measures change, but the sum remains 180°.

2. 73°. $x + 52° + 55° = 180°$, so $x + 107° = 180°$, and $x = 73°$.

3. 60°. All three angles of the triangle are congruent, so $3v = 180°$. Therefore, $v = 60°$.

4. 110°. Ignore the 100° angle and the line that intersects the large triangle. Find the angle measures for the large triangle: The supplement of the 120° angle measures 60°, and the supplement of the 130° angle measures 50° (Linear Pair Conjecture). Then, by the Triangle Sum Conjecture, the measure of the third angle is 180° − (60° + 50°) = 70°. Because $z + 70° = 180°$, $z = 110°$.

5. 24°. Let x represent the measure of each of the marked congruent angles. Then $x + x + 48° = 180°$, so $2x = 132°$, and $x = 66°$. Now, to find w, look at the right triangle in which the measures of the acute angles are x and w.

$$w + x + 90° = 180°$$
$$w + 66° + 90° = 180°$$
$$w + 156° = 180°$$
$$w = 24°$$

6. 900°. At each vertex of the triangle, four angles are formed, the sum of whose measures is 360°. The three (interior) angles of the triangle are unmarked, so the sum of their measures, which is 180°, must be subtracted from the total. Therefore, the sum of the measures of the marked angles is $3 \cdot 360° − 180° = 900°$.

7. 360°. At each vertex of the triangle, a linear pair is formed by a marked angle and an interior angle of the triangle. Because the sum of the measures of the angles in a linear pair is 180°, the sum of the measures of the marked angles is $3 \cdot 180° − 180° = 540° − 180° = 360°$.

8. $a = 69°$, $b = 47°$, $c = 116°$, $d = 93°$, and $e = 86°$. First look at the large triangle that contains angles with measures a, 40°, and 71°. By the Triangle Sum Conjecture, $a + 40° + 71° = 180°$, so $a = 69°$. The angle with measure b forms a linear pair with the 133° angle, so $b + 133° = 180°$, and $b = 47°$. Next look at the triangle that includes angles with measures a and b. By the Triangle Sum Conjecture, the measure of the unmarked angle in this triangle is $180° − a − b = 180° − 69° − 47° = 64°$. The angle with measure c forms a linear pair with the 64° angle, so $c = 180° − 64° = 116°$ (Linear Pair Conjecture). Now look at the triangle that includes angles with measures d and 47°. The unmarked angle in this triangle forms a linear pair with the 140° angle, so its measure is $180° − 140° = 40°$. Therefore, $d + 47° + 40° = 180°$ (Triangle Sum Conjecture), so $d = 93°$. Next look at the triangle containing the 40° angle. One of its angles is a vertical angle of the angle with measure d, so the measure of this angle is 93° (Vertical Angles

Conjecture). The measure of the third angle of this triangle is $180° − 40° − 93° = 47°$ (Triangle Sum Conjecture). Finally, look at the small triangle at the top of the figure that includes the angle with measure e. The angle in the lower left measures 47° (vertical angle of angle of measure b or supplement of 133° angle), and the angle in the lower right measures 47° (vertical angle of angle found in the triangle containing the 40° angle). Therefore, $e + 47° + 47° = 180°$ (Triangle Sum Conjecture), so $e = 86°$.

9. $m = 30°$, $n = 50°$, $p = 82°$, $q = 28°$, $r = 32°$, $s = 78°$, $t = 118°$, and $u = 50°$. First look at the right triangle that contains a 60° angle. Here, $m + 60° + 90° = 180°$ (Triangle Sum Conjecture), so $m = 30°$. Now look at the right triangle that contains a 40° angle. Here, by the Triangle Sum Conjecture, the unmarked angle measures $180° − 90° − 40° = 50°$. Because this angle and the angle with measure n are vertical angles, they have the same measure (Vertical Angles Conjecture), so $n = 50°$. Now look at the small triangle with three unmarked angles, which is below the triangle that includes the angle with measure m. In this triangle, one angle measures $180° − 112° = 68°$ (Linear Pair Conjecture), and another measures 30° because it is a vertical angle with the angle of measure m (Vertical Angles Conjecture). Therefore, the third angle in the small triangle measures $180° − 68° − 30° = 82°$. Because this angle is a vertical angle with the angle of measure p, $p = 82°$ (Vertical Angles Conjecture). Next look at the triangle that includes angles with measures p and q. The unmarked angle in this triangle measures 70° (Vertical Angles Conjecture), so $82° + q + 70° = 180°$ (Triangle Sum Conjecture), and $q = 28°$. Now look at the triangle that contains the angle with measure n, the angle that forms a linear pair with the angle of measure p, and the vertical angle of the angle with measure r. The angle measures in this triangle are 50°, $180° − p = 98°$, and r. $50° + 98° + r = 180°$, so $r = 32°$. Next look at the large triangle that includes the angles with measures n and q. In this triangle, the measure of the unmarked angle is $180° − n − q = 180° − 50° − 28° = 102°$ (Triangle Sum Conjecture), so $s = 78°$ (Linear Pair Conjecture). Now look at the triangle that includes the angle with measure n and the angles that form linear pairs with the 112° angle and the angle with measure t. The supplement of the 112° angle measures 68°. Thus, the angle in this triangle that forms a linear pair with the angle of measure t has measure $180° − n − 68° = 180° − 50° − 68° = 62°$, so $t = 180° − 62° = 118°$. Now look at the triangle that includes the angle with measure s and an angle that forms a linear pair with the angle of measure t. Because $s = 78°$ and $180° - t = 62°$, the third angle of this triangle measures $180° - 78° - 62° = 40°$. Finally, look at the right triangle that includes the angle with measure u. The other acute angle in this triangle measures $40°$ (Vertical Angles Conjecture), so $90° + 40° + u = 180°$, and $u = 50°$.

10. Draw a line with a straightedge and duplicate $\angle A$ with one side along this line. Duplicate $\angle R$ so that angles R and A have a common vertex and a common side that is not along the original line. The side of $\angle R$ that is not common with $\angle A$ and the ray opposite the one that forms the first side of $\angle A$ will form $\angle M$ because $m\angle M + m\angle R + m\angle A = 180°$.

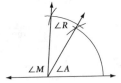

This construction could also be done by constructing the given angles at the ends of a line segment; then $\angle M$ is the third angle formed where the sides of the angles meet.

11. Draw a line with a straightedge and duplicate $\angle L$ with one side along this line. Bisect the angle that forms a linear pair with $\angle L$. Either of the two congruent angles formed can be used as $\angle G$.

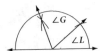

12. First construct $\angle E$, using the method used in Exercise 10. Then duplicate $\overline{AE}$ and $\angle A$. Extend the sides of $\angle A$ and $\angle E$ that are not along $\overline{AE}$ until they intersect. The intersection point of these two rays will be R, the third vertex of the triangle.

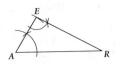

13. For Exercise 10: Use the method described for Exercise 10, but duplicate $\angle A$ and $\angle R$ by tracing them onto patty paper rather than using compass and straightedge. No folding is necessary.

For Exercise 11: Use the method described for Exercise 11, but duplicate $\angle L$ by tracing it onto patty paper, and then bisect the angle that forms a linear pair with $\angle L$ by folding the patty paper.

For Exercise 12: Use the method described for Exercise 12, but duplicate the side and two angles by tracing them onto patty paper. No folding is necessary.

14. By the Triangle Sum Conjecture, $m\angle A + m\angle S + m\angle M = 180°$. Because $\angle M$ is a right angle, $m\angle M = 90°$. By substitution, $m\angle A + m\angle S + 90° = 180°$. By subtraction, $m\angle A + m\angle S = 90°$. So, two wrongs make a right!

15. Answers will vary. See the proof on page 202. To prove the Triangle Sum Conjecture, the Linear Pair Conjecture and the Alternate Interior Angles Conjecture must be accepted as true.

16. It is easier to draw $\triangle PDQ$ if the Triangle Sum Conjecture is used to find that the measure of $\angle D$ is $85°$. Then $\overline{PD}$ can be drawn to be 7 cm, and angles P and D can be drawn at each endpoint using the protractor.

17. Sample answer: Draw $\triangle ABC$ with $m\angle A = 110°$, $m\angle B = 40°$, and $AB = 3$ cm.

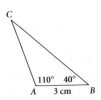

Now trace angles A and B and make the segment connecting the new angles 5 cm long. Call the new triangle $\triangle DEF$, where $m\angle D = 110°$, $m\angle E = 40°$, and $DE = 5$ cm.

Discovering Geometry Solutions Manual
©2008 Key Curriculum Press

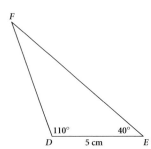

Measure the third angle of each triangle with a protractor to find that $m\angle C = 30°$ and $m\angle F = 30°$, so the third angles are also equal in measure. Conjecture: If two angles of one triangle have the same measures as two angles of another triangle, then the third angles are have the same measure (Third Angle Conjecture).

18. You know from the Triangle Sum Conjecture that $m\angle A + m\angle B + m\angle C = 180°$, and $m\angle D + m\angle E + m\angle F = 180°$. Thus, $m\angle A + m\angle B + x = 180°$ and $m\angle D + m\angle E + y = 180°$, so by the transitive property, $m\angle A + m\angle B + x = m\angle D + m\angle E + y$. Because the figures show that $m\angle A = m\angle D$ and that $m\angle B = m\angle E$, subtracting equal terms from both sides results in the equation $x = y$, that is, $m\angle C = m\angle F$.

19. For any triangle, the sum of the angle measures is 180° by the Triangle Sum Conjecture. Because the triangle is equiangular, each angle has the same measure, say x. So $x + x + x = 180°$, and $x = 60°$.

20. False. The angles between the two given sides may differ, which will result in triangles that differ in both size and shape.

21. False. The triangles will be the same shape, but may not be the same size.

22. False. The other sides and angles of the triangle may differ.

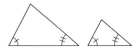

23. False. The triangles will be the same shape, but may not be the same size.

24. True

25. Draw the next house in the series. A four-story house will need $15 + 11 = 26$ cards. Use inductive reasoning to find a pattern.

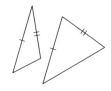

The number of cards added when a new story is added to the tower increases by 3 each time, so a five-story house will need $26 + 14 = 40$ cards. Complete the table, stopping with the largest number of cards that is less than $2 \cdot 52 = 104$.

Number of stories	1	2	3	4	5	6	7	8
Number of cards	2	7	15	26	40	57	77	100

Thus, the tallest house you can build with two 52-card decks is eight stories. It will take 100 cards to build this house.

IMPROVING YOUR VISUAL THINKING SKILLS

1. Each part is a right trapezoid. If you are having difficulty, see if you can divide the hexagon into two congruent parts.

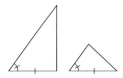

2. Start by dividing the hexagon into two congruent parts; then divide each part into four congruent parts. Each part is a trapezoid with three congruent sides.

EXTENSION

See the solution to Take Another Look activity 1 on page 83.

LESSON 4.2

EXERCISES

1. 79°. Because $m\angle H + m\angle O + m\angle T = 180°$ and $m\angle T = 22°$, $m\angle H + m\angle O = 180° - 22° = 158°$. By the Isosceles Triangle Conjecture, $m\angle H = m\angle O$. Therefore, $2m\angle H = 158°$, and $m\angle H = 79°$.

2. 54°. By the Isosceles Triangle Conjecture, $m\angle O = m\angle D$, so $m\angle O = 63°$. Then $m\angle G = 180° - (2 \cdot 63°) = 54°$.

3. 107.5°. By the Triangle Sum Conjecture, $m\angle S + m\angle SLO + 35° = 180°$. By the Isosceles Triangle Conjecture, $m\angle S = m\angle SLO$. Therefore, $2m\angle SLO + 35° = 180°$, so $2m\angle SLO = 145°$ and $m\angle SLO = 72.5°$. $\angle SLO$ and $\angle OLE$ form a linear pair, so, by the Linear Pair Conjecture, $m\angle OLE = 180° - 72.5° = 107.5°$.

4. $m\angle R = 44°$, $RM = 35$ cm. Use the Triangle Sum Conjecture to find $m\angle R = 180° - (2 \cdot 68°) = 44°$. By the Converse of the Isosceles Triangle Conjecture, $\triangle ARM$ is isosceles with $\overline{RA} \cong \overline{RM}$. Therefore, $RM = RA = 35$ cm.

5. $m\angle Y = 76°$, $RD = 3.5$ cm. $m\angle Y + m\angle R = 180° - 28° = 152°$ and $m\angle R = m\angle Y$, so $m\angle Y = 76°$. $RD = YD = 3.5$ cm.

6. $m\angle D = 72°$, $m\angle U = 36°$, $MD = 8.6$ cm. The markings on the figure show that $\overline{UD} \cong \overline{UM}$, so $\triangle MUD$ is isosceles with $\angle M$ and $\angle D$ as the base angles. Therefore, by the Isosceles Triangle Conjecture, $\angle D \cong \angle M$, so $m\angle D = 72°$. By the Triangle Sum Conjecture, $m\angle U + m\angle M + m\angle D = 180°$, so $m\angle U = 180° - 2 \cdot 72° = 36°$. Because $\overline{UD} \cong \overline{UM}$, $UD = 14$ cm. The perimeter of $\triangle MUD$ is 36.6 cm, so $MD = 36.6$ cm $- (2 \cdot 14$ cm$) = 8.6$ cm.

7. $m\angle T = 78°$; 93 cm. By the Triangle Sum Conjecture, $m\angle T + m\angle B + m\angle S = 180°$, so $m\angle T = 180° - 24° - 78° = 78°$. This shows that $\angle T \cong \angle S$, so the triangle is isosceles by the Converse of the Isosceles Triangle Conjecture. Because $\angle T$ and $\angle S$ are the base angles, the two congruent sides (or bases) of $\triangle TBS$ are $\overline{SB}$ and $\overline{TB}$. Therefore, $y + 22.5$ cm $= 38.5$ cm, so $y = 16$ cm. Thus, the perimeter of $\triangle TBS$ is 16 cm $+ 2 \cdot 38.5$ cm $= 93$ cm.

8. $NB = 75$ m; $m\angle N = 81°$. From the figure, $\overline{CN} \cong \overline{CB}$, so $CN = 2x + 90$ m. Because the perimeter of $\triangle NBC$ is 555 m, $2(2x + 90$ m$) + x = 555$ m. Solve this equation.

$$2(2x + 90) + x = 555$$
$$4x + 180 + x = 555$$
$$5x + 180 = 555$$
$$5x = 375$$
$$x = 75 \text{ m}$$

Therefore, $NB = 75$ m.

By the Triangle Sum Conjecture, $m\angle N + m\angle B + m\angle C = 180°$. Because $\triangle NBC$ is isosceles with $\overline{CN} \cong \overline{CB}$, by the Isosceles Triangle Conjecture,

$m\angle N = m\angle B$. Therefore, $2(m\angle N) + 18° = 180°$, so $m\angle N = 81°$.

9. $MV = 160$ in., $m\angle M = 126°$. Using the fact that the perimeter is 605 in., $MV + VT + TM = 605$ in. Therefore, $MV = 605 - 285 - 160 = 160$ in. Because $MV = TM = 160$ in., $\triangle MTV$ is isosceles with $\overline{MV}$ and $\overline{TM}$ as the legs and angles V and T as the base angles. Therefore, by the Isosceles Triangle Conjecture, $m\angle T = m\angle V = x$. Apply the Triangle Sum Conjecture to get $x + x + (x + 99°) = 180°$, so $x = 27°$. Then $x + 99° = 126°$, so $m\angle M = 126°$.

10. $a = 124°$, $b = 56°$, $c = 56°$, $d = 38°$, $e = 38°$, $f = 76°$, $g = 66°$, $h = 104°$, $k = 76°$, $n = 86°$, and $p = 38°$. $a + 56° = 180°$ by the Linear Pair Conjecture, so $a = 124°$. $b = 56°$ by the Vertical Angles Conjecture. The angle with measure c and the angle marked 56° are alternate interior angles formed when the parallel lines are cut by a transversal, so $c = 56°$ by the AIA Conjecture. Now look at the large triangle with angle measures 66°, d, and $2e$. Here, $66° + d + 2e = 180°$, but $d = e$, so $66° + 3d = 180°$, and $d = e = 38°$. Now look at the tall triangle on the left: $66° + 38° + f = 180°$, so $f = 76°$. Next look at the isosceles triangle containing the angle with measure d. Because $d = 38°$, the other base angle (not labeled) also measures 38°. Then $76° + 38° + g = 180°$, so $g = 66°$. Also, from the isosceles triangle, $h = 180° - (2 \cdot 38°) = 104°$. The angles with measures k and h form a linear pair, so $k = 180° - 104° = 76°$. $d + c + n = 180°$, so $n = 180° - 38° - 56° = 86°$. d and p are the measures of corresponding angles, so $p = d$ by the CA Conjecture; thus, $p = 38°$.

11. $a = 36°$, $b = 36°$, $c = 72°$, $d = 108°$, $e = 36°$; none. There are 10 congruent central angles at the center of the star decagon, and a is the measure of one of these angles, so $a = \frac{360°}{10} = 36°$. Because $b = a$, $b = 36°$, and the triangle containing the angles with measures a and b is isosceles by the Converse of the Isosceles Triangle Conjecture. Now look at the smaller isosceles triangle in which the angle of measure a is the vertex. (You also know that this triangle is isosceles by the Converse of the Isosceles Triangle Conjecture.) Here, the measure of each base angle is $\frac{1}{2}(180° - 36°) = \frac{1}{2}(144°) = 72°$. This tells you that the measure of the third angle in the triangle containing angles with measures b and c is also 72°. Thus, $b + c + 72° = 180°$ or $36° + c + 72° = 180°$, so $c = 72°$. Therefore, this triangle has two congruent angles and is thus also isosceles. The angle with measure d forms a linear pair with a 72° angle, so $d = 108°$. The measure of the third angle in the triangle containing the angles of measures d

and e is $180° − 72° − c = 180° − 72° − 72° = 36°$. Therefore, $e = 180° − 36° − d = 180° − 36° − 108° = 36°$. Thus, this triangle has two 36° angles and is also isosceles.

Every triangle in the design is isosceles. (In other words, none of the triangles is not isosceles.)

12. a. Yes. Two sides are radii of a circle. Radii must be congruent; therefore, each triangle must be isosceles.

b. 60°. If the vertex angle of an isosceles triangle measures 60°, each of the base angles will measure $\frac{1}{2}(180° − 60°) = \frac{1}{2}(120°) = 60°$. In other words, this isosceles triangle is equilateral.

13. $\triangle GEA \cong \triangle NCA$. From the information given in the figure, the correct correspondence of vertices is *G* to *N*, *E* to *C*, and *A* to *A*, and all pairs of corresponding parts are congruent, so $\triangle GEA \cong \triangle NCA$.

14. $\triangle JAN \cong \triangle IEC$. Notice that $m\angle N = 40°$ and $m\angle I = 50°$. From the information given in the figure, the correct correspondence of vertices is *J* to *I*, *A* to *E*, and *N* to *C*, and all pairs of corresponding parts are congruent, so $\triangle JAN \cong \triangle IEC$.

15. Possible answer: The three angles of $\triangle ABC$ will be congruent to the corresponding angles of $\triangle DEF$, but the corresponding sides should not be congruent. To construct $\triangle ABC$, duplicate $\angle D$ to make $\angle A$, and duplicate $\angle E$ to make $\angle B$, but make $AB \neq DE$.

16. Possible answer: Duplicate $\overline{MN}$ to make $\overline{GH}$ and duplicate $\angle M$ to make $\angle G$. Draw an arc with center at *H* and length *NP*, intersecting the ray that forms the side of $\angle G$ that does not lie along $\overline{GH}$. This arc will intersect the ray in two points, giving two possible positions for *K*, which are labeled as K_1 and K_2.

$\triangle GHK_2 \cong \triangle MNP$, so choose K_1 for *K*, and complete the triangle.

17. Possible answer: Construct a 60° angle (one angle of an equilateral triangle) and a 45° angle (bisect a right angle). $60° + 45° = 105°$, so you obtain a 105° angle.

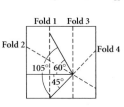

18. Perpendicular

Slope $\overleftrightarrow{AB} = \dfrac{0 − 3}{6 − 1} = \dfrac{−3}{5} = −\dfrac{3}{5}$

Slope $\overleftrightarrow{CD} = \dfrac{−2 − 3}{1 − 4} = \dfrac{−5}{−3} = \dfrac{5}{3}$

The slopes, $−\frac{3}{5}$ and $\frac{5}{3}$, are opposite reciprocals of each other, so by the perpendicular slope property, $\overleftrightarrow{AB}$ and $\overleftrightarrow{CD}$ are perpendicular.

19. Parallel

Slope $\overleftrightarrow{FG} = \dfrac{6 − 1}{−1 − (−4)} = \dfrac{5}{3}$

From Exercise 18, slope $\overleftrightarrow{CD} = \frac{5}{3}$.

The slopes are equal, so by the parallel slope property, $\overleftrightarrow{FG}$ and $\overleftrightarrow{CD}$ are parallel.

20. Parallel. $\overleftrightarrow{AD}$ is a vertical line because the *x*-coordinates of points *A* and *D* are equal. $\overleftrightarrow{CH}$ is also a vertical line because the *x*-coordinates of points *C* and *H* are equal. Any two vertical lines are parallel, so $\overleftrightarrow{AD}$ and $\overleftrightarrow{CH}$ are parallel. (Note that slopes cannot be used here because the slope of a vertical line is undefined.)

21. Neither

Slope $\overleftrightarrow{DE} = \dfrac{8 − (−2)}{−3 − 1} = \dfrac{10}{−4} = −\dfrac{5}{2}$

Slope $\overleftrightarrow{GH} = \dfrac{−4 − 6}{4 − (−1)} = \dfrac{−10}{5} = −2$

The slopes are neither equal nor opposite reciprocals, so $\overleftrightarrow{DE}$ and $\overleftrightarrow{GH}$ are neither parallel nor perpendicular.

22. Parallelogram. In quadrilateral *FGCD*, $\overline{FG}$ and $\overline{CD}$ are opposite sides, and $\overline{GC}$ and $\overline{FD}$ are opposite sides. From Exercise 19, $\overline{FG} \parallel \overline{CD}$. Find the slopes of the other two sides:

Slope $\overline{GC} = \dfrac{3 − 6}{4 − (−1)} = \dfrac{−3}{5} = −\dfrac{3}{5}$

Slope $\overline{FD} = \dfrac{−2 − 1}{1 − (−4)} = \dfrac{−3}{5} = −\dfrac{3}{5}$

Because their slopes are equal, $\overline{GC} \parallel \overline{FD}$.

Both pairs of opposite sides of *FGCD* are parallel, so *FGCD* is a parallelogram.

23. 40. From the figure, you can see that point *P* will land at 20 on the number line after one cycle and at 40 after two cycles.

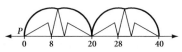

24. Move each point of the original triangle to the right 5 units and down 3 units to obtain the new triangle. Original triangle: $(1, 0)$, $(−3, −2)$, $(−2, 3)$. New triangle: $(6, −3)$, $(2, −5)$, $(3, 0)$. The original triangle was translated (moved to the right and downward), but its size and shape were not changed, so the two triangles are congruent.

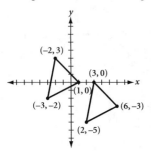

25. Reflect each point of the original triangle across the x-axis to obtain the new triangle. Original triangle: (3, 3), (−3, 1), (−1, 5). New triangle: (3, −3), (−3, −1), (−1, −5). The original triangle has been flipped over the x-axis, but its size and shape were not changed, so the two triangles are congruent.

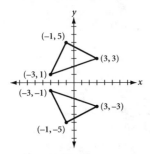

IMPROVING YOUR REASONING SKILLS

First notice which digits are missing, and find what number they have to equal when combined.

1. $1 + 2 + 3 − 4 + 5 + 6 + \mathbf{78} + 9 = 100$

2. $1 + 2 + 3 + 4 + 5 + \mathbf{6 + 7 + 8 \cdot 9} = 100$

3. $1 + 2 + 3 \cdot 4 \cdot 5 \div 6 + \mathbf{78} + 9 = 100$

4. $(−1 − \mathbf{2 − 3 − 4}) \div 5 + 6 + 7 + 89 = 100$

5. $1 + 23 − 4 + \mathbf{56 + 7 + 8} + 9 = 100$

Many other identities using all nine digits in order are possible, including $12 + 34 + 5 \cdot 6 + 7 + 8 + 9 = 100$, $123 − 4 − 5 − 6 − 7 + 8 − 9 = 100$, and $−1 + 2 + 3 + 4 \cdot 5 \cdot 6 − 7 − 8 − 9 = 100$.

EXTENSIONS

A. The conjecture is false; any scalene triangle is a counterexample. It is possible to divide any triangle into a kite and two triangles, but the triangles will be *isosceles* only if the original triangle is isosceles. (Recall that equilateral triangles are isosceles.)

This extension can be explored with geometry software or with compass-and-straightedge or patty-paper constructions. Here is one possible approach using compass and straightedge: Starting with $\triangle PQR$, to construct the kite, make an arc to find two points, S and T, one on each side of $\angle P$, that are equidistant from point P. Connect these two points with $\overline{ST}$ and then construct the perpendicular bisector of $\overline{ST}$. U is the point where the perpendicular bisector intersects the third side of the triangle, $\overline{QR}$. Draw $\overline{SU}$ and $\overline{TU}$. By construction, $PS = PT$ and $SU = TU$, so *PSUT* is a kite.

The figures below show this construction for an isosceles triangle (using the vertex angle of the triangle as one vertex of the kite) and a scalene triangle. Observe that the two smaller triangles that are formed are each isosceles when the original triangle is isosceles, but are scalene when the original triangle is scalene.

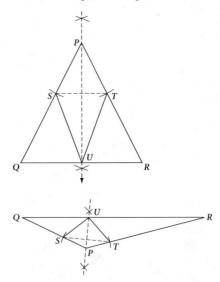

B. See the solutions to Take Another Look activities 2 and 3 on page 83.

USING YOUR ALGEBRA SKILLS 4

EXERCISES

1. False. $2(4 + 5) = 2(9) = 18 \neq 13$.

2. True. Use the order of operations to simplify each side of the given equation.

$$2 + [3(−4) − 4] = 2 + [−12 − 4] = 2 + (−16) = −14$$
$$2(−4 − 3) = 2(−7) = −14$$

Because $−14 = −14$ is true, the given equation is true.

Discovering Geometry Solutions Manual
©2008 Key Curriculum Press

3. Not a solution. Substitute 6 for x in the given equation and see whether a true statement results.

$x - 8 = 2$ Original equation.

$6 - 8 \overset{?}{=} 2$ Substitute 6 for x.

$-2 \overset{?}{=} 2$ Subtract; equation is false.

The false statement shows that 6 is not a solution.

4. Solution.

$4(3y - 1) = -40$ Original equation.

$4[3(-3) - 1] \overset{?}{=} -40$ Substitute -3 for y.

$4[-9 - 1] \overset{?}{=} -40$ Multiply 3(–3).

$4[-10] \overset{?}{=} -40$ Subtract –9 – 1.

$-40 \overset{?}{=} -40$ Multiply; equation is true.

5. Not a solution.

$\frac{3}{4}n - \frac{1}{2} = \frac{1}{8}$ Original equation.

$\frac{3}{4}\left(\frac{1}{4}\right) - \frac{1}{2} \overset{?}{=} \frac{1}{8}$ Substitute $\frac{1}{4}$ for n.

$\frac{3}{16} - \frac{1}{2} \overset{?}{=} \frac{1}{8}$ Multiply fractions.

$-\frac{5}{16} \overset{?}{=} \frac{2}{16}$ Subtract fractions; equation is false.

6. $6x - 3 = 39$ Original equation.

$6x = 42$ Add 3 to both sides.

$x = 7$ Divide both sides by 7.

Check the solution.

$6(7) - 3 \overset{?}{=} 39$ Substitute 7 for x.

$42 - 3 \overset{?}{=} 39$

$39 = 39$ The solution checks.

7. $3y - 7 = 5y + 1$ Original equation.

$3y = 5y + 8$ Add 7 to both sides.

$-2y = 8$ Subtract 5y from both sides.

$y = -4$ Divide both sides by -2.

Check the solution.

$3(-4) - 7 \overset{?}{=} 5(-4) + 1$ Substitute -4 for y.

$-12 - 7 \overset{?}{=} -20 + 1$

$-19 = -19$ The solution checks.

8. $6x - 4(3x + 8) = 16$ Original equation.

$6x - 12x - 32 = 16$ Distributive property.

$-6x - 32 = 16$ Subtract $6x - 12x$.

$-6x = 48$ Add 32.

$x = -8$ Divide by -6.

Check the solution.

$6(-8) - 4[3(-8) + 8] \overset{?}{=} 16$ Substitute -8 for x.

$6(-8) - 4[-24 + 8] \overset{?}{=} 16$

$6(-8) - 4[-16] \overset{?}{=} 16$

$-48 + 64 \overset{?}{=} 16$

$16 = 16$ The solution checks.

For Exercises 9–12, the solutions should be checked by the method shown for Exercises 6–8.

9. $7 - 3(2x - 5) = 1 - x$ Original equation.

$7 - 6x + 15 = 1 - x$ Distributive property.

$22 - 6x = 1 - x$ Add 7 + 15.

$21 = 5x$ Add $6x - 1$ to both sides.

$x = \frac{21}{5}$ or 4.2   Divide both sides by 5.

10. $5(n - 2) - 14n = -3n - (5 - 4n)$ Original equation.

$5n - 10 - 14n = -3n - 5 + 4n$ Distributive property.

$-9n - 10 = n - 5$ Combine like terms.

$-10n = 5$ Add $-n + 10$ to both sides.

$n = -\frac{1}{2}$, or -0.5 Divide both sides by -10.

11. The denominators are 6, 10, and 15; the least common denominator is 30.

$\frac{1}{6} = \frac{3}{10} - \frac{1}{15}x$ Original equation.

$30\left(\frac{1}{6}\right) = 30\left(\frac{3}{10} - \frac{1}{15}x\right)$ Multiply both sides by 30.

$\frac{30}{6} = \frac{90}{10} - \frac{30x}{15}$ Distributive property.

$5 = 9 - 2x$ Reduce the fractions.

$-4 = -2x$ Subtract 9 from both sides.

$x = 2$ Divide both sides by -2.

12. The denominators are t and 6; the least common denominator is $6t$.

$\frac{4}{t} - \frac{1}{6} = \frac{1}{t}$ Original equation.

$6t\left(\frac{4}{t} - \frac{1}{6}\right) = 6t\left(\frac{1}{t}\right)$ Multiply both sides by $6t$.

$\frac{24t}{t} - \frac{6t}{6} = \frac{6t}{t}$ Distributive property.

$24 - t = 6$ Reduce the fractions.

$t = 18$ Add $t - 6$ to both sides.

13. The denominators are 3, 4, and 6; the least common denominator is 12.

$$\frac{3n}{4} - \frac{1}{3} = \frac{2n-1}{6}$$ Original equation.

$$12\left(\frac{3n}{4} - \frac{1}{3}\right) = 12\left(\frac{2n-1}{6}\right)$$ Multiply both sides by 12.

$$\frac{36n}{4} - \frac{12}{3} = \frac{12(2n-1)}{6}$$ Distributive property.

$$9n - 4 = 2(2n - 1)$$ Reduce the fractions.

$$9n - 4 = 4n - 2$$ Distributive property.

$$5n = 2$$ Add $-4n + 4$ to both sides.

$$n = 0.4$$ Divide both sides by 5.

14. a. The denominators are 4 and 3; the least common denominator is 12.

$$\frac{3}{4} = \frac{x}{3}$$ Original equation.

$$12\left(\frac{3}{4}\right) = 12\left(\frac{x}{3}\right)$$ Multiplication property of equality.

$$9 = 4x$$ Multiply and reduce the fractions.

$$x = \frac{9}{4} \text{ or } 2.25$$ Divide both sides by 4.

b. $$\frac{3}{4} = \frac{x}{3}$$ Original equation.

$$3 \cdot 3 = 4 \cdot x$$ Cross multiply.

$$9 = 4x$$ Multiply.

$$x = \frac{9}{4}, \text{ or } 2.25$$ Divide both sides by 4.

The two methods produce identical results. Multiplying by the least common denominator (which is comprised of the factors of both denominators) and then reducing common factors (which clears the denominators on either side) is the same as simply multiplying each numerator by the opposite denominator (or cross multiplying). Algebraically you could show that the two methods are equivalent as follows:

$$\frac{a}{b} = \frac{c}{d}$$

$$bd\left(\frac{a}{b}\right) = bd\left(\frac{c}{d}\right)$$ The method of "clearing fractions . . ."

$$\frac{a\cancel{b}d}{\cancel{b}} = \frac{bc\cancel{d}}{\cancel{d}}$$

$$ad = bc$$ . . . results in the method of "cross multiplying."

15. $2(3x + 1) = 6x + 3$ Original equation.

$$6x + 2 = 6x + 3$$ Distributive property.

$$2 = 3$$ Subtract $6x$ from both sides.

The last equation is always false, so the original equation has no solution.

16. Camella is incorrect. Because the equation $0 = 0$ is always true, the truth of the equation does not depend on the value of x. Therefore, x can be any real number, and 0 is only one of infinitely many solutions.

17. If the measure of the vertex angle is x, then the measure of each base angle is $2x$.

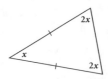

Apply the Triangle Sum Conjecture to get the equation $x + 2x + 2x = 180°$. Solve this equation.

$$x + 2x + 2x = 180°$$

$$5x = 180°$$

$$x = 36°$$

$$2x = 72°$$

The measure of the vertex angle is 36°, and the measure of each base angle is 72°.

LESSON 4.3

EXERCISES

1. Yes. The sum of the lengths of any two sides is greater than the length of the third side.

2. No. $4 + 5 = 9$, so the sum of the two shorter sides is not greater than the length of the longest side.

3. No. $5 + 6 = 11 < 12$

4. Yes. The sum of the lengths of any two sides is greater than the length of the third side.

5. a, b, c. The measure of the third angle is $180° - 70° - 35° = 75°$ (Triangle Sum Conjecture), so the angle measures from greatest to least are 75°, 70°, 35°. By the Side-Angle Inequality Conjecture, the order of the sides opposite those angles is the same: a, b, c.

6. c, b, a. The measure of the third angle is 57°, so the angle measures from greatest to least are 68°, 57°, 55°, and the order of the sides opposite those angles is the same: c, b, a.

7. *b, a, c.* The lengths of the sides, from longest to shortest, are 12 cm, 9 cm, 5 cm, so the order of the angles opposite those sides is the same: *b, a, c.*

8. *a, c, b.* The lengths of the sides, from longest to shortest, are 28 in., 17 in., 15 in., so the order of the angles opposite those sides is the same: *a, c, b.*

9. *a, b, c.* There are two isosceles triangles in the figure. In the larger triangle, the vertex angle measures 30°, so each base angle measures $\frac{1}{2}(180° - 30°) = 75°$. You can see by referring to the isosceles triangle on the right that the length of the base of the triangle on the left is *b.* By the Side-Angle Inequality Conjecture, you know that $a > b$ because $75° > 30°$. In the smaller triangle, one base angle measures 72°, so the other base angle must also measure 72°, and therefore the vertex angle measures $180° - 72° - 72° = 36°$. Apply the same conjecture to the triangle on the right: Because $72° > 36°$, you know that $b > c$. Thus, $a > b > c$, so the correct order is *a, b, c.*

10. *v, z, y, w, x.* Apply the Side-Angle Inequality Conjecture first to the larger triangle and then to the smaller one, noticing that the two triangles share a side. In the larger triangle, the third angle measures 122°. Therefore, the angle measures in this triangle, from largest to smallest, are 122°, 30°, 28°, and the order of the side lengths, from largest to smallest, is *v, z, y.* Now look at the smaller triangle. Here, the third angle measures 104°, so the angle measures from largest to smallest are 104°, 42°, 34°, and the order of the side lengths from largest to smallest is *y, w, x.* Putting together the results from the two triangles, the order of all the side lengths in the figure is *v, z, y, w, x.*

11. $6 < \text{length} < 102$. The third side must be greater than $54 - 48 = 6$ and less than $54 + 48 = 102$, so that the sum of the lengths of any two sides will be greater than the length of the third side.

12. By the Triangle Inequality Conjecture, the sum of 11 cm and 25 cm should be greater than 48 cm, but $11 + 25 = 36$ cm.

13. $b = 55°$, but $55° + 130° > 180°$, which is impossible by the Triangle Sum Conjecture. Another way to see that this situation is impossible is to apply the Triangle Exterior Angle Conjecture. The exterior angle shown in the figure measures 125°, which must be the sum of the two remote interior angles. But one of the remote interior angles measures 130° and *a* must be a positive angle measure, so this is impossible.

14. 135°. By the Triangle Exterior Angle Conjecture, $t + p = 135°$.

15. 72°. By the Triangle Exterior Angle Conjecture, $r + 58° = 130°$, so $r = 72°$.

16. 72°. The triangle is isosceles with base angles of measure *x.* By the Triangle Exterior Angle Conjecture, $x + x = 144°$, or $2x = 144°$, so $x = 72°$.

17. To show that the Triangle Exterior Angle Conjecture is true, we must show that $x = a + b$. By the Triangle Sum Conjecture, $a + b + c = 180°$. Because $\angle BCA$ and $\angle BCD$ are a linear pair, $x + c = 180°$. Then, by substitution, $x + c = a + b + c$. Subtracting *c* from both sides gives $x = a + b$.

18. 45°. When the perpendicular distance is measured, the bearing will be 90°. Because this is double the bow angle when you begin recording, that angle must measure 45°.

19. $a = 52°$, $b = 38°$, $c = 110°$, and $d = 35°$. First $a + 38° + 90° = 180°$ (Triangle Sum Conjecture), so $a = 52°$. The angle with measure *b* and the 38° angle are alternate interior angles, so $b = 38°$ (AIA Conjecture). Then, in the triangle with angles of measure *c* and 32°, the third angle also measures 38°, so $c + 32° + 38° = 180°$, and $c = 110°$ (Triangle Sum Conjecture). In the small isosceles triangle at the top of the diagram, the vertex angle measures 110° (Vertical Angles Conjecture) and the third angle measures *d* (Isosceles Triangle Conjecture), so $2d + 110° = 180°$ (Triangle Sum Conjecture), and thus $d = 35°$.

20. $a = 90°$, $b = 68°$, $c = 112°$, $d = 112°$, $e = 68°$, $f = 56°$, $g = 124°$, and $h = 124°$. First, the angle with measure *a* and the angle marked as a right angle are corresponding angles formed when two parallel lines are cut by a transversal, so $a = 90°$ (CA Conjecture). $a + b + 22° = 180°$ (Triangle Sum Conjecture), so $b = 68°$. $b + c = 180°$ (Linear Pair Conjecture), so $c = 112°$. The angles with measures *c* and *d* are alternate interior angles, so $d = c = 112°$ by the AIA Conjecture. The angles with measures *b* and *e* are alternate exterior angles, so $e = b = 68°$. In the isosceles triangle containing the angles with measures *e* and *f*, the angle with measure *e* is the vertex angle, so $2f + e = 180°$ (Triangle Sum Conjecture); therefore, $f = 56°$. Then $56° + g = 180°$ (Isosceles Triangle Conjecture and Linear Pair Conjecture), so $g = 124°$. Finally, the angles with measures *g* and *h* are alternate interior angles, so $h = g = 124°$ (AIA Conjecture).

21. By the Triangle Sum Conjecture, the third angle must measure 36° in the small triangle, but measure 32° in the large triangle. These are the same angle, so they can't have different measures.

22. $\triangle BAR \cong \triangle ABE$. All pairs of corresponding parts are congruent. Two pairs of congruent sides are marked and the shared side is congruent to itself. Two pairs of angles are congruent by the AIA Conjecture, and the third pair of angles must be congruent by the Triangle Sum Conjecture.

23. $\triangle FAR \cong \triangle FNK$. All pairs of corresponding parts are congruent. Two pairs of congruent sides are marked. Applying the Converse of the Isosceles Triangle Conjecture to $\triangle ANF$ shows that $\overline{AF} \cong \overline{NF}$, which gives the third pair of congruent sides. One pair of angles is congruent because they are both right angles and the other two pairs can be shown to be congruent using the Triangle Sum Conjecture.

24. Cannot be determined. Only one pair of congruent sides and one pair of congruent angles are given, so it is not possible to determine congruence of the triangles.

PROJECT

Project should satisfy the following criteria:

- Presentation of data is organized and clear.

- Explanations of predictions and descriptions of the results are consistent.

- For students cutting straws, lengths probably won't be random. If lengths are generated using a graphing calculator, Fathom, or another random-length generator, the experimental probability (of getting a triangle) for large samples will be around 25%.

Extra credit

- A graph of the sample space uses shading to show cut combinations that do produce a triangle. Sample graph:

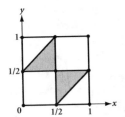

EXTENSIONS

A. Research results will vary.

B. See the solution to Take Another Look activity 4 on page 83.

LESSON 4.4

EXERCISES

1. Answers will vary. Possible answer: If three sides of one triangle are congruent to three sides of another triangle, then the triangles are congruent. (All corresponding angles are also congruent.)

2.   If you know this: then you also know this:

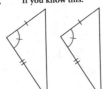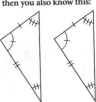

Answers will vary. Possible answer: The picture statement means that if two sides of one triangle are congruent to two sides of another triangle, and the angles between those sides are also congruent, then the two triangles are congruent.

3. Answers will vary. Possible answer:

4. SAS. Notice that if one of the triangles is rotated 180° in either direction, it will coincide with the other, with L coinciding with I, U with D, and Z with A, which confirms the congruence.

5. SSS. Use the shared side, $\overline{FD}$, as the third pair of congruent sides. Every side is congruent to itself.

6. Cannot be determined. Matching congruent sides and angles give $\triangle COT \cong \triangle NAP$, rather than $\triangle COT \cong \triangle NPA$.

7. SSS. Use the shared side, $\overline{CV}$, as the third pair of congruent sides. Every side is congruent to itself.

8. SAS. Use the shared side, $\overline{KA}$, for the second pair of congruent sides.

9. SSS. Because Y is a midpoint, $\overline{AY} \cong \overline{RY}$, and by the Converse of the Isosceles Triangle Conjecture, $\overline{YB} \cong \overline{YN}$.

10. Yes; SAS. Because the perimeter of $\triangle ABC$ is 180 m, $x + (x + 11) + (x - 11) = 180$. Solve this equation to get $x = 60$ m, so $x + 11 = 71$ m. Therefore, $AC = 60$ m and $AB = 71$ m, so $\overline{AC} \cong \overline{AE}$ and $\overline{AB} \cong \overline{AD}$. Also, $\angle BAC \cong \angle DAE$ by the Vertical Angles Conjecture. Hence, $\triangle ABC \cong \triangle ADE$ by SAS.

11. Possible answer: Boards nailed diagonally in the corners of the gate form triangles in those corners. Triangles are rigid, so the triangles in the gate's corners will increase the stability of those corners and keep them from changing shape.

12. $\triangle ANT \cong \triangle FLE$ by SSS. Match congruent sides.

13. Cannot be determined. SSA is not a congruence conjecture.

14. $\triangle GIT \cong \triangle AIN$ by SSS. Or use the vertical angles as the pair of included congruent angles for SAS.

Discovering Geometry Solutions Manual
©2008 Key Curriculum Press

15. Cannot be determined. Parts do not correspond. Notice that the marked side is included between the two marked angles in △BOY, but not in △MAN.

16. △SAT ≅ △SAO by SAS. Use the shared side for one pair of congruent sides.

17. Cannot be determined. Parts do not correspond. Notice that the shared side is included between the two marked angles in △WOM, but not in △WTO.

18. △SUN ≅ △RAY by SAS. $UN = AY = 4$, $SU = RA = 3$, and $m\angle U = m\angle A = 90°$.

19. △DRO ≅ △SPO by SAS. The midpoint of both $\overline{SD}$ and $\overline{PR}$ is (0, 0), giving two pairs of congruent sides. Use the vertical angles as the pair of included congruent angles.

20. Because the LEV is marking out two triangles that are congruent by SAS, measuring the length of the segment leading to the finish will also approximate the diameter of the crater.

21. Draw a baseline with your straightedge and copy the length of one side along this baseline to form one side of the new triangle. Place the point of your compass at one endpoint of this segment and draw an arc with radius equal to the length of a second side of the original triangle. Then place your compass point at the other endpoint of the same segment and draw an arc using a radius equal to the length of the third side of the original triangle. The intersection point of the two arcs will be the third vertex of the new triangle.

22. Duplicate one side of the triangle. Using the resulting segment as one side of the angle, duplicate an angle adjacent to this side. Then duplicate a second side of the original triangle so that the duplicate angle will be included between the two duplicate sides.

23. $a = 37°$, $b = 143°$, $c = 37°$, $d = 58°$, $e = 37°$, $f = 53°$, $g = 48°$, $h = 84°$, $k = 96°$, $m = 26°$, $p = 69°$, $r = 111°$, and $s = 69°$. $a + 143° = 180°$ (Linear Pair Conjecture), so $a = 37°$. $b = 143°$ (Vertical Angles Conjecture). $c = a = 37°$ (AIA Conjecture). $c + d + 85° = 180°$ (Triangle Sum Conjecture), so $d = 58°$. $e = c = 37°$ (Vertical Angles Conjecture). $e + f + 90° = 180°$ (Triangle Sum Conjecture), so $f = 53°$. $g = 48°$ (Isosceles

Triangle Conjecture). $g + h + 48° = 180°$ (Triangle Sum Conjecture), so $h = 84°$. $h + k = 180°$ (Linear Pair Conjecture), so $k = 96°$. $d + k + m = 180°$ (Triangle Sum Conjecture), so $m = 26°$. In the triangle containing angles with measures p and 85°, the third angle has measure m, so $p + m + 85° = 180°$ (Triangle Sum Conjecture), and $p = 69°$. $p + r = 180°$ (Linear Pair Conjecture), so $r = 111°$. Finally, $s = p = 69°$ (CA Conjecture).

24. 3 cm < third side < 19 cm. The length of the third side must be greater than $11 - 8 = 3$ cm and less than $11 + 8 = 19$ cm.

25.

Side length	1	2	3	4	5	n	20
Elbows	4	4	4	4	4	4	4
T's	0	4	8	12	16	$4n - 4$	76
Crosses	0	1	4	9	16	$(n - 1)^2$	361

There is one elbow at each corner, so the number of elbows is always 4. The T's are used around the edges; there are $(n - 1)$ of these at each edge and 4 edges, so the number of T's is $4(n - 1) = 4n - 4$. A cross is used at each interior intersection point; there are $(n - 1)(n - 1)$, or $(n - 1)^2$, such intersections, so there are $(n - 1)^2$ crosses.

26. a. $2y - 5(8 - y) = 2$

$2y - 40 + 5y = 2$

$7y - 40 = 2$

$7y = 42$

$y = 6$

b. The denominators are 2, 3, and 4. The least common denominator is 12.

$$12\left(\frac{y}{2} - \frac{1}{3}\right) = 12 \cdot \frac{y + 3}{4}$$

$$6y - 4 = 3(y + 3)$$

$$6y - 4 = 3y + 9$$

$$3y = 13$$

$$y = \frac{13}{3}$$

c. $3x + 4y = 8$

$4y = -3x + 8$

$$y = -\frac{3}{4}x + 2$$

27. $(-5, -3)$. The orthocenter of a triangle is the point of concurrency of the three altitudes. In a right triangle, two of the altitudes are sides of the triangle, so, because you are told that △ABC is a right triangle, the orthocenter will be the right-angle vertex of this triangle. To identify this vertex, find the slopes of the three sides:

Slope $\overline{AB} = \dfrac{-3-2}{-5-(-8)} = \dfrac{-5}{3} = -\dfrac{5}{3}$

Slope $\overline{BC} = \dfrac{0-(-3)}{0-(-5)} = \dfrac{3}{5}$

Slope $\overline{AC} = \dfrac{0-2}{0-(-8)} = \dfrac{-2}{8} = -\dfrac{1}{4}$

Because $-\dfrac{5}{3}$ and $\dfrac{3}{5}$ are opposite reciprocals, $\overline{AB} \perp \overline{BC}$, so $B(-5, -3)$ is the vertex of the right angle. Therefore, the orthocenter has coordinates $(-5, -3)$.

IMPROVING YOUR REASONING SKILLS

Fill the cylinder twice to the 150 mL mark and once to the 50 mL mark. Or fill the small container twice to the 250 mL mark, pouring the contents into the large container each time. Pour 150 mL from the large container back into the small container. It is not possible in fewer than three steps.

EXTENSION

See the solution to Take Another Look activity 9 on page 83.

LESSON 4.5

EXERCISES

1. If two angles and the included side of one triangle are congruent to two angles and the included side of another triangle, then the triangles are congruent.

2.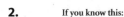
If you know this:
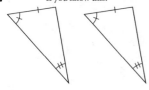

then you also know this:
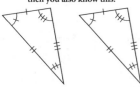

If two angles and a non-included side of one triangle are congruent to two angles and a non-included side of another triangle, then the triangles are congruent.

3. Answers will vary. Possible answer:
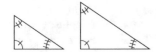

4. $\triangle AMD \cong \triangle RMC$ by ASA. Use the vertical angles at M as one pair of congruent angles.

5. Cannot be determined. Using the shared side as a pair of congruent sides, you have SSA, which is not a congruence shortcut.

6. $\triangle GAS \cong \triangle IOL$ by SAA. To confirm the congruence and correspondence of vertices, flip over one of the triangles and slide it to coincide with the other.

7. Cannot be determined. There is only one pair of congruent sides given, and the only pair of angles that you know are congruent are the vertical angles. This is not enough information to determine congruence.

8. $\triangle BOX \cong \triangle CAR$ by ASA.

9. Cannot be determined. The parallel lines and two transversals give two pairs of congruent angles, and the vertical angles at T are congruent, but you don't have any information about the sides. AAA is not a congruence shortcut.

10. $\triangle FAD \cong \triangle FED$ by SSS. Use the shared side as the third pair of congruent sides.

11. $\triangle WHO \cong \triangle WTA$ by ASA or SAA. $\overleftrightarrow{HT}$ and $\overleftrightarrow{OA}$ are transversals of the parallel sides, so $\angle H \cong \angle T$ and $\angle O \cong \angle A$ by the AIA Conjecture. Also, $\angle HWO \cong \angle TWA$ by the Vertical Angles Conjecture. If you use $\angle H$ and $\angle T$ and the pair of vertical angles, the congruence is true by ASA, or if you use both pairs of alternate interior angles, or $\angle O$ and $\angle A$ and the pair of vertical angles, the congruence is true by SAA.

12. $\triangle LAT \cong \triangle SAT$ by SAS. Because $\overline{AT}$ is an angle bisector, $\angle LAT \cong \angle SAT$, and the shared side, $\overline{AT}$, is congruent to itself.

13. $\triangle POE \cong \triangle PRN$ by ASA or SAS, $\triangle SON \cong \triangle SRE$ by ASA. For $\triangle POE$ and $\triangle PRN$ by ASA, use the shared right angle, $\angle P$, as one pair of congruent angles. Every angle is congruent to itself.

14. Cannot be determined. Parts do not correspond. Note that $\angle A$ is adjacent to $\overline{AM}$ but $\angle C$ is opposite $\overline{RM}$.

15. $\triangle RMF \cong \triangle MRA$ by SAS. $\angle FMR \cong \angle ARM$ because both are right angles, and the shared side, $\overline{MR}$, is congruent to itself.

16. Cannot be determined. Using alternate interior angles formed by the two transversals to the parallel lines and the vertical angles, you have three pairs of congruent angles, but no information about the sides. AAA does not guarantee congruence.

17. $\triangle LAW \cong \triangle WKL$ by ASA. Use the shared side, the right angles, and the other marked angles.

18. Yes; SAA or ASA. Because the perimeter of $\triangle ABC$ is 138 m, $x + (x + 4) + (x - 4) = 138$. Solve this equation to get $x = 46$. Therefore, $AC = 46$ m, so

$\overline{AC} \cong \overline{AE}$. Because $\overline{BC} \parallel \overline{DE}$ and $\overleftrightarrow{EC}$ is a transversal through $\overleftrightarrow{BC}$ and $\overleftrightarrow{DE}$, $\angle E \cong \angle C$ by the AIA Conjecture. Similarly, $\overleftrightarrow{BD}$ is also a transversal through $\overleftrightarrow{BC}$ and $\overleftrightarrow{DE}$, so $\angle B \cong \angle D$ by the AIA Conjecture. Therefore, $\triangle ABC \cong \triangle ADE$ by SAA.

Alternate solution: Notice that $\angle BAC \cong \angle DAE$ by the Vertical Angles Conjecture. Using this pair of angles, $\overline{AC} \cong \overline{AE}$, and $\angle E \cong \angle C$, $\triangle ABC \cong \triangle ADE$ by ASA.

19. $\triangle ABC \cong \triangle CDA$ by SAA. Find the slopes of the sides of quadrilateral $ABCD$: slope $\overline{AB}$ = slope $\overline{CD}$ = 3 and slope $\overline{BC}$ = slope $\overline{DA}$ = $-\frac{1}{3}$. Therefore, $\overline{AB} \perp \overline{BC}$ and $\overline{CD} \perp \overline{DA}$, which tells us that $\angle B$ and $\angle D$ are both right angles, so they are congruent. Also, from the slopes, $\overline{BC} \parallel \overline{DA}$, so $\angle BCA \cong \angle CDA$ by the AIA Conjecture. Using these two pairs of congruent angles and the shared side, $\overline{AC}$, $\triangle ABC \cong \triangle CDA$ by SAA.

20. Duplicate one side of the original triangle. Then duplicate the two angles that include that side. Use one endpoint of the new segment as the vertex of one of these angles and the other endpoint of the segment as the vertex of the second angle. Find the intersection of the rays of the two angles that you duplicated.

Because a side and the angles that include that side in the new triangle are congruent to the corresponding parts of the original triangle, the second triangle is congruent to the first by ASA.

21. The construction is the same as the construction in Exercise 20 once you find the third angle, which is used here. (Finding the third angle is not shown.)

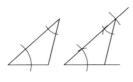

22. Draw any triangle. Duplicate any two angles of the original triangle, but make the included side a different length from the one in the original triangle. By the Third Angle Conjecture, the two triangles will have three pairs of congruent angles. The new triangle will have the same shape, but not the same size, as the original. Because the sides of the new triangle are not congruent to those of the original, the triangles are not congruent. Possible answer:

23. Draw a line segment. Construct a perpendicular. Bisect the right angle. Construct a triangle with two congruent sides and with a vertex that measures 135°.

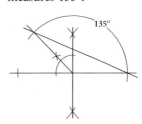

24. 125. Look for a pattern. Two concurrent lines divide the plane into 4 parts, 3 concurrent lines divide it into 6 parts, and 4 concurrent lines divide it into 8 parts. Each time another line is drawn, two more parts are added. Thus, n concurrent lines divide the plane into $2n$ parts; if $2n = 250$, then $n = 125$.

25. False. One possible counterexample is a kite.

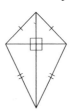

26. None. Because the triangle is isosceles, both legs will have length KM. By SAS, the two pairs of congruent sides and the included right angles will guarantee that all isosceles right triangles with a given length for one of the legs will be congruent.

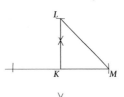

27.

28. a. About 100 km southeast of San Francisco

b. Yes. No, two towns would narrow it down to two locations. The third circle narrows it down to one.

EXTENSIONS

A. See the solutions to Take Another Look activities 5–8 on page 83.

B. See the solution to Take Another Look activity 9 on page 83.

The next terms in the sequences are $21x + 23y$, $34x + 37y$; and $64x - 23y$, $128x - 28y$.

In the first sequence, add the coefficients of two consecutive x-terms to get the coefficient of the next x-term, and add the coefficients of two consecutive y-terms to get the coefficient of the next y-term. In the second sequence, double the coefficient of each x-term to find the coefficient of the next x-term, and subtract 5 from the coefficient for any y-term to get the coefficient of the next y-term.

LESSON 4.6

EXERCISES

1. Yes. $\overline{BD} \cong \overline{BD}$ (same segment), $\angle A \cong \angle C$ (given), and $\angle ABD \cong \angle CBD$ (given), so $\triangle DBA \cong \triangle DBC$ by SAA. Therefore, $\overline{AB} \cong \overline{CB}$ by CPCTC.

2. Yes. $\overline{CN} \cong \overline{WN}$ and $\angle C \cong \angle W$ (given), and $\angle RNC \cong \angle ONW$ (Vertical Angles Conjecture), so $\triangle CRN \cong \triangle WON$ by ASA. Therefore, $\overline{RN} \cong \overline{ON}$ by CPCTC.

3. Cannot be determined. The given congruent parts and $\overline{CH} \cong \overline{CH}$ lead to SSA for triangles CHS and HCR, but SSA does not prove triangle congruence.

4. Yes. $\angle S \cong \angle I$, $\angle G \cong \angle A$ (given), and $\overline{TS} \cong \overline{IT}$ (definition of midpoint), so $\triangle ATI \cong \triangle GTS$ by SAA. Therefore, $\overline{SG} \cong \overline{IA}$ by CPCTC.

5. Yes. Draw $\overline{UF}$ to form $\triangle FOU$ and $\triangle FRU$. Then $\overline{FO} \cong \overline{FR}$ and $\overline{UO} \cong \overline{UR}$ (given), and $\overline{UF} \cong \overline{UF}$ (same segment), so $\triangle FOU \cong \triangle FRU$ by SSS. Therefore, $\angle O \cong \angle R$ by CPCTC.

6. Yes. $\overline{MN} \cong \overline{MA}$ (given), $\overline{ME} \cong \overline{MR}$ (given), and $\angle M \cong \angle M$ (same angle), so $\triangle EMA \cong \triangle RMN$ by SAS. Therefore, $\angle E \cong \angle R$ by CPCTC.

7. Yes. Draw $\overline{UT}$ to form triangles TUB and UTE. $\overline{BT} \cong \overline{EU}$ (given), $\overline{BU} \cong \overline{ET}$ (given), and $\overline{UT} \cong \overline{UT}$ (same segment), so $\triangle TUB \cong \triangle UTE$ by SSS. Therefore, $\angle B \cong \angle E$ by CPCTC.

8. Cannot be determined. $\triangle HLF \cong \triangle LHA$ by ASA (using two pairs of alternate interior angles and the shared side), but $\overline{HA}$ and $\overline{HF}$ are not corresponding sides.

9. Cannot be determined. AAA does not guarantee congruence. There is no information given about the sides.

10. Yes. $RO = GE = 2$, $FO = TE = 4$, and the included angles are congruent because they are both right angles. Therefore, $\triangle FRO \cong \triangle TGE$ by SAS and $\overline{FR} \cong \overline{GT}$ by CPCTC.

11. Yes. $\triangle DNO \cong \triangle RCO$ by SAS, and $\angle OND \cong \angle OCR$ by CPCTC.

12. Draw $\overline{AC}$ and $\overline{DF}$ to form $\triangle ABC$ and $\triangle DEF$. $\overline{AB} \cong \overline{CB} \cong \overline{DE} \cong \overline{FE}$ because all were drawn with the same radius. $\overline{AC} \cong \overline{DF}$ for the same reason. $\triangle ABC \cong \triangle DEF$ by SSS. Therefore, $\angle B \cong \angle E$ by CPCTC.

13. Cannot be determined. You have two pairs of congruent sides ($\overline{CM} \cong \overline{PM}$ from the median, and $\overline{AM} \cong \overline{AM}$), but that is not enough information to show that the triangles are congruent.

14. $\triangle HEI \cong \triangle KEI$ by ASA. The shared side is included between the two pairs of given congruent angles.

15. $\triangle ULF \cong \triangle UTE$ by SAS. Because U is the midpoint of $\overline{FE}$, $\overline{UF} \cong \overline{UE}$, and because U is also the midpoint of $\overline{LT}$, $\overline{UL} \cong \overline{UT}$. The included angles are vertical angles.

16. Copy one side of the original triangle, then one of the angles adjacent to that side using an endpoint of the segment as a vertex. Then use a compass to mark off an arc whose length is equal to the other side of the original triangle that is adjacent to the same angle. Connect the endpoints of the two segments you have constructed that are not the vertex of the angle between them to form the third side of the new triangle.

17. Make the included angles different.

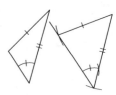

18. $a = 112°$, $b = 68°$, $c = 44°$, $d = 44°$, $e = 136°$, $f = 68°$, $g = 68°$, $h = 56°$, $k = 68°$, $l = 56°$, and $m = 124°$. $a + 68° = 180°$ (Linear Pair Conjecture), so $a = 112°$. $b = 68°$ (AIA Conjecture). $68° + 68° + c = 180°$ (Linear Pair Conjecture), so $c = 44°$. $d = c = 44°$ (AIA Conjecture). $d + e = 180°$ (Linear Pair Conjecture), so $e = 136°$. In the triangle with angle measures f and g, the unmarked angle measures $44°$ (Vertical Angles Conjecture). This is an isosceles triangle with base angles of measures f and g, so $2f + 44° = 180°$. Therefore, $f = 68°$ and $g = 68°$. In the isosceles triangle with base angle of measure h, the measure of the vertex angle is $68°$ (Vertical Angles Conjecture), so $2h + 68° = 180°$ and $h = 56°$. $k = 68°$ (AIA Conjecture). $k + h + l = 180°$, so $l = 56°$. Finally, $m = k + h$ (AIA Conjecture), so $m = 124°$.

19. ASA. The "long segment in the sand" is a shared side of both triangles.

20. $(-4, 1)$. In Lesson 3.7, Exercise 10, you discovered that the circumcenter of a right triangle is the midpoint of the hypotenuse. Using slopes, you can determine that $\overline{AB} \perp \overline{BC}$, so $\angle B$ is the right angle and $\overline{AC}$ is the hypotenuse. Therefore, the circumcenter is the midpoint of $\overline{AC}$, and its coordinates are $(-4, 1)$.

21.

Number of sides	3	4	5	6	7	12	n
Number of struts needed to make polygon rigid	0	1	2	3	4	9	$n - 3$

The number of struts needed to make a polygon with n sides rigid is $n - 3$. This is the number of diagonals needed to divide the polygon into triangles by connecting one of the n vertices to all of the other vertices that are not adjacent to it.

22. Value C always decreases. The distance from point P to point C decreases until $\overline{PB} \perp \ell$; then the distance begins to increase. The distance from C to $\overline{AB}$ remains constant; it is always half the distance between the two parallel lines. Because AP is increasing and AB is not changing, the ratio $\frac{AB}{AP}$ is decreasing. Because C is the midpoint of $\overline{BP}$, the ratio $\frac{BC}{BP}$ is always equal to $\frac{1}{2}$.

23. $x = 3$, $y = 10$. Add or subtract given lengths: $x = 5 - 2 = 3$ and $y = 3 + 4 + 3 = 10$.

PROJECT

One way to understand the answer of 26 regions is to see that the number of parts of space added at each step is the number of regions into which the new plane is divided by the lines that are its intersections with previously existing planes. For example, the fourth plane intersects the three existing planes in three lines, and three lines divide a plane into seven parts, so seven new regions are added by the third plane.

Project should satisfy the following criteria:

- The answer is correct: 26 regions.

- The student has looked for analogies to the cases in other dimensions.

- Tables are used to look for patterns across dimensions.

- The student has described the different strategies used in solving the problem and analyzed the effectiveness of each one.

Extra credit

- The problem is solved in more than one way.

- The student considered bounded and unbounded regions.

- The student used finite differences to find the cubic formula for the number of parts into which n random planes divide space: $f(n) = \frac{1}{6}n^3 + \frac{5}{6}n + 1$.

LESSON 4.7

EXERCISES

1. 1. Given; 2. Given; 3. Vertical Angles Conjecture; 4. $\triangle ESM \cong \triangle USO$; 5. CPCTC

2. 2. Given; 4. Definition of midpoint; 5. Vertical Angles Conjecture; 6. $\triangle CIL \cong \triangle MIB$ by SAS; 7. $\overline{CL} \cong \overline{MB}$

3. 5. Given; 6. $\triangle WSN \cong \triangle ESN$ by SSS; 7. $\angle W \cong \angle E$ by CPCTC

4. 2. $\angle 1 \cong \angle 2$, Definition of angle bisector; 3. Given; 4. Same segment; 5. $\triangle WNS \cong \triangle ENS$ by SAA; 6. CPCTC; 7. Definition of isosceles triangle

5. 1. Given; 2. Given; 4. $\angle 1 \cong \angle 2$ by AIA Conjecture; 6. $\triangle ESN \cong \triangle ANS$ by ASA; 7. $\overline{SA} \cong \overline{NE}$ by CPCTC. This proof shows that in a parallelogram, opposite sides are congruent.

6.

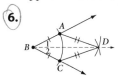

Given: $\angle ABC$ with $\overline{BA} \cong \overline{BC}$ and $\overline{CD} \cong \overline{AD}$

Show: $\overrightarrow{BD}$ is the angle bisector of $\angle ABC$

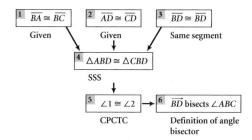

7. The angle bisector does not go to the midpoint of the opposite side in every triangle, only in isosceles triangles.

8. $\overline{NE}$. Apply the Side-Angle Inequality Conjecture twice, noticing that $\overline{EA}$ is a side of both triangles. First in $\triangle EAL$, $\overline{EA}$ is the shortest side because it is opposite the smallest angle. Now look at $\triangle NAE$. The measure of the unmarked angle is $180° - 61° - 58° = 60°$. In this triangle, $\angle EAN$ is the smallest angle, so the side opposite this angle, which is $\overline{NE}$, is the shortest side. Because $\overline{EA}$ is also a side of this triangle, you are able to compare the side lengths of the two triangles and conclude that $\overline{NE}$ is the shortest segment in the figure.

9. The triangles are congruent by SSS, so the two central angles cannot have different measures.

10. $\triangle POE \cong \triangle PRN$ by ASA, $\triangle SON \cong \triangle SRE$ by ASA. For the first pair of triangles, use the shared right angle and ignore the marks for $\overline{OS} \cong \overline{RS}$. For the second pair, use the vertical angles and ignore the right-angle marks and the given statement, $\overline{PO} \cong \overline{PR}$.

11. Cannot be determined. The parts do not correspond.

12. $\triangle RCK \cong \triangle ACK$ by SSS. $KA = KR$ because $\overline{CK}$ is a median, and $\overline{CK}$ is the shared side.

13. $a = 72°$, $b = 36°$, $c = 144°$, $d = 36°$, $e = 144°$, $f = 18°$, $g = 162°$, $h = 144°$, $j = 36°$, $k = 54°$, and $m = 126°$. $a = 72°$ (AIA Conjecture). $2a + b = 180°$, so $b = 36°$. $b + c = 180°$, so $c = 144°$. $72° + 72° + d = 180°$ (Triangle Sum Conjecture), so $d = 36°$. $d + e = 180°$, so $e = 144°$. The triangle with the angles with measures e and f is isosceles, so $2f + e = 180°$, and $f = 18°$. $g + 18° = 180°$, so $g = 162°$ (Linear Pair Conjecture). $h = e = 144°$ (CA Conjecture). $j = b = 36°$ (CA Conjecture). The unmarked angle in the right triangle containing the angle with measure k is $180° - c = 36°$, so $k + 36° + 90° = 180°$, and therefore $k = 54°$. Finally, in the isosceles triangle with vertex angle of measure a, the measure of each base angle is $\frac{1}{2}(180° - 72°) = 54°$, so $m + 54° = 180°$ and $m = 126°$.

14. The circumcenter is equidistant from all three vertices because it is on the perpendicular bisector of each side. Every point of the perpendicular bisector of a segment is equidistant from the endpoints. The incenter is equidistant from all three sides because it is on the angle bisector of each angle, and every point of an angle bisector is equidistant from the sides of the angle.

15. ASA. The fishing pole forms the side. "Perpendicular to the ground" forms one angle. "Same angle on her line of sight" forms the other angle.

16. $\frac{10}{35} = \frac{2}{7}$. Divide the number of shortest diagonals by the total number of diagonals. Each of the 10 vertices can be connected by a diagonal to each of the 7 non-adjacent diagonals, but this counts each diagonal twice, once from each endpoint. The total number of diagonals is $\frac{10 \cdot 7}{2} = 35$. A shortest diagonal occurs whenever a vertex is connected to another vertex that is two vertices away. Each of the 10 vertices can be connected to 2 other vertices in this way, but again, each diagonal would be counted twice. Therefore, the number of shortest diagonals is $\frac{10 \cdot 2}{2} = 10$.

17.

18. The vertices of the original rectangle are $B(1, 2)$, $O(3, 2)$, $X(3, 3)$, and $Y(1, 3)$. The vertices of the rotated rectangle are $B'(2, -1)$, $O'(2, -3)$, $X'(3, -3)$, and $Y'(3, -1)$. Under this rotation, each point (x, y) is replaced by the point $(y, -x)$.

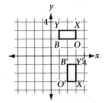

IMPROVING YOUR REASONING SKILLS

In effect, the problem states that there is a unique solution, so finding any solution is sufficient. If you are stuck, systematically try all possible locations of, for example, two jacks. You can use symmetry to diminish the number of possibilities; that is, for every placement of the jacks, you can rotate or reflect the entire square to account for other possibilities. (There are eight different placements of two identical cards in a 3-by-3 array.)

Solution: An ace is in the center.

K	A	K
Q	A	Q
J	K	J

LESSON 4.8

EXERCISES

1. 6. The perimeter of $\triangle ABC$ is 48, so $AB + BC + AC = 48$. Because $AC = BC = 18$, $AB + (2 \cdot 18) = 48$, so $AB = 12$. By the Vertex Angle Bisector Conjecture, altitude $\overline{CD}$ is also a median, so $AD = \frac{1}{2}(AB) = 6$.

2. $m\angle ADC = 90°$; $m\angle ACD = 18°$. By the Vertex Angle Bisector Conjecture, the angle bisector of the vertex angle of isosceles triangle ABC is also the altitude to the base, so $m\angle ADC = 90°$. By the Triangle Sum Conjecture, $\angle ACD$ must measure $18°$.

3. $45°$. Because $DB = DA$, $\overline{CD}$ is the median from the vertex of the isosceles triangle, so it is also an altitude. Therefore, $m\angle CDA = 90°$. $\angle CAD$ and $\angle CAB$ are the same angle, so $m\angle CAD = 45°$. Thus, $m\angle ACD = 180° - 90° - 45° = 45°$.

Discovering Geometry Solutions Manual
©2008 Key Curriculum Press

4. 2. ∠1 ≅ ∠2; 5. SAS

5. 4. CPCTC; 7. Definition of perpendicular; 8. $\overline{CD}$ is an altitude

6.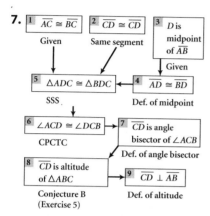

7.

```
1 AC ≅ BC    2 CD ≅ CD    3 D is
  Given        Same segment    midpoint
                              of AB
                              Given
```

```
5 △ADC ≅ △BDC ←── 4 AD ≅ BD
  SSS                Def. of midpoint
```

```
6 ∠ACD ≅ ∠DCB ──→ 7 CD is angle
  CPCTC               bisector of ∠ACB
                      Def. of angle bisector
```

```
8 CD is altitude      9 CD ⊥ AB
  of △ABC
  Conjecture B          Def. of altitude
  (Exercise 5)
```

8. Yes. First show that the three exterior triangles are congruent by SAS. Because △SLN is equilateral, $SN = NL = LS$. The figure shows that $TN = EL = IS$, so by subtraction, $ST = NE = LI$. Therefore, you have two sets of congruent sides in the three triangles: $\overline{TN} \cong \overline{EL} \cong \overline{IS}$ and $\overline{NE} \cong \overline{LI} \cong \overline{ST}$. Also, because △SLN is equilateral, each of its angles measures 60°, so ∠N ≅ ∠L ≅ ∠S. Therefore, △TNE ≅ △ELI ≅ △IST by SAS. Because all corresponding parts of congruent triangles are congruent, $\overline{TE} \cong \overline{EI} \cong \overline{IT}$, which means that △TIE is equilateral.

9. Drawing the vertex angle bisector as an auxiliary segment, you have two triangles. You can show them to be congruent by SAS, as you did in Exercise 4. Then, ∠A ≅ ∠B by CPCTC. Therefore, base angles of an isosceles triangle are congruent.

10. The proof is similar to the proof of the Equilateral Triangle Conjecture on page 245 of the student book, but in reverse, and using the Converse of the Isosceles Triangle Conjecture in place of the Isosceles Triangle Conjecture.

11. First construct a 60° angle by drawing arcs that determine an equilateral triangle. Then bisect the 60° angle to form two 30° angles.

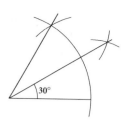

12. $a = 128°$, $b = 128°$, $c = 52°$, $d = 76°$, $e = 104°$, $f = 104°$, $g = 76°$, $h = 52°$, $j = 70°$, $k = 70°$, $l = 40°$, $m = 110°$, and $n = 58°$. $a + 52° = 180°$ (Linear Pair Conjecture), so $a = 128°$. $b = 128°$ (AIA Conjecture with ℓ_1 and ℓ_2). $b + c = 180°$ (Linear Pair Conjecture), so $c = 52°$. $d = 180° - 2c$ (Triangle Sum Conjecture), so $d = 76°$. The angle directly below the angle with measure d has measure $180° - d$ (Linear Pair Conjecture), so its measure is 104°. Then $e = 104°$ (AIA Conjecture with ℓ_1 and ℓ_2). Next, $f = e = 104°$ (AIA Conjecture with ℓ_3 and ℓ_4). $g = d = 76°$ (CA Conjecture with ℓ_3 and ℓ_4). $h = \frac{1}{2}(180° - g) = 52°$. $j = 70°$ (marked congruent to other 70° angle). Look at the triangle containing the angle with measure n. The unmarked angle in this triangle measures 70° (CA Conjecture with ℓ_1 and ℓ_2). Then $k = 70°$ (Vertical Angles Conjecture). $l + k + 70° = 180°$ (Triangle Sum Conjecture), so $l = 40°$. $m + k = 180°$ (Linear Pair Conjecture), so $m = 110°$. Finally, $n + 70° + 52° = 180°$ (Triangle Sum Conjecture), so $n = 58°$.

13. Between 16 and 17 minutes. First find a five-minute interval during which this happens, and then narrow it down to a one-minute interval. At 3:15, the hands have not yet crossed each other because the minute hand is at the 3, but the hour hand has moved one-fourth of the way between the 3 and the 4. At 3:20, the hands have already crossed because the minute hand is on the 4, but the hour hand is only one-third of the way from the 3 to the 4. To get closer to the time where the hands overlap, try some times between 3:15 and 3:20. At 3:17, the hour hand has gone $\frac{17}{60}$ of the way from the 3 to the 4, while the minute hand has gone $\frac{2}{5}$ of the way from the 3 to the 4. Compare these fractions by changing them to decimals: $\frac{17}{60} = 0.28\overline{3}$ and $\frac{2}{5} = 0.4$, so $\frac{2}{5} > \frac{17}{60}$. This means that at 3:17, the minute hand has already crossed the hour hand, so try 3:16. At 3:16, the hour hand has gone $\frac{16}{60}$ of the way from the 3 to the 4, while the minute hand has gone $\frac{1}{5}$ of the way from the 3 to the 4. Again, compare the fractions by changing them to decimals: $\frac{16}{60} = 0.2\overline{6}$ and $\frac{1}{5} = 0.2$. $\frac{16}{60} > \frac{1}{5}$, so at 3:16, the minute hand has not yet crossed the hour hand. Therefore, the hands overlap sometime between 3:16 and 3:17, or between 16 and 17 minutes after 3:00.

14. $y = -\frac{5}{3}x + 16$. First find the slope of $\overline{AB}$: $\frac{-2-3}{4-1} = \frac{-5}{3} = -\frac{5}{3}$. Parallel lines have equal slopes, so find the equation in the form $y = mx + b$ of the line through $C(6, 6)$ with slope $-\frac{5}{3}$.

$$\frac{y-6}{x-6} = \frac{-5}{3}$$

$$3(y-6) = -5(x-6)$$

$$3y - 18 = -5x + 30$$

$$3y = -5x + 48$$

$$y = -\frac{5}{3}x + 16$$

15. 120. n concurrent lines divide the plane into $2n$ parts; if $n = 60$, $2n = 120$. (See solution for Lesson 4.5, Exercise 24.)

16. Any point at which the x-coordinate is either 1 or 7 and the y-coordinate does not equal 3, or the points $(4, 6)$ or $(4, 0)$.

17. Hugo and Duane can locate the site of the fireworks by creating a diagram using SSS.

18.

Because "hept" means 7, cycloheptane has 7 C's. There are 2 H's branching off each C, so there are 14 H's. In general, a cycloparaffin has n C's and $2n$ H's, so the general rule for a cycloparaffin is C_nH_{2n}.

IMPROVING YOUR ALGEBRA SKILLS

Let x represent the month you were born, and let y represent the day.

$2x$

$2x - 16$

$5(2x - 16) = 10x - 80$

$10x - 80 + 100 = 10x + 20$

$10x + 20 - 20 = 10x$

$10x \cdot 10 = 100x$

$100x + y$

EXTENSION

If any two segments coincide, all three will. (This happens when the three segments are drawn from the vertex angle of an isosceles triangle or from any vertex of an equilateral triangle.)

EXPLORATION · NAPOLEON'S THEOREM

PROJECT

Project should satisfy the following criteria:

- Equations and graphs are clearly labeled.

- At least three of the questions are answered correctly.

  1. Any pair that has the same y-intercepts and slopes with the same absolute values, but opposite signs.

  2. Any pair that has the same x-intercepts and slopes with the same absolute values, but opposite signs.

  3. $y = -mx + b$; $y = -mx - b$

  4. The lines form an isosceles triangle with the base on the line $y = -x$ and with line of symmetry the line $y = x$. Other such triangles are formed on the base $y = -x$ by lines with equations in the form $y = mx - m$ and $y = \left(\frac{1}{m}\right)x + 1$.

Extra credit

- All project questions are answered correctly.

- Student gives general equations in the answer to Question 4.

CHAPTER 4 REVIEW

EXERCISES

1. Their rigidity gives strength.

2. The Triangle Sum Conjecture states that the sum of the measures of the angles in every triangle is 180°. Possible answers: It applies to all triangles; many other conjectures rely on it.

3. Possible answer: The angle bisector of the vertex angle is also the median and the altitude.

4. The distance between A and B is along the segment connecting them. The distance from A to C to B can't be shorter than the distance from A to B. Therefore, $AC + CB > AB$. Points A, B, and C form a triangle. Therefore, the sum of the lengths of any two sides is greater than the length of the third side.

5. SSS, SAS, ASA, or SAA

6. In some cases, two different triangles can be constructed using the same two sides and non-included angle.

Discovering Geometry Solutions Manual
©2008 Key Curriculum Press

7. Cannot be determined. SSA does not guarantee congruence.

8. $\triangle TOP \cong \triangle ZAP$ by SAA.

9. $\triangle MSE \cong \triangle OSU$ by SSS.

10. Cannot be determined. SSA does not guarantee congruence.

11. $\triangle TRP \cong \triangle APR$ by SAS.

12. $\triangle CGH \cong \triangle NGI$ by SAS. Use the Converse of the Isosceles Triangle Conjecture to get $\overline{HG} \cong \overline{IG}$, and use the vertical angles.

13. Cannot be determined. You have two pairs of congruent sides, but there is no information about the third pair of sides or about any of the pairs of angles.

14. $\triangle ABE \cong \triangle DCE$ by SAA or ASA.

15. $\triangle ACN \cong \triangle RBO \cong \triangle OBR$ by SAS. In a regular polygon, all sides are congruent and all interior angles are congruent.

16. $\triangle AMD \cong \triangle UMT$ by SAS; $\overline{AD} \cong \overline{UT}$ by CPCTC.

17. Cannot be determined. AAA does not guarantee congruence.

18. Cannot be determined. SSA does not guarantee congruence.

19. $\triangle TRI \cong \triangle ALS$ by SAA; $\overline{TR} \cong \overline{AL}$ by CPCTC. Use alternate interior angles to show the triangles are congruent.

20. $\triangle SVE \cong \triangle NIK$ by SSS; $\overline{EI} \cong \overline{KV}$ by the overlapping segments property. $EV + VI = EI$ and $KI + IV = KV$. Because $EV = KI$ and $VI = IV$, $EI = KV$ and thus $\overline{EI} \cong \overline{KV}$.

21. Cannot be determined. Parts don't correspond. Notice that the shared side is not opposite congruent angles.

22. Cannot be determined. There is not sufficient information to determine that the triangles are congruent. By the AIA Conjecture, $\angle MNT \cong \angle CTN$. With the shared side, this gives SSA, which does not guarantee that the triangles are congruent. You are not able to determine whether $\overline{MT} \parallel \overline{NC}$, so you cannot tell whether quadrilateral $NCTM$ has one pair of opposite parallel sides or two pairs, and thus cannot determine whether it is a parallelogram or a trapezoid.

23. $\triangle LAZ \cong \triangle IAR$ by ASA, $\triangle LRI \cong \triangle IZL$ by ASA, and $\triangle LRD \cong \triangle IZD$ by ASA. There are actually two isosceles triangles in the figure, $\triangle LAI$ and $\triangle LDI$, and there are three pairs of congruent triangles. For $\triangle LAZ \cong \triangle IAR$, use the shared angle, $\angle A$. For $\triangle LRI \cong \triangle IZL$, use the common side, $\overline{LI}$. Also, $m\angle RLI = m\angle ZIL$ (Isosceles Triangle Conjecture), and $m\angle RLZ = m\angle ZIR$ (given), so by subtraction, $m\angle ZLI = m\angle RIL$, and thus, $\angle ZLI \cong \angle RIL$. Thus, the triangles are congruent by ASA. Because $\angle ZLI \cong \angle RIL$, $\overline{DI} \cong \overline{DL}$ by the Converse of the Isosceles Triangle Conjecture. Using this pair of sides, the marked angles, and the vertical angles, $\triangle LRD \cong \triangle IZD$ by ASA.

24. $\triangle PTS \cong \triangle TPO$ by ASA or SAA; yes. Use the shared side to show that the triangles are congruent. By the Converse of the Parallel Lines Conjecture, you can show that $\overline{PS} \parallel \overline{TO}$ and $\overline{PO} \parallel \overline{ST}$, so $STOP$ is a parallelogram.

25. $\triangle ANG$ is isosceles, so $\angle A \cong \angle G$. Then, $m\angle A + m\angle N + m\angle G = 188°$. The sum of the measures of the three angles of a triangle must be 180°, so an isosceles triangle with the given angle measures is impossible.

26. $\triangle ROW \cong \triangle NOG$ by ASA, implying that $\overline{OW} \cong \overline{OG}$. However, the two segments shown are not the same length.

27. c is the longest segment, and a and g are the shortest. Apply the Side-Angle Inequality Conjecture to all three triangles in succession. First, in the triangle with side lengths a and g, the third angle measure is 30°, so this triangle is isosceles with $a = g < f$. Now look at the triangle with side lengths d, e, and f. The angle opposite the side with length e measures 60°, because the measure of this angle + 30° + 90° = 180°. So the angle opposite the side with length f must also measure 60°. Thus, this triangle is equilateral, and $f = d = e$. Finally, look at the right triangle. The unmarked angle measures 45°, so this is an isosceles right triangle with $b = d$. In this triangle, c (the hypotenuse) is the longest side, so $b = d < c$. Putting the inequalities from the three triangles together, you have $a = g < f = d = e = b < c$, so c is the longest segment and a and g are the shortest.

28. $x = 20°$. Apply the Triangle Sum Conjecture to both the large triangle and the triangle containing the angle marked as 100°. From the large triangle, $2a + 2b + x = 180°$, and from the triangle with the 100° angle, $a + b + 100° = 180$, or $a + b = 80°$, which is equivalent to $2a + 2b = 160°$. Substituting 160° for $2a + 2b$ in the equation $2a + 2b + x = 180°$ gives $x = 20°$.

29. Yes

Given: $\overline{RE} \cong \overline{AE}$, $\angle S \cong \angle T$, $\angle ERL \cong \angle EAL$

Show: $\overline{SA} \cong \overline{TR}$

Flowchart Proof

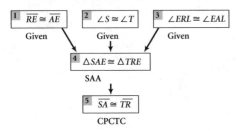

30. Yes

Given: $\angle A \cong \angle M$, $\overline{AF} \perp \overline{FR}$, $\overline{MR} \perp \overline{FR}$

Show: $\triangle FRD$ is isosceles

Flowchart Proof

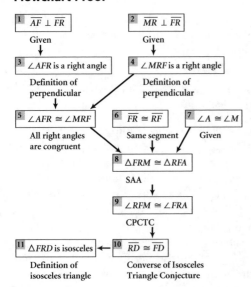

31. $x = 48°$. The sum of the measures of the interior angles of any quadrilateral is 360° because it can be subdivided into two triangles. Therefore, $x + 90° + 132° + 90° = 360°$, so $x = 48°$.

32. The legs form two triangles that are congruent by SAS, using the vertical angles as the included angles. Alternate interior angles are congruent by CPCTC, so by the Converse of the Parallel Lines Conjecture, the seat must be parallel to the floor.

33. Construct $\angle P$ and $\angle A$ to be adjacent. The angle that forms a linear pair with the conjunction of $\angle P$ and $\angle A$ is $\angle L$. Construct $\angle A$. Mark off the length AL on one ray. Construct $\angle L$. Extend the unconnected sides of the angles until they meet. Label the point of intersection P.

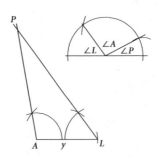

34. Construct $\angle P$. Mark off the length PB on one ray. From point B, mark off the two segments that intersect the other ray of $\angle P$ at distance x.

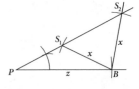

35. 1. M is midpoint of $\overline{TE}$ and $\overline{IR}$, Given; 2. $\angle TMI \cong \angle RME$, Vertical angles; 3. $\overline{TM} \cong \overline{ME}$, Definition of midpoint; 4. $\overline{IM} \cong \overline{MR}$, Definition of midpoint; 5. $\triangle TMI \cong \triangle EMR$, SAS; 6. $\angle T \cong \angle E$ or $\angle R \cong \angle I$, CPCTC; 7. $\overline{TI} \parallel \overline{RE}$, Converse of AIA Conjecture.

36. Given three sides, only one triangle is possible; therefore, the shelves on the right hold their shape. The shelves on the left have no triangles and move freely as a parallelogram.

37. Possible method: With a compass and straightedge, construct an equilateral triangle, and bisect one angle to obtain two 30° angles. Adjacent to that angle, construct a right angle, and bisect it to obtain two 45° angles. The 30° angle and 45° angles that share a common side form a 75° angle.

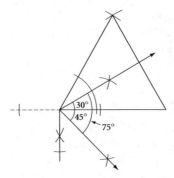

For a patty-paper construction, see the solution for Lesson 4.2, Exercise 17, which shows the construction of a 105° angle. If you use just the lower half of the 60° angle shown there, you will have a 30° angle adjacent to a 45° angle, which makes a 75° angle.

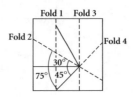

38. $d, a = b, c, e, f$. The figure shows that $\overline{AC} \parallel \overline{BD}$, so $a = b$ by the AIA Conjecture. It is given that $m\angle CAD > m\angle CBD$, which means that $a + f > b + e$. Because $a = b$, we can substitute a for b in this inequality to obtain $a + f > a + e$. Then subtract a from both sides of the last inequality to obtain $f > e$. Now apply the Side-Angle Triangle Inequality to each of the triangles. In $\triangle ABC$, $AC > AB$ gives $e > c$, and $AB > BC$ gives $c > a$. In $\triangle ABD$, $BD > AD$ gives $f > b$, and $AD > AB$ gives $b > d$. Putting all of this information together, we have $f > e > c > a = b > d$.

TAKE ANOTHER LOOK

1. On a sphere or a globe, angles are measured along tangent lines. It is indeed possible to draw a triangle with two or more obtuse angles or with three right angles. The sum of the interior angle measures of any triangle drawn on a sphere is always greater than 180°.

2. Both conjectures are true on a sphere, but the angles in an equilateral triangle no longer measure 60°.

3. A triangle with the measure of one angle twice that of another can be divided into two isosceles triangles for certain only if the smallest angle measures less than 45°. When the angle with twice the measure is acute, it works, but when this angle measures, for example, 100°, it doesn't work.

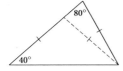

4. The claim must always be true. Let a and b be the measures of interior angles A and B, respectively, and let x be the measure of the exterior angle to $\angle C$, with $x = 2a$. Then $2a = a + b$, so $a = b$.

5. The measure of an exterior angle of a convex quadrilateral is 180° less than the sum of the measures of the remote interior angles. (In a concave quadrilateral, with appropriate interpretation, the exterior angle at an angle with measure more than 180° is the supplement of the sum of the measures of the remote interior angles.)

6. Two possible answers: (1) The sum of the lengths of any three sides of a quadrilateral is greater than the length of the remaining side. (2) The sum of the lengths of any two consecutive sides of a quadrilateral is greater than the length of the diagonal joining their endpoints.

7. Use this construction to bisect $\overline{AB}$: From points A and B, draw arcs that have the same radius and have length greater than $\frac{1}{2}AB$, intersecting at points C and D. $\overleftrightarrow{CD}$ is the perpendicular bisector, bisecting $\overline{AB}$ at point E.

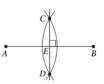

Proof: $\overline{AC} \cong \overline{BC} \cong \overline{AD} \cong \overline{BD}$ and $\overline{CD} \cong \overline{CD}$, so $\triangle ACD \cong \triangle BCD$ by SSS. Therefore, $\angle ACE \cong \angle BCE$. $\overline{CE} \cong \overline{CE}$, so $\triangle ACE \cong \triangle BCE$ by SAS. $\overline{AE} \cong \overline{BE}$ by CPCTC, so $\overline{AB}$ is bisected by $\overleftrightarrow{CD}$. $\angle AEC \cong \angle BEC$. $\angle AEC$ and $\angle BEC$ form a linear pair. Therefore, $\angle AEC$ and $\angle BEC$ are right angles. Therefore, $\overleftrightarrow{CD} \perp \overline{AB}$.

8. Use this construction of the perpendicular to a line through point P: With a compass, mark off points A and B on the line, equidistant from point P. Choose a longer radius for the compass, and draw arcs with centers at points A and B and meeting at point Q. Draw $\overline{PQ}$. $\overline{PQ}$ is perpendicular to the line.

Proof: $\overline{AP} \cong \overline{BP}$, $\overline{AQ} \cong \overline{BQ}$, and $\overline{PQ} \cong \overline{PQ}$. So, $\triangle APQ \cong \triangle BPQ$ by SSS. Therefore, $\angle APQ \cong \angle BPQ$, and these angles form a linear pair, so they are right angles. Therefore, $\overline{PQ} \perp \overline{AB}$.

9. Neither SSSS nor SSSD guarantee congruence, but SSSDD does.

Draw diagonals and consider triangle congruence. Four sides and an angle will guarantee congruence of quadrilaterals, and there are other possibilities.

SASA does not guarantee congruence, but SASAS does. SASA is similar to the SSA case for triangles.

CHAPTER 5

LESSON 5.1

EXERCISES

1. *(See table at bottom of page.)*

For each given value of n (the number of sides of the polygon), calculate $180°(n - 2)$ (the sum of the measures of the interior angles).

2. *(See table at bottom of page.)*

For each given value of n (number of sides), calculate $180°(n - 2)$ to find the sum of the measures of the interior angles, and then divide by n to find the measure of each interior angle. In an equiangular polygon, all interior angles have the same measure.

3. 122°. In the quadrilateral, the unmarked angle measures 90° (Linear Pair Conjecture). Then, by the Quadrilateral Sum Conjecture, $a + 72° + 76° + 90° = 360°$, so $a = 122°$.

4. 136°. The two unmarked angles in the hexagon measure 112° and 110° (Linear Pair Conjecture), and the sum of the interior angles of a hexagon is $180° \cdot 4 = 720°$ (Polygon Sum Conjecture). Therefore, $2b + 110° + 112° + 116° + 110° = 720°$, so $2b = 272°$ and $b = 136°$.

5. $e = 108°$, $f = 36°$. In the equiangular pentagon, $5e = 540°$ (Pentagon Sum Conjecture), so $e = 108°$. The triangle is isosceles with base angles of measure 72° (Linear Pair Conjecture), so $f + 2 \cdot 72° = 180°$ and $f = 36°$.

6. $c = 108°$, $d = 106°$. One of the unmarked angles is a vertical angle of the angle marked as 44°, so its measure is also 44°, and the other unmarked angle of the quadrilateral measures 102° (Linear Pair Conjecture). Look at the triangle containing the angle with measure d. Here, $d + 44° + 30° = 180°$ (Triangle Sum Conjecture), so $d = 106°$. Then apply the Quadrilateral Sum Conjecture: $c + d + 102° + 44° = 360°$, so $c = 108°$.

7. $g = 105°$, $h = 82°$. In the pentagon, $3g + 108° + 117° = 540°$, so $g = \frac{1}{3}[540° - (117° + 108°)] = 105°$. Now look at the vertex on the right side of the figure that is shared by the pentagon and the quadrilateral. The sum of the measures of the three angles at this vertex is 360°, so the unmarked angle in the quadrilateral measures 122°. In the quadrilateral, $h + 90° + 66° + 122° = 360°$, so $h = 82°$.

8. $j = 120°$, $k = 38°$. The hexagon is equiangular, so $6j = 180° \cdot 4 = 720°$, and $j = 120°$. Now look at the parallel lines to see that $k = 38°$ (AIA Conjecture).

9. The sum of the interior angle measures of this quadrilateral is 358°, but it should be 360°. Use vertical angles to find that three of the angle measures in the quadrilateral are 102°, 76°, and 82°. Using the CA Conjecture and the Linear Pair Conjecture shows that the fourth angle of the quadrilateral is $180° - 82° = 98°$. Then the sum of the four interior angles of the quadrilateral would be $76° + 102° + 82° + 98° = 358°$, which is impossible.

10. The sum of the measures of the interior angles is 554°. However, the figure is a pentagon, so the sum of the measures of its interior angles should be 540°. Three exterior angles of the pentagon each measure 49°, so the interior angles at these three vertices each measure 131°. Another exterior angle measures 154°, so the exterior angle at that vertex measures 26°. Thus, the sum of the interior angle measures would be $3 \cdot 131° + 135° + 26° = 554°$, which is impossible.

11. 18 sides. The figure shows an equilateral triangle, a regular nonagon, and a third regular polygon meeting at point A. The sum of the measures of the angles sharing A as a common vertex must be 360°. The measure of each interior angle of an equilateral triangle is 60°, and the measure of each interior angle of a regular nonagon is $\frac{180° \cdot 7}{9} = 140°$. Therefore, the measure of each interior angle of the third regular polygon is $360° - 60° - 140° = 160°$. Because all angles of a regular polygon have the

---

Lesson 5.1, Exercises 1, 2

1.

Number of sides of polygon	7	8	9	10	11	20	55	100
Sum of measures of angles	900°	1080°	1260°	1440°	1620°	3240°	9540°	17,640°

2.

Number of sides of equiangular polygon	5	6	7	8	9	10	12	16	100
Measure of each angle of equiangular polygon	108°	120°	$128\frac{4}{7}°$	135°	140°	144°	150°	$157\frac{1}{2}°$	$176\frac{2}{5}°$

same measure, the measure of each interior angle is $\frac{180°(n-2)}{n}$. Use this expression to find n when each interior angle measures 160°.

$$\frac{180°(n-2)}{n} = 160°$$

$$180°(n-2) = 160°n$$

$$180°n - 360° = 160°n$$

$$20°n = 360°$$

$$n = 18$$

Therefore, the largest polygon has 18 sides.

12. $a = 116°$, $b = 64°$, $c = 90°$, $d = 82°$, $e = 99°$, $f = 88°$, $g = 150°$, $h = 56°$, $j = 106°$, $k = 74°$, $m = 136°$, $n = 118°$, and $p = 99°$. $a = 116°$ (Vertical Angles Conjecture). $b = 64°$ (CA or AIA Conjecture, and Linear Pair Conjecture). $c = 90°$ (CA or AIA Conjecture, and Linear Pair Conjecture). $a + b + d + 98° = 360°$ (Quadrilateral Sum Conjecture), so $d = 82°$. Now look at the quadrilateral containing angles with measures e and p. Here, $p = e$, and the unmarked angles measure 98° and 64° (Linear Pair Conjecture), so $2e + 98° + 64° = 360°$. Therefore, $2e = 198°$ and $e = 99°$. Next look at the pentagon in the lower left. By the Linear Pair Conjecture, the two unmarked angles measure 82° and 116°. The sum of the measures of the interior angles of a pentagon is 540°, so $f + 138° + 116° + 82° + 116° = 540°$, and $f = 88°$. $f + g + 122° = 360°$, so $g = 150°$. Next look at the quadrilateral that includes the angles with measures g and h. By the Linear Pair Conjecture, the unmarked angles measure 64° and 90°, so $g + h + 64° + 90° = 360°$, and thus $h = 56°$. Now look at the quadrilateral in the lower right that includes the angle with measure j. The unmarked angle is 90° (vertical angle with angle of measure c), so $j + 90° + 77° + 87° = 360°$, and thus $j = 106°$. Either of the angles that form a linear pair with the angle of measure j measures 74°, so $k = 74°$ (AIA Conjecture or CA Conjecture). Next look at the quadrilateral in the upper right that includes the angle with measure m. Here, the unmarked angles measure 90° and 74° (Linear Pair Conjecture and Vertical Angles Conjecture), so $m + 60° + 74° + 90° = 360°$, and thus $m = 136°$. $n + m + 106° = 360°$, so $n = 118°$. Finally, $p = e$, so $p = 99°$.

13. 17 sides. Find the value of n for which $180°(n-2) = 2700°$. Solve this equation.

$$180°(n-2) = 2700°$$

$$n - 2 = 15$$

$$n = 17$$

Therefore, if the sum of the measures of the interior angles is 2700°, the polygon has 17 sides.

14. 15 sides. The measure of each interior angle of an equiangular polygon is $\frac{180°(n-2)}{n}$, so solve the equation $\frac{180°(n-2)}{n} = 156°$.

$$\frac{180°(n-2)}{n} = 156°$$

$$180°(n-2) = 156°n$$

$$180°n - 360° = 156°n$$

$$24°n = 360°$$

$$n = 15$$

Therefore, an equiangular polygon in which each interior angle measures 156° has 15 sides.

15. The 12th century. Compare the measures of each interior angle in a regular 16-gon to those in a regular 18-gon. Each interior angle of a 16-gon measures $\frac{180° \cdot 14}{16} = 157.7°$, while each interior angle of an 18-gon measures $\frac{180° \cdot 16}{18} = 160°$. Therefore, the plate is probably from the 12th century.

16. The angles of the trapezoid measure 67.5° and 112.5°. 67.5° is half the value of each angle of a regular octagon, and 112.5° is half the value of 360° − 135°.

17. First proof: Apply the Triangle Sum Conjecture to $\triangle QDU$ to obtain $q + d + u = 180°$, and to $\triangle ADU$ to obtain $a + e + v = 180°$. The sum of the angle measures in quadrilateral $QDAU$ is $m\angle Q + m\angle QDA + m\angle A + m\angle AUQ = q + d + e + a + u + v$. Rearrange terms to obtain $q + d + u + a + e + v = (q + d + u) + (a + e + v) = 180° + 180° = 360°$.

Second proof: Using the Triangle Sum Conjecture, $(a + b + j) + (c + d + k) + (e + f + l) + (g + h + i) = 4(180°)$, or 720°. The four angles in the center sum to 360°, so $j + k + l + i = 360°$. Subtract to get $a + b + c + d + e + f + g + h = 360°$.

18. $x = 120°$. The sum of the angle measures at a vertex of the tiling must be 360°, so $90° + 60° + 90° + x = 360°$, and $x = 120°$.

19. The segments joining the opposite midpoints of a quadrilateral always bisect each other.

20. D. As vertex P moves from left to right: The distance PA decreases and then soon increases, the perimeter of the triangle decreases before it increases, and the measure of $\angle APB$ increases for a while, but then decreases.

21. The base angles of an isosceles right triangle measure 45°; thus, they are complementary.

IMPROVING YOUR VISUAL THINKING SKILLS

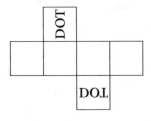

EXTENSIONS

A. The angles of a quadrilateral completely surround a point, so the sum of their measures is 360°. The angles of a pentagon will begin to overlap and will surround a point $1\frac{1}{2}$ times (for a sum of 540°).

B. Results will vary.

C. See the solutions to Take Another Look activities 1 and 2 on pages 105–106.

LESSON 5.2

EXERCISES

1. 360°. By the Exterior Angle Sum Conjecture, the sum of the measures of a set of exterior angles for *any* polygon is 360°.

2. 72°; 60°. In an equiangular polygon, all interior angles are congruent, so all exterior angles are also congruent. For a polygon with n sides, the measure of each exterior angle is $\frac{360°}{n}$, so the measure of each exterior angle of an equiangular pentagon is $\frac{360°}{5} = 72°$, and the measure of each exterior angle of an equilateral hexagon is $\frac{360°}{6} = 60°$.

3. 15 sides. The measure of each exterior angle of a regular polygon is $\frac{360°}{n}$. (See solution for Exercise 2.) If $\frac{360°}{n} = 24°$, 360° = 24° · n, so $n = 15$. Thus, if each exterior angle of a regular polygon measures 24°, the polygon has 15 sides.

4. 43 sides. Use the Polygon Sum Conjecture. Find n if $180°(n-2) = 7380°$.

$$180°(n-2) = 7380°$$

$$180° \cdot n - 360° = 7380°$$

$$180° \cdot n = 7740°$$

$$n = 43$$

Thus, if the sum of the measures of the interior angles of a polygon is 7380°, the polygon has 43 sides.

5. $a = 108°$. Use the Exterior Angle Sum Conjecture. The figure shows a set of exterior angles (one at each vertex) for a pentagon. The measure of the unmarked exterior angle is 180° − 140° = 40° (Linear Pair Conjecture). Therefore, $a + 68° + 84° + 60° + 40° = 360°$, so $a = 108°$.

6. $b = 45\frac{1}{3}°$. Use the Exterior Angle Sum Conjecture. The measure of the unmarked exterior angle is 180° − 68° = 112° (Linear Pair Conjecture). There are three exterior angles with measure b. Therefore, $3b + 69° + 43° + 112° = 360°$, so $3b = 136°$, and $b = 45\frac{1}{3}°$.

7. $c = 51\frac{3}{7}°$, $d = 115\frac{5}{7}°$. By the Equiangular Polygon Conjecture, the measure of an interior angle of an equiangular heptagon is $\frac{5 \cdot 180°}{7} = 128\frac{4}{7}°$. Then $c = 180° - 128\frac{4}{7}° = 51\frac{3}{7}°$ (Linear Pair Conjecture). Now look at the common vertex of the heptagon and the two quadrilaterals. The sum of the angle measures at this vertex is 360°, so $2d + 128\frac{4}{7}° = 360°$. Therefore, $2d = 231\frac{3}{7}°$, and $d = 115\frac{5}{7}°$.

8. $e = 72°$, $f = 45°$, $g = 117°$, and $h = 126°$. Use the Equiangular Polygon Conjecture. In the regular pentagon, the measure of each interior angle is $\frac{3 \cdot 180°}{5} = 108°$, so $e = 180° - 108° = 72°$. In the regular octagon, the measure of each interior angle is $\frac{6 \cdot 180°}{8} = 135°$, so $f = 180° - 135° = 45°$. g is the measure of one of three angles whose sum is 360°. Because one of these angles is an interior angle of the pentagon and another is an interior angle of the octagon, $g + 108° + 135° = 360°$, so $g = 117°$. Finally, $h + e + f + g = 360°$ (Quadrilateral Sum Conjecture), so $h + 234° = 360°$, and $h = 126°$.

9. $a = 30°$, $b = 30°$, $c = 106°$, and $d = 136°$. First, $a + 56° + 94° = 180°$ (Triangle Sum Conjecture), so $a = 30°$. Next, $b = a$ (AIA Conjecture), so $b = 30°$. From the triangle on the left, $b + c + 44° = 180°$, so $c = 106°$. Finally, look at the quadrilateral that contains angles with measures 56°, 94°, and d, as well as an unmarked angle. The measure of the unmarked angle is 180° − c = 74° (Linear Pair Conjecture), so $d + 94° + 56° + 74° = 360°$ (Quadrilateral Sum Conjecture), and $d = 136°$.

10. $a = 162°$, $b = 83°$, $c = 102°$, $d = 39°$, $e = 129°$, $f = 51°$, $g = 55°$, $h = 97°$, and $k = 83°$. $a = 180° - 18° = 162°$. To find b, look at the exterior angles of the large pentagon (which is subdivided into a triangle, a quadrilateral, and a pentagon). The unmarked exterior angle at the lower right forms a linear pair with an angle that is marked as congruent to the angle with measure h, so the measure of this exterior angle is b. The Exterior Angle Sum Conjecture says that the sum of the measures of a set of exterior angles (one at each vertex) of any polygon is 360°. Therefore, $86° + b + 18° + b + 90° = 360°$, or $2b + 194° = 360°$, and $b = 83°$. Next look at the isosceles triangle. Here, $d = 39°$ (Isosceles Triangle Conjecture), and $2 \cdot 39° + c = 180°$ (Triangle Sum Conjecture), so $c = 102°$. Next look at the vertex of the triangle with measure c. Here, $2e + c = 360°$, so $2e = 258°$ and $e = 129°$. Now look at the upper-right corner of the figure. Here, $d + f + 90° = 180°$, so $f = 51°$. Next look at the upper-left corner of the figure. Here, $86° + g + 39° = 180°$, so $g = 55°$. Now look at the lower-left corner. $h + b = 180°$, so $h = 97°$. Finally, look at the quadrilateral. The angle in the lower-right corner of the quadrilateral is congruent to the angle with measure h, so its measure is also 97°. By the Quadrilateral Sum Conjecture, $k + 97° + f + 129° = 360°$, or $k + 277° = 360°$, so $k = 83°$.

11. 1. Linear Pair Conjecture; 2. Linear Pair Conjecture; 3. Linear Pair Conjecture; 4. 540°; 5. 180°, Triangle Sum Conjecture; 6. 360°

12. Yes, the maximum number of obtuse exterior angles that a polygon can have is three. This is because the measure of an obtuse angle is greater than 90°, and if there were four or more exterior angles that each measured more than 90°, their sum would be greater than 360°. That is impossible because the sum of *all* the exterior angles (one at each vertex) is 360° for *any* polygon.

The minimum number of acute interior angles that a polygon must have is 0. It's possible for a polygon to have no acute interior angles. A simple example of this situation is a rectangle, which has four right angles.

13. First proof: Use the diagram on the left. $m\angle U = b + c$, $m\angle I = d + e$, $m\angle T = g + h + i$, so $m\angle Q + m\angle U + m\angle I + m\angle N + m\angle T = a + b + c + d + e + f + g + h + i$.
$a + b + i = 180°$, $c + d + h = 180°$, and $e + f + g = 180°$ by the Triangle Sum Conjecture.
$a + b + c + d + e + f + g + h + i = 540°$ by the addition property of equality. Therefore, the sum of the measures of the angles of a pentagon is 540°.

Second proof: Use the diagram on the right. By the Triangle Sum Conjecture, $(a + b + l) + (c + d + m) + (e + f + n) + (g + h + o) + (i + j + k) = 5(180°)$, or 900°. The five angles in the

center sum to 360°, so $l + m + n + o + k = 360°$. Subtract to get $a + b + c + d + e + f + g + h + i + j = 540°$.

14. Regular polygons: triangle and dodecagon. Angle measures: 60°, 150°, and 150°. Point A is surrounded by an interior angle of a triangle and an interior angle of two dodecagons. The measure of each interior angle of an equilateral triangle is 60°, while the measure of each interior angle of a regular dodecagon is $\frac{10 \cdot 180°}{12} = 150°$.

15. Regular polygons: square, hexagon, and dodecagon. Angle measures: 90°, 120°, and 150°.

16. Yes. $\triangle RAC \cong \triangle DCA$ by SAS. $\overline{AD} \cong \overline{CR}$ by CPCTC.

17. Yes. $\triangle DAT \cong \triangle RAT$ by SSS. $\angle D \cong \angle R$ by CPCTC. (Draw $\overline{AT}$ to form the two triangles.)

IMPROVING YOUR VISUAL THINKING SKILLS

Eleven possible answers are shown.

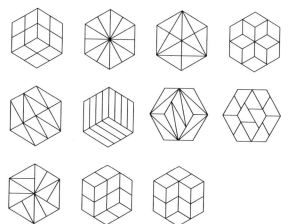

EXTENSIONS

A. Because it is easy to construct angles with measures 60° and 90° with compass and straightedge, and these angles may be bisected to obtain angles with measures 30° and 45°, you can construct regular polygons that have any of these four interior angle measures or angle measures that can be found by adding or subtracting these angles. This includes equilateral triangles (interior angle measure = 60°), squares (interior angle measure = 90°), regular hexagons (interior angle measure = 120° = 2 · 60°), regular octagons (interior angle measure = 135° = 90° + 45°), and dodecagons (interior angle measure = 150° = 2 · 60° + 30°). It is also possible (but difficult) to construct regular polygons with 10, 16, 17, and 20 sides.

B. See the solutions to Take Another Look activities 3, 4, and 5 on page 106.

EXERCISES

1. 64 cm. Because *ABCD* is a kite, $AB = AD = 20$ cm and $BC = DC = 12$ cm. Therefore, the perimeter is $2 \cdot 12 + 2 \cdot 20 = 64$ cm.

2. $x = 21°$, $y = 146°$. By the Kite Angles Conjecture, $y = 146°$. Then, by the Quadrilateral Sum Conjecture, $x + 2 \cdot 146° + 47° = 360°$, so $x = 21°$.

3. $x = 52°$, $y = 128°$. By the Isosceles Trapezoid Conjecture, $y = 128°$. Also, by the Isosceles Triangle Conjecture, the fourth angle of the trapezoid has measure x. By the Quadrilateral Sum Conjecture, $2x + 2 \cdot 128° = 360°$, so $2x = 104°$ and $x = 52°$.

4. 15 cm. The perimeter of the trapezoid is 85 cm, so $2x + 18 + 37 = 85$. Thus, $2x = 30$ and $x = 15$ cm.

5. $x = 72°$, $y = 61°$. The Kite Diagonals Conjecture says that the diagonals of a kite are perpendicular, so the two diagonals form four right triangles. Also, the diagonal that connects the vertices of the nonvertex angles divides the kite into two isosceles triangles. Look at the small right triangle in the upper right. The smallest angle in this triangle measures 18° because this is one of the base angles of the smaller isosceles triangle (Isosceles Triangle Conjecture). Then $x + 90° + 18° = 180°$ (Triangle Sum Conjecture), so $x = 72°$. In the right triangle in the lower right, the acute angles are 29° and $90° - 29° = 61°$. The 61° angle in this triangle is a base angle of the larger isosceles triangle, so $y = 61°$ (Isosceles Triangle Conjecture).

6. $x = 99°$, $y = 38$ cm. Notice that the figure is an isosceles trapezoid. First look at the unmarked angle at the lower-right corner of the trapezoid. By the Trapezoid Consecutive Angles Conjecture, the measure of this angle is $180° - 81° = 99°$. By the Isosceles Triangle Conjecture, this angle is congruent to x, so $x = 99°$. The perimeter of this isosceles trapezoid is 164 cm, so $y + 2(y + 12) + (y - 12) = 164$. Solve this equation.

$$y + 2y + 24 + y - 12 = 164$$
$$4y + 12 = 164$$
$$4y = 152$$
$$y = 38$$

7. $w = 120°$, $x = 45°$, $y = 30°$. From the hint, $\triangle PAT \cong \triangle APR$. Then, by CPCTC, $\angle PAT \cong \angle APR$, so $y = 30°$. By the Isosceles Trapezoid Conjecture, $\angle PAR \cong \angle APT$, so $x + 30° = y + 45°$. Because $y = 30°$, this gives $x = 45°$. Now look at $\triangle ZAP$. By the Vertical Angles Conjecture, $m\angle AZP = w$. Thus,

by the Triangle Sum Conjecture, $w + y + 30° = 180°$. Substitute 30° for y to obtain $w + 30° + 30° = 180°$, so $w = 120°$.

8. $w = 1.6$ cm, $x = 48°$, $y = 42°$. By the definition of a kite, *FLYE* must have two distinct pairs of consecutive congruent sides. Because $FL = LY$ is given, we also know that $FE = EY$. Therefore, $\angle FLY$ and $\angle FEY$ are the vertex angles of the kite, so, by the Kite Diagonal Bisector Conjecture, $\overline{LE}$ bisects $\overline{FY}$; thus, $w = 1.6$ cm. $\triangle FEY$ is isosceles with $FE = EY$, so by the Isosceles Triangle Conjecture, $\angle RFE \cong \angle RYE$; thus, $x = 48°$. Finally, $\triangle YRE$ is a right triangle because $\overline{LE} \perp \overline{FY}$ by the Kite Diagonals Conjecture. Therefore, by the Triangle Sum Conjecture, $x + y + 90° = 180°$. Substitute 48° for x to obtain $y + 48° + 90° = 180°$, so $y = 42°$.

9. 3. $\overline{BN} \cong \overline{BN}$; 4. $\triangle BEN \cong \triangle BYN$ by SSS; 5. $\angle 1 \cong \angle 2$ and $\angle 3 \cong \angle 4$ by CPCTC; 6. $\overline{BN}$ bisects $\angle B$, $\overline{BN}$ bisects $\angle N$.

10. First proof: This proof uses the Kite Angle Bisector Conjecture. Given: Kite *BENY* with vertex angles $\angle B$ and $\angle N$, and diagonals intersecting at point X.

$\angle 1 \cong \angle 2$ by the Kite Angle Bisector Conjecture. By SAS, $\triangle BXY \cong \triangle BXE$, so $\overline{XY} \cong \overline{XE}$ by CPCTC. Because $\angle YXB$ and $\angle EXB$ form a linear pair, they are supplementary, that is, $m\angle YXB + m\angle EXB = 180°$. By CPCTC, $\angle YXB \cong \angle EXB$, so $2m\angle YXB = 180°$, or $m\angle YXB = m\angle EXB = 90°$. Hence, $\overline{BN}$ is the perpendicular bisector of $\overline{YE}$.

Second proof: This proof uses the Converse of the Perpendicular Bisector Conjecture. The definition of a kite says that $\overline{KI} \cong \overline{IT}$ and $\overline{TE} \cong \overline{EK}$. So point I is equidistant from points K and T. Likewise, point E is equidistant from points K and T. Therefore, by the Converse of the Perpendicular Bisector Conjecture, both I and E lie on the perpendicular bisector of $\overline{KT}$. So diagonal $\overline{IE}$ is the perpendicular bisector of diagonal $\overline{KT}$.

11. $\angle E \cong \angle I$

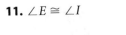

12. The other base is $\overline{ZI}$. $\angle Q$ and $\angle U$ are a pair of base angles. $\angle Z$ and $\angle I$ are a pair of base angles.

13. $\overline{OW}$ is the other base. $\angle S$ and $\angle H$ are a pair of base angles. $\angle O$ and $\angle W$ are a pair of base angles. $\overline{SW} \cong \overline{HO}$.

14. Start by duplicating $\overline{BN}$, which will form one diagonal of the kite. Next, draw an arc centered at N with radius NE and a second arc centered at B with radius BE. Draw these two arcs large enough so that they will intersect twice on opposite sides of $\overline{BN}$. Label the two points of intersection of the arcs as F and E. Connect the four vertices B, E, N, and F in order, forming the kite.

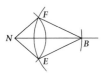

Only one kite is possible because three sides determine a triangle. (*Note:* The two points labeled E and F are interchangeable, so the figure can be labeled in two ways, but there is only one possible figure.)

15. Duplicate $\overline{WI}$. Duplicate $\angle I$ and $\angle W$, using the endpoints of $\overline{WI}$ as their vertices. Duplicate $\overline{IS}$ along the side of $\angle I$ that does not lie on $\overline{WI}$. Construct a line through point S parallel to $\overline{WI}$. Label the point where this line intersects the side of $\angle W$ that does not lie along $\overline{WI}$ as H. $WISH$ is the required trapezoid.

16. Possible construction: Duplicate $\overline{NE}$. Use congruent corresponding angles to construct a line parallel to $\overline{NE}$, and duplicate the length BO along this line. Connect the vertices B, O, N, and E to form a trapezoid.

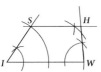

Infinitely many trapezoids can be drawn. Notice that none of the angles of the trapezoid, nor the lengths of either of the nonparallel sides, are given. In the construction shown above, the angle that was used to construct the parallel lines is arbitrary as is the position of point O along one of the rays of that angle.

17. 80°, 80°, 100°, 100°. Look at one of the common vertices where two of the trapezoids and the 18-gon

meet. The sum of the three angles that meet at this vertex must be 360°. Let x represent the measure of one of the base angles of the trapezoid along the inner edge of the arch. Each interior angle of a regular 18-gon measures $\frac{(18-2) \cdot 180°}{18} = \frac{16 \cdot 180°}{18} = 160°$. Therefore, $2x + 160° = 360°$, so $x = 100°$. The two base angles of the isosceles trapezoid along the inner edge of the arch each measure 100°, and the two base angles along the outer edge of the arch each measure 80°.

Notice that the exercise asks you to *draw* the arch, not to *construct* it, so you may use a protractor to measure angles.

To draw the arch, begin by drawing a horizontal line. Using a point on the line as the center, draw two concentric semicircles above the line. To form half of the regular 18-gons inscribed in the semicircles, draw central angles of measure $\frac{180°}{9} = 20°$. On each semicircle, draw line segments connecting consecutive intersections of the semicircles with the rays of the central angles. Then draw segments connecting the two semicircles at those points.

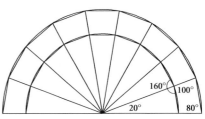

18. Because $ABCD$ is an isosceles trapezoid, $\angle A \cong \angle B$. $\triangle AGF \cong \triangle BHE$ by SAA. Thus, $\overline{AG} \cong \overline{BH}$ by CPCTC.

19. $a = 80°$, $b = 20°$, $c = 160°$, $d = 20°$, $e = 80°$, $f = 80°$, $g = 110°$, $h = 70°$, $m = 110°$, and $n = 100°$. First $a + 100° = 180°$ (Linear Pair Conjecture), so $a = 80°$. In the isosceles triangle that contains the angles with measures a and b, notice that b is the measure of the vertex angle. Therefore, $b + 2a = 180°$ (Triangle Sum Conjecture), so $b = 20°$. $c + b = 180°$ (Linear Pair Conjecture), so $c = 160°$. The angles with measures b and d are corresponding angles, so $d = b$ (CA Conjecture), and $d = 20°$. Next $2e + d = 180°$, so $e = 80°$. The angle that forms a linear pair with the angle of measure f has the same measure as the angle formed by combining the angles of measures e and d, so its measure is $80° + 20° = 100°$, and thus $f = 180° - 100° = 80°$. Now look at the small right triangle in the lower left that contains the angle with measure h. The measure of the other acute angle of this triangle is d (Vertical Angles Conjecture), so $h + d = 90°$ and $h = 70°$. Then $g = 180° - h$ (Linear Pair Conjecture), so $g = 110°$. Finally, by the CA Conjecture, $m = g$, so $m = 110°$, and similarly $n = 100°$.

Think about which pairs of items can be together. One solution: Take the rabbit across and leave it there. Go back. Take the carrots across and return with the rabbit. Leave the rabbit on the original side. Take the dog across, leave it there, and go back. Finally, bring the rabbit across again.

LESSON 5.4

EXERCISES

1. A triangle has three midsegments, one parallel to each of its sides, while a trapezoid has just one, which is parallel to the two bases.

2. 28. By the Triangle Midsegment Conjecture, $PO = \frac{1}{2}(RA) = 10$. From the figure, $PT = PR = 8$, and $OT = OA = 10$, so the perimeter of $\triangle TOP$ is $8 + 10 + 10 = 28$.

3. $x = 60°$, $y = 140°$. By the Triangle Midsegment Conjecture, the midsegment shown is parallel to the third side, so $x = 60°$ (AIA Conjecture). Also, the angle that forms a linear pair with the angle of measure y measures 40°, so $y = 180° - 40° = 140°$.

4. 65°. By the Three Midsegments Conjecture, the midsegments divide the large triangle into four smaller congruent triangles. The three angles of the large triangle measure 65°, 42°, and $180° - (65° + 42°) = 73°$. Because all four triangles are congruent, each must have angle measures of 65°, 42°, and 73°. By the Triangle Midsegment Conjecture, each of the three midsegments is parallel to the third side. By using the CA Conjecture, you can find the angle measures in the three outer triangles. (Notice that all three of these triangles are oriented the same way, while the inner triangle is oriented differently.) From these angle measures, you can see that $42° + z + 73° = 180°$, so $z = 65°$.

5. 23. By the Triangle Midsegment Conjecture, each side of $\triangle TEN$ is half the length of the parallel side of $\triangle UPA$: $TN = \frac{1}{2}(PA) = 9$, $TE = \frac{1}{2}(UA) = 8$, and $NE = \frac{1}{2}(UP) = 6$. Therefore, the perimeter of $\triangle TEN$ is $9 + 8 + 6 = 23$.

6. $m = 129°$, $n = 73°$, $p = 42$ cm. By the Trapezoid Midsegment Conjecture, the midsegment is parallel to the two bases, so $n = 73°$ (CA Conjecture). By the Interior Supplements Conjecture, $m = 180° - 51° = 129°$. By the Trapezoid Midsegment Conjecture, $p = \frac{1}{2}(36 \text{ cm} + 48 \text{ cm}) = \frac{1}{2}(84 \text{ cm}) = 42$ cm.

7. 35. By the Trapezoid Midsegment Conjecture, $24 = \frac{1}{2}(13 + q)$, so $48 = 13 + q$ and $q = 35$. Another way to find q is to notice that the length of the shorter base is 11 less than the length of the midsegment,

so the length of the longer base must be 11 more than the midsegment: $q = 24 + 11 = 35$.

8. 3. Triangle Midsegment Conjecture; 4. $\overline{OA} \parallel \overline{RD}$; 5. $\overline{LN} \parallel \overline{RD}$

9. Parallelogram. Draw a diagonal of the original quadrilateral. The diagonal forms two triangles. Each of the two midsegments is parallel to the diagonal, and thus the midsegments are parallel to each other. Now draw the other diagonal of the original quadrilateral. By the same reasoning, the second pair of midsegments is parallel. Therefore, the quadrilateral formed by joining the midpoints is a parallelogram.

10. The length of the edge of the top base is 30 m by the Trapezoid Midsegment Conjecture. If x represents the length of the edge of the top, $\frac{52 + x}{2} = 41$, so $52 + x = 82$, and $x = 30$. You can also figure this out by noticing that the bottom base is 11 meters longer than the midsegment, so the top edge must be 11 meters shorter than the midsegment: $41 - 11 = 30$.

11. Ladie drives a stake into the ground to create a triangle for which the trees are the other two vertices. She finds the midpoint from the stake to each tree. The distance between these midpoints is half the distance between the trees.

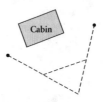

12. Possible explanation: Use the original picture to find the volume of water, $V = 60 \cdot 80 \cdot 30 = 144,000$ cm³. Let x be the height of the water when the container is resting on its smallest face. The volume must be the same, so $144,000 = 40 \cdot 60 \cdot x$. Therefore, $x = \frac{144,000}{40 \cdot 60} = 60$ cm.

13. If a quadrilateral is a kite, then exactly one diagonal bisects a pair of opposite angles. Yes, both the original and converse statements are true. (By definition, a kite is not a rhombus.)

14. $a = 54°$, $b = 72°$, $c = 108°$, $d = 72°$, $e = 162°$, $f = 18°$, $g = 81°$, $h = 49.5°$, $i = 130.5°$, $k = 49.5°$, $m = 162°$, and $n = 99°$. $a = 54°$ (AIA Conjecture). $2a + b = 180°$, so $b = 180° - 2 \cdot 54° = 72°$. The angle with measure c is a remote exterior angle of base angles in the isosceles triangle whose base angles measure 54°, so $c = 54° + 54° = 108°$ (Triangle Exterior Angle Conjecture). The angles with measures b and d are corresponding angles

formed when the parallel lines are cut by a transversal, so $d = b$, and $d = 72°$ (CA Conjecture). (Also, $d = 180° - b = 180° - 108° = 72°$ by the Linear Pair Conjecture.) Next look at the right triangle in which the angle with measure d is one of the acute angles. The other acute angle of this triangle measures $90° - 72° = 18°$. Then $e = 180° - 18° = 162°$ (Linear Pair Conjecture), and $f = 18°$ (Vertical Angles Conjecture). The triangle containing angles with measures f and g is isosceles with f the measure of the vertex angle, so $2g + f = 180°$, and $g = 81°$. Now look at the isosceles triangle that contains the angle with measure h as one of its base angles. In this triangle, the vertex angle measures $81°$ (Vertical Angles Conjecture), so $2h + 81° = 180°$, and therefore, $2h = 99°$, so $h = 49.5°$. The angle with measure i forms a linear pair with one of the base angles of that isosceles triangle, so $i = 180° - 49.5° = 130.5°$. The angle with measure k and the angle of the small isosceles triangle that forms a linear pair with the angle of measure i are corresponding angles formed when the parallel lines are cut by a transversal, so $k = 49.5°$. Next look at the pentagon that contains angles of measures i, k, and m. The two unmarked angles each measure $99°$ because each of them forms a linear pair with one of the base angles of the isosceles triangle that contains the angles of measures f and g; and in that triangle, it was found earlier that the base angles each measure $81°$. By the Pentagon Sum Conjecture, the sum of the measures of the interior angles of a pentagon is $540°$, so $k + i + 2 \cdot 99° + m = 540°$, or $49.5° + 130.5° + 198° + m = 360°$, so $m = 162°$. Finally, look at the pentagon that contains angles of measures b, c, e, and n. The unmarked angle in this pentagon forms a linear pair with the angle of measure g, so its measure is $180° - 81° = 99°$. Then, by the Pentagon Sum Conjecture, $b + c + e + 99° + n = 540°$, or $72° + 108° + 162° + 99° + n = 540°$. Therefore, $441° + n = 540°$, and $n = 99°$.

15. $(3, 8)$. Find the y-coordinate first. Because $\overline{TR} \parallel \overline{CA}$, $\overline{TR}$ is a horizontal segment, so the y-coordinate of T must be 8. Because of the symmetry of an isosceles trapezoid, the slopes of $\overline{TC}$ and $\overline{RA}$ must be opposite signs. Because the slope of $\overline{RA}$ is $\frac{8 - 0}{12 - 15} = \frac{8}{-3} = -\frac{8}{3}$, the slope of $\overline{TC}$ is $\frac{8}{3}$. Let x represent the x-coordinate of T. Then $\frac{8 - 0}{x - 0} = \frac{8}{3}$, so $x = 3$, and the coordinates of T are $(3, 8)$.

16. $(0, -8)$. By the Kite Diagonals Conjecture, $\overline{HS}$ is the perpendicular bisector of $\overline{ER}$. The diagonals of this kite intersect at the origin, so $(0, 0)$ is the midpoint of $\overline{ER}$. Therefore, because E is 8 units directly above the origin, R must be 8 units directly below the origin. This means that the coordinates of R are $(0, -8)$.

17. Coordinates: $E(2, 3.5)$, $Z(6, 5)$; both slopes are $\frac{3}{8}$. E is the midpoint of $\overline{RY}$, so its coordinates are $\left(\frac{4 + 0}{2}, \frac{7 + 0}{2}\right) = (2, 3.5)$, and Z is the midpoint of $\overline{RT}$, so its coordinates are $\left(\frac{4 + 8}{2}, \frac{7 + 3}{2}\right) = (6, 5)$. The slope of $\overleftrightarrow{EZ} = \frac{5 - 3.5}{6 - 2} = \frac{1.5}{4} = \frac{3}{8}$, and the slope of $\overleftrightarrow{YT} = \frac{3 - 0}{8 - 0} = \frac{3}{8}$.

18. Possible construction: Copy $\overline{FN}$, which will form one of the diagonals of the kite, and then construct its perpendicular bisector. Because the diagonals of a kite are perpendicular, the other diagonal, $\overline{RK}$, will lie along this perpendicular bisector, but you must locate the points R and K. To do this, draw an arc centered at N with radius NK. Label the point where this arc intersects the perpendicular bisector as K. Now use your compass to mark off a distance equal to RK along the perpendicular bisector to locate K. Connect the vertices F, R, N, and K to form the kite.

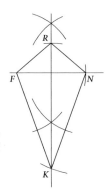

There is only one kite, but more than one way to construct it.

Project

Project should satisfy the following criteria:

- The project shows knowledge of the properties of isosceles trapezoids.

- The diagram includes the measure of one voussoir and the number in the arch.

- Measurement of each angle is determined from the number of sides of the circle that contains the arch's arc.

Extra credit

- There is an estimate of the rise and the span.

Extension

Triangle: Place a triangle on a coordinate system with one vertex at the origin and one side along the x-axis. Draw the midsegment that connects the endpoints of the two sides of the triangle that don't lie on the x-axis. Assign coordinates to the three vertices of the triangle, and use the midpoint formula to find the coordinates of the endpoints of the midsegment.

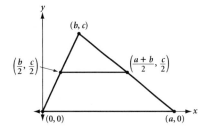

Trapezoid: Place a trapezoid on a coordinate system with one vertex at the origin and one side along the x-axis. Draw the midsegment of the trapezoid, which connects the midsegments of the two nonparallel sides. Assign coordinates to the four coordinates of the trapezoid. The two vertices that do not lie on the x-axis will lie on the same horizontal line and therefore have the same y-coordinate because the two bases of a trapezoid are parallel. Use the midpoint formula to find the coordinates of the endpoints of the midsegment.

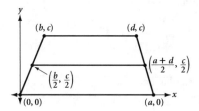

In both the triangle and the trapezoid, the two endpoints of the midsegment have the same y-coordinates, so each of the midsegments lies on a horizontal line (or has slope 0) and is therefore parallel to the x-axis. Therefore, the midsegment of the triangle is parallel to the third side, and the midsegment of the trapezoid is parallel to the two bases.

LESSON 5.5

EXERCISES

1. $c = 34$ cm, $d = 27$ cm. Use the Parallelogram Opposite Sides Conjecture.

2. $a = 132°$, $b = 48°$. By the Parallelogram Consecutive Angles Conjecture, $a = 180° - 48° = 132°$, and by the Parallelogram Opposite Angles Conjecture, $b = 48°$.

3. $g = 16$ in., $h = 14$ in. Use the Parallelogram Opposite Sides Conjecture to find g and the Parallelogram Diagonals Conjecture to find h.

4. 63 m. Use the Parallelogram Diagonals Conjecture to find $VN = \frac{1}{2}(VF) = 18$ m and $NI = \frac{1}{2}(EI) = 21$ m, and use the Parallelogram Opposite Sides Conjecture to find that $VI = EF = 24$ m. Then the perimeter of $\triangle NVI = 18 + 21 + 24 = 63$ m.

5. 80. By the Parallelogram Opposite Sides Conjecture, $x - 3 = 17$, so $x = 20$, and therefore, $x + 3 = 23$. Therefore, the perimeter of the parallelogram is $2 \cdot 17 + 2 \cdot 23 = 34 + 46 = 80$.

6. $e = 63°$, $f = 78°$. By the definition of a parallelogram, both pairs of opposite sides are parallel, so $e = 63°$ by the AIA Conjecture, and $f = 78°$ by the Parallelogram Opposite Angles Conjecture.

7. Possible construction: First, duplicate $\overline{LA}$; then, duplicate $\angle L$ with one of its sides along $\overrightarrow{LA}$. Mark off an arc of length AS along the other side of $\angle L$,

and label the intersection point of this arc with the ray that forms the second side of the angle as T. Draw an arc of length AS centered at A and an arc of length LA centered at T. Label the intersection mark of these two arcs as S. Connect the vertices in order to form parallelogram $LAST$. Notice that you used two pairs of parallel sides in this construction.

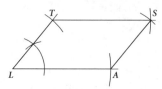

8. Possible construction: Recall that the diagonals of a parallelogram bisect each other (Parallelogram Diagonals Conjecture). First duplicate $\overline{DO}$, which will form the longer diagonal of the parallelogram. Bisect $\overline{DO}$ to locate its midpoint. Also, bisect the given segment $\overline{PR}$, and then open your compass to a radius of $\frac{1}{2}PR$. Draw arcs (or a complete circle) with centers at the midpoint of $\overline{DO}$ and radius $\frac{1}{2}PR$. Also, draw arcs with centers at D and O and with lengths DR. Label as R the point where the arc centered at D intersects one of the arcs (or the circle) with radius $\frac{1}{2}PR$. Label as P the point where the arc centered at O intersects one of the arcs (or the circle) with radius $\frac{1}{2}PR$. Connect the vertices D, R, O, and P to form the parallelogram.

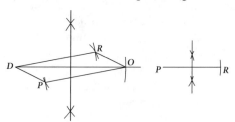

9. Complete the parallelogram with the given vectors as sides. The resultant vector is the diagonal of the parallelogram.

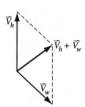

10. Follow the same procedure as in Exercise 9.

11. $(b - a, c)$. Use the definition of a parallelogram and slopes. By the definition of a parallelogram, $\overline{MA} \parallel \overline{PR}$; because $\overline{PR}$ is a horizontal segment (and has a slope of 0), so is $\overline{MA}$, and therefore, the y-coordinate of M is c. Also, by the definition of a

Discovering Geometry Solutions Manual
©2008 Key Curriculum Press

parallelogram, $\overline{PM} \parallel \overline{RA}$, so $\overline{PM}$ and $\overline{RA}$ have equal slopes. The slope of $\overline{RA}$ is $\frac{c-0}{b-a} = \frac{c}{b-a}$. The coordinates of P are $(0, 0)$, so if you let x represent the x-coordinate of M, then the slope of $\overline{PM}$ is $\frac{c-0}{x-0} = \frac{c}{x}$. Equating the slopes of $\overline{RA}$ and $\overline{PM}$ gives $\frac{c}{b-a} = \frac{c}{x}$. Therefore, $x = b - a$ and the coordinates of M are $(b - a, c)$.

12. Possible answer:

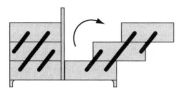

13. 1. Given; 2. Definition of parallelogram; 4. $\angle EAL \cong \angle NLA$; 5. $\overline{AE} \cong \overline{LN}$; 6. $\triangle AET \cong \triangle LNT$; 8. $\overline{AT} \cong \overline{LT}$; 9. $\overline{EN}$ and $\overline{LA}$ bisect each other

14. The parallelogram linkage is used for the sewing box so that the drawers remain parallel to each other (and to the ground) and the contents cannot fall out.

15. $a = 135°$, $b = 90°$. a is the measure of an interior angle of a regular octagon, so $a = \frac{180° \cdot 6}{8} = 135°$ (Equiangular Polygon Conjecture), and b is the measure of an interior angle of a square, so $b = 90°$.

16. $a = 120°$, $b = 108°$, $c = 90°$, $d = 42°$, and $e = 69°$. Start by applying the Equiangular Polygon Conjecture to the three equiangular polygons in the figure. Recall that the Equiangular Polygon Conjecture says that the measure of each interior angle of an equiangular n-gon is $\frac{(n-2)180°}{n}$. a is the measure of an interior angle of an equiangular hexagon, so

$$a = \frac{180° \cdot 4}{6} = 120°$$

b is the measure of an interior angle of an equiangular pentagon, so

$$b = \frac{180° \cdot 3}{5} = 108°$$

c is the measure of an interior angle of an equiangular quadrilateral, so

$$c = \frac{180° \cdot 2}{4} = 90°$$

The four polygons share a common vertex, so $a + b + c + d = 360°$, and $d = 360° - 120° - 108° - 90° = 42°$. Now look at the isosceles triangle. Here, d is the measure of the vertex angle, so $d + 2e = 180°$ (Triangle Sum Conjecture). Therefore, $2e = 138°$, and $e = 69°$.

17. $x = 104°$, $y = 98°$. The quadrilaterals on the left and right sides are kites, and the nonvertex angles of a kite are congruent (Kite Angles Conjecture). The quadrilateral at the bottom of the figure is an isosceles trapezoid. Base angles are congruent (Isosceles Trapezoid Conjecture), and consecutive angles are supplementary (Trapezoid Consecutive Angles Conjecture). Look at the three angles that share a common vertex on the left side of the figure, one of which has angle measure x. The other two angles measure 154° (Kite Angles Conjecture) and $180° - 78° = 102°$ (Trapezoid Consecutive Angles Conjecture). Therefore, $x + 154° + 102° = 360°$, and $x = 104°$. Now look at the three angles that share a common vertex on the right side of the figure, one of which has angle measure y. The other two angles measure 160° (Kite Angles Conjecture) and 102° (Isosceles Trapezoid Conjecture), so $y + 102° + 160° = 360°$, and $y = 98°$.

18. $a = 84°$, $b = 96°$. The arch is semicircular, so the complete regular polygon on which the arch is constructed has 30 sides, and each of its interior angles measures $\frac{(30-2) \cdot 180°}{30} = 168°$. Look at a common vertex along the inside edge of the arch where a base angle from each of two isosceles trapezoids meets an interior angle of the 30-gon. Here, $2b + 168° = 360°$, so $b = 96°$. By the Trapezoid Consecutive Angles Conjecture, $a + b = 180°$, so $a = 84°$.

19. No. The congruent angles and the common side do not correspond. Notice that the common side of the two triangles, $\overline{WY}$, is opposite the 83° angle in $\triangle WYZ$, but is opposite the 58° angle in $\triangle XYW$.

20. The section is an isosceles trapezoid.

21. Parallelogram. Possible construction: Construct a segment, $\overline{AC}$, of any length, and bisect it to find its midpoint, M. Construct any line that passes through M; call this line p. Open your compass to a radius that is *not* equal to $\frac{1}{2}AC$. Place your compass point at M, and use this new radius to mark off arcs on p on either side of $\overleftrightarrow{AC}$. Label the two points where these arcs intersect p as B and D. Connect the vertices A, B, C, and D to form a parallelogram. Notice that M is the midpoint of both diagonals, $\overline{AC}$ and $\overline{BD}$, so the diagonals bisect each other as required.

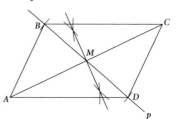

To explain why the quadrilateral you have constructed is a parallelogram, look at the figure with the construction marks removed. The marks on the figure show that the diagonals bisect each other.

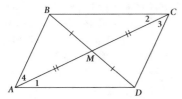

Because $\overline{MB} \cong \overline{MD}$ and $\overline{MA} \cong \overline{MC}$ (diagonals bisect each other, by construction) and also $\angle BMC \cong \angle DMA$ (vertical angles), $\triangle BMC \cong \triangle DMA$ by SAS. Then $\angle 1 \cong \angle 2$ by CPCTC, and because $\angle 1$ and $\angle 2$ are alternate interior angles, $\overline{BC} \parallel \overline{AD}$ by the Converse of the Parallel Lines Conjecture. Likewise, using the same sides and vertical angles AMB and CMD, $\triangle AMB \cong \triangle CMD$ by SAS. Then $\angle 3 \cong \angle 4$ by CPCTC, and because $\angle 3$ and $\angle 4$ are alternate interior angles, $\overline{AB} \parallel \overline{DC}$. Therefore, both pairs of opposite sides are parallel, and $ABCD$ is a parallelogram by the definition of a parallelogram.

22. Kite, dart, or rhombus. Construct two intersecting circles.

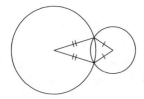

The figure is a kite or a dart because all radii of a given circle are congruent, which gives the two pairs of consecutive congruent sides. It is only a rhombus if the two circles have the same radius, so the quadrilateral has four congruent sides. Here, it is a kite. If the center of the smaller circle were inside the larger circle, the figure would be a dart.

PROJECT

Project should satisfy the following criteria:

- The polygons are regular. (A friendly window was used.)

- At least three questions are answered correctly.

1. Sample answers: Regular triangles have central angles of measure 120°, regular quadrilaterals have central angles of measure 90°, and regular pentagons have central angles of measure 72°. Use t-steps of 120, 90, and 72, respectively, to draw these polygons on a graphing calculator.

2. The measure of each central angle gets smaller.

3. Setting different t-min and t-max values will rotate the polygon.

4. One way to draw a star polygon with an odd number of points is to set the t-step to twice the central angle of the corresponding regular convex polygon, and change the t-range to 720°. For example, for a 5-pointed star, use t-min = 0, t-max = 720, t-step = 144. Descriptions will be different for drawing star polygons with even numbers of points, or for drawing different types of star polygons.

Extra credit

- All questions are answered correctly.

- The measure of the central angle of a polygon is given as a formula.

EXTENSIONS

A. Yes, the converses of the parallelogram conjectures are true.

Converse of the Parallelogram Opposite Angles Conjecture: If both pairs of opposite angles of a quadrilateral are congruent, then the quadrilateral is a parallelogram.

Converse of the Parallelogram Consecutive Angles Conjecture: If consecutive angles of a quadrilateral are supplementary, then the quadrilateral is a parallelogram.

Converse of the Parallelogram Opposite Sides Conjecture: If both pairs of opposite sides of a quadrilateral are congruent, then the quadrilateral is a parallelogram.

Converse of the Parallelogram Diagonals Conjecture: If the diagonals of a quadrilateral bisect each other, then the quadrilateral is a parallelogram.

Investigations will vary.

B. A coordinate geometry verification of the Parallelogram Diagonals Conjecture is given here. Other parallelogram conjectures could also be verified. Place a parallelogram on a coordinate system with one vertex at the origin and another along the positive x-axis. In order for opposite sides of the parallelogram to be parallel, the side opposite the side that lies on the x-axis must also lie on a horizontal line (slope = 0), so the y-coordinates of its endpoints will be equal.

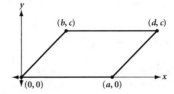

The Parallelogram Diagonals Conjecture states that the diagonals of a parallelogram bisect each other, so that is what you need to show for this figure.

Discovering Geometry Solutions Manual
©2008 Key Curriculum Press

Two segments bisect each other if they have the same midpoint, so if you can show that the two diagonals of the parallelogram have the same midpoint, you will have verified the conjecture.

The midpoint of the diagonal with endpoints $(0, 0)$ and (d, c) is $\left(\frac{0 + d}{2}, \frac{0 + c}{2}\right) = \left(\frac{d}{2}, \frac{c}{2}\right)$, and the midpoint of the diagonal with endpoints $(a, 0)$ and (d, c) is $\left(\frac{a + b}{2}, \frac{c + 0}{2}\right) = \left(\frac{a + b}{2}, \frac{c}{2}\right)$. Now look at the slopes of the opposite sides of the parallelogram that are not horizontal. The slope of the side with endpoints $(0, 0)$ and (b, c) is $\frac{c - 0}{b - 0} = \frac{c}{b}$, and the slope of the side with endpoints $(a, 0)$ and (d, c) is $\frac{c - 0}{d - a} = \frac{c}{d - a}$. Because opposite sides of a parallelogram are parallel (definition of a parallelogram) and parallel lines have the same slope, the two slopes you have found must be equal. Therefore, $\frac{c}{b} = \frac{c}{d - a}$, so $b = d - a$, and $d = a + b$. By substituting $a + b$ for d in the midpoint coordinates $\left(\frac{d}{2}, \frac{c}{2}\right)$, you can see that both diagonals have the same midpoint, $\left(\frac{a + b}{2}, \frac{c}{2}\right)$. Therefore, the diagonals of the parallelogram bisect each other.

USING YOUR ALGEBRA SKILLS 5

EXERCISES

1. The equation $y = 1 - 2x$ is in the form $y = a + bx$ with $a = 1$ and $b = -2$, so its graph is the line with slope -2 and y-intercept 1. To graph this line, first use the y-intercept to plot the point $(0, 1)$. From this point, use the slope to move to the right 1 unit and down 2 units to reach the point $(1, -1)$. Draw the line through these two points.

2. The line with equation $y = \frac{4}{3}x + 4$ is in the form $y = mx + b$ with $m = \frac{4}{3}$ and $b = 4$, so its graph is the line with slope $\frac{4}{3}$ and y-intercept 4. To graph this line, first use the y-intercept to plot the point $(0, 4)$. From this point, use the slope to move to the right 3 units and up 4 units to reach the point $(3, 8)$. Draw the line through these two points.

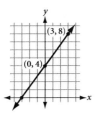

3. To find the slope and y-intercept of the line, rewrite the given equation in the form $y = mx + b$ by solving it for y.

$$2y - 3x = 12$$
$$2y = 3x + 12$$
$$y = \frac{3}{2}x + 6$$

The slope is $\frac{3}{2}$ and the y-intercept is 6. To graph this line, first use the y-intercept to plot the point $(0, 6)$. From this point, use the slope to move to the right 2 units and up 3 units to reach the point $(2, 9)$. Draw a line through these two points.

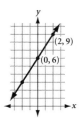

4. $y = -x + 2$. Find the y-intercept and then the slope. From the point $(0, 2)$, the y-intercept is 2. The second point shown is $(4, -2)$, so the slope is $\frac{-2 - 2}{4 - 0} = \frac{-4}{4} = -1$. Therefore, the equation of the line in point-slope form is $y = -x + 2$.

5. $y = -\frac{6}{13}x + \frac{74}{13}$. First use the two points shown on the graph to find the slope.

$$\text{Slope} = \frac{2 - 8}{8 - (-5)} = \frac{-6}{13} = -\frac{6}{13}$$

The slope between any point (x, y) and either of the given points must also be $-\frac{6}{13}$. Choose the point $(8, 2)$.

$$\frac{y - 2}{x - 8} = -\frac{6}{13} = \frac{-6}{13}$$
$$13(y - 2) = -6(x - 8)$$
$$13y - 26 = -6x + 48$$
$$13y = -6x + 74$$
$$y = -\frac{6}{13}x + \frac{74}{13}$$

Once you find the slope, an alternative method for finding the equation is to use the point-slope form, $y = y_1 + m(x - x_1)$, with either of the two points. As before, choose the point $(8, 2)$ so that $x_1 = 8$ and $y_1 = 2$.

$$y = 2 - \frac{6}{13}(x - 8)$$
$$y = 2 - \frac{6}{13}x + \frac{48}{13}$$
$$y = -\frac{6}{13}x + \frac{48}{13} + \frac{26}{13}$$
$$y = -\frac{6}{13}x + \frac{74}{13}$$

6. $y = x + 1$. First find the slope of the line through the points $(1, 2)$ and $(3, 4)$, which is $\frac{4 - 2}{3 - 1} = \frac{2}{2} = 1$. The slope between any point (x, y) and either

of the given points must also be 1. Choose the point (1, 2).

$$\frac{y-2}{x-1} = 1$$

$$y - 2 = 1(x - 1)$$

$$y - 2 = x - 1$$

$$y = x + 1$$

7. $y = -3x + 5$. First find the slope of the line through the two points (1, 2) and (3, −4), which is $\frac{-4-2}{3-1} = \frac{-6}{2} = -3$. The slope between any point (x, y) and either of the given points must also be −3. Choose the point (1, 2).

$$\frac{y-2}{x-1} = -3$$

$$y - 2 = -3(x - 1)$$

$$y - 2 = -3x + 3$$

$$y = -3x + 5$$

8. $y = \frac{2}{5}x - \frac{8}{5}$. First find the slope of the line through the given points (−1, −2) and (−6, −4), which is $\frac{-4-(-2)}{-6-(-1)} = \frac{-2}{-5} = \frac{2}{5}$. Use the point-slope form, $y = y_1 + m(x - x_1)$, with $m = \frac{2}{5}$, $x_1 = -1$, and $y_1 = -2$.

$$y = -2 + \frac{2}{5}[x - (-1)]$$

$$y = -2 + \frac{2}{5}(x + 1)$$

$$y = -2 + \frac{2}{5}x + \frac{2}{5}$$

$$y = \frac{2}{5}x - \frac{8}{5}$$

9. $y = 80 + 4x$. The set-up fee is a fixed cost, so if this equation were graphed, 80 would be the y-intercept. The cost of the T-shirts varies with the number of T-shirts, so 4 is the slope.

10. $y = -3x + 26$. First find the midpoint of the segment with endpoints (3, 4) and (11, 6). The coordinates of the midpoint are $\left(\frac{3+11}{2}, \frac{4+6}{2}\right) =$ (7, 5). Now find an equation of the line with slope −3 that passes through the point (7, 5).

$$\frac{y-5}{x-7} = -3$$

$$y - 5 = -3(x - 7)$$

$$y - 5 = -3x + 21$$

$$y = -3x + 26$$

11. $y = -\frac{1}{4}x - 3$. The slope of the line $y = 4x + 5$ is 4, so the slope of any line perpendicular to it will be the opposite reciprocal of 4, which is $-\frac{1}{4}$. The

required line passes through the point (0, −3), so its y-intercept is −3. Thus, the equation is $y = -\frac{1}{4}x - 3$.

12. $y = \frac{6}{5}x$. O is the midpoint of $\overline{HY}$.

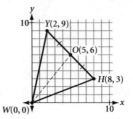

Find the coordinates of O: $\left(\frac{2+8}{2}, \frac{9+3}{2}\right) = (5, 6)$. Now find the equation of the line containing the median $\overline{WO}$, which is the line through (0, 0) and (5, 6). The slope of this line is $\frac{6-0}{5-0} = \frac{6}{5}$. Because this line passes through the origin, the y-intercept is 0. Therefore, the equation of the line is $y = \frac{6}{5}x$.

13. $y = x + 1$. The perpendicular bisector of $\overline{HY}$ passes through the midpoint of $\overline{HY}$ and is perpendicular to it. From Exercise 12, the midpoint of $\overline{HY}$ is O, which has coordinates (5, 6).

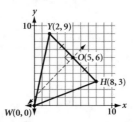

The slope of $\overline{HY}$ is $\frac{9-3}{2-8} = \frac{6}{-6} = -1$, so the slope of a line perpendicular to $\overline{HY}$ is the opposite reciprocal of −1, which is 1. Find the equation of the line with slope 1 that passes through (5, 6).

$$\frac{y-6}{x-5} = 1$$

$$y - 6 = x - 5$$

$$y = x + 1$$

14. $y = -\frac{2}{9}x + \frac{43}{9}$. The line containing altitude $\overline{HT}$ is the altitude to $\overline{YW}$.

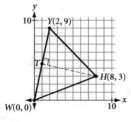

The slope of $\overline{YW}$ is $\frac{9-0}{2-0} = \frac{9}{2}$, so the slope of a line perpendicular to $\overline{YW}$ is $-\frac{2}{9}$.

Find an equation for the line passing through
$H(8, 3)$ with slope $-\frac{2}{9}$.
$$\frac{y - 3}{x - 8} = -\frac{2}{9} = \frac{-2}{9}$$
$$9(y - 3) = -2(x - 8)$$
$$9y - 27 = -2x + 16$$
$$y = -\frac{2}{9}x + \frac{43}{9}$$

IMPROVING YOUR REASONING SKILLS

Beginner Puzzle: green left, red up, red right, red down

Intermediate Puzzle: orange down, orange right, red up, red right, red down

Advanced Puzzle: orange down, orange left, red up, red right, yellow down, yellow left, red down

LESSON 5.6

EXERCISES

1. Sometimes true. It is only true if the parallelogram is a rectangle.

2. Always true. By the definition of rectangle, all the angles are congruent. By the Quadrilateral Sum Conjecture and division, each angle measures 90°, so any two angles of a rectangle, including consecutive angles, are supplementary.

3. Always true by the Rectangle Diagonals Conjecture

4. Sometimes true; it is only true if the rectangle is a square.

5. Always true by the Square Diagonals Conjecture

6. Sometimes true. It is true only if the rhombus is equiangular.

7. Always true. All squares fit the definition of rectangle.

8. Always true. All sides of a square are congruent and form right angles, so the sides become the legs of

the isosceles right triangle, and the diagonal is the hypotenuse.

9. Always true by the Parallelogram Opposite Angles Conjecture

10. Sometimes true. It is true only if the parallelogram is a rectangle. Consecutive angles of a parallelogram are always supplementary, but are only congruent if they are right angles.

11. 20. By the Rectangle Diagonals Conjecture, the diagonals of a rectangle bisect each other and are congruent. By the "bisect each other" part, $KC = CR = 10$, so $KR = 20$, and by the "are congruent" part, $WE = KR$, so $WE = 20$.

12. 37°. By the Parallelogram Consecutive Angles Conjecture, $\angle P$ and $\angle PAR$ are supplementary, so $48° + (y + 95°) = 180°$. Then $y + 95° = 132°$, so $y = 37°$.

13. $x = 45°$, $y = 90°$. A diagonal divides a square into two isosceles right triangles, so $x = 45°$. The diagonals of a square are perpendicular (Square Diagonals Conjecture), so $y = 90°$.

14. *DIAM* is not a rhombus because it is not equilateral and opposite sides are not parallel. You can use slopes to determine that opposite sides of this quadrilateral are not parallel, so it is not even a parallelogram.

15. *BOXY* is a rectangle because its adjacent sides are perpendicular.

16. Yes. *TILE* is a rhombus, and every rhombus is a parallelogram.

17. Possible construction: You know by the Square Diagonals Conjecture that the diagonals of a square are perpendicular and congruent. Duplicate $\overline{LV}$. Construct its perpendicular bisector. From the intersection point of the diagonals, set the radius of your compass at $\frac{1}{2}(LV)$. Draw a circle with this center and radius. Label the two points where the circle intersects the perpendicular bisector of $\overline{LV}$ as E and O. Connect the points L, O, V, and E to form the square.

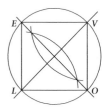

18. One possible construction: Duplicate ∠B. Bisect it. Mark off distance *BK* along the bisector. At *K* duplicate angles of measure $\frac{1}{2}m\angle B$ on either side of $\overline{BK}$. Label as *A* and *E* the intersections of the rays of ∠B with the rays of the new angles which are not $\overline{BK}$.

Another possible construction: Duplicate ∠B and then bisect it. Mark off the length *BK* on the angle bisector. Then construct the perpendicular bisector of $\overline{BK}$. Label the points where this perpendicular intersects the sides of ∠B as *E* and *K*. Connect the points *B, A, K,* and *E* to form the rhombus.

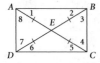

19. Possible construction: Duplicate $\overline{PS}$ and construct a perpendicular to $\overline{PS}$ through *S*. Open your compass to radius *PE* and draw an arc intersecting the perpendicular line that you have constructed. Label the intersection point of the arc and the perpendicular line as *E*. Construct arcs of length *PI* and *EI*. Label their intersection as *I*. Connect the points *P, I, E,* and *S* to form the rectangle.

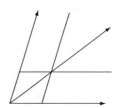

20. Converse: If the diagonals of a quadrilateral are congruent and bisect each other, then the quadrilateral is a rectangle.

Given: Quadrilateral *ABCD* with diagonals $\overline{AC} \cong \overline{BD}$. $\overline{AC}$ and $\overline{BD}$ bisect each other

Show: *ABCD* is a rectangle

Paragraph Proof: Because the diagonals are congruent and bisect each other, $\overline{AE} \cong \overline{BE} \cong \overline{DE} \cong \overline{EC}$. Using the Vertical Angles Conjecture, ∠*AEB* ≅ ∠*CED* and ∠*BEC* ≅ ∠*DEA*. So △*AEB* ≅ △*CED* and △*AED* ≅ △*CEB* by SAS. Using the Isosceles Triangle Conjecture and CPCTC, ∠1 ≅ ∠2 ≅ ∠5 ≅ ∠6, and ∠3 ≅ ∠4 ≅ ∠7 ≅ ∠8. Each angle of the quadrilateral is the sum of two angles, one from each set, so for example, $m\angle DAB = m\angle 1 + m\angle 8$. By the addition property of equality, $m\angle 1 + m\angle 8 = m\angle 2 + m\angle 3 = m\angle 5 + m\angle 4 = m\angle 6 + m\angle 7$. So $m\angle DAB = m\angle ABC = m\angle BCD = $

$m\angle CDA$. So the quadrilateral is equiangular. Using ∠1 ≅ ∠5 and the Converse of AIA, $\overline{AB} \parallel \overline{CD}$. Using ∠3 ≅ ∠7 and the Converse of AIA, $\overline{BC} \parallel \overline{AD}$. Therefore *ABCD* is an equiangular parallelogram, so it is a rectangle.

21. If the diagonals are congruent and bisect each other, then the room is rectangular (Rectangle Diagonals Conjecture).

22. The platform stays parallel to the floor because opposite sides of a rectangle are parallel. (The Parallelogram Opposite Sides Conjecture applies because a rectangle is a parallelogram.)

23. The crosswalks form a parallelogram: The streets are of different widths, so the crosswalks are of different lengths. The streets would have to cross at right angles for the crosswalks to form a rectangle. The streets would have to cross at right angles and also be of the same width for the crosswalk to form a square.

24. Place one side of the ruler along one side of the angle. Draw a line with the other side of the ruler. Repeat with the other side of the angle. Draw a line from the vertex of the angle to the point where the two lines meet.

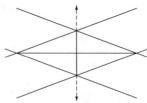

25. Rotate your ruler so that each endpoint of the segment barely shows on each side of the ruler. Draw the parallel lines on each side of your ruler. Now rotate your ruler the other way and repeat the process to get a rhombus. The original segment is one diagonal of the rhombus. The other diagonal will be the perpendicular bisector of the original segment.

26. 2. Given; 4. SSS; 5. CPCTC; 9. Definition of rhombus

27. Yes, it is true for rectangles.

Given: ∠1 ≅ ∠2 ≅ ∠3 ≅ ∠4

Show: *ABCD* is a rectangle

Paragraph Proof: By the Quadrilateral Sum Conjecture, $m\angle 1 + m\angle 2 + m\angle 3 + m\angle 4 = 360°$. Because all four angles are congruent, each angle measures 90°. Because ∠4 and ∠5 form a linear

Discovering Geometry Solutions Manual
©2008 Key Curriculum Press

pair, $m\angle 4 + m\angle 5 = 180°$. Substitute $90°$ for $m\angle 4$ and solve to get $m\angle 5 = 90°$. By definition of congruent angles, $\angle 5 \cong \angle 3$, and they are alternate interior angles, so $\overline{AD} \parallel \overline{BC}$ by the Converse of the Parallel Lines Conjecture. Similarly, $\angle 1$ and $\angle 5$ are congruent corresponding angles, so $\overline{AB} \parallel \overline{CD}$ by the Converse of the Parallel Lines Conjecture. Thus, $ABCD$ is a parallelogram by the definition of parallelogram. Because it is an equiangular parallelogram, $ABCD$ is a rectangle.

28. $a = 54°$, $b = 36°$, $c = 72°$, $d = 108°$, $e = 36°$, $f = 144°$, $g = 18°$, $h = 48°$, $j = 48°$, and $k = 84°$. First, $a = 54°$ (CA Conjecture). Now look at the right triangle in which the measure of one of the acute angles is b. The other acute angle in this triangle is the vertical angle of the angle of measure a, so its measure is $54°$, and $b = 90° - 54° = 36°$. Next, $2c + b = 180°$, so $2c = 144°$, and $c = 72°$. The angle with measure d forms a linear pair with the alternate interior angle of the angle with measure c, so $d = 180° - 72° = 108°$. In the triangle that contains the angle with measure e, both of the other angle measures have been found to be $72°$, so this is an isosceles triangle with vertex angle of measure e. Therefore, $e + 2 \cdot 72° = 180°$, so $e = 36°$. (Or, by the CA Conjecture, $e = b = 36°$.) Now look at the quadrilateral that contains the angle with measure f. This is a parallelogram because both pairs of opposite sides are parallel (from the given pairs of parallel lines). Notice that the angle that forms a linear pair with the angle of measure e is the angle opposite the angle of measure f in the parallelogram. Therefore, by the Parallelogram Opposite Angles Conjecture and the Linear Pair Conjecture, $f = 180° - e = 144°$. Now look at the isosceles triangle in which g is the measure of a base angle. In this triangle, the vertex angle measures $144°$ (Vertical Angles Conjecture), so $2g + 144° = 180°$; then $2g = 36°$, and $g = 18°$. Along the upper horizontal line, there are three marked angles, all of measure h, and one unmarked angle. The unmarked angle is the alternate interior angle of the supplement of the angle of measure f, so its measure is $180° - 144° = 36°$. Then $3h + 36° = 180°$, so $3h = 144°$, and $h = 48°$. Next, j is an alternate interior angle of one of the angles of measure h, so $j = 48°$. Finally, $k + j + 48° = 180°$ (Triangle Sum Conjecture), so $k = 84°$.

29. Possible answers: $(1, 0)$; $(0, 1)$; $(-1, 2)$; $(-2, 3)$. Find an equation for the line passing through the points $(2, -1)$ and $(-3, 4)$, and then find points on that line. First find the slope: $m = \frac{4 - (-1)}{-3 - 2} = \frac{5}{-5} = -1$. Now use the slope and one of the points on the line to find an equation for the line. Here, $(2, -1)$ is used.

$$\frac{y - (-1)}{x - 2} = -1$$
$$\frac{y + 1}{x - 2} = -1$$
$$y + 1 = -1(x - 2)$$
$$y + 1 = -x + 2$$
$$y = -x + 1$$

To find points on this line in addition to the two that are given, substitute any number for x other than 2 and -3 into the equation $y = -x + 1$ to find the corresponding value for y. If $x = 1$, $y = 0$; if $x = 0$, $y = 1$; if $x = -1$, $y = 2$; if $x = -2$, $y = 3$. Therefore, four additional points on the line are $(1, 0)$, $(0, 1)$, $(-1, 2)$, and $(-2, 3)$. Any three of these points would be sufficient; there are infinitely many other points on the line.

30. $y = \frac{8}{9}x + \frac{86}{9}$, or $8x - 9y = -86$. The perpendicular bisector of the segment with endpoints $(-12, 15)$ and $(4, -3)$ is the line through the midpoint of this segment and perpendicular to it. First find the midpoint:

$$\left(\frac{-12 + 4}{2}, \frac{15 + (-3)}{2}\right) = \left(\frac{-8}{2}, \frac{12}{2}\right) = (-4, 6)$$

The slope of this segment is

$$\frac{-3 - 15}{4 - (-12)} = \frac{-18}{16} = -\frac{9}{8}$$

So, its perpendicular bisector will have slope $\frac{8}{9}$. Find an equation of the line with $m = \frac{8}{9}$ through $(-4, 6)$.

$$\frac{y - 6}{x - (-4)} = \frac{8}{9}$$
$$\frac{y - 6}{x + 4} = \frac{8}{9}$$
$$9(y - 6) = 8(x + 4)$$
$$9y - 54 = 8x + 32$$
$$y = \frac{8}{9}x + \frac{86}{9}, \text{ or } 8x - 9y = -86$$

31. $y = -\frac{7}{10}x - \frac{12}{5}$, or $7x + 10y = -24$. The median to $\overline{AB}$ goes through $C(8, -8)$ and the midpoint of $\overline{AB}$, which is $(-2, -1)$. Find an equation of the line that contains $(8, -8)$ and $(-2, -1)$. First find the slope.

$$m = \frac{-8 - (-1)}{8 - (-2)} = -\frac{7}{10}$$

Now use the slope and either point to find the equation of the line. Here, the point $(-2, -1)$ is used.

$$\frac{y - (-1)}{x - (-2)} = \frac{-7}{10}$$
$$\frac{y + 1}{x + 2} = \frac{-7}{10}$$
$$10(y + 1) = -7(x + 2)$$
$$10y + 10 = -7x - 14$$
$$7x + 10y = -24, \text{ or } y = -\frac{7}{10}x - \frac{12}{5}$$

32. Velocity = 1.8 mi/h. Angle of path = 106.1° clockwise from the north.

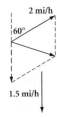

Improving your Visual Thinking Skills

The matching pairs are (A1, B3), (B1, D3), (A2, C2), (B2, C4), (A3, B4), (C1, C3), (A4, D2), and (D1, D4).

LESSON 5.7

Exercises

1. Completion of flowchart proof: 3. $\overline{OA} \parallel \overline{SK}$, definition of parallelogram; 5. AIA; 6. $\overline{SA} \cong \overline{SA}$, Same segment; 7. △SOA ≅ △AKS by ASA

Paragraph Proof: By the definition of a parallelogram, $\overline{SO} \parallel \overline{KA}$ and $\overline{OA} \parallel \overline{SK}$. Because ∠3 and ∠4 are alternate interior angles formed when the parallel lines $\overleftrightarrow{SO}$ and $\overleftrightarrow{KA}$ are cut by the transversal $\overleftrightarrow{SA}$, ∠3 ≅ ∠4 by the AIA Conjecture. Similarly, ∠1 and ∠2 are alternate interior angles formed when parallel lines $\overleftrightarrow{OA}$ and $\overleftrightarrow{SK}$ are cut by the same transversal, so ∠1 ≅ ∠2 by the AIA Conjecture. $\overline{SA}$ is a shared side of the two triangles; every segment is congruent to itself. Therefore, △SOA ≅ △AKS by ASA.

2. Completion of flowchart proof: 4. Given; 5. △THA, Conjecture proved in Exercise 1; 6. ∠HBA ≅ ∠ATH by CPCTC

Paragraph Proof: Diagonal $\overline{BT}$ divides parallelogram BATH into two congruent triangles because either diagonal of a parallelogram divides the parallelogram into two congruent triangles. (This is the conjecture that you proved in Exercise 1.) Therefore, △BAT ≅ △THB, and ∠BAT ≅ ∠THB by CPCTC. Also, $\overline{HT}$ divides parallelogram BATH into two congruent triangles for the same reason, so △BAH ≅ △THA, and ∠HBA ≅ ∠ATH by CPCTC.

3. Completion of flowchart proof: 1. $\overline{WA} \cong \overline{RT}$, Given; 2. $\overline{WR} \cong \overline{AT}$, Given; 3. $\overline{WT} \cong \overline{WT}$, Same segment; 4. △WRT ≅ △TAW by SSS; 5. ∠1 ≅ ∠2 by CPCTC; 6. $\overline{RT} \parallel \overline{WA}$ by Converse of the Parallel Lines Conjecture; 7. ∠4 ≅ ∠3 by CPCTC; 8. $\overline{RW} \parallel \overline{TA}$ by Converse of the Parallel Lines Conjecture; 9. Definition of parallelogram

Paragraph Proof: Because $\overline{WA} \cong \overline{RT}$ and $\overline{WR} \cong \overline{AT}$ (both given) and also $\overline{WT} \cong \overline{WT}$, △WRT ≅ △TAW by SSS. Then ∠1 ≅ ∠2 by CPCTC, so $\overline{RT} \parallel \overline{WA}$ by the Converse of the Parallel Lines Conjecture. Similarly, ∠3 ≅ ∠4, so $\overline{RW} \parallel \overline{TA}$.

Because both pairs of opposite sides are parallel, WATR is a parallelogram.

4. Flowchart Proof

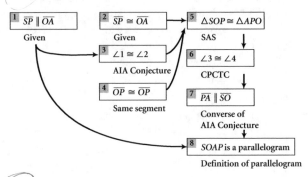

5. parallelogram

6. Flowchart Proof

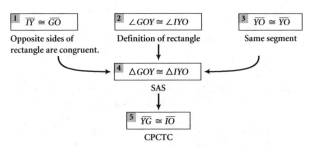

Paragraph Proof: Look at two overlapping triangles: △GOY and △IYO. $\overline{IY} \cong \overline{GO}$ because opposite sides of a rectangle are congruent. (Opposite sides of a parallelogram are congruent, and a rectangle is a parallelogram.) ∠GOY ≅ ∠IYO by the definition of a rectangle. (All angles of a rectangle are congruent.) Therefore, △GOY ≅ △IYO by SAS, and $\overline{YG} \cong \overline{OI}$ by CPCTC.

7. Flowchart Proof

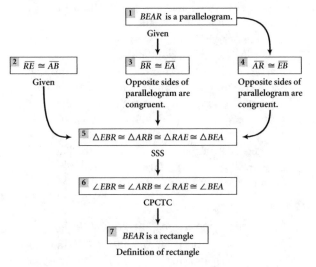

Paragraph Proof: $\overline{RE} \cong \overline{AB}$ is given, and $\overline{BR} \cong \overline{EA}$ and $\overline{AR} \cong \overline{EB}$ because opposite sides of a parallelogram are congruent (Parallelogram Opposite Sides Conjecture). Therefore,

$\triangle EBR \cong \triangle ARB \cong \triangle RAE \cong \triangle BEA$ by SSS, so $\angle EBR \cong \angle ARB \cong \angle RAE \cong \angle BEA$ by CPCTC. Thus, all four angles of parallelogram *BEAR* are congruent, and therefore, *BEAR* is a rectangle by the definition of a rectangle.

8.

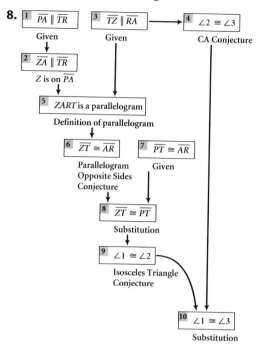

9. Flowchart Proof

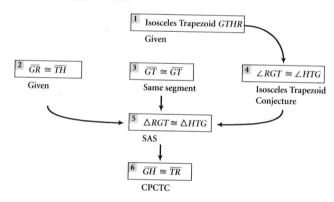

Paragraph Proof: Look at the overlapping triangles in the figure, $\triangle RGT$ and $\triangle HTG$. It is given that *GTHR* is an isosceles trapezoid with nonparallel sides $\overline{GR} \cong \overline{TH}$. Also, $\overline{GT} \cong \overline{GT}$ (same segment), and $\angle RGT \cong \angle HTG$ by the Isosceles Triangle Conjecture. Then $\triangle RGT \cong \triangle HTG$ by SAS, so $\overline{GH} \cong \overline{TR}$ by CPCTC.

10. If the fabric is pulled along the warp or the weft, nothing happens. However, if the fabric is pulled along the bias, it can be stretched because the rectangles are pulled into parallelograms.

11. 30° angles in 4-pointed star, 30° angles in 6-pointed star; yes

4-pointed star: At each vertex of the tiling, two hexagons, one square, and one vertex of the star

meet. Each interior angle of the hexagon measures $\frac{4 \cdot 180°}{6} = 120°$, and each interior angle of the square measures 90°. The sum of the angles around any point is 360°, so the measure of each angle of the 4-pointed star is $360° - 2 \cdot 120° - 90° = 30°$.

6-pointed star: At each vertex of the tiling, three squares and three stars meet. Again, the sum of the angles around any point is 360°, so the measure of each acute angle of the 6-pointed star is $\frac{1}{3}(360° - 3 \cdot 90°) = \frac{1}{3}(90°) = 30°$.

The acute angles of both stars are the same, 30°.

12. He should measure the alternate interior angles to see if they're congruent. If they are, the edges are parallel.

13. $\overleftrightarrow{ES}$: $y = -2x - 3$, $\overleftrightarrow{QI}$: $y = \frac{1}{2}x + 2$. The two diagonals of any quadrilateral connect nonconsecutive vertices, so the diagonals of rhombus *EQSI* are $\overline{ES}$ and $\overline{QI}$. The graph illustrates this.

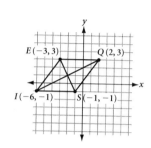

The slope of $\overleftrightarrow{ES}$ is $\frac{y_2 - y_1}{x_2 - x_1} = \frac{-1 - 3}{-1 - (-3)} = \frac{-4}{2} = -2$. The line passes through the point $E(-3, 3)$, so $\frac{y - 3}{x - (-3)} = -2$. Solve this equation for *y*.

$$\frac{y - 3}{x + 3} = -2$$
$$y - 3 = -2(x + 3)$$
$$y = -2x - 3$$

Use the same method to find the equation of $\overleftrightarrow{QI}$. The slope of $\overleftrightarrow{QI}$ is $\frac{y_2 - y_1}{x_2 - x_1} = \frac{3 - (-1)}{2 - (-6)} = \frac{4}{8} = \frac{1}{2}$. The line passes through the point $Q(2, 3)$, so $\frac{y - 3}{x - 2} = \frac{1}{2}$. Solve this equation for *y*.

$$\frac{y - 3}{x - 2} = \frac{1}{2}$$
$$y - 3 = \frac{1}{2}(x - 2)$$
$$y = \frac{1}{2}x + 2$$

14. (12, 7). Solve the system of equations by substitution. Substitute $\frac{2}{3}x - 1$ for *y* in the second equation, and solve for *x*.

$$3x - 4\left(\frac{2}{3}x - 1\right) = 8$$
$$3x - \frac{8}{3}x + 4 = 8$$
$$\frac{1}{3}x = 4$$
$$x = 12$$

Now substitute 12 for x in the first equation to find y.

$$y = \frac{2}{3}(12) - 1 = 8 - 1 = 7$$

Graph both lines to see that they intersect at $(12, 7)$.

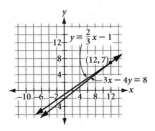

15. $\frac{1}{3}$. You miss 5 minutes out of 15 minutes, so the probability of missing the bus is $\frac{5}{15} = \frac{1}{3}$.

16. The container is $\frac{8}{12} = \frac{2}{3}$ full, so it will be $\frac{2}{3}$ full no matter which of the faces it rests on, which tells you that the height of the liquid in the new position will be $\frac{2}{3}(9 \text{ in.}) = 6 \text{ in.}$

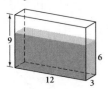

PROJECT

Project should satisfy the following criteria:

• At least two of the project questions are answered correctly.

1. At least two colors are needed.

2. In a quilt of four colors, around any pseudoblock of one color there can be six different arrangements of pseudoblocks of the other three colors (not counting rotations); three of these arrangements require four different quilt blocks. If four colors are used with no touching, then the quilt can be made with two different quilt blocks, each with kites of all four colors. If the colors of one block are considered in clockwise order beginning with a kite in the smaller angle of the rhombus, then the other block will have the same colors in counterclockwise order beginning with a kite in the larger angle of the rhombus.

3. None of the four-color quilts requires more than four different quilt blocks.

• A two- or four-color quilt is correctly assembled.

Extra credit

• A quilt is designed with five or six colors.

• All three questions are answered correctly.

CHAPTER 5 REVIEW

EXERCISES

1. Divide 360° by the number of sides.

2. Sample answers: Using the measure of an interior angle, set the expression in the interior angle measure formula equal to the angle measure and solve for n. Using the measure of an exterior angle, divide the angle measure into 360° to find n.

3. Trace both sides of the ruler as shown below.

4. Make a rhombus using the double-edged straight-edge, and draw a diagonal connecting the vertex of the original angle to the opposite vertex of the rhombus.

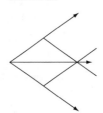

5. Sample answer: Measure the diagonals with string to see if they are congruent and bisect each other.

6. Draw a third point and connect it with each of the two points to form two sides of a triangle. Find the midpoints of the two sides and connect them to construct the midsegment. The distance between the two points is twice the length of the midsegment.

7. $x = 10°$, $y = 40°$. This figure is a kite, so the diagonals are perpendicular and form two pairs of congruent right triangles. In the larger right triangles (on the right), one of the acute angles of each triangle measures 80°, so the other acute angle measures 10°, that is, $x = 10°$. In the smaller right triangles (on the left), one of the acute angles of each triangle measures 50°, so the other acute angles measure 40°. Thus, $y = 40°$.

8. $x = 60$ cm. $2x + 52 + 64 = 266$, so $2x = 120$, and $x = 60$ cm.

9. $a = 116°$, $c = 64°$. This figure is an isosceles trapezoid, so $a = 116°$ (Isosceles Trapezoid Conjecture) and $c = 180° - 116° = 64°$ (Trapezoid Consecutive Angles Conjecture).

10. Perimeter = 100. By the Triangle Midsegment Conjecture, $MS = \frac{1}{2}(OI)$, so $OI = 36$. Also, because S is the midpoint of $\overline{IT}$ and M is the midpoint of

$\overline{OT}$ (definition of midsegment), $IS = 20$ and $OM = 26$. Therefore, the perimeter of $MOIS$ (which is a trapezoid) is $36 + 20 + 18 + 26 = 100$.

11. $x = 38$ cm. Use the Trapezoid Midsegment Conjecture.

$$32 = \frac{1}{2}[x + (x - 12)]$$

$$32 = \frac{1}{2}(2x - 12)$$

$$32 = x - 6$$

$$38 = x$$

Thus, $x = 38$ cm.

12. $y = 34$ cm, $z = 51$ cm. The key to finding y and z is to look for smaller polygons contained within the large triangle. First look at the triangle in which y is one of the lengths of the sides. In this triangle, 17 cm is the length of the midsegment and y is the length of the third side, so $17 = \frac{1}{2}y$, or $y = 2 \cdot 17 = 34$ cm by the Triangle Midsegment Conjecture. Now look at the trapezoid in which one of the bases has length 17 cm and the other has length z. In this trapezoid, x is the length of the midsegment, so by the Trapezoid Midsegment Conjecture, $y = \frac{17 + z}{2}$. Because $y = 34$ cm, this equation becomes $34 = \frac{17 + z}{2}$, or $68 = 17 + z$. Therefore, $z = 51$ cm.

13. (See table at bottom of page.)

14. $a = 72°$, $b = 108°$. The measure of each interior angle of a regular decagon is

$$\frac{(10 - 2) \cdot 180°}{10} = \frac{8 \cdot 180°}{10} = 144°$$

By looking at a common vertex of two isosceles trapezoids and the decagon along the inner edge of the frame and by using the fact that the sum of all angles around a point is 360°, you can see that $2b + 144° = 360°$, so $2b = 216°$ and $b = 108°$. Then, by the Trapezoid Consecutive Angles Conjecture, $a + b = 180°$, so $a = 72°$.

15. $a = 120°$, $b = 60°$, $c = 60°$, $d = 120°$, $e = 60°$, $f = 30°$, $g = 108°$, $m = 24°$, and $p = 84°$. First, look at the equiangular hexagon on the left. Because a is the measure of an interior angle of this hexagon,

$$a = \frac{(6 - 2) \cdot 180°}{6} = \frac{4 \cdot 180°}{6} = 120°$$

The angle with measure b forms a linear pair with one of the interior angles of the hexagon, so $b = 180° - 120° = 60°$. The third angle in the triangle containing angles with measures b and c also forms a linear pair with an interior angle of the hexagon, so this angle also measures 60°. Thus $b + c + 60° = 180°$, so $c = 60°$. The angle that forms a linear pair with the angle of measure c is the alternate interior angle of the angle with measure d. Therefore, $d = 180° - 60°$, so $d = 120°$. The measure of the angle that forms a linear pair with the angle of measure d is 60°, so $2e + 60° = 180°$, and $e = 60°$. Now look at the triangle that contains the angle of measure f. One of the angles of this triangle forms a linear pair with an angle that is marked as a right angle, so this angle of the triangle is also a right angle and this is a right triangle. The measure of one of the acute angles of this triangle is f and the measure of the other acute angle is $e = 60°$, so $e + f = 90°$, and $f = 30°$. Now look at the equiangular pentagon on the right. Here, g is the measure of one of the interior angles, so

$$g = \frac{(5 - 2) \cdot 180°}{5} = \frac{3 \cdot 180°}{5} = 108°$$

Next, look at the small triangle with three unmarked angles, one of which forms a linear pair with the angle of measure d. That angle measures $180° - d = 60°$, and another angle of the triangle is an exterior angle of the equiangular pentagon, so its measure is $\frac{360°}{5} = 72°$ (or $180° - 108° = 72°$). Thus, the measure of the third angle of this triangle is $180° - 60° - 72° = 48°$. Then $m + 108° + 48° = 180°$, so $m = 24°$. Finally, look at the small

Chapter 5 Review, Exercise 13

	Kite	Isosceles trapezoid	Parallelogram	Rhombus	Rectangle	Square
Opposite sides are parallel	No	No	Yes	Yes	Yes	Yes
Opposite sides are congruent	No	No	Yes	Yes	Yes	Yes
Opposite angles are congruent	No	No	Yes	Yes	Yes	Yes
Diagonals bisect each other	No	No	Yes	Yes	Yes	Yes
Diagonals are perpendicular	Yes	No	No	Yes	No	Yes
Diagonals are congruent	No	Yes	No	No	Yes	Yes
Exactly one line of symmetry	Yes	Yes	No	No	No	No
Exactly two lines of symmetry	No	No	No	Yes	Yes	No

triangle that contains an angle of measure m. Another angle of this triangle measures 72° (exterior angle of pentagon or supplement of g), and the third angle measures p (Vertical Angles Conjecture), so $p + m + 72° = 180°$, and $p = 84°$.

16. 15 stones. Let x represent the measure of an interior angle in the regular polygon. Two obtuse angles measuring 96° (from two adjacent isosceles trapezoids) and one interior angle of the regular polygon meet at a common vertex, so $2 \cdot 96° + x = 360°$, which gives $x = 168°$. Use algebra to find the number of sides in a regular polygon in which each interior angle measures 96°.

$$\frac{(n - 2) \cdot 180°}{n} = 168°$$
$$180°n - 360° = 168°n$$
$$12°n = 360°$$
$$n = 30$$

Thus, the regular polygon is a 30-gon, but because the arch is semicircular, the original arch contained 15 stones.

17. (1, 0). Sketch the kite and observe that $\angle A$ and $\angle C$ are the vertex angles.

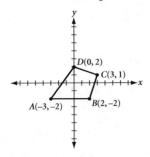

By the Kite Diagonal Bisector Conjecture, $\overline{AC}$ is the perpendicular bisector of $\overline{BD}$, so the diagonals of the kite intersect at the midpoint of $\overline{BD}$, which has coordinates $\left(\frac{0 + 2}{2}, \frac{2 + (-2)}{2}\right) = (1, 0)$.

18. When the swing is motionless, the seat, the bar at the top, and the chains form a rectangle. When you swing left to right, the rectangle changes to a parallelogram. The opposite sides stay equal in length, so they stay parallel. The seat and the bar at the top are also parallel to the ground.

19. $a = 60°$, $b = 120°$. Corresponding (and therefore congruent) angles of six of the pentagons meet at a common vertex in the center of the figure, so $6a = 360°$, and $a = 60°$. By looking at the tiling, you can see that four of the interior angles of each pentagon are congruent, with measure b, while the fifth angle has measure a. The sum of the measures of all the interior angles of any pentagon is 540°

(Pentagon Sum Conjecture), so $4b + 60° = 540°$, and thus $b = 120°$.

Another way to find b is to notice that three angles with this measure meet at a common vertex, and the sum of the measures of all the angles around a point is 360°, so $3b = 360°$, and thus $b = 120°$.

20. Speed ≈ 901.4 km/h. Direction: slightly west of north. Figure is approximate.

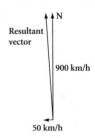

21. Recall that the diagonals of a rhombus are perpendicular and bisect each other (Rhombus Diagonals Conjecture); use this conjecture as the basis of your construction.

First, copy the segment of length y and label the copied segment as $\overline{SR}$. Construct the perpendicular bisector of $\overline{SR}$. Also, bisect the given segment of length x. Using the midpoint of $\overline{SR}$ as the center and $\frac{1}{2}x$ as the radius, mark off arcs on both sides of $\overline{SR}$ along its perpendicular bisector. Label the points where these arcs intersect the perpendicular bisector as E and Q. To form the rhombus, connect the vertices S, Q, R, and E.

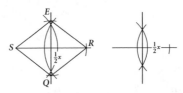

22. Possible construction: Duplicate $\angle F$ and draw an arc centered at F with radius x, intersecting both sides of the angle. Label the points where this arc intersects the angle as R and L. Bisect $\angle F$. Duplicate $\angle L$ with vertex at L and one side along $\overline{FL}$. Label the point where this angle intersects the angle bisector of $\angle F$ as Y. Connect the vertices F, L, Y, and R to form the kite.

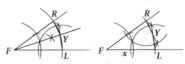

23. Construct $\overline{LP}$ of length z and duplicate $\angle L$ with one side along $\overline{LP}$. Placing your compass point at L, mark off a distance of x along the other side of $\angle L$ and label the point where the arc intersects the angle as N. Construct the line parallel to $\overleftrightarrow{LP}$ through N. Placing your compass point at N, mark off a distance of y along this parallel line to form

$\overline{NE}$. Connect the vertices E and P to form the fourth side of the trapezoid.

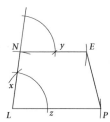

24. Compare this situation with Exercise 23. Notice that Exercise 23 gives the lengths of both bases of the trapezoid, whereas Exercise 24 gives only the length of one possible base. Use the same method as outlined in the solution for Exercise 23, but notice that now you can make $\overline{RY}$ any length you wish. The figures below show two possible trapezoids obtained with different choices for RY.

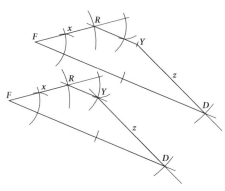

25. 20 sides. Notice that a square, a regular pentagon, and the third regular polygon with an unknown number of sides meet at the common vertex, B. The measure of each interior angle of a regular pentagon is $\frac{3 \cdot 180°}{5} = 108°$, and the measure of each interior angle of a square is $90°$. Because the sum of the measures of the angles around any point is $360°$, the measure of an interior angle of the third polygon is $360° - 108° - 90° = 162°$. Now find the number of sides that a regular polygon has if the measure of its interior angles is $162°$.

$$\frac{(n-2) \cdot 180°}{n} = 162°$$
$$180°n - 360° = 162°n$$
$$18°n = 360°$$
$$n = 20$$

Therefore, the third polygon has 20 sides.

26. 12 cm. First look at the two triangles with solid sides and ignore the dashed segments. The lower triangle is isosceles, so the shared side of the two triangles has length 48 cm (Converse of the Isosceles Triangle Conjecture). The middle of the three dashed segments is the midsegment of the upper solid triangle, so its length is $\frac{1}{2}(48) = 24$ cm

(Triangle Midsegment Conjecture). Now look at the smaller triangle in which the dashed segment of length x is the midsegment and the dashed segment of the larger triangle (of length 24 cm) is the third side. Apply the Triangle Midsegment Conjecture to this smaller triangle to find x: $x = \frac{1}{2}(24) = 12$ cm.

27. 1. Given; 2. $\overline{DE} \cong \overline{DI}$ by definition of rhombus; 3. $\overline{NE} \cong \overline{NI}$ by definition of rhombus; 4. $\overline{DN} \cong \overline{DN}$, Same segment; 5. $\triangle DEN \cong \triangle DIN$ by SSS; 6. $\angle 1 \cong \angle 2$, $\angle 3 \cong \angle 4$ by CPCTC; 7. definition of angle bisector

28. Possible answer:

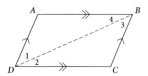

Given: Parallelogram $ABCD$

Show: $\overline{AB} \cong \overline{CD}$ and $\overline{AD} \cong \overline{CB}$

Flowchart Proof

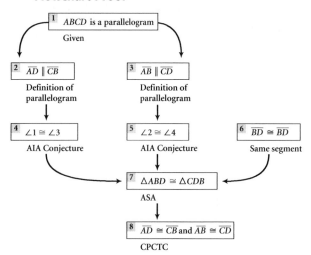

Paragraph Proof: By the definition of parallelogram, $\overline{AD} \parallel \overline{BC}$ and $\overline{AB} \parallel \overline{CD}$. Because parallel lines $\overleftrightarrow{AD}$ and $\overleftrightarrow{BC}$ are cut by transversal $\overleftrightarrow{BD}$, $\angle 1 \cong \angle 3$ by the AIA Conjecture. Also, because parallel lines $\overleftrightarrow{AB}$ and $\overleftrightarrow{CD}$ are cut by transversal $\overleftrightarrow{BD}$, $\angle 4 \cong \angle 2$ by the AIA Conjecture. We also have $\overline{BD} \cong \overline{BD}$ because they are the same segment. Therefore, $\triangle ABD \cong \triangle CDB$ by ASA, and thus $\overline{AB} \cong \overline{CD}$ and $\overline{AD} \cong \overline{CB}$ by CPCTC.

TAKE ANOTHER LOOK

1. Sample answer: There are $(n-2)$ triangles and for each triangle, the sum of angle measures is $180°$, so the total is $180°(n-2)$. The proof, with adaptations in particular cases, holds for concave polygons.

2. It's not possible for a "rectangle" on a sphere to have four right angles, because the sum of the angles of any quadrilateral on a sphere is greater than 360°. The proof from Take Another Look activity 1, using inequalities, extends to the sphere, on which the sum of angle measures of each triangle is more than 180°. Sample answer: On a sphere, the sum of the angle measures of an *n*-sided polygon is greater than 180°$(n - 2)$.

3. Arranging the angles about a point is one way of finding their sum. Because this arrangement forms a complete circle about the point, the sum of the angle measures is 360°.

4. In effect, the measure of an exterior angle on a concave side is 180° minus the measure of the interior angle and thus is negative. Other definitions of *exterior angle* are possible, so results may vary. All the kite conjectures also hold for darts (if the diagonal joining the vertices is extended to intersect the diagonal lying outside the figure).

5. The sum of the angle measures at a vertex is still 360°. However, the exterior angles, cut and arranged around a point, will not quite completely surround the point, showing that the exterior angle sum is less than 360°. For instance, a triangle with three right angles would have an exterior angle sum of 90° + 90° + 90° = 270°.

CHAPTER 6

LESSON 6.1

EXERCISES

1. $w = 50°$. Look at the quadrilateral in the figure. Notice that the figure contains two tangents to the circle and that the two unmarked angles of the quadrilateral are formed when radii are drawn to the points of tangency. Therefore, both of these angles are right angles by the Tangent Conjecture. Now apply the Quadrilateral Sum Conjecture: $130° + 90° + w + 90° = 360°$, so $w = 50°$.

2. $x = 55°$. By the Tangent Segments Conjecture, the triangle in the figure is isosceles with a vertex angle of 70°. Therefore, by the Isosceles Triangle Conjecture, each of the base angles has measure *x*. Thus, $x + x + 70° = 180°$, so $2x = 110°$, and $x = 55°$.

3. $y = 30°$. Look at the triangle in the figure. Its angle measures are *y*, 90° (Tangent Conjecture), and 60° (supplement to a 120° angle). Therefore, $y + 90° + 60° = 180°$ (Triangle Sum Conjecture), so $y = 30°$.

4. $z = 105°$. Look at the quadrilateral in the figure. The two unmarked angles are right angles (Tangent

Conjecture), so $z + 75° + 90° + 90° = 360°$ (Quadrilateral Sum Conjecture). Therefore, $z = 105°$.

5. 76. Apply the Tangent Segments Conjecture four times: From point *P*, $PA = PC$. From *O*, $OA = OR$. From *S*, $SR = SD$. From *T*, $TD = TC$. Also, by markings in the figure, $PA = OA$, and $SR = TC$. Therefore, $PC = PA = OA = OR = 13$, and $SD = SR = TC = TD = \frac{1}{2}(ST) = 6$, so the perimeter of *POST* is $4(13) + 4(6) = 52 + 24 = 76$.

6. When viewed from the side, the ball's path is actually a parabola, but the overhead view shows a tangent line. Possible answer:

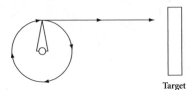

Target

7. Possible answer: The perpendicular to the tangent line passes through the center of the circle. Use the T-square to find two diameters of the Frisbee. The intersection of these two lines is the center.

8. From the Tangent Conjecture, you know that the tangent is perpendicular to the radius at the point of tangency. Construct $\overrightarrow{OT}$. Construct a line through point *T* perpendicular to $\overrightarrow{OT}$. Possible construction:

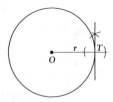

9. Construct $\overrightarrow{OX}$, $\overrightarrow{OY}$, and $\overrightarrow{OZ}$. Construct tangents through points *X*, *Y*, and *Z*. The three intersection points of pairs of these tangents are the vertices of the circumscribed triangle. Possible construction:

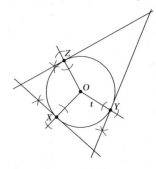

10. Construct tangent circles *M* and *N*, each with radius *s*. Construct equilateral triangle *MNP*.

Then construct circle P with radius s. Possible construction:

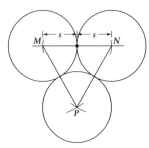

11. Construct a line, and label a point T on it. On the line, mark off two points, L and M, each on the same side of T at distances r and t from T, respectively. Construct circle L with radius r. Construct circle M with radius t. Possible construction:

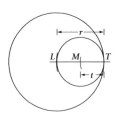

12. Start with the construction from Exercise 11. On line $\overleftrightarrow{LM}$, mark off length TK so that $TK = s$ and K is on the opposite side of T from L and M. Construct circle K with radius s. Possible construction:

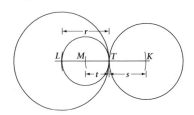

13. Sample answer: If the three points do not lie on the same semicircle, the tangents form a triangle that circumscribes the original circle. If two of the three points are on opposite sides of a diameter, the tangent lines to those two points are parallel. If the points lie on the same semicircle, they form a triangle outside the circle, with one side touching (called an *exscribed triangle*).

14. Sample answer: Internally tangent: wheels on a roller-coaster car in a loop, one bubble inside another. Externally tangent: touching coins, a snowman, a computer mouse ball and its roller balls. Note that sample answers include tangent spheres whose great circles through the point of tangency are tangent.

15. Draw a diameter. Then bisect each of the radii that form the diameter to find the centers of the two

inside circles, which are also the centers of the two small circles inside of them. Possible construction:

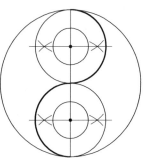

16. $41.\overline{6}\%$. Look at the angles in the quadrilateral in the figure. Two of these angles are formed by radii drawn to points of tangency, so each of these is a right angle (Tangent Conjecture). Therefore, by the Quadrilateral Sum Conjecture, the measure of the central angle, and thus the arc marked with a question mark, is $360° - 30° - 90° - 90° = 150°$. Because $\frac{150°}{360°} = 41.\overline{6}\%$, $41.\overline{6}\%$ of the equator is observable from the satellite.

17. Angles A and B must be right angles by the Tangent Conjecture, but this would make the sum of the angle measures in the quadrilateral shown greater than $360°$.

18. a. Rhombus

b. Rectangle

c. Kite

d. Parallelogram

19. $78°$. From the figure below, you can see that the measure of the angle to be found is the sum of the measures of two angles. The portion of the angle between the two paths that is to the left of the vertical (North) line is the alternate interior angle of the angle marked as $15°$, so it also measures $15°$ (AIA Conjecture), while the portion of the angle to the right of the vertical line is the supplement of the $117°$ angle, so its measure is $180° - 117° = 63°$. Thus, the measure of the angle between the two paths is $15° + 63° = 78°$.

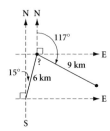

20. 9.7 km. In the figure below, C is the location of the camp, L is the location of the lake, and F is the place where the family meets their friends. (0.5 cm represents 1 km, so 1 cm represents 2 km.)

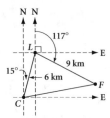

The distance to be found is CF. Carefully measure to find that, in this figure, $CF = 4.85$ cm, so, to the nearest tenth of a kilometer, the distance from the camp to the lake is 4.85 cm $\cdot \frac{2 \text{ km}}{1 \text{ cm}} = 9.7$ km.

21. The triangle on the left is isosceles, with the angle of measure x as its vertex angle, so $x + 55° + 55° = 180°$, and therefore, $x = 70°$. Also, the triangle on the right is isosceles, with the 40° angle as its vertex angle, so $40° + y + y = 180°$, and thus, $y = 70°$. Therefore, $x = y$.

22. $\frac{11}{21}$. Find the number of possible right triangles, and divide this by the number of ways of randomly selecting three points from the nine points in the grid. To find the number of right triangles, consider the number of possible triangles with right angles at the corners of the grid, at the middle of the sides, and at the middle of the grid. There are four distinct triangles that have right angles at each corner (giving $4 \cdot 4 = 16$ triangles); five right triangles (including one tilted) have right angles at the middle point of each side (so $4 \cdot 5 = 20$); and eight triangles (four tilted) have right angles at the middle point ($1 \cdot 8 = 8$). The total, 44, is divided by the number of ways of choosing three points from the nine points, which is $\frac{9(8)(7)}{1(2)(3)}$ = 84. Therefore, the probability of selecting three points from the grid that form the vertices of a right triangle is $\frac{44}{84} = \frac{11}{21}$.

IMPROVING YOUR VISUAL THINKING SKILLS

EXTENSIONS

A. Constructions will vary.

B. Conjectures and results will vary.

C. See solutions for Take Another Look activities 1 and 2 on page 132.

LESSON 6.2

EXERCISES

1. $x = 165°$ by the definition of the measure of an arc. The measure of an arc is defined as the measure of its central angle.

2. $z = 84°$ by the Chord Arcs Conjecture. The two marked chords are congruent, so their intercepted arcs are congruent, and the measure of the unmarked arc is 128°. The sum of the measures of all arcs of a circle is 360°; $z + 128° + 20° + 128° = 360°$, so $z = 84°$.

3. $w = 70°$ by the Chord Central Angles Conjecture.

4. $OQ = 8$ cm by the Chord Distance to Center Conjecture. The distance between a point and a segment of a line is measured along the perpendicular.

5. $m\overarc{AC} = 68°$ by the definition of the measure of an arc; $m\angle B = 34°$ by the Isosceles Triangle Conjecture and the Triangle Exterior Angle Conjecture: $\overline{OC} \cong \overline{OB}$ because all radii of a circle are congruent, so $\triangle OBC$ is isosceles, and $\angle B \cong \angle C$ by the Isosceles Triangle Conjecture. Also, $m\angle B + m\angle C = 68°$ (Triangle Exterior Angle Conjecture), so $2m\angle B = 68°$, and $m\angle B = 34°$.

6. $w = 115°$, $x = 115°$, $y = 65°$. By the definition of arc measure, $w = 115°$. $\overline{OA} \cong \overline{OG}$ because both segments are radii, therefore $AOGN$ is a kite. By the Kite Diagonal Bisector Conjecture, $\overline{ON}$ bisects $\angle AOG$, so $m\angle GON = m\angle AON = 115°$, hence $x = 115°$. Because $\angle GON$ and $\angle IOG$ form a linear pair, $m\angle IOG = 180° - m\angle GON = 65°$. Therefore, $y = 65°$.

7. 20 cm; Perpendicular to a Chord Conjecture. $\overline{OP} \perp \overline{AB}$, so $\overline{OP}$ bisects $\overline{AB}$, and therefore $PB = \frac{1}{2}(AB) = 3$ cm. Likewise, $\overline{OQ} \perp \overline{CD}$, so $QD = \frac{1}{2}(CD) = 4$ cm. Thus the perimeter of pentagon $OPBDQ$ is $4 + 3 + 6 + 4 + 3 = 20$ cm.

8. $w = 110°$, $x = 48°$, $y = 82°$, $z = 120°$. First, $w = 110°$ and $x = 48°$ by the definition of arc measure. Next, $m\overarc{AB} = 130° - 48° = 82°$, so $y = 82°$ by the definition of arc measure. Finally, $130° + w + z = 360°$. Substituting 110° for w, this equation becomes $130° + 110° + z = 360°$, so $z = 120°$.

9. $x = 96°$, $y = 96°$, $z = 42°$. By the definition of the measure of an arc and by the Chord Central Angles Conjecture, $x = y$. The three marked chords are congruent, so their intercepted arcs are congruent by the Chord Arcs Conjecture. Therefore, $3y + 72° = 360°$, so $3y = 288°$ and $y = 96°$. Hence, $x = y = 96°$. Finally, find z: Look at the small triangle containing the angle with measure z. This is an isosceles triangle because two of its sides are radii of the circle. The vertex angle of this triangle is a central angle of the circle and is 96° by the Chord Central Angles Conjecture. By the Isosceles Triangle Conjecture, the third angle of the triangle also has measure z. Then, by the Triangle Sum Conjecture, $2z + 96° = 180°$, so $2z = 84°$ and $z = 42°$.

10. $x = 66°$, $y = 48°$, $z = 66°$. Because $m\overset{\frown}{CI} = 66°$, $m\angle COI = 66°$ by the definition of arc measure. Because $\overline{AB} \parallel \overline{CO}$, $\angle ABO \cong \angle COI$ by the CA Conjecture, so $x = 66°$. By the definition of arc measure, $m\angle AOC = z$, and by the AIA Conjecture, $\angle COA \cong \angle BAO$, so $m\angle BAO = z$. However, because both $\overline{OA}$ and $\overline{OB}$ are radii of the same circle, $\triangle AOB$ is isosceles with base angles OAB and OBA, so, by the Isosceles Triangle Conjecture, $\angle OAB \cong \angle OBA$. Therefore, $z = x$, so $z = 66°$. Finally, because $\overline{BI}$ is a diameter, $m\angle BOA + m\angle AOC + m\angle COI = 180°$. Thus, $y + z + 66° = 180°$, or $y + 66° + 66° = 180°$, so $y = 48°$.

11. The length of the chord is greater than the length of the diameter. Because the radius of the circle is 18 cm, the diameter is 36 cm, and a diameter is the longest chord in any circle.

12. The perpendicular bisector of the segment does not pass through the center of the circle. This is impossible by the Perpendicular Bisector of a Chord Conjecture.

13. The longer chord is closer to the center; the longest chord, which is the diameter, passes through the center.

14. The central angle of the smaller circle is larger because in the smaller circle the chord is closer to the center.

15. $M(-4, 3)$, $N(-4, -3)$, $O(4, -3)$. Possible method: Because the rectangle is centered at the origin, it must be symmetric to both axes. Reflect P across the y-axis to get the coordinates of M: $(-4, 3)$. Then reflect M across the x-axis to get the coordinates of N: $(-4, -3)$. Finally, either reflect N across the y-axis or reflect P across the x-axis to get the coordinates of O: $(4, -3)$.

16. The center of the circle is the circumcenter of the triangle. The circumcenter of a triangle is the point of concurrency of three perpendicular bisectors. Construct the perpendicular bisectors of two sides of the triangle. Use their intersection point as the center of the circle. The radius is the distance from the center to any of the three vertices of the triangle. Possible construction:

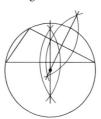

17. Compass-and-straightedge construction: Draw any two chords of the circle and construct their perpendicular bisectors. The intersection point of the perpendicular bisectors is the center of the circle. Possible construction:

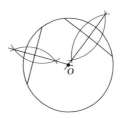

Patty-paper construction: Fold a piece of patty paper so that two semicircles coincide and make a crease. Repeat with a second pair of semicircles. The intersection point of the two creases is the center of the circle.

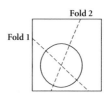

18. ≈ 13.8 cm. Draw two chords that connect pairs of points on the arc. Find the center by the compass-and-straightedge construction method used in Exercise 17. Measure the radius, and double it to find the diameter. (*Note:* In order to find the diameter accurately, trace the arc from the drawing of the plate on page 321 of your book, and use this arc for your construction.)

19. They can draw two chords and locate the intersection of their perpendicular bisectors. The radius is just over 5 km.

20. 1. Given; 3. All radii of a circle are congruent; 4. $\triangle AOB \cong \triangle COD$ by the SSS Congruence Conjecture; 5. $\angle AOB \cong \angle COD$ by CPCTC

21. $y = \frac{1}{7}x$. $(0, 0)$ is a point on this line. The perpendicular bisector of $\overline{AB}$ is the line that is perpendicular to $\overline{AB}$ and passes through its midpoint. The midpoint of $\overline{AB}$ is $\left(\frac{3+4}{2}, \frac{4+(-3)}{2}\right) = \left(\frac{7}{2}, \frac{1}{2}\right)$. The slope of $\overline{AB}$ is $\frac{-3-4}{4-3} = \frac{-7}{1} = -7$, whose opposite reciprocal is $\frac{1}{7}$. Find an equation of the line with slope $\frac{1}{7}$ and passing through $\left(\frac{7}{2}, \frac{1}{2}\right)$:

$$\frac{y - \frac{1}{2}}{x - \frac{7}{2}} = \frac{1}{7}$$

$$\frac{2\left(y - \frac{1}{2}\right)}{2\left(x - \frac{7}{2}\right)} = \frac{1}{7}$$

Multiply fraction on left by $\frac{2}{2}$ to eliminate fractions.

$$\frac{2y - 1}{2x - 7} = \frac{1}{7}$$

$$7(2x-7)\left(\frac{2y-1}{2x-7}\right) = 7(2x-7)\left(\frac{1}{7}\right)$$

Multiply both sides of equation by least common denominator.

$$7(2y - 1) = 1(2x - 7)$$

$$14y - 7 = 2x - 7$$

$$14y = 2x$$

$$y = \frac{1}{7}x$$

If $x = 0$, $y = \frac{1}{7}(0) = 0$, so $(0, 0)$ is on this line. Therefore, the perpendicular bisector of $\overline{AB}$ passes through the center of the circle.

22. a. True. If diagonals were perpendicular bisectors of each other, it would be a square. Because only one diagonal bisects the other, opposite sides can't be the same length.

b. False. It can be an isosceles trapezoid or a kite, so an isosceles trapezoid is a counterexample.

c. False. A nonsquare rectangle is a counterexample.

23. $x = 140°$; $y = 160°$; $z = 60°$. In each of the three diagrams, $m\angle P + m\angle A + m\angle Q + m\angle B = 360°$ by the Quadrilateral Sum Conjecture. Also, by the Tangent Conjecture, $\overline{QA} \perp \overline{PA}$ and $\overline{QB} \perp \overline{PB}$, so $m\angle A = 90°$ and $m\angle B = 90°$, and $m\angle A + m\angle B = 180°$. In the first diagram, $m\angle Q = 360° - 180° - 40° = 180° - 40° = 140°$. Then, by the definition of arc measure, $x = 140°$. In the second diagram, using

the same reasoning, $m\angle Q = 360° - 180° - 20° = 160°$, so $y = 160°$. In the third diagram, $z = 360° - 180° - 120° = 60°$. Conjecture: The measure of the angle formed by two intersecting tangents to a circle is 180° minus the measure of the intercepted arc.

24. By the Tangent Conjecture, $\angle 2$ and $\angle 4$ are right angles, so $m\angle 2 + m\angle 4 = 180°$. According to the Quadrilateral Sum Conjecture, $m\angle 1 + m\angle 2 + m\angle 3 + m\angle 4 = 360°$, so, by the Subtraction Property of Equality, $m\angle 1 + m\angle 3 = 180°$, or $m\angle 1 = 180° - m\angle 3$. By the definition of arc measure, the measure of a central angle equals the measure of its arc, so by substitution, $m\angle 1 = 180° - m\widehat{AB}$.

25. The circumcenter of the triangle formed by the three light switches. Draw the triangle formed by the three light switches, and find its circumcenter by constructing the perpendicular bisectors of two of the sides of the triangle.

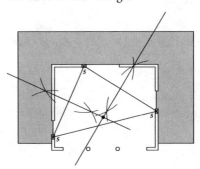

The circumcenter of the triangle (or center of the circumscribed circle, if it were constructed) is equidistant from the three points, so it is the most efficient location for the junction box.

26. 7. Make a list of powers of 3, beginning with $3^0 = 1$, and look for a pattern in the units digits:

$3^0 = 1$	$3^4 = 81$
$3^1 = 3$	$3^5 = 343$
$3^2 = 9$	$3^6 = 1029$
$3^3 = 27$	$3^7 = 3087$

Notice that in all powers of 3, the units digit is 1, 3, 9, or 7 and that the digits go through this pattern in a repeating cycle. Look at the remainders when the exponents are divided by 4: When the remainder is 0, the units digit of the power is 1; when the remainder is 1, the units digit is 3; when the remainder is 2, the units digit is 9; and when the remainder is 3, the units digit is 7. When 23 is divided by 4, the remainder is 3, so the units digit of 3^{23} is 7.

Discovering Geometry Solutions Manual
©2008 Key Curriculum Press

27. Station Beta is closer. Use a protractor and a centimeter rule to make a careful drawing.

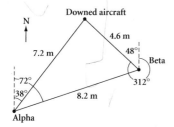

28. D. By the Triangle Midsegment Conjecture, $DC = \frac{1}{2}AB$, which remains constant. The distance from D to $\overleftrightarrow{AB}$ is always half the distance from l to $\overleftrightarrow{AB}$, so it is constant. The ratio $DC : AB$ is always $\frac{1}{2}$, as noted in part A. The lengths AP and BP will change, and will eventually increase infinitely, so the perimeter of $\triangle ABP$ is not constant. Therefore, D is the only correct answer.

IMPROVING YOUR ALGEBRA SKILLS

These terms occur in expansions of $(x + y)^n$ for $n = 6$, 7, and 8, respectively. If you are familiar with Pascal's triangle, you can see the pattern in the coefficients. The exponents move up or down by 1 in each subsequent term. You might find a missing exponent by symmetry, or you might see a different pattern: To calculate the kth term in a sequence, multiply the coefficient and first exponent of the previous term, and divide by $n - 1$. For example, the sixth term of the first sequence has coefficient $\frac{(15)(2)}{5} = 6$.

1. $6xy^5$, y^6 **2.** $7xy^6$, y^7 **3.** $8xy^7$, y^8

4. $36x^2y^7$, $9xy^8$, y^9

EXTENSIONS

A. Results will vary.

B. If a segment is drawn from the center of the circle to the midpoint of a chord (any chord that is not a diameter), two triangles will be formed that are congruent by SSS, so you know by CPCTC that two right angles are formed. Therefore, the median of the chord must be perpendicular to the chord, so it coincides with the given perpendicular bisector, forcing the latter to go through the circle's center.

LESSON 6.3

EXERCISES

1. $a = 65°$. The arc intercepted by the angle of measure a is also intercepted by the central angle of measure 130°. The measure of this arc is 130° (definition of the measure of an arc), so $a = \frac{1}{2}(130°) = 65°$ (Inscribed Angle Conjecture).

2. $b = 30°$. One of the sides of the triangle is a diameter, so the unmarked angle is inscribed in a semicircle. Therefore, the unmarked angle in the triangle is a right angle (Angles Inscribed in a Semicircle Conjecture). Thus, $b + 60° + 90° = 180°$, so $b = 30°$.

3. $c = 70°$. The 95° angle is an inscribed angle whose intercepted arc measures $c + 120°$. Therefore, $95° = \frac{1}{2}(c + 120°)$, or $c + 120° = 2(95°)$, by the Inscribed Angle Conjecture, so $c = 70°$.

4. $h = 50°$. Draw the radius to the point of tangency. By the Tangent Conjecture, the radius is perpendicular to the tangent at the point of tangency, so the triangle that has been formed is a right triangle. The figure shows that one of its acute angles measures 40°, so the other acute angle measures 50°. This is the central angle that intercepts the arc of measure h, so $h = 50°$ by the definition of arc measure.

5. $d = 140°$, $e = 42°$. The diameter divides the circle into two semicircles, and the sum of the measures of the arcs that make up a semicircle is 180°. The arc intercepted by the 20° angle measures 40° (Inscribed Angle Conjecture), so $d + 40° = 180°$, and $d = 140°$. Likewise, the measure of the arc intercepted by the inscribed angle of measure e is $2e$, so $2e + 96° = 180°$; thus, $2e = 84°$, and $e = 42°$.

6. $f = 90°$, $g = 100°$. The quadrilateral in the figure is a cyclic quadrilateral, so its opposite angles are supplementary (Cyclic Quadrilateral Conjecture). Therefore, $f = 90°$, and the angle opposite the 75° angle measures 105°. The 105° angle is an inscribed angle that intercepts an arc of measure $g + 110°$, so the measure of this arc must be $2(105°) = 210°$ (Inscribed Angle Conjecture). Therefore, $g + 110° = 210°$, and $g = 100°$.

7. $w = 50°$. The angle that intercepts the arc that is marked as 130° is a central angle, so its measure is 130°, and the measure of its vertical angle is also 130° (Vertical Angles Conjecture). This vertical angle, also a central angle of the circle, is one of the angles of the smallest quadrilateral that contains the angle of measure w. Also, two of the angles of the quadrilateral are right angles because they are formed by radii drawn to points of tangency (Tangent Conjecture). Therefore, by the Quadrilateral Sum Conjecture, $w + 90° + 130° + 90° = 360°$, so $w = 50°$.

8. $x = 148°$. $CALM$ is a rectangle, so its opposite sides are parallel. (A rectangle is a parallelogram.) Because $\overline{CM} \parallel \overline{AL}$, $\overarc{CA} \cong \overarc{ML}$ by the Parallel Lines Intercepted Arcs Conjecture, so $m\overarc{ML} = m\overarc{CA} = 32°$. Likewise, because $\overline{CA} \parallel \overline{ML}$, $\overarc{CM} \cong \overarc{AL}$ by the Parallel Lines Intercepted Arcs Conjecture, so $m\overarc{CM} = m\overarc{AL} = x$. Therefore, $2x + 2(32°) = 360°$, so $2x = 296°$, and $x = 148°$. (*Note:* You could also use the Chord Arcs Conjecture to conclude that $\overline{AL} \cong \overline{CA}$ and $\overline{CM} \cong \overline{AL}$ because opposite sides of a rectangle, or any parallelogram, are congruent.)

9. $y = 44°$. Because *DOWN* is a kite, $\overline{DO} \cong \overline{OW}$, so $\overparen{DO} \cong \overparen{WO}$ (Chord Arcs Conjecture), and therefore $m\overparen{DO} = m\overparen{WO} = y$. Likewise, $\overline{DN} \cong \overline{WN}$, so $\overparen{DN} \cong \overparen{WN}$, and therefore $m\overparen{WN} = m\overparen{DN} = 136°$. Thus, $2y + 2(136°) = 360°$, so $2y = 88°$, and $y = 44°$.

10. $k = 142°$. The triangle is isosceles with vertex angle of measure 38°, so each of its base angles measures $\frac{1}{2}(180° - 38°) = \frac{1}{2}(142°) = 71°$. Each of the base angles of the isosceles triangle is an inscribed angle in the circle, and one of these angles intercepts the arc of measure *k*. Therefore, by the Inscribed Angle Conjecture, $71° = \frac{1}{2}k$, or $k = 2(71°) = 142°$.

11. $r = 120°$, $s = 60°$. Notice that the sides of the hexagon are chords of the circle. Because the hexagon is equilateral, the six arcs intercepted by these chords are all congruent. Therefore, $6s = 360°$, so $s = 60°$. Also, the angle with measure *r* is an inscribed angle that intercepts an arc of measure $4s = 240°$, so $r = \frac{1}{2}(240°) = 120°$ (Inscribed Angle Conjecture). (Notice that each interior angle of the hexagon intercepts an arc of measure 4s, so the hexagon is equiangular as well as equilateral; that is, it is a regular hexagon. Therefore, you could also find *r* by using the Equiangular Polygon Conjecture: $r = \frac{(6-2) \cdot 180°}{6} = 120°$.)

12. $m = 140°$, $n = 111°$. Apply the Cyclic Quadrilateral Conjecture and the Inscribed Angle Conjecture. Because opposite angles of a cyclic quadrilateral are supplementary, the angle opposite the angle marked as a right angle is also a right angle. This is an inscribed angle that intercepts an arc of measure $m + 40°$, so $90° = \frac{1}{2}(m + 40°)$ (Inscribed Angle Conjecture). Therefore, $m + 40° = 180°$, and $m = 140°$. The measure of the fourth (unmarked) arc of the circle is $360° - 140° - 40° - 98° = 82°$. The angle of measure *n* is an inscribed angle that intercepts an arc of measure $m + 82° = 140° + 82° = 222°$, so $n = \frac{1}{2}(222°) = 111°$.

13. $p = 71°$, $q = 41°$. First apply the Parallel Lines Intercepted Arcs Conjecture. Because $\overline{AB} \parallel \overline{CD}$, $\overparen{AC} \cong \overparen{BD}$, so $m\overparen{BD} = p$. Next, $m\overparen{AB} = 120°$ and $m\overparen{CD} = 98°$ because these are the measures of their central angles. Adding all the arc measures in the circle, $120° + 2p + 98° = 360°$, so $2p = 142°$, and $p = 71°$. Now look at the triangle whose vertices are *C*, *D*, and the center of the circle. Because two of its sides are radii and all radii of a circle are congruent,

this is an isosceles triangle with vertex angle of measure 98°. Therefore, $2q + 98° = 180°$, so $2q = 82°$, and $q = 41°$.

14. 180°. Each of the five angles whose vertices are the points of the star is an inscribed angle, so the measure of each of them is half the measure of its intercepted arc. Notice that the five intercepted arcs add up to one complete circle (360°). Therefore, $a + b + c + d + e = \frac{1}{2}(360°) = 180°$. (Another way to approach this exercise is to recall your work with star polygons in the Sketchpad Exploration in Chapter 5. There, you found that the sum of the measures of the angles of a 5-pointed star is 180°.)

15. $y = 75°$. Label the figure as shown. The angles with measures *a* and *b* are both inscribed angles, so $a = \frac{1}{2}(70°) = 35°$, and $b = \frac{1}{2}(80°) = 40°$ (Inscribed Angle Conjecture). Notice that the angle with measure *y* is an exterior angle of the triangle, with *a* and *b* the measures of its remote interior angles. Therefore, $y = a + b$ (Triangle Exterior Angle Conjecture), so $y = 35° + 40° = 75°$.

16. The two inscribed angles intercept the same arc, so they should be congruent (Inscribed Angles Intercepting Arcs Conjecture). In the figure, they have different measures, so they are not congruent.

17. $\angle BFE \cong \angle DFA$ (Vertical Angles Conjecture), and $\angle BGD \cong \angle FHD$ (all right angles congruent). Therefore, $\angle B \cong \angle D$ (Third Angle Conjecture). $\angle B$ and $\angle D$ are inscribed angles, so by the Inscribed Angle Conjecture, $m\angle B = \frac{1}{2}m\overparen{AC}$, and $m\angle D = \frac{1}{2}m\overparen{EC}$. Because $m\angle B = m\angle D$, it follows that $\overparen{AC} \cong \overparen{EC}$.

18. Possible answer: Place the corner so that it is an inscribed angle. Trace the inscribed angle. Use the side of the paper to construct the hypotenuse of the right triangle (which is the diameter). Repeat the process. The place where the two diameters intersect is the center.

19. Possible answer:

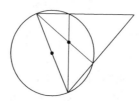

It works on acute and right triangles. To use this method on an obtuse triangle, you must construct the circle with the longest side of the triangle as the diameter; the altitudes will intersect the circle at the extensions of the sides.

20. The camera can be placed anywhere on the major arc (measuring 268°) of a circle such that the row of students is a chord intersecting the circle to form a minor arc measuring 92°. This illustrates the Inscribed Angles Intercepting Arcs Conjecture, which says that inscribed angles that intercept the same arc are congruent.

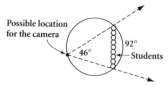

21. You will get two congruent externally tangent circles with half the diameter of the original circle.

22. $a = 108°$, $b = 72°$, $c = 36°$, $d = 108°$, $e = 108°$, $f = 72°$, $g = 108°$, $h = 90°$, $l = 36°$, $m = 18°$, $n = 54°$, and $p = 36°$. First, a is the measure of an interior angle of an equiangular pentagon, so
$$a = \frac{(5-2) \cdot 180°}{5} = 108°$$
by the Equiangular Polygon Conjecture. Then $b = 180° - 108° = 72°$ (Linear Pair Conjecture). (Also, the angle with measure b is an exterior angle of the equiangular polygon, so $b = \frac{360°}{5} = 72°$.) Look at the triangle that contains the angles with measures b and c. The unmarked angle in this triangle is also an exterior angle of the equiangular pentagon, so its measure is also b. Therefore, the triangle is isosceles, and $2b + c = 180°$, and $c = 36°$. The angle with measure d is a vertical angle of one of the interior angles of the equiangular pentagon, so $d = a = 108°$. Because $\ell_1 \parallel \ell_2$, $e = d$ (AIA Conjecture), so $e = 108°$. Notice that e and f are the measures of consecutive angles of a parallelogram, so $e + f = 180°$ (Parallelogram Consecutive Angles Conjecture), and $f = 72°$. Also, e and g are opposite angles of a parallelogram, so $g = e = 108°$ (Parallelogram Opposite Angles Conjecture). The angle with measure h forms a linear pair with a right angle, so $h = 90°$ (Linear Pair Conjecture). To find l, look at the triangle that contains the vertical angle of the angle with measure l. The other two angles of this triangle are exterior angles of the equiangular pentagon, so this is an isosceles triangle with base angles of measure 72°. So, the third angle measures $180° - 2(72°) = 36°$, and therefore $l = 36°$ (Vertical Angles Conjecture). Now look at the small triangle whose angles measure n, h, and l. $n + h + l = 180°$, so $n + 90° + 36° = 180°$, and $n = 54°$. Next look at the triangle that includes the angle of measure m. One of the other angles of this triangle is a

corresponding angle of the angle with measure h, and the other is the vertical angle of the angle of measure f. Therefore, these angles measure 90° (CA Conjecture) and 72° (VA Conjecture), so $m + 90° + 72° = 180°$, and $m = 18°$. Finally, look at the large triangle whose angles measure p, e, and c. Here $p + e + c = 180°$, so $p + 108° + 36° = 180°$, and thus $p = 36°$.

23. $(-2, -1)$. Possible method: Plot the three points. Construct the midpoint and the perpendicular bisectors of the segments connecting two different pairs of points. The center is the point of intersection of the two lines. To check, construct the circle through the three given points. Notice that the circumcenter of the triangle (which is the center of the circle) lies outside the triangle. This is because the angle with vertex at (3, 11) is obtuse.

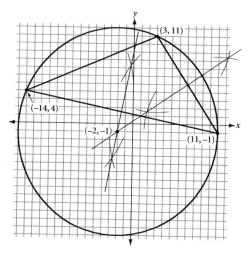

Note: It may be difficult to find the exact coordinates of the center by this geometric method, especially when the coordinates are not integers. Finding the center of a circle that passes through three given points is equivalent to finding the circumcenter of the triangle with the three given points as vertices. You will learn an algebraic way to do this in Using Your Algebra Skills 6 Example C. The algebraic method requires several steps, but has the advantage of always giving the exact coordinates of the center.

24. 1. Given; 2. Definition of perpendicular lines; 3. Definition of right angle; 4. Substitution property; 5. All radii of a circle are congruent; 6. Definition of isosceles triangle; 7. $\angle C \cong \angle D$ by the Isosceles Triangle Conjecture; 8. $\triangle OCR \cong \triangle ODR$ by SAA; 9. $\overline{CR} \cong \overline{DR}$ by CPCTC; 10. Definition of bisect

25. Start with an equilateral triangle whose vertices are the centers of the three congruent circles. Then locate the incenter/circumcenter/orthocenter/centroid (all the same point because the triangle is equilateral) to find the center of the larger circle. To find the radius, construct a segment from the incenter of the triangle through the vertex of the triangle to a point on the circle.

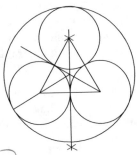

26. Look at the three smaller triangles inside △*ABC*, each of which shares a side with one of the equiangular polygons. Notice that in each case, two of the angles of the smaller triangle are exterior angles of the equiangular polygon; therefore, each of the small triangles is isosceles, with angles *A*, *B*, and *C* as their vertex angles.

The polygon near ∠*A* is an equiangular hexagon, so the measure of each of its exterior angles is $\frac{360°}{6} = 60°$, and therefore $m\angle A = 180° - 2(60°) = 60°$. (Thus, the small isosceles triangle containing ∠*A* is equiangular.) The polygon near ∠*B* is an equiangular pentagon, so the measure of each of its exterior angles is $\frac{360°}{5} = 72°$, and $m\angle B = 180° - 2(72°) = 36°$. The polygon near ∠*C* is an equiangular octagon, so the measure of each of its exterior angles is $\frac{360°}{8} = 45°$, and $m\angle C = 180° - 2(45°) = 90°$.

Using the angle measures that you have found, $m\angle A + m\angle B + m\angle C = 60° + 36° + 90° = 186°$. This is impossible because the sum of the measures of the angles in any triangle is 180° (Triangle Sum Conjecture).

IMPROVING YOUR REASONING SKILLS

The second vowel in *dinosaur* is *o*, and the letter that is three letters after *o* is *u*. The sixteenth letter of the alphabet is *p*. In the alphabet, *u* comes after *p*, not

before it. Therefore the word *dinosaur* should be printed vertically. The first vowel is *i*, and the second letter after *i* is *o*, so *o* should be crossed out.

d
i
n
~~o~~
s
a
u
r

EXTENSIONS

A. Research results will vary.

B. See the solutions for Take Another Look activities 3 and 4 on page 132.

LESSON 6.4

EXERCISES

1. Paragraph Proof: By the Inscribed Angle Conjecture, $m\angle ACD = \frac{1}{2}m\widehat{AD}$ and also $m\angle ABD = \frac{1}{2}m\widehat{AD}$. Therefore, by substitution, $m\angle ACD = m\angle ABD$, so $\angle ACD \cong \angle ABD$ by the definition of congruence.

Flowchart Proof (*See flowchart at bottom of page.*)

2. Paragraph Proof: ∠*ACB* is an inscribed angle that intercepts $\widehat{ADB}$. Because $\overline{AB}$ is a diameter of the circle, it divides the triangle into two semicircles, so $\widehat{ADB}$ is a semicircle. So, by the Inscribed Angle Conjecture, $m\angle ACB = \frac{1}{2}m\widehat{ADB} = \frac{1}{2}(180°) = 90°$. Therefore, ∠*ACB* is a right angle.

Flowchart Proof (*See flowchart at bottom of next page.*)

3. Paragraph Proof: By the Inscribed Angle Conjecture, $m\angle C = \frac{1}{2}m\widehat{YLI}$, and $m\angle L = \frac{1}{2}m\widehat{YCI} = \frac{1}{2}(360° - m\widehat{YLI}) = 180° - \frac{1}{2}m\widehat{YLI} = 180° - m\angle C$. Therefore, ∠*L* and ∠*C* are supplementary.

Lesson 6.4, Exercise 1

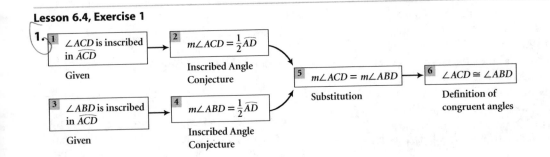

1.

| 1 | ∠*ACD* is inscribed in $\widehat{ACD}$ | → | 2 | $m\angle ACD = \frac{1}{2}\widehat{AD}$ |

Given — Inscribed Angle Conjecture

| 3 | ∠*ABD* is inscribed in $\widehat{ACD}$ | → | 4 | $m\angle ABD = \frac{1}{2}\widehat{AD}$ |

Given — Inscribed Angle Conjecture

| 5 | $m\angle ACD = m\angle ABD$ | → | 6 | $\angle ACD \cong \angle ABD$ |

Substitution — Definition of congruent angles

(A similar proof can be used to show that $\angle I$ and $\angle Y$ are supplementary.)

Flowchart Proof *(See flowchart at bottom of page.)*

4. **Paragraph Proof:** Angles 1 and 2 are inscribed angles, so, by the Inscribed Angle Conjecture, $m\angle 1 = \frac{1}{2}(m\widehat{AD})$ and $m\angle 2 = \frac{1}{2}(m\widehat{BC})$. Because $\overleftrightarrow{AB} \parallel \overleftrightarrow{DC}$, $\angle 1 \cong \angle 2$ by the AIA Conjecture. Therefore, $\frac{1}{2}m\widehat{BC} = \frac{1}{2}m\widehat{AD}$, so $m\widehat{BC} = m\widehat{AD}$. $\widehat{BC} \cong \widehat{AD}$ by the definition of congruence.

Flowchart Proof *(See flowchart at bottom of page.)*

5. True

Paragraph Proof: Opposite angles of a parallelogram are congruent (Parallelogram Opposite Angles Conjecture), and opposite angles of any quadrilateral inscribed in a circle are supplementary (Cyclic Quadrilateral Conjecture). If two angles are both

congruent and supplementary, each of them must be a right angle. Here, there are two pairs of opposite angles that are congruent and supplementary, so *GOLD* has four right angles. The definition of a rectangle says that a rectangle is a parallelogram with four right angles, so *GOLD* is a rectangle.

Flowchart Proof *(See flowchart at bottom of next page.)*

6. True

Paragraph Proof: Diagonal $\overline{RG}$ is the perpendicular bisector of $\overline{BD}$ by the Kite Diagonal Bisector Conjecture. Because kite *BRDG* is inscribed in the circle, $\overline{BD}$ and $\overline{RG}$ are chords of the circle. By the Perpendicular Bisector of a Chord Conjecture, the perpendicular bisector of $\overline{BD}$ passes through the center of the circle. Because $\overline{RG}$ is a chord of the circle that passes through the center, by the definition of diameter, $\overline{RG}$ is a diameter.

Lesson 6.4, Exercises 2, 3, 4

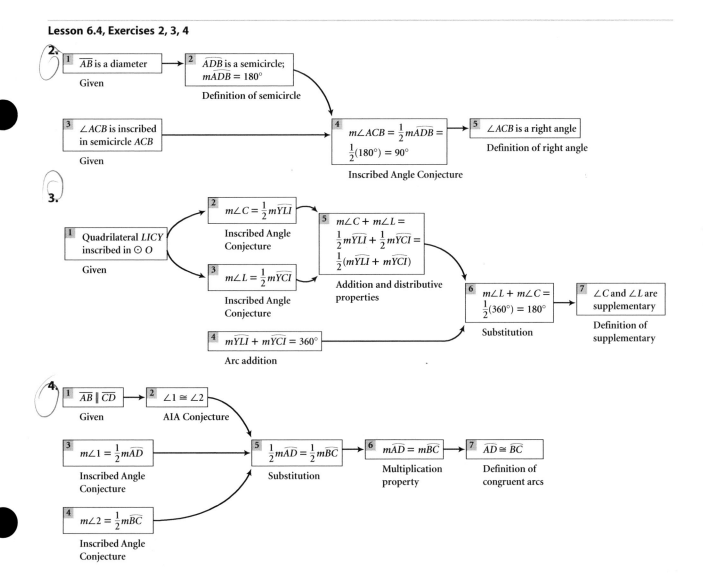

7. True

Start by drawing radii $\overline{GR}$, $\overline{ER}$, $\overline{TR}$, and $\overline{AR}$.

Paragraph Proof: Because they are radii of the same circle, $\overline{GR} \cong \overline{ER}$ and $\overline{AR} \cong \overline{TR}$. By the Parallel Lines Intercepted Arcs Conjecture, $\overset{\frown}{GA} \cong \overset{\frown}{ET}$. Their central angles must also be congruent, so $\angle GRA \cong \angle ERT$. Thus $\triangle GRA \cong \triangle ERT$ by SAS, so $\overline{GA} \cong \overline{ET}$ by CPCTC. $\therefore$ *GATE* is an isosceles trapezoid.

Flowchart Proof *(See flowchart at bottom of page.)*

8. $x = 65°$, $y = 40°$, $z = 148°$. Conjecture: The measure of the angle formed by the intersection of a tangent and chord at the point of tangency is half the measure of the intercepted arc.

First diagram: $\triangle AOB$ is isosceles and $\angle AOB$ is a central angle of the circle, so $m\angle AOB = 130°$ and $m\angle ABO = \frac{1}{2}(180° - 130°) = \frac{1}{2}(50°) = 25°$. By the Tangent Conjecture, $\overline{OB} \perp \overleftrightarrow{BC}$, so $x = m\angle ABC = 90° - 25° = 65°$.

Second diagram: $m\angle OBA = \frac{1}{2}(180° - 80°) = \frac{1}{2}(100°) = 50°$, so $y = m\angle ABC = 90° - 50° = 40°$.

Third diagram: $m\angle OBA = 90° - 74° = 16°$. Because $\triangle AOB$ is isosceles, $m\angle AOB = 180° - 2(16°) = 180° - 32° = 148°$, so $z = 148°$.

9. Because the radii of a circle are congruent, $\overline{OA} \cong \overline{OB}$, so $\triangle OAB$ is isosceles. By the Isosceles Triangle Conjecture, $\angle 2 \cong \angle 3$, so $m\angle 2 = m\angle 3$. By the Triangle Sum Conjecture, $m\angle 1 + m\angle 2 + m\angle 3 = 180°$, so by substitution, $m\angle 1 + 2(m\angle 2) = 180°$, or

$\angle 1 = 180° - 2(m\angle 2)$. By the Tangent Conjecture, $\overline{OB} \perp \overleftrightarrow{BC}$, so $m\angle OBC = 90°$. By Angle Addition, $m\angle 2 + m\angle 4 = m\angle OBC$, so $m\angle 2 + m\angle 4 = 90°$, or $m\angle 2 = 90° - m\angle 4$. Substitute $90° - m\angle 4$ for $m\angle 2$ in the earlier equation: $m\angle 1 = 180° - 2(90° - m\angle 4)$. Simplifying gives $m\angle 1 = 2(m\angle 4)$. Because $m\overset{\frown}{AB} = m\angle 1$, substitution gives $m\overset{\frown}{AB} = 2(m\angle 4)$, or $m\angle 4 = \frac{1}{2}m\overset{\frown}{AB}$.

10. a. S. An equilateral triangle is equiangular, but a rhombus is not always equiangular.

b. A

c. N. (Only one diagonal is the perpendicular bisector of the other.)

d. A

e. S. An equilateral triangle has rotational symmetry and three lines of reflectional symmetry; a parallelogram has rotational symmetry, but no line of reflectional symmetry.

11. L   **12.** J   **13.** K

14. D   **15.** E   **16.** B

17. H   **18.** G   **19.** N

20. $a + b + b + a = 180°$, so $2a + 2b = 180°$, or $2(a + b) = 180°$, and therefore $a + b = 90°$.

21. $\frac{2}{21}$. In Exercise 22 of Lesson 6.1, you worked with the same 3-by-3 grid and determined that the number of ways to select three points from the nine

---

Lesson 6.4, Exercises 5, 7

5.

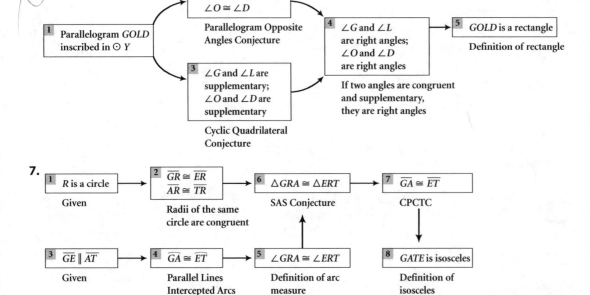

7.

points in the grid is $\frac{9(8)(7)}{1(2)(3)} = 84$. Now count the number of triples of collinear points: There is a collinear triple across each row (3), down each column (3), and along each diagonal (2). Therefore, there are 8 triples of collinear points out of 84 selections of any three points, so the probability of selecting three collinear points is $\frac{8}{84} = \frac{2}{21}$.

22. It is given that $\overline{PQ} \cong \overline{RS}$. $\overline{OP} \cong \overline{OQ} \cong \overline{OR} \cong \overline{OS}$ because all radii in a circle are congruent. Therefore, $\triangle OPQ \cong \triangle ORS$ by SSS, and $\angle 2 \cong \angle 1$ by CPCTC. Now look at the smaller right triangles inside $\triangle OPQ$ and $\triangle ORS$. It is given that $\overline{OT} \perp \overline{PQ}$ and $\overline{OV} \perp \overline{RS}$. Therefore, $\angle OTQ$ and $\angle OVS$ are right angles by the definition of perpendicular lines, and $\angle OTQ \cong \angle OVS$ because all right angles are congruent. Thus, $\triangle OTQ \cong \triangle OVS$ by SAA, and $\overline{OT} \cong \overline{OV}$ by CPCTC.

IMPROVING YOUR VISUAL THINKING SKILLS

The rotating quarter makes two full turns. Visualize what would happen if the two quarters were enmeshed gears and were turning together. Both would be facing the same way after a half turn. The same thing happens when one of the two quarters is stationary.

LESSON 6.5

EXERCISES

1. $d = 5$ cm. Substitute 5π cm for C in the formula $C = \pi d$, and solve for d.

$$C = \pi d$$
$$5\pi = \pi d$$
$$d = 5 \text{ cm}$$

2. $C = 10\pi$ cm. Substitute 5 cm for r in the formula $C = 2\pi r$, and solve for C.

$$C = 2\pi r$$
$$C = 2\pi(5) = 10\pi \text{ cm}$$

3. $r = \frac{12}{\pi}$ m. Substitute 24 m for C in the formula $C = 2\pi r$, and solve for r.

$$C = 2\pi r$$
$$24 \text{ m} = 2\pi r$$
$$r = \frac{24}{2\pi} = \frac{12}{\pi} \text{ m}$$

4. $C = 5.5\pi$ m. $C = \pi d = \pi(5.5) = 5.5\pi$ m.

5. $C = 12\pi$ cm. $C = \pi d = \pi(12) = 12\pi$ cm.

6. $d = 46$ m. Use the formula $C = \pi d$: $46\pi = \pi d$, so $d = 46$ m.

7. $C \approx 15.7$ cm. $C = \pi d = \pi(5) = 5\pi$ cm ≈ 15.7 cm.

8. $C \approx 25.1$ cm. $C = 2\pi r = 2\pi(4) = 8\pi$ cm $\approx$ 25.1 cm.

9. $r \approx 7.0$ m. Use the formula $C = 2\pi r$: $44 = 2\pi r$, so $r = \frac{44}{2\pi} = \frac{22}{\pi}$ m ≈ 7.0 m.

10. $C \approx 84.8$ in. $C = \pi d = \pi(27) = 27\pi$ in. ≈ 84.8 in.

11. A seated person travels about 565 ft. The distance from the center to one of the seats is the radius of the Ferris wheel, and the distance traveled by a seated person in one revolution is the circumference, so find the circumference of a circle with radius 90 ft. $C = 2\pi r = 2\pi(90) = 180\pi$ ft ≈ 565 ft.

12. $C = 6\pi$ cm. Sketch a circle inscribed in a square.

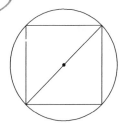

Notice that the diameter of the circle has the same length as a side of the square. The perimeter of the square is 24 cm, so the length of each side is 6 cm. Therefore, the diameter of the circle is also 6 cm, and the circumference of the circle is $\pi d = 6\pi$.

13. 16 in. Sketch a circle circumscribed about a square.

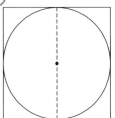

Notice that the diameter of the circle is a diagonal of the square. Find the diameter of the circle: $C = \pi d$, so $16\pi = \pi d$, and $d = 16$ in. Therefore, the length of the diagonal of the square is also 16 in.

14. 244 yr. Possible answer: The size of the ring indicates the amount of growth in a particular year, which varies from year to year depending on weather patterns.

To find the age of "Old Fred," first find its radius.

$$C = 2\pi r$$
$$766 = 2\pi r$$
$$r = \frac{766}{2\pi} \approx 122 \text{ cm}$$

If each ring has a thickness of 0.5 cm, the tree will have about $\frac{122 \text{ cm}}{0.5 \text{ cm}} = 244$ rings and is therefore about 244 years old.

15. 1399 tiles. Find the perimeter of the figure. Add the lengths of the two 30-foot sides of the rectangle and the circumference of two semicircles each with diameter 18 ft, which is the same as the circumference of one circle with diameter 18 ft: $2(30) + \pi(18) = (60 + 18\pi)$ ft $= 12(60 + 18\pi)$ in. ≈ 1399 in. Therefore, 1399 1-inch tiles will be needed.

16. $n = 30°$, $g = 40°$, $x = 70°$; $y = 142°$; $z = 110°$.

First diagram: By the Inscribed Angle Conjecture, $n = \frac{1}{2}(m\widehat{LG}) = 30°$ and $g = \frac{1}{2}(m\widehat{AN}) = 40°$. By the Triangle Exterior Angle Conjecture, $x = n + g = 70°$.

Second diagram: By the Inscribed Angle Conjecture, $m\angle N = \frac{1}{2}(m\widehat{LG}) = 92°$ (where $\widehat{LG}$ is the major arc) and $m\angle G = \frac{1}{2}(m\widehat{AN}) = 50°$. Then, by the Triangle Exterior Angle Conjecture, $y = 92° + 50° = 142°$.

Third diagram: Draw $\overline{NG}$. Using the same reasoning as for the second diagram, $m\angle N = 65°$, $m\angle G = 45°$, and $z = 65° + 45° = 110°$.

Conjecture: The measure of the angle formed by two intersecting chords is equal to one-half the sum of the measures of the two intercepted arcs. In the diagrams, $m\angle NEA = \frac{1}{2}(m\widehat{AN} + m\widehat{LG})$.

You could also say, "The measure of the angle formed by two intersecting chords is the average of the measures of the two intercepted arcs."

17. $m\angle AGN = \frac{1}{2}m\widehat{AN}$ and $m\angle LNG = \frac{1}{2}m\widehat{LG}$ by the Inscribed Angle Conjecture. $m\angle NEA = m\angle AGN + m\angle LNG$ by the Triangle Exterior Angle Conjecture. By substitution, $m\angle NEA = \frac{1}{2}(m\widehat{AN}) + \frac{1}{2}(m\widehat{LG}) = \frac{1}{2}(m\widehat{AN} + m\widehat{LG})$.

18. 1. $\overline{MA} \cong \overline{MT}$; 2. $\overline{SA} \cong \overline{ST}$; 3. Definition of kite; 4. $\overline{MS}$ is the perpendicular bisector of $\overline{AT}$ by the Kite Diagonal Bisector Conjecture.

19. $b = 90°$, $c = 42°$, $d = 70°$, $e = 48°$, $f = 132°$, and $g = 52°$. First, $b = 90°$ by the Cyclic Quadrilateral Conjecture. Next, $c = 42°$ (Inscribed Angles Intercepting Arcs Conjecture). Now look at the right triangle in which the measures of the acute angles are e and 42°. Here, $e = 90° - 42° = 48°$. Then $f = 180° - 48° = 132°$. Next apply the Quadrilateral Sum Conjecture to the quadrilateral in which the angle measures are d, f, 68°, and 90°: $d + 132° + 68° + 90° = 360°$, so $d = 70°$. Finally, look at the triangle that contains the 76° angle and the angle of measure g. This triangle is isosceles with vertex angle of measure 76° (Tangent Segments Conjecture). Therefore, $2g + 76° = 180°$, so $2g = 104°$, and $g = 52°$.

20. $\frac{150°}{360°}$, or $\frac{5}{12}$. $m\widehat{AB} = 2\left(22\frac{1}{2}°\right) = 45°$ (Inscribed Angle Conjecture). $m\angle A + 22\frac{1}{2}° + 105° = 180°$ (Triangle Sum Conjecture), so $m\angle A = 52\frac{1}{2}°$, and $m\widehat{CD} = 2\left(52\frac{1}{2}°\right) = 105°$ (Inscribed Angle Conjecture). Then $m\widehat{AB} + m\widehat{CD} = 45° + 105° = 150°$. Therefore, the probability that a random point on the circle will lie on either $\widehat{AB}$ or $\widehat{CD}$ is $\frac{150°}{360°}$, or $\frac{5}{12}$.

21. Look at the isosceles triangle that is formed when the two slanted lines intersect line n. One of the base angles of this triangle forms a linear pair with the 141° angle, so its measure is $180° - 141° = 39°$. Therefore, the other base angle must also have a measure of 39° (Isosceles Triangle Conjecture). Notice that this second base angle (lower left angle of triangle) and the angle marked 39° are corresponding angles formed when lines m and n are cut by one of the transversals. Because the corresponding angles are congruent, $m \parallel n$ by the Converse of the Parallel Lines Conjecture.

22. $10x + 2y$. Look for a pattern in the lengths of the outside edges, whose sum is the perimeter of each figure. The nth shape has n outside edges of length x. If n is odd, there is 1 edge of length y and 1 of length w, whereas if n is even, there are 2 edges of length y and none of length w. For the tenth shape, $n = 10$, an even number, so there are 10 edges of length x and 2 of length y. Therefore, the perimeter of the tenth shape is $10x + 2y$.

PROJECT

Project should satisfy the following criteria:

- For a large number of trials, the ratio $\frac{2N}{C}$ will be close to π.

- Explanations will take into account that the experiment involves lines and segments, but the result suggests a circle. They might suggest that the different possible orientations of the toothpick lie in a circle.

Extra credit

- Student does experiments with different line widths and finds that for a toothpick with length L tossed on lines a distance D apart, P(crossing a line) $= \frac{2L}{\pi D}$. (If L is longer than D, however, calculating the probability is more complicated and requires calculus.)

EXTENSIONS

A. Research results will vary.

B. Ratios should be close to π.

C. See the solution for Take Another Look activity 5 on page 132.

D. Poems will vary.

Discovering Geometry Solutions Manual
©2008 Key Curriculum Press

EXERCISES

1. ≈ 4398 km/h

$$\text{speed} = \frac{\text{distance}}{\text{time}} = \frac{\text{circumference}}{12 \text{ h}}$$

$$= \frac{2\pi(2000 \text{ km} + 6400 \text{ km})}{12 \text{ h}}$$

$$\approx 4398 \text{ km/h}$$

2. ≈ 11 m/s

$$\text{speed} = \frac{\text{distance}}{\text{time}} = \frac{\text{circumference}}{16 \text{ s}}$$

$$= \frac{2\pi \cdot 28 \text{ m}}{16 \text{ s}} \approx 11 \text{ m/s}$$

3. ≈ 37,000,000 revolutions. First convert 60 cm to kilometers: 60 cm = 0.6 m = 0.0006 km. The diameter of the tire is 0.0006 km, so the circumference, which is the length of one revolution, is $\pi d = 0.0006\pi$ km.

Let x represent the number of revolutions of the tire before the warranty is up, and write a proportion; then solve the proportion.

$$\frac{1 \text{ revolution}}{0.00006\pi \text{ km}} = \frac{x \text{ revolutions}}{70,000 \text{ km}}$$

$$x = \frac{70,000}{0.0006\pi} \approx 37,000,000$$

The tire will make about 37,000,000 revolutions before the warranty is up.

4. ≈ 637 revolutions. 1 revolution = $\pi d = 0.5\pi$ m. Use a proportion.

$$\frac{1 \text{ revolution}}{0.5\pi \text{ m}} = \frac{x \text{ revolutions}}{1000 \text{ m}}$$

$$x = \frac{1000}{0.5\pi} \approx 637$$

The tire will make about 637 revolutions.

5. Mama; $C \approx 50$ in. First, find the circumference of each pizza.

Baby Bear: $C = 2\pi r = 12\pi$ in.

Mama Bear: $C = 2\pi r = 16\pi$ in.

Papa Bear: $C = \pi d = 20\pi$ in.

Now use the prices for the three pizzas to find the number of inches of edge per dollar for each pizza.

Baby Bear: $\frac{12\pi \text{ in.}}{\$9.75} \approx 3.87$ in./dollar

Mama Bear: $\frac{16\pi \text{ in.}}{\$12.00} \approx 4.19$ in./dollar

Papa Bear: $\frac{20\pi \text{ in.}}{\$16.50} \approx 3.81$ in./dollar

Therefore, the Mama Bear pizza has the most pizza edge per dollar. Its circumference is 16π in. ≈ 50 in.

6. ≈ 168 cm. Find the circumference of the tree, and then use the circumference to find the diameter. The circumference is about $138 + 136 + 128 + 126 \approx 528$ cm. Then $d = \frac{C}{\pi} = \frac{528}{\pi} \approx 168$ cm, so the diameter of the redwood tree is about 168 cm.

7. $d \approx 7.6$ ft. The table will fit, but the chairs may be a little tight in a 12-by-14 ft room. 12 chairs = 192 in., and 12 spaces = 96 in., so the circumference of the circle should be $C = 288$ in. For this table, $d = \frac{C}{\pi} = \frac{288}{\pi} \approx 91.7$ in. ≈ 7.6 ft.

8. ≈ 0.35 ft/s. Calculate the distance traveled in one revolution, which is the circumference, for each record.

45 rpm record: $d = 7$ in., so $C = 7\pi$ in.

33 rpm record: $d = 12$ in., so $C = 12\pi$ in.

Now find the speed of a point on the edge of each record.

45 rpm record:

$$\text{speed} = \frac{\text{distance}}{\text{time}} = \frac{(7\pi \text{ in./rev})(45 \text{ rev})}{1 \text{ min}}$$

$$= 315\pi \text{ in./min}$$

33 rpm record:

$$\text{speed} = \frac{\text{distance}}{\text{time}} = \frac{(12\pi \text{ in./rev})(33 \text{ rev})}{1 \text{ min}}$$

$$= 396\pi \text{ in./min}$$

So, the difference in speeds between the two records is $396\pi - 315\pi = 81\pi$ in./min. Now convert this difference from in./min to ft/s, and use your calculator to approximate π:

$$\frac{81\pi \text{ in.}}{\text{min}} \cdot \frac{1 \text{ ft}}{12 \text{ in.}} \cdot \frac{1 \text{ min}}{60 \text{ s}} \approx 0.35 \text{ ft/s}$$

So, the difference in speeds between points on the edges of the 33 rpm record and the 45 rpm record is about 0.35 ft/s.

9. $a = 37.5°$, $s = 17.5°$, $x = 20°$; $y = 80°$; $z = 61°$. $m\angle ECA = \frac{1}{2}(m\widehat{SN} - m\widehat{EA})$. Conjecture: The measure of an angle formed by two intersecting secants through a circle is equal to one-half the difference of the larger arc measure and the smaller arc measure.

First diagram: By the Inscribed Angle Conjecture, $a = \frac{1}{2}(m\widehat{STN}) = 37.5°$ and $s = \frac{1}{2}(m\widehat{EA}) = 17.5°$. Then, by the Triangle Exterior Angle Conjecture, $a = s + x$, so $x = s - a = 37.5° - 17.5° = 20°$.

Second diagram: By the Inscribed Angle Conjecture, $m\angle SAN = \frac{1}{2}(m\widehat{STN}) = 100°$ and $m\angle S = \frac{1}{2}(m\widehat{EA}) = 20°$. Then, by the Triangle Exterior Angle Conjecture, $m\angle SAN = m\angle S + y$, so $y = 100° - 20° = 80°$.

Third diagram: Draw $\overline{SA}$. Using the same reasoning as for the other two diagrams, $m\angle SAN = 73.5°$, $m\angle S = 12.5°$, and $z = 73.5° - 12.5° = 61°$.

10. Draw $\overline{SA}$ to form inscribed angles ESA and SAN. $m\angle ESA = \frac{1}{2}m\widehat{EA}$ and $m\angle SAN = \frac{1}{2}m\widehat{SN}$ by the Inscribed Angle Conjecture. $m\angle SAN = m\angle ESA + m\angle ECA$ by the Triangle Exterior Angle Conjecture, so $\frac{1}{2}m\widehat{SN} = \frac{1}{2}m\widehat{EA} + m\angle ECA$ by substitution. So, $m\angle ECA = \frac{1}{2}m\widehat{SN} - \frac{1}{2}m\widehat{EA} = \frac{1}{2}(m\widehat{SN} - m\widehat{EA})$.

11. Both triangles are isosceles, so the base angles in each pair are congruent (Isosceles Triangle Conjecture). Also, the unmarked base angles of the two triangles are vertical angles, so they are congruent (Vertical Angles Conjecture). Therefore, $a = b$ by transitivity.

12. C. The measure of $\angle ABP$ increases as it changes from an acute angle to a right angle to an obtuse angle. The other measures either increase and then decrease or do not change as P moves.

13. 38°. By the Intersecting Chords Conjecture that you discovered in Lesson 6.5, Exercise 16 and proved in Exercise 17, $a = \frac{1}{2}(32° + 44°) = \frac{1}{2}(76°) = 38°$.

14. 48°. By the Parallel Lines Intercepted Arcs Conjecture, the unmarked arc has measure b. Therefore, $2b + 96° + 168° = 360°$, so $2b = 96°$, and $b = 48°$.

15. 30 cm. The figure is a trapezoid, and the segment of length 24 cm is its midsegment. Therefore, $24 = \frac{1}{2}(d + 18)$ by the Trapezoid Midsegment Conjecture, so $48 = d + 18$, and $d = 30$ cm.

16. $\frac{400 \text{ rev}}{1 \text{ min}} \cdot \frac{2\pi \cdot 26 \text{ ft}}{1 \text{ rev}} \cdot \frac{1 \text{ min}}{60 \text{ s}} \approx 1089$ ft/s

17. 12 cm < third side < 60 cm. By the Triangle Inequality Conjecture, the length of the third side must be between $36 - 24 = 12$ cm and $24 + 36 = 60$ cm.

IMPROVING YOUR VISUAL THINKING SKILLS

1. Rule: $(n + 1)n + 1 = n^2 + n + 1$

2. Rule: $(n + 2)n + 2 = n^2 + 2n + 2$

EXTENSION

Problems and solutions will vary.

USING YOUR ALGEBRA SKILLS 6

EXERCISES

Note: Each of the systems in Exercises 1–6 can be solved by either the substitution or elimination method.

1. $\left(-\frac{1}{2}, 3\right)$. The substitution method is a good choice for solving this system because the first equation is already solved for y. Substitute $-2x + 2$ for y in the second equation and solve for x.

$$6x + 2(-2x + 2) = 3$$
$$6x - 4x + 4 = 3$$
$$2x = -1$$
$$x = -\frac{1}{2}$$

Then substitute x back into the first equation to find y.

$$y = -2x + 2$$
$$y = -2\left(-\frac{1}{2}\right) + 2$$
$$y = 3$$

The solution of the system is $\left(-\frac{1}{2}, 3\right)$.

2. $(-3, -3)$. Multiply the first equation by 3 and then add the resulting equation to the second equation.

$$-12x + 9y = 9$$
$$+ 7x - 9y = 6$$
$$\overline{-5x = 15}$$
$$x = -3$$

Now substitute -3 for x in either of the original equations and solve for y. Here, it is substituted into the first original equation.

$$-4(-3) + 3y = 3$$
$$12 + 3y = 3$$
$$3y = -9$$
$$y = -3$$

The solution of the system is $(-3, -3)$.

3. $\left(\frac{2}{5}, 3\right)$. Solve the first equation for y to get $y = 5x + 1$. Then substitute $5x + 1$ for y in the second equation and solve for x.

$$15x = 2(5x + 1)$$
$$15x = 10x + 2$$
$$5x = 2$$
$$x = \frac{2}{5}$$

Now substitute $\frac{2}{5}$ for x in the equation $5x - y = -1$ and find the corresponding value of y.

$$5\left(\frac{2}{5}\right) - y = -1$$

$$2 - y = -1$$

$$3 = y$$

The solution of the system is $\left(\frac{2}{5}, 3\right)$.

4. $(7, -2)$. To solve by the elimination method, multiply both sides of the second equation by 2 and add the resulting equation to the first equation.

$$\begin{array}{r} x + 2y = 3 \\ + \; 4x - 2y = 32 \\ \hline 5x = 35 \end{array}$$

$$x = 7$$

Now substitute 7 for x in either of the original equations and solve for y. Here, it is substituted into the first original equation.

$$7 + 2y = 3$$

$$2y = -4$$

$$y = -2$$

The solution of the system is $(7, -2)$.

5. Infinitely many solutions: any solution to one equation will also be a solution to the other equation. Multiply the second equation by 3 and subtract the resulting equation from the first equation.

$$\begin{array}{r} x + 3y = 6 \\ -(x + 3y = 6) \\ \hline 0 = 0 \end{array}$$

Notice that all the variables cancelled out and you're left with a true statement. Multiplying the second equation by 3 showed that the two equations are equivalent, so they have the same solutions.

6. No solution. Substitute $-2x - 1$ for y in the first equation.

$$2x + (-2x - 1) = 9$$

$$2x - 2x + 1 = 9$$

$$1 = 9$$

Notice that all of the variables cancel out and you're left with a false statement. Therefore, no values of x and y can satisfy both equations simultaneously.

7. To graph the systems, solve each equation for y.

The first equation in Exercise 4 is equivalent to $y = -\frac{1}{2}x + \frac{3}{2}$, and the second equation is equivalent to

$y = 2x - 16$. The solution to the system, $(7, -2)$, is the point where the lines intersect.

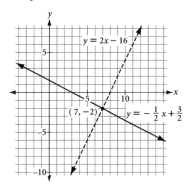

Both equations in Exercise 5 are equivalent to $y = -\frac{2}{3}x + 2$. Every point on the line is a solution to the system.

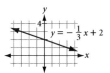

The first equation in Exercise 6 is equivalent to $y = -2x + 9$, and the second equation is $y = -2x - 1$. The graphs of these two equations are lines with the same slope and different y-intercepts, so they are parallel. There is no solution to the system because the lines don't intersect.

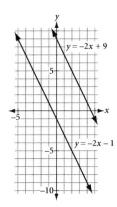

8. $\left(\frac{22}{7}, \frac{18}{7}\right)$; all three perpendicular bisectors are concurrent, so finding the intersection of any two will give the circumcenter. The midpoint of $\overline{AP}$ is $(2, 6)$, and the slope of the line containing $\overline{AP}$ is $\frac{1}{3}$. Therefore, the perpendicular bisector of $\overline{AP}$ has slope -3 and passes through $(2, 6)$. Its equation is $y = -3x + 12$. Through similar reasoning, you can find that the equation of the perpendicular bisector of $\overline{AZ}$ is $y = \frac{1}{2}x + 1$. Solve the system $\begin{cases} y = -3x + 12 \\ y = \frac{1}{2}x + 1 \end{cases}$ to find the circumcenter. Substitute $-3x + 12$ for y in the second equation, and solve for x.

$$-3x + 12 = \frac{1}{2}x + 1$$

$$11 = \frac{7}{2}x$$

$$\frac{22}{7} = x$$

Now substitute $\frac{22}{7}$ for x in either equation to find the corresponding value of y. $y = \frac{1}{2}\left(\frac{22}{7}\right) + 1 = \frac{18}{7}$, so the circumcenter is at $\left(\frac{22}{7}, \frac{18}{7}\right)$.

9. a. Plan A: $y = 4x + 20$; Plan B: $y = 7x$. To solve the system formed by these two equations by the substitution method, substitute $7x$ for y in the first equation and solve for x.

$$7x = 4x + 20$$

$$3x = 20$$

$$x = \frac{20}{3}$$

Substitute $\frac{20}{3}$ for x in the second equation and solve for y.

$$y = 7\left(\frac{20}{3}\right) = \frac{140}{3}$$

The value of x, $\frac{20}{3} = 6\frac{2}{3}$, represents $6\frac{2}{3}$ h, or 6 h 40 min. The value of y, $\frac{140}{3} = 46\frac{2}{3} = 46.\overline{6}$, represents \$46.67 (rounded to the nearest cent).

b. The point of intersection shows when both plans cost the same, 6 h 40 min of rental time for \$46.67.

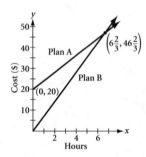

c. The best deal for 5 hours is Plan B. Look at the graph. The line representing Plan B is below the line representing Plan A when $x = 5$, which is to the left of the intersection point, so Plan B is the better deal (less expensive) when $x = 5$.

The most you can snowboard for \$50 is $7\frac{1}{2}$ hours, with Plan A. The line $y = 50$ intersects the line representing Plan A farther to the right than it intersects the line representing Plan B, indicating that \$50 corresponds to more hours under Plan A than it does under Plan B. To find the number of hours of snowboarding that you can get for \$50 with Plan A, substitute 50 for y in the equation for Plan A and solve for x: $50 = 4x + 20$, so $4x = 30$ and $x = \frac{30}{4} = \frac{15}{2} = 7\frac{1}{2}$.

10. $(-3, 1)$, $(0, 3)$, $(3, -1)$. Find the intersection point for each pair of equations by solving that pair simultaneously.

$y = 3 + \frac{2}{3}x$ and $y = -\frac{1}{3}x$: Substitute $3 + \frac{2}{3}x$ for y in the second equation and solve for x. Then substi-

tute the value of x into the second equation to find the corresponding value of y.

$$3 + \frac{2}{3}x = -\frac{1}{3}x$$

$$x = -3$$

$$y = -\frac{1}{3}(-3) = 1$$

The first and second lines intersect at the point $(-3, 1)$.

$y = 3 + \frac{2}{3}x$ and $y = -\frac{4}{3}x + 3$: Substitute $3 + \frac{2}{3}x$ for y in the second equation and solve for x; then find the corresponding value of y.

$$3 + \frac{2}{3}x = -\frac{4}{3}x + 3$$

$$2x = 0$$

$$x = 0$$

$$y = 3 + \frac{2}{3}(0) = 3$$

The first and third lines intersect at the point $(0, 3)$.

$y = -\frac{1}{3}x$ and $y = -\frac{4}{3}x + 3$: Substitute $-\frac{1}{3}x$ for y in the third equation and solve for x; then find the corresponding value of y.

$$-\frac{1}{3}x = -\frac{4}{3}x + 3$$

$$x = 3$$

$$y = -\frac{1}{3}(3) = -1$$

The second and third lines intersect at the point $(3, -1)$.

Therefore, the vertices of the triangle are $(-3, 1)$, $(0, 3)$, and $(3, -1)$.

11. a. $\begin{cases} y = \frac{3}{4}x + \frac{3}{2} \\ y = -x + 12 \end{cases}$. The slope of the line containing $\overline{AC}$ is $\frac{y_2 - y_1}{x_2 - x_1} = \frac{9 - 3}{10 - 2} = \frac{6}{8} = \frac{3}{4}$. The line passes through the point $A(2, 3)$, so $\frac{y - 3}{x - 2} = \frac{3}{4}$. Solve this equation for y.

$$\frac{y - 3}{x - 2} = \frac{3}{4}$$

$$4(y - 3) = 3(x - 2)$$

$$4y - 12 = 3x - 6$$

$$4y = 3x + 6$$

$$y = \frac{3}{4}x + \frac{3}{2}$$

The slope of the line containing $\overline{BD}$ is $\frac{y_2 - y_1}{x_2 - x_1} = \frac{8 - 4}{4 - 8} = \frac{4}{-4} = -1$. The line passes through the point $B(8, 4)$, so $\frac{y-4}{x-8} = -1$. Solve this equation for y.

$$\frac{y-4}{x-8} = -1$$

$$y - 4 = -1(x - 8)$$

$$y = -x + 12$$

b. $(6, 6)$. The system from part a may be solved by either the substitution or elimination method. To solve by substitution, substitute $\frac{3}{4}x + \frac{3}{2}$ for y in the second equation. Multiply both sides by the least common denominator, 4, to eliminate fractions.

$$\frac{3}{4}x + \frac{3}{2} = -x + 12$$

$$4\left(\frac{3}{4}x + \frac{3}{2}\right) = 4(-x + 12)$$

$$3x + 6 = -4x + 48$$

$$7x + 6 = 48$$

$$7x = 42$$

$$x = 6$$

Now substitute 6 for x in the second equation of the system from 11a and solve for y. $y = -6 + 12 = 6$.

c. $(6, 6)$; $(6, 6)$. Use the Coordinate Midpoint Property to find the midpoint of each diagonal.

Midpoint of $\overline{AC}$: $= \left(\frac{x_1 + x_2}{2}, \frac{y_1 + y_2}{2}\right)$

$$= \left(\frac{2 + 10}{2}, \frac{3 + 9}{2}\right) = \left(\frac{12}{2}, \frac{12}{2}\right)$$

$$= (6, 6)$$

Midpoint of $\overline{BD}$: $= \left(\frac{x_1 + x_2}{2}, \frac{y_1 + y_2}{2}\right)$

$$= \left(\frac{8 + 4}{2}, \frac{4 + 8}{2}\right) = \left(\frac{12}{2}, \frac{12}{2}\right)$$

$$= (6, 6)$$

d. The diagonals intersect at their midpoints, which supports the conjecture that the diagonals of a parallelogram bisect each other.

12. $y = \frac{2}{3}x - \frac{13}{3}$. The perpendicular bisector of $\overline{RE}$ is the line perpendicular to $\overline{RE}$ and passing through its midpoint. The midpoint of $\overline{RE}$ is $\left(\frac{0+4}{2}, \frac{0+(-6)}{2}\right) = (2, -3)$, and the slope of $\overline{RE}$ is $\frac{-6-0}{4-0} = \frac{-6}{4} = -\frac{3}{2}$. The slope of the perpendicular bisector is the opposite reciprocal of $-\frac{3}{2}$, which is $\frac{2}{3}$.

Find the equation in the form $y = mx + b$ of the line with slope $\frac{2}{3}$ passing through $(2, -3)$.

$$\frac{y - (-3)}{x - 2} = \frac{2}{3}$$

$$\frac{y + 3}{x - 2} = \frac{2}{3}$$

$$3(y + 3) = 2(x - 2)$$

$$3y + 9 = 2x - 4$$

$$3y = 2x - 13$$

$$y = \frac{2}{3}x - \frac{13}{3}$$

13. $(4, -7)$. Find the perpendicular bisectors of any two sides of the triangle, and then find the point where they intersect. Any two of the perpendicular bisectors can be chosen; in this solution, the perpendicular bisectors of $\overline{TR}$ and $\overline{RM}$ will be used to find the circumcenter.

First find the perpendicular bisector of $\overline{TR}$.

Midpoint of $\overline{TR} = \left(\frac{-2 + 4}{2}, \frac{1 + 3}{2}\right) = (1, 2)$

Slope of $\overline{TR} = \frac{3 - 1}{4 - (-2)} = \frac{2}{6} = \frac{1}{3}$

The slope of the perpendicular bisector of $\overline{TR}$ is the opposite reciprocal of $\frac{1}{3}$, which is -3. Find the equation in the form $y = mx + b$ for the line with slope -3 that passes through $(1, 2)$.

$$\frac{y - 2}{x - 1} = -3$$

$$y - 2 = -3(x - 1)$$

$$y - 2 = -3x + 3$$

$$y = -3x + 5$$

Now find the perpendicular bisector of $\overline{RM}$.

Midpoint of $\overline{RM} = \left(\frac{4 + (-4)}{2}, \frac{3 + (-1)}{2}\right) = (0, 1)$

Slope of $\overline{RM} = \frac{-1 - 3}{-4 - 4} = \frac{-4}{-8} = \frac{1}{2}$

The perpendicular bisector of $\overline{RM}$ has slope -2 and y-intercept 1, so its equation is $y = -2x + 1$.

Now solve the system formed by the equations of the perpendicular bisectors.

$$\begin{cases} y = -3x + 5 \\ y = -2x + 1 \end{cases}$$

To solve this system by the substitution method, substitute $-2x + 1$ for y in the first equation, and solve for x.

$$-2x + 1 = -3x + 5$$

$$x = 4$$

Now substitute 4 for x in the second equation, and solve for y.

$$y = -2(4) + 1 = -7$$

The solution of the system gives the coordinates of the point where the two perpendicular bisectors intersect, which is the circumcenter of the triangle. Therefore the circumcenter of $\triangle TRM$ is $(4, -7)$.

14. $\left(\frac{69}{14}, -\frac{6}{7}\right)$. Follow the method given in the solution for Exercise 13. In this solution, the perpendicular bisectors of $\overline{FG}$ and $\overline{FH}$ will be found, but you could choose any pair of perpendicular bisectors.

Midpoint of $\overline{FG} = \left(\dfrac{0 + 3}{2}, \dfrac{-6 + 6}{2}\right) = \left(\dfrac{3}{2}, 0\right)$

Slope of $\overline{FG} = \dfrac{6 - (-6)}{3 - 0} = \dfrac{12}{3} = 4$

The slope of the perpendicular bisector of $\overline{FG}$ is $-\frac{1}{4}$.

Find the equation in the form $y = mx + b$ for the line with slope $-\frac{1}{4}$ that passes through the point $\left(\frac{3}{2}, 0\right)$.

$$\dfrac{y - 0}{x - \dfrac{3}{2}} = -\dfrac{1}{4}$$

$$\dfrac{y}{x - \dfrac{3}{2}} = \dfrac{-1}{4}$$

$$4y = -1\left(x - \dfrac{3}{2}\right)$$

$$4y = -x + \dfrac{3}{2}$$

$$y = -\dfrac{1}{4}x + \dfrac{3}{8}$$

Midpoint of $\overline{FH} = \left(\dfrac{0 + 12}{2}, \dfrac{-6 + 0}{2}\right) = (6, -3)$

Slope of $\overline{FH} = \dfrac{0 - (-6)}{12 - 0} = \dfrac{6}{12} = \dfrac{1}{2}$

The slope of the perpendicular bisector of $\overline{FH}$ is -2. Find the equation in the form $y = mx + b$ for the line with slope -2 that passes through $(6, -3)$.

$$\dfrac{y - (-3)}{x - 6} = -2$$

$$y + 3 = -2(x - 6)$$

$$y + 3 = -2x + 12$$

$$y = -2x + 9$$

Now solve the system formed by the equations of the perpendicular bisectors.

$$\begin{cases} y = -\dfrac{1}{4}x + \dfrac{3}{8} \\ y = -2x + 9 \end{cases}$$

To solve this system by substitution, substitute $-2x + 9$ for y in the first equation, and solve for x.

$$-2x + 9 = -\dfrac{1}{4}x + \dfrac{3}{8}$$

$$8(-2x + 9) = 8\left(-\dfrac{1}{4}x + \dfrac{3}{8}\right)$$

$$-16x + 72 = -2x + 3$$

$$-14x = -69$$

$$x = \dfrac{69}{14}$$

Now substitute $\frac{69}{14}$ for x in the second equation, and solve for y.

$$y = -2\left(\dfrac{69}{14}\right) + 9 = \dfrac{-69}{7} + \dfrac{63}{7} = -\dfrac{6}{7}$$

Therefore, the circumcenter of $\triangle FGH$ is $\left(\frac{69}{14}, -\frac{6}{7}\right)$.

15. $\left(3, -\frac{3}{2}\right)$. Find the perpendicular bisectors of $\overline{MO}$ and $\overline{NO}$, and then find their point of intersection.

Midpoint of $\overline{MO} = \left(\dfrac{-4 + 10}{2}, \dfrac{0 + (-3)}{2}\right)$

$$= \left(3, -\dfrac{3}{2}\right)$$

Slope of $\overline{MO} = \dfrac{-3 - 0}{10 - (-4)} = \dfrac{-3}{14}$

Slope of perpendicular bisector of $\overline{MO} = \dfrac{14}{3}$

Solve the equation $\dfrac{y - \left(-\frac{3}{2}\right)}{x - 3} = \dfrac{14}{3}$ for y to rewrite this equation in the form $y = mx + b$:
$y = \dfrac{14}{3}x - \dfrac{31}{2}$.

Midpoint of $\overline{NO} = \left(\dfrac{0 + 10}{2}, \dfrac{5 + (-3)}{2}\right) = (5, 1)$

Slope of $\overline{NO} = \dfrac{-3 - 5}{10 - 0} = \dfrac{-8}{10} = -\dfrac{4}{5}$

Slope of perpendicular bisector of $\overline{NO} = \dfrac{5}{4}$

Solve the equation $\dfrac{y - 1}{x - 5} = \dfrac{5}{4}$ for y to obtain $y = \dfrac{5}{4}x - \dfrac{21}{4}$.

Now solve the system formed by the equations of the two perpendicular bisectors.

$$\begin{cases} y = \dfrac{14}{3}x - \dfrac{31}{2} \\ y = \dfrac{5}{4}x - \dfrac{21}{4} \end{cases}$$

Substitute $\frac{5}{4}x - \frac{21}{4}$ for y in the first equation.

$$\dfrac{5}{4}x - \dfrac{21}{4} = \dfrac{14}{3}x - \dfrac{31}{2}$$

$$12\left(\dfrac{5}{4}x - \dfrac{21}{4}\right) = 12\left(\dfrac{14}{3}x - \dfrac{31}{2}\right)$$

$$15x - 63 = 56x - 186$$

$$-41x = -123$$

$$x = 3$$

To find the value of y, substitute 3 for x in the first equation of the system.

$$y = \frac{14}{3}(3) - \frac{31}{2} = 14 - \frac{31}{2} = \frac{28}{2} - \frac{31}{2} = -\frac{3}{2}$$

The circumcenter is $\left(3, -\frac{3}{2}\right)$.

16. The circumcenter is the midpoint of the side opposite the right angle (the hypotenuse). For a right triangle, the perpendicular bisectors of the two legs adjacent to the right angle are two of the midsegments of the triangle. As with any pair of triangle midsegments, they intersect at the midpoint of the third side.

LESSON 6.7

EXERCISES

1. $\frac{4\pi}{3}$ in. $m\overset{\frown}{CD} = 80°$, so $\overset{\frown}{CD}$ is $\frac{80}{360} = \frac{2}{9}$ of the circumference. $r = 3$ in., so $C = 2\pi r = 2\pi(3) = 6\pi$ in. Therefore, by the Arc Length Conjecture, the length of $\overset{\frown}{CD}$ is $\frac{2}{9}C = \frac{2}{9}(6\pi) = \frac{4\pi}{3}$ in.

2. 8π m. $m\overset{\frown}{EF} = 120°$, so $\overset{\frown}{EF}$ is $\frac{120}{360} = \frac{1}{3}$ of the circumference. $r = 12$ m, so $C = 2\pi(12) = 24\pi$ m. Therefore, the length of $\overset{\frown}{EF} = \frac{1}{3}C = \frac{1}{3}(24\pi) = 8\pi$ m.

3. 14π cm. $m\overset{\frown}{GB} = 150°$, so $m\overset{\frown}{BIG} = 360° - 150° = 210°$, and $\overset{\frown}{BIG}$ is $\frac{210}{360} = \frac{7}{12}$ of the circumference. $r = 12$ cm, so $C = 24\pi$ cm, and the length of $\overset{\frown}{BIG} = \frac{7}{12}(24\pi) = 14\pi$ cm.

4. 9 m. $m\overset{\frown}{AB} = 120°$, so $\overset{\frown}{AB}$ is $\frac{1}{3}$ of the circumference. Use the Arc Length Conjecture to find the radius.

$$6\pi = \frac{1}{3}C$$
$$6\pi = \frac{1}{3}(2\pi r)$$
$$18\pi = 2\pi r$$
$$r = 9 \text{ m}$$

5. 6π ft. By the Inscribed Angle Conjecture, $m\overset{\frown}{RT} = 2(30°) = 60°$, so $\overset{\frown}{RT}$ is $\frac{60}{360} = \frac{1}{6}$ of the circumference. $C = 2\pi r = 2\pi(18) = 36\pi$ ft. Therefore, the length of $\overset{\frown}{RT}$ is $\frac{1}{6}(36\pi) = 6\pi$ ft.

6. 4π m. $\overline{CO}$ is a diameter of the circle, so $\overset{\frown}{CSO}$ is a semicircle, and $m\overset{\frown}{SO} = 180° - 100° = 80°$. $C = 2\pi r = 18\pi$ m. Therefore, the length of $\overset{\frown}{SO}$ is $\frac{80}{360}(18\pi) = \frac{2}{9}(18\pi) = 4\pi$ m.

7. 27 in. $\angle TAV$ is an inscribed angle, so $m\overset{\frown}{TV} = 2(80°) = 160°$ by the Inscribed Angle Conjecture, and $\overset{\frown}{TV}$ is $\frac{160}{360} = \frac{4}{9}$ of the circumference. Use the Arc Length Conjecture to find the diameter.

$$12\pi = \frac{4}{9}C$$
$$12\pi = \frac{4}{9}(\pi d)$$
$$108\pi = 4\pi d$$
$$d = 27 \text{ in.}$$

8. 100 cm. By the Parallel Lines Intercepted Arcs Conjecture, $m\overset{\frown}{CE} = m\overset{\frown}{AR}$, so $2m\overset{\frown}{AR} + 146° + 70° = 360°$. Therefore, $2m\overset{\frown}{AR} = 144°$, and $m\overset{\frown}{AR} = 72°$, so $\overset{\frown}{AR}$ is $\frac{72}{360} = \frac{1}{5}$ of the circumference. Use the Arc Length Conjecture to find the radius.

$$40\pi = \frac{1}{5}(2\pi r)$$
$$200\pi = 2\pi r$$
$$r = 100 \text{ cm}$$

9. 217 m/min. Sketch the racetrack.

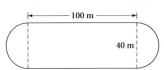

To make one complete lap around the track, a go-cart must cover two straightaways and two semicircles. The circumference of the two semicircles is the same as the circumference of one circle with a diameter of 40 m. Thus, the length of one complete lap is $2(100) + 40\pi = (200 + 40\pi)$ m. The go-cart covers four laps in 6 minutes. Find its speed:

$$\text{speed} = \frac{\text{distance}}{\text{time}} = \frac{4(200 + 40\pi) \text{ m}}{6 \text{ min}} \approx 217 \text{ m/min}$$

10. ≈ 4200 mi. Because $\frac{15 \text{ min}}{90 \text{ min}} = \frac{1}{6}$, Polly has made $\frac{1}{6}$ of a trip around Earth during her lunch. The distance along the equator over which she has passed is $\frac{1}{6}$ of the circumference of Earth, or $\frac{1}{6}(8000\pi) \approx 4200$ miles.

11. The desks are about 17 m from the center. Use the Arc Length Conjecture.

$$12 = \frac{1}{9}C$$
$$12 = \frac{1}{9}(2\pi r)$$
$$108 = 2\pi r$$
$$r \approx 17 \text{ m}$$

About four desks will fit because an arc with one-half the radius and the same central angle will be one-half as long as the outer arc.

12. 25,000 mi. The measure of the central angle is 7.2° because of the Corresponding Angles Conjecture. Therefore, $500 = \frac{7.2}{360} \cdot C$. So, according to this method, $C = 25,000$, that is, the circumference of Earth is about 25,000 mi.

13. 18°/s. No, the angular velocity is the same at every point on the carousel.

$$\text{angular velocity} = \frac{360°}{20 \text{ s}} = 18°/\text{s}.$$

14. Outer horse ≈ 2.5 m/s, inner horse ≈ 1.9 m/s. One horse has traveled farther in the same amount of time (tangential velocity), but both horses have

rotated the same number of times (angular velocity).

Calculation of tangential velocities:

Outer horse:

$C = 2\pi r = 2\pi(8) = 16\pi$ m

tangential velocity $= \dfrac{\text{distance along circular path}}{\text{time}}$

$= \dfrac{16\pi \text{ m}}{20 \text{ s}} \approx 2.5$ m/s

Inner horse:

$C = 2\pi r = 2\pi(6) = 12\pi$ m

tangential velocity $= \dfrac{\text{distance along circular path}}{\text{time}}$

$= \dfrac{12\pi \text{ m}}{20 \text{ s}} \approx 1.9$ m/s

15. $a = 50°$, $b = 75°$, $x = 25°$; $z = 45°$; $y = 35°$. Conjecture: The measure of the angle formed by an intersecting tangent and secant to a circle is one-half the difference of the larger intercepted arc measure and the smaller intercepted arc measure.

First diagram: By the Inscribed Angle Conjecture, $a = m\angle CAB = 50°$. The measure of the angle formed by the intersection of a tangent and chord at the point of tangency is half the measure of the intercepted arc (Tangent-Chord Conjecture), so $b = 75°$. By the Triangle Exterior Angle Conjecture, $b = x + a$, so $x = b - a = 75° - 50° = 25°$.

Second diagram: Let $a = m\angle PAB$ and b be the measure of the exterior angle of $\triangle PAB$ formed by $\overline{BA}$ and tangent $\overleftrightarrow{PB}$. By the Inscribed Angle Conjecture, $a = 25°$, and by the Tangent-Chord Conjecture, $b = 70°$. By the Triangle Exterior Angle Conjecture, $b = y + a$, so $y = b - a = 70° - 25° = 45°$.

Third diagram: Again, let $a = m\angle PAB$ and b be the measure of the exterior angle of $\triangle PAB$ formed by $\overline{BA}$ and tangent $\overleftrightarrow{PB}$. By the Inscribed Angle Conjecture, $a = 40°$, and by the Tangent-Chord Conjecture, $b = 75°$. By the Triangle Exterior Angle Conjecture, $b = y + a$, so $y = b - a = 75° - 40° = 35°$.

16. Let z represent the measure of the exterior angle of $\triangle PBA$ formed by $\overline{BA}$ and tangent $\overleftrightarrow{PB}$. By the Tangent-Chord Conjecture, $z = \frac{1}{2}m\widehat{AB}$. By the Inscribed Angle Conjecture, $m\angle BAP = \frac{1}{2}m\widehat{BC}$. By the Triangle Exterior Angle Conjecture, $z = m\angle BPA + m\angle BAP$, or $m\angle BPA = z - m\angle BAP$. By substitution, $m\angle BPA = \frac{1}{2}m\widehat{AB} - \frac{1}{2}m\widehat{BC}$. Using the Distributive Property, $m\angle BPA = \frac{1}{2}(m\widehat{AB} - m\widehat{BC})$.

17. $a = 70°$, $b = 110°$, $c = 110°$, $d = 70°$, $e = 20°$, $f = 20°$, $g = 90°$, $h = 70°$, $k = 20°$, $m = 20°$, $n = 20°$, $p = 140°$, $r = 80°$, $s = 100°$, $t = 80°$,

and $u = 120°$. First, $a = 180° - 110° = 70°$ (Linear Pair Conjecture). The segment on the left between the two parallel lines is the midsegment of a trapezoid, so it is parallel to the bases of the trapezoid (Trapezoid Midsegment Conjecture). Therefore, $b = 110°$ and $c = 110°$ (CA Conjecture). Also, by the CA Conjecture, $d = a$, so $d = 70°$. Next look at the right triangle in the lower left. The acute angles of this triangle have measures d and e, so $e = 90° - d = 20°$. $f = 20°$ (Vertical Angles Conjecture). Now look at the large isosceles triangle in which f and k are the measures of the base angles. The figure shows the median to the base of this triangle. In an isosceles triangle, the median to the base is also an altitude, so $g = 90°$. f and h are the measures of the acute angles of a right triangle, so $h = 90° - f = 70°$. Also, $k = f$ (Isosceles Triangle Conjecture), so $k = 20°$. Next, by the AIA Conjecture, $m = k$, so $m = 20°$, and $n = f$, so $n = 20°$. By the Triangle Sum Conjecture, $m + n + p = 180°$, so $p = 180° - 2(20°) = 140°$. Now $e + 2r = 180°$, so $2r = 160°$, and $r = 80°$. Now look at the trapezoid in which c and s are opposite angles. (You know that this is a trapezoid from the Trapezoid Midsegment Conjecture.) By the Trapezoid Consecutive Angles Conjecture, $s = 180° - r = 100°$. By the CA Conjecture, $t = r$, so $t = 80°$. Finally, look at the small triangle at the top of the figure in which all three angles are unmarked. In this triangle, the lower left angle forms a linear pair with the angle of measure t, so its measure is $180° - t = 100°$, and the lower right angle is the vertical angle of the angle of measure m, so its measure is $20°$. The angle with measure u is an exterior angle of this triangle, with its remote interior angles being the two angles whose measures have just been found. Therefore, by the Triangle Exterior Angle Conjecture, $u = 100° + 20° = 120°$.

18. The overlaid figure consists of two pairs of congruent equilateral triangles. The length of a side in the smaller pair is half the length of a side in the larger pair. All of the arcs use the lengths of the sides of the triangles as radii. Possible construction:

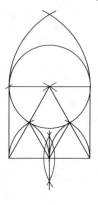

19. 170°. Sketch the clock at 10:20, and observe the position of the hands.

From 10:00 to 10:20, the minute hand has moved from the 12 to the 4, while the hour hand has moved $\frac{1}{3}$ of the way from the 10 to the 11 (because 20 min $= \frac{1}{3}$ hr), which is $\frac{1}{3}\left(\frac{1}{12}\right) = \frac{1}{36}$ of the way around the clock. Because $\frac{1}{36}(360°) = 10°$, this corresponds to an arc or a central angle of 10°. If the hands were at exactly 10 and 4, the angle between them would be 180°, but because the hour hand has moved 10° closer to the minute hand, the angle between the hands is $180° - 10° = 170°$.

20. $y = -\frac{8}{15}x + \frac{289}{15}$. Because $\overline{PA}$ is a radius and $\overleftrightarrow{AT}$ is a tangent to the circle, $\overleftrightarrow{AT}$ is the line perpendicular to $\overline{PA}$ and passing through the point $A(8, 15)$ (Tangent Conjecture). The slope of $\overline{PA}$ is $\frac{15}{8}$, so the slope of $\overleftrightarrow{AT}$ is the opposite reciprocal of $\frac{15}{8}$, which is $-\frac{8}{15}$. Find the equation of the line through $(8, 15)$ with slope $-\frac{8}{15}$:

$$\frac{y - 15}{x - 8} = \frac{-8}{15}$$
$$15(y - 15) = -8(x - 8)$$
$$15y - 225 = -8x + 64$$
$$15y = -8x + 289$$
$$y = -\frac{8}{15}x + \frac{289}{15}$$

21. 45°. Look at the angles in quadrilateral $PAQC$. $\angle CQA$ is a central angle that intercepts $\overarc{CA}$, so $m\angle CQA = m\overarc{CA} = 78°$ (definition of arc measure). $\overline{QA} \perp \overleftrightarrow{PA}$ (Tangent Conjecture), so $m\angle QAP = 90°$. In order to find $m\angle PCQ$, it is necessary to find some other angle measures. First, $\angle BQA$ is a central angle that intercepts $\overarc{BA}$, so $m\angle BQA = m\overarc{BA} = 168°$. Then $m\angle BQC + 168° + 78° = 360°$ (sum of angle measures around a point), so $m\angle BQC = 114°$. Now look at $\triangle BQC$: $\overline{BQ} \cong \overline{CQ}$ because all radii of a circle are congruent, so $\triangle BQC$ is isosceles, with vertex angle BQC. Then $2m\angle BCQ + 114° = 180°$, so $2m\angle BCQ = 66°$, and $m\angle BCQ = 33°$. Therefore, $m\angle PCQ = 180° - 33° = 147°$ (Linear Pair Conjecture). Now apply the Quadrilateral Sum Conjecture to $PAQC$ to find $m\angle P$: $m\angle P + 147° + 78° + 90° = 360°$, so $m\angle P = 45°$.

22. Case 1: 8π cm; Case 2: 8π cm; Case 3: 8π cm; Case 10: 8π cm. By the Circumference Conjecture, the circumference of a circle is given by the formula $C = 2\pi r$, so the circumference of a semicircle with radius r is πr. The table summarizes the results.

Case number	Diameter of each bump	Length of each bump	Number of bumps	Sum of lengths of bumps
1	16	8π	1	8π
2	8	4π	2	8π
3	4	2π	4	8π

Notice that each time you go from one case to the next, the diameter and therefore circumference of each bump is halved, while the number of bumps is doubled, so their product, which is the sum of the lengths of the bumps, remains constant at 8π cm. Therefore, for Case 10, the sum of the lengths of the bumps would also be 8π cm.

23. 6. Make an orderly list of the routes, and then count them. The routes are $\overline{RA}$ to $\overline{AL}$ to $\overline{LG}$, $\overline{RA}$ to $\overline{AN}$ to $\overline{NG}$, $\overline{RE}$ to $\overline{EC}$ to $\overline{CG}$, $\overline{RE}$ to $\overline{EN}$ to $\overline{NG}$, $\overline{RT}$ to $\overline{TC}$ to $\overline{CG}$, and $\overline{RT}$ to $\overline{TL}$ to $\overline{LG}$.

24. Yes, as long as the three points are noncollinear. Possible answer: Connect the points with segments, then find the point of concurrency of the perpendicular bisectors (same as circumcenter construction).

PROJECT

Project should satisfy the following criteria:

- A detailed drawing is included with lengths labeled.

- The track will have straightaways with lengths of about 320 meters.

- The runner in the inner lane starts at the finish line.

- Assumptions about the width of the lanes are stated.

- If the lanes are 1 meter wide, the runner in the outer lane will start about 18.8 meters ahead of the runner in the inner lane.

- Complete explanations of all the factors used in the calculations are given.

EXTENSION

Assuming the angle is measured in degrees, students' findings should confirm the Arc Length Conjecture. That is, the length of the arc is given by the measure of the arc divided by 360°, times the circumference.

EXERCISES

1. Possible answer: The Inscribed Angle Conjecture is very important because several other conjectures build on it, and it can be used in many different situations.

2. Possible answers:

   With compass and straightedge: Draw two nonparallel chords, and construct their perpendicular bisectors. The intersection of their perpendicular bisectors is the center of the circle.

   With patty paper: Fold the paper along a diameter so that two semicircles coincide. Repeat with a different diameter. The center is the intersection of the two folds.

   With the right-angled corner of a carpenter's square: Place the corner in the circle so that it is an inscribed right angle. Trace the sides of the corner. Use the square to construct the hypotenuse of the right triangle (which is the diameter of the circle). Repeat. The center is the intersection of the two diameters.

3. The velocity vector is always perpendicular to the radius at the point of tangency to the object's circular path.

4. Sample answer: An arc measure is between 0° and 360°. An arc length is proportional to arc measure and depends on the radius of the circle.

5. 55°. Draw the radius to the point of tangency. By the Tangent Conjecture, the radius is perpendicular to the tangent, so a right triangle has been formed. Therefore the measure of the central angle that intercepts the arc of measure b is $90° - 35° = 55°$, so $b = 55°$ by the definition of the measure of an arc.

6. 65°. The 110° angle is an inscribed angle that intercepts an arc of measure $a + 155°$, so by the Inscribed Angle Conjecture, $110° = \frac{1}{2}(a + 155°)$; $220° = a + 155°$, and $a = 65°$.

7. 128°. Congruent chords intercept congruent arcs (Chord Arcs Conjecture), so the unmarked arc has measure c. Then $2c + 104° = 360°$, so $2c = 256°$, and $c = 128°$.

8. 118°. First find the measure of either of the two vertical angles that form a linear pair with the angle of measure e. The measure of an angle formed by two intersecting chords is half the sum of the measures of the intercepted arcs (Intersecting Chords Conjecture), so the measure of either one of these angles is $\frac{1}{2}(60° + 64°) = 62°$. Then $e = 180° - 62°$ (Linear Pair Conjecture), so $e = 118°$.

9. 91°. The angle marked as a right angle intercepts a semicircle and is therefore inscribed in the opposite semicircle, so $d + 89° = 180°$, and $d = 91°$. (You could also use the Cyclic Quadrilateral Conjecture to see that the angle opposite the marked right angle is the supplement of a right angle, and therefore, it is also a right angle. Then the intercepted arc of this right angle must measure 180°, so $d + 89° = 180°$.)

10. 66°. Look at either of the angles that form a linear pair with the 88° angle. The supplement of an 88° angle is a 92° angle. Because the measure of an angle formed by two intersecting chords is one-half the sum of the measures of their intercepted arcs (Intersecting Chords Conjecture), $92° = \frac{1}{2}(f + 118°)$, so $184° = f + 118°$, and $f = 66°$.

11. 125.7 cm. $C = 2\pi r = 2\pi(20) \approx 125.7$ cm.

12. 42.0 cm. $C = \pi d$, so $132 = \pi d$, and $d = \frac{132}{\pi} \approx 42.0$ cm.

13. 15π cm. $m\widehat{AB} = 100°$ (Chord Arcs Conjecture), so by the Arc Length Conjecture, the length of $\widehat{AB}$ is $\frac{100°}{360°}C = \frac{5}{18}(2\pi \cdot 27) = 15\pi$ cm.

14. 14π ft. By the Intersecting Secants Conjecture, $50° = \frac{1}{2}(m\widehat{DL} - 60°)$, so $100° = m\widehat{DL} - 60°$, and $m\widehat{DL} = 160°$. By the Chord Arcs Conjecture, $m\widehat{CD} = m\widehat{OL}$, so $2m\widehat{CD} + 160° + 60° = 360°$. Then $2m\widehat{CD} = 140°$, and $m\widehat{CD} = 70°$. Now apply the Arc Length Conjecture. The length of $\widehat{CD}$ is $\frac{70°}{360°}C = \frac{7}{36}(2\pi \cdot 36 \text{ ft}) = 14\pi$ ft.

15. Look at the inscribed angles with measures 57° and 35°. By the Inscribed Angle Conjecture, the sum of the measures of their intercepted arcs is $2(57°) + 2(35°) = 184°$. However, the sum of these two arcs is a semicircle, and the measure of a semicircle is 180°, so this is impossible.

   Another way to look at this is to add the angle measures in the triangle. The third angle of the triangle must be a right angle because it is inscribed in a semicircle (Angles Inscribed in a Semicircle Conjecture). Therefore, the sum of the three angles of the triangle would be $57° + 35° + 90° = 182°$, which is impossible by the Triangle Sum Conjecture.

16. By the Parallel Lines Intercepted Arcs Conjecture, the unmarked arc measures 56°. Then the sum of the arcs would be $84° + 56° + 56° + 158° = 354°$, but this is impossible because the sum of the measures of the arcs of a circle must be 360°.

17. $m\angle EKL = \frac{1}{2}m\widehat{EL} = \frac{1}{2}(180° - 108°) = 36° = m\angle KLY$. Therefore, $\overline{KE} \parallel \overline{YL}$ by the Converse of the Parallel Lines Conjecture.

18. $m\widehat{JI} = 360° − 56° − 152° = 152° = m\widehat{MI}$. Therefore, $m\angle J = m\angle M$ (Inscribed Angles Intercepting Arcs Conjecture), and $\triangle JIM$ is isosceles by the Converse of the Isosceles Triangle Conjecture.

19. $m\widehat{KIM} = 2m\angle KEM = 140°$. Then $m\widehat{KI} = 140° − 70° = 70° = m\widehat{MI}$. Therefore, $m\angle IKM = \frac{1}{2}m\widehat{MI} = \frac{1}{2}m\widehat{KI} = m\angle IMK$, so $\angle IKM \cong \angle IMK$. So, $\triangle KIM$ is isosceles by the Converse of the Isosceles Triangle Conjecture.

20. Ertha can trace the incomplete circle on paper. She can lay the corner of the pad on the circle to trace an inscribed right angle. Then Ertha should mark the endpoints of the intercepted arc and use the pad to construct the hypotenuse of the right triangle, which is the diameter of the circle.

21. Sample answer: Construct perpendicular bisectors of two sides of the triangle. The point at which they intersect (the circumcenter) is the center of the circle. The distance from the circumcenter to each vertex is the radius.

22. Sample answer: Construct the incenter (from the angle bisectors) of the triangle. From the incenter, which is the center of the circle, construct a perpendicular to a side. The distance from the incenter to the foot of the perpendicular is the radius.

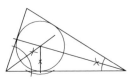

23. Sample answer: Construct a right angle, and label the vertex R. Mark off $\overline{RE}$ and $\overline{RT}$ with any lengths. From point E, swing an arc with radius RT. From point T, swing an arc with radius RE. Label the intersection of the arcs as C. Construct the diagonals $\overline{ET}$ and $\overline{RC}$. Their intersection is the center of the circumscribed circle. The circle's radius is the distance from the center to a vertex. It is not possible to construct the inscribed circle unless the rectangle is a square.

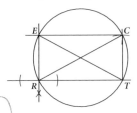

24. Sample answer: Construct acute angle R. Mark off equal lengths RM and RH. From points M and H, swing arcs of lengths equal to RM and RH. Label

the intersection of the arcs as O. Construct $RHOM$. The intersection of the diagonals is the center of the inscribed circle. Construct a perpendicular to a side to find the radius. It is not possible to construct the circumscribed circle unless the rhombus is a square.

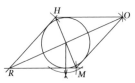

25. $4x + 3y = 32$ or $y = −\frac{4}{3}x + \frac{32}{3}$. A tangent is perpendicular to a radius drawn to the point of tangency (Tangent Conjecture). Here, the slope of the radius to the point of tangency is $\frac{4−1}{5−1} = \frac{3}{4}$, so the slope of the tangent is the opposite reciprocal of $\frac{3}{4}$, which is $−\frac{4}{3}$. The tangent is the line with slope $−\frac{4}{3}$ passing through $(5, 4)$. Find an equation for this line.

$$\frac{y − 4}{x − 5} = −\frac{4}{3} = \frac{−4}{3}$$

$$3(y − 4) = −4(x − 5)$$

$$3y − 12 = −4x + 20$$

$$4x + 3y = 32$$

or

$$3y = −4x + 32$$

$$y = −\frac{4}{3}x + \frac{32}{3}$$

26. $(−3, 2)$. This is equivalent to finding the circumcenter of the triangle with the three given points as vertices. For reference, label the three points as $A(−7, 5)$, $B(0, 6)$, and $C(1, −1)$. Draw the triangle on a coordinate grid.

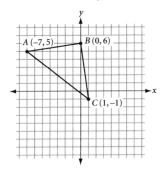

It appears from the drawing that $\triangle ABC$ is a right triangle with $\angle B$ as the right angle. Verify this by finding slopes of the two sides of $\angle B$: Slope $\overline{AB} = \frac{6 − 5}{0 − (−7)} = \frac{1}{7}$, and slope $\overline{BC} = \frac{−1 − 6}{1 − 0} = \frac{−7}{1} = −7$. Therefore, $\overline{AB} \perp \overline{BC}$, so $\angle B$ is a right angle, and $\overline{AC}$ is the hypotenuse of the right triangle. Thus, the circumcenter of the triangle (or the center of the circle) is the midpoint of $\overline{AC}$, which has coordinates $\left(\frac{-7+1}{2}, \frac{5+(-1)}{2}\right) = (-3, 2)$.

Note: You could also use the more general method of finding equations of two perpendicular bisectors of the triangle and then finding their intersection by solving a system of equations. The method shown above is a shortcut that works for right triangles only.

27. ≈ 0.318 m. Use the formula $C = \pi d$ to find the diameter of a circle whose circumference (one revolution) is 1 m: $1 = \pi d$, so $d = \frac{1}{\pi}$ m ≈ 0.318 m.

28. Melanie: 151 m/min or 9 km/h; Melody: 94 m/min or 6 km/h. For Melanie, the radius is 8 m, so the circumference (or length of one revolution) is 16π m, and for Melody, the radius is 5 m, so the circumference is 10π m.

The merry-go-round makes 30 revolutions in 10 minutes, or 3 revolutions/minute. Find the average speeds for Melanie and Melody in kilometers per hour.

Melanie:

$$\text{speed} = \frac{\text{distance}}{\text{time}} = \frac{3C}{1 \text{ min}}$$
$$= \frac{3(16\pi \text{ m})}{1 \text{ min}} \approx 151 \text{ m/min}$$
$$= \frac{3(16\pi \text{ m})}{1 \text{ min}} \cdot \frac{60 \text{ min}}{1 \text{ h}} \cdot \frac{0.001 \text{ km}}{1 \text{ m}}$$
$$\approx 9 \text{ km/h}$$

Melody:

$$\text{speed} = \frac{\text{distance}}{\text{time}} = \frac{3C}{1 \text{ min}}$$
$$= \frac{3(10\pi \text{ m})}{1 \text{ min}} \approx 94 \text{ m/min}$$
$$= \frac{3(10\pi \text{ m})}{1 \text{ min}} \cdot \frac{60 \text{ min}}{1 \text{ h}} \cdot \frac{0.001 \text{ km}}{1 \text{ m}}$$
$$\approx 6 \text{ km/h}$$

29. $\frac{2\pi(6357)}{360 \cdot 60} \approx 1.849 < 1.852 < 1.855 \approx \frac{2\pi(6378)}{360 \cdot 60}$

30.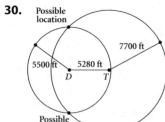

31. $\frac{200}{\pi}$ ft ≈ 63.7 ft. The circumference of the table is $100(2) = 200$ ft. Use the formula $C = \pi d$ to find the diameter of the table: $d = \frac{C}{\pi} = \frac{200}{\pi} \approx 63.7$ ft.

32. 8π m ≈ 25.1 m. Use the formula $C = 2\pi r$. If the radius of the moat is 10 m, the circumference

would be 20π m, whereas if the radius is 6 m, the circumference would be 12π m. Therefore, the larger moat's circumference should have been $20\pi - 12\pi = 8\pi$ m ≈ 25.1 m greater.

33. 12 cm. The circumference of the base of the cone will be the length of the arc of the sector shown in the figure. The circumference of the original circle is $2\pi(45) = 90\pi$ cm, so the length of the arc is $\frac{48}{360}C = \frac{2}{15}(90\pi) = 12\pi$ cm, and the diameter of the base is 12 cm.

34. False. Any obtuse isosceles triangle is a counter-example, such as a triangle with angles of measures 20°, 20°, and 140°.

35. True

36. False

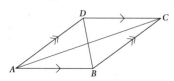

37. True   **38.** True   **39.** True   **40.** True

41. False. $(7 - 2) \cdot 180° = 900°$, so it could have seven sides.

42. False. The sum of the measures of any triangle is 180°.

43. False. The sum of the measures of one set of exterior angles for any polygon is 360°. The sum of the measures of the interior angles of a triangle is 180° and of a quadrilateral is 360°. Neither is greater than 360°, so these are two counterexamples.

44. False. The consecutive angles between the bases are supplementary.

45. False. $48° + 48° + 132° \neq 180°$.

46. False. Inscribed angles that intercept the same arc are congruent.

47. False. The measure of an inscribed angle is half the measure of the arc.

48. True

49. False. $\overline{AC}$ and $\overline{BD}$ bisect each other, but $\overline{AC}$ is not perpendicular to $\overline{BD}$.

50. False. It could be isosceles. (Remember that an equilateral triangle is a special kind of isosceles triangle.)

51. False. $100° + 100° + 100° + 60° = 360°$.

Discovering Geometry Solutions Manual
©2008 Key Curriculum Press

52. False. $\overset{\frown}{AB} \not\cong \overset{\frown}{CD}$

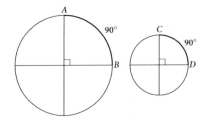

53. False. The ratio of the circumference to the diameter is π.

54. False. $24 + 24 + 48 + 48 \neq 96$.

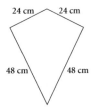

55. True

56. This is a paradox. All but seven of the statements in Exercises 34–55 are false. What about the statement in Exercise 56? If it is true, then all but eight of the statements in Exercises 34–56 will be true, which would make the statement in Exercise 56 false. And if the statement in Exercise 56 is false, then all but seven of the statements in Exercises 34–56 are false, so the statement in Exercise 56 is true.

57. $a = 58°$, $b = 61°$, $c = 58°$, $d = 122°$, $e = 58°$, $f = 64°$, $g = 116°$, $h = 52°$, $i = 64°$, $k = 64°$, $l = 105°$, $m = 105°$, $n = 105°$, $p = 75°$, $q = 116°$, $r = 90°$, $s = 58°$, $t = 122°$, $u = 105°$, $v = 75°$, $w = 61°$, $x = 29°$, and $y = 151°$. First, $a = 58°$ (Vertical Angles Conjecture). Then $2b + 58° = 180°$, so $b = 61°$. Next, $c = 58°$ (CA Conjecture), and $d = 180° - c$ (Linear Pair Conjecture), so $d = 122°$. Also, $e = c$ (Vertical Angles Conjecture), so $e = 58°$. Next, $f = 180° - 116°$ (Linear Pair Conjecture), so $f = 64°$, and $g = 116°$ (Vertical Angles Conjecture).

Next look at the isosceles triangle in which the vertex angle has measure h. Each of the base angles of this triangle measures $64°$ because one of these angles is the vertical angle of the angle with measure f. Then $h + 2(64°) = 180°$, so $h = 52°$, and $i = 64°$ (CA Conjecture), using the $64°$ angle in the upper left of the isosceles triangle. Next, $h + i + k = 180°$, so $k = 64°$. Now, $l = 180° - 75°$ (Linear Pair Conjecture), so $l = 105°$. Then $m = l$ (AIA Conjecture), so $m = 105°$, $n = l$ (CA Conjecture), so $n = 105°$, and $p = 75°$ (Vertical Angles Conjecture). Also, $q = g$ (CA Conjecture), so $q = 116°$, and $r = 180° - 90°$ (Linear Pair Conjecture), so $r = 90°$.

Next, $s = c$ (CA Conjecture), so $s = 58°$, and $t = d$ (CA Conjecture), so $t = 122°$. Now $u = n$ (CA Conjecture), so $u = 105°$, and $v = 75°$ (CA Conjecture). Also, $w = b$ (CA Conjecture), so $w = 61°$. Now look at the right triangle with an acute angle of measure w. The other acute angle in this triangle measures $90° - w = 90° - 61° = 29°$, so $x = 29°$ (AIA Conjecture). Finally, $y = 180° - 29°$ (Linear Pair Conjecture), so $y = 151°$.

58. $\triangle TAR \cong \triangle YRA$ by SAS; $\triangle TAE \cong \triangle YRE$ by ASA

59. $\triangle FTO \cong \triangle YTO$ by SAA, SAS, or SSS; $\triangle FLO \cong \triangle YLO$ by SAA, SAS, or SSS; $\triangle FTL \cong \triangle YTL$ by SSS, SAS, or SAA

60. $\triangle PTR \cong \triangle ART$ by SAS; $\triangle TPA \cong \triangle RAP$ by SAS, SAA, or ASA; $\triangle TLP \cong \triangle RLA$ by SAA or ASA

61. ASA

62. $m\overset{\frown}{AC} = 84°$, length of $\overset{\frown}{AC} = 11.2\pi$ in. or about 35.2 in. By the Inscribed Angle Conjecture, $m\overset{\frown}{AC} = 2m\angle ABC = 2(42°) = 84°$. $\overset{\frown}{AC}$ is $\frac{84}{360} = \frac{7}{30}$ of the circumference, and $C = 2\pi r = 2\pi(24) = 48\pi$ in. Therefore, the length of $\overset{\frown}{AC}$ is $\frac{7}{30}C = \frac{7}{30}(48\pi) = 11.2\pi$ in. ≈ 35.2 in.

63. $x = 63°$, $y = 27°$, $w = 126°$. Let O be the center of the circle. Look at the angles in quadrilateral $ECOD$, which is a kite. Angles ECO and EDO are right angles (Tangent Conjecture), so $54° + 90° + w + 90° = 360°$ (Quadrilateral Sum Conjecture), and thus $w = 126°$. The angle with measure w is the central angle that intercepts $\overset{\frown}{CD}$, so $m\overset{\frown}{CD} = 126°$ (definition of the measure of an arc). Then $x = \frac{1}{2}(m\overset{\frown}{CD})$ (Inscribed Angle Conjecture), so $x = 63°$. Now look at $\triangle AOB$. $\overline{AB} \cong \overline{CD}$ (given) and $\overline{OA} \cong \overline{OB} \cong \overline{OC} \cong \overline{OD}$ (radii of same circle.) Therefore, $\triangle AOB \cong \triangle COD$ by SSS, so $\angle AOB \cong \angle COD$ by CPCTC, and therefore $m\angle AOB = w = 126°$. $\triangle AOB$ is isosceles, so $126° + 2y = 180°$. Therefore, $2y = 54°$, and $y = 27°$.

64. Sample answer:

65. $f(n) = 9 - 4n$; -71. Notice that as n increases by 1, $f(n)$ decreases by 4, so the function rule must involve subtracting 4 n times to get the nth term. To find the number from which $4n$ is subtracted (call this number a), look at the first term: $f(1) = 5 = a - 4(1)$, so $a = 9$. Therefore, the function rule is $f(n) = 9 - 4n$. Now use this rule to find the 20th term: $f(20) = 9 - 4(20) = 9 - 80 = -71$.

66. a. The circle with its contents has 3-fold rotational symmetry; the entire tile does not.

b. No, it does not have reflectional symmetry.

67. Possible construction: Draw a segment for the width. Construct two perpendiculars at the endpoints of this segment. Mark off the width twice along each perpendicular to get the lengths. Connect the last two vertices to form the rectangle.

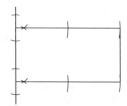

68. 9.375 cm. Sketch the situation described in the exercise.

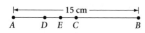

From the figure, you can see that $EC = \frac{1}{8}(AB)$ and $CB = \frac{1}{2}(AB)$. Then $EB = EC + CB = \frac{1}{8}(AB) + \frac{1}{2}(AB) = \frac{5}{8}(AB) = \frac{5}{8}(15) = 9.375$ cm.

69.

70.

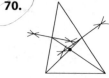

TAKE ANOTHER LOOK

1. $\angle EAN$ and $\angle EGN$ are right angles because the Tangent Conjecture says that a tangent is perpendicular to the radius. $\overline{EA} \cong \overline{EG}$ because all radii in a circle are congruent. Because point E is equidistant from the sides of $\angle ANG$, the converse of the Angle Bisector Conjecture says that $\angle ANE \cong \angle GNE$. Therefore, $\triangle ANE \cong \triangle GNE$ by SAA, so $\overline{AN} \cong \overline{GN}$ by CPCTC. Thus, the tangent segments are congruent.

2. Sample answer: The quadrilateral is a kite because $\overline{EA} \cong \overline{EG}$ (all radii in a circle are congruent) and $\overline{AN} \cong \overline{GN}$ (Tangent Segments Conjecture).

3. The converse of the conjecture "If a quadrilateral is inscribed in a circle, then its opposite angles are supplementary" is "If the opposite angles of a quadrilateral are supplementary, then the quadrilateral can be inscribed in a circle." To show that this is true, for quadrilateral $ABCD$, draw a circle containing A, B, and C, and show D is also on the circle. You know $m\widehat{ABC} + m\widehat{AC} = 360°$, $m\angle B + m\angle D = 180°$, and $m\angle B = \frac{1}{2}m\widehat{AC}$. Combining these equations, you get the result $m\widehat{ABC} = 2m\angle D$. This is true only if D is on the circle.

4. Rectangles and squares are always cyclic because their opposite angles are right angles and thus are supplementary. An isosceles trapezoid is always cyclic.

In isosceles trapezoid *PART*, $\angle A$ and $\angle R$ are consecutive interior angles and therefore supplementary. $\angle R$ and $\angle T$ are base angles and therefore congruent. Thus, opposite angles A and T are supplementary. A rhombus has opposite angles congruent, so any rhombus inscribed in a circle is a square. A kite is cyclic only if its nonvertex angles are right angles.

5. Possible answer: $y = a + bx$; thus $C = 0 + 3.1d$, or $C = 3.1d$. This confirms the Circumference Conjecture.

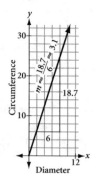

6. Construct circle O and point P outside the circle. Construct segment $\overline{OP}$ and its midpoint. Then construct a semicircle with $\overline{OP}$ as its diameter. Let T be the intersection of the semicircle and O, and construct $\overrightarrow{PT}$. If you were to construct $\angle OTP$, then by the Angles Inscribed in a Semicircle Conjecture, $\angle T$ would be a right angle. Therefore, by the converse of the Tangent Conjecture, $\overrightarrow{PT}$ is tangent to the circle.

7. Start with the fact that $m\widehat{SN} = m\widehat{ST} + m\widehat{TN}$. By the Parallel Lines Intercepted Arcs Conjecture, $\widehat{EA} \cong \widehat{ST}$, hence $m\widehat{EA} = m\widehat{ST}$. Use substitution in the first equation to obtain $m\widehat{SN} = m\widehat{EA} + m\widehat{TN}$, or $m\widehat{TN} = m\widehat{SN} - m\widehat{EA}$. By the Inscribed Angle Conjecture and the definition of arc measure, $m\angle TAN = \frac{1}{2}m\widehat{TN}$. $m\angle C = m\angle TAN$ by the Corresponding Angles Conjecture, so by substitution, $m\angle C = \frac{1}{2}m\widehat{TN} = \frac{1}{2}(m\widehat{SN} - m\widehat{EA})$.

CHAPTER 7

LESSON 7.1

EXERCISES

1. Rigid. The size and shape do not change.

2. Nonrigid. The shape changes.

3. Nonrigid. The size changes.

4. 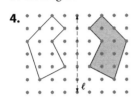 **5.**

6.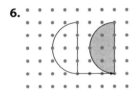

7. Possible answer: a boat moving across the water

8. Possible answer: a Ferris wheel

9. a. Sample answer: Fold the paper so that the images coincide, and crease.

b. Construct a segment that connects two corresponding points. Construct the perpendicular bisector of that segment.

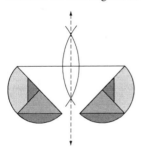

10. a. Extend the three horizontal segments onto the other side of the reflection line. Use your compass to measure lengths of segments and distances from the reflection line.

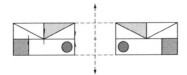

b.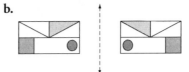

11.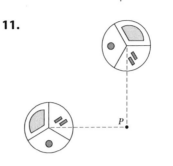

12. Reflectional symmetry

13. 4-fold rotational and reflectional symmetry

14. Reflectional symmetry

15. 7-fold symmetry: Possible answers are F or J. 9-fold symmetry: Possible answers are E or H. Basket K has 3-fold rotational symmetry, but not reflectional symmetry.

16.

Number of sides of regular polygon	3	4	5	6	7	8	n
Number of reflectional symmetries	3	4	5	6	7	8	n
Number of rotational symmetries ($\leq 360°$)	3	4	5	6	7	8	n

A regular polygon of n sides has n reflectional symmetries and n rotational symmetries.

17. Notice that each figure is made up of a capital letter attached to its "mirror image" (reflection across a vertical line). Because the letters are in alphabetical order starting with C, the next two figures will use the letters H and I.

18. The capital letters are in alphabetical order, and their position moves clockwise through the four small squares. Also, the placement of the letter is rotated 90° clockwise each time. Therefore, the next two figures will have F placed like B, and G placed like C. The circle that is divided into four parts is always opposite the letter, and the quarter that is shaded moves clockwise through four positions, so the circle for F is the same as that for B, and the circle for G is the same as that for C.

19. $P(-a, b)$, $Q(-a, -b)$, $R(a, -b)$. A rectangle has 2-fold reflectional symmetry. In this case, the y-axis and the x-axis are the lines of symmetry. The reflection of $S(a, b)$ across the y-axis is $P(-a, b)$, the reflection of $P(-a, b)$ across the x-axis is $Q(-a, -b)$, and the reflection of $Q(-a, -b)$ across the y-axis is $R(a, -b)$. Notice that you can also find the coordinates of R by considering it as the reflection of S across the x-axis.

20. Compass-and-straightedge construction: Place your compass point at one endpoint of the arc, and draw an arc with a radius that is greater than half the length of the original arc. Repeat, using the other endpoint as center and the same radius. Use your straightedge to draw a segment connecting the two points of intersection of the arcs you have drawn. The point where this segment intersects the original arc is P. Possible construction:

Patty-paper construction: Fold the patty paper so that the two endpoints of the arc coincide, and crease. The point where the crease intersects the arc is P, the midpoint of the arc.

Fold

21. 50th figure: 154 (50 shaded, 104 unshaded); nth figure: $n + 2(n + 2)$, or $3n + 4$ (n shaded, $2(n + 2)$ unshaded). Find patterns for the number of shaded circles and for the number of unshaded circles, and then add to find the total number of circles. Shaded circles: 1 in the first figure, 2 in the second figure, 3 in the third figure, so there are n shaded circles in the nth figure. Unshaded circles: 6 in the first figure, 8 in the second figure, 10 in the third figure, so there is always an even number of unshaded circles. Notice that $6 = 2(3)$, $8 = 2(4)$, $10 = 2(5)$, so there are $2(n + 2)$ unshaded circles in the nth figure. Then the total number of circles in the nth figure is $n + 2(n + 2)$, which can also be written as $3n + 4$. By substituting 50 for n in this expression, you can find the total number of circles in the 50th figure: $3n + 4 = 3(50) + 4 = 154$.

22. 46. Use the Tangent Segments Conjecture and subtraction to find the lengths of all the tangent segments that aren't given. $HI = HM$, so $HI = 4$. $SI = ST$, so $SI = 5$. $WT = WS - ST = 11 - 5 = 6$. $WE = WT$, so $WE = 6$. $OE = WO - WE = 14 - 6 = 8$. $OM = OE$, so $OM = 8$. Therefore, the perimeter of $SHOW = SW + WO + OH + HS = 11 + 14 + 12 + 9 = 46$.

23. From the given information, $\angle 1 \cong \angle 2$. Also, by the Vertical Angles Conjecture, $\angle 2 \cong \angle 3$. Therefore, $\angle 1 \cong \angle 3$. Segment DC is congruent to itself. $\angle DCE$ and $\angle DCB$ are both right angles, so they are congruent. Therefore, $\triangle DCB \cong \triangle DCE$ by ASA, and $\overline{BC} \cong \overline{CE}$ by CPCTC.

IMPROVING YOUR ALGEBRA SKILLS

Using the formula for factoring differences of squares, $a^2 - b^2 = (a - b)(a + b)$, in the case where $a - b = 1$ gives $a^2 - b^2 = (a - b)(a + b) = a + b$, so you can find $a^2 - b^2$ by adding a and b. You can also use the fact that the base numbers are consecutive, so $a = b + 1$, and substitute into the expression $a^2 - b^2$ to get $(b + 1)^2 - b^2 = b^2 + 2b + 1 - b^2 = 2b + 1 = (b + 1) + b = a + b$.

Another explanation uses a picture:

The quantity $a + b$ represents $a(1) + b(1)$, the sum of the areas of the rectangles between the perimeters of the two squares.

EXTENSIONS

A. Research and discussions results will vary.

B. Any number x and the number formed by rotating x 180° are both in the same 2-by-2 corner square.

96	11	89	68
88	69	91	16
61	86	18	99
19	98	66	81

LESSON 7.2

EXERCISES

1. Translation. $x + 5$ means "move right 5 units." Every point of the polygon moves right 5 units. Find the image of each vertex of the given triangle, and then connect the image points to form the translated triangle.

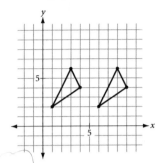

2. Reflection. By the Coordinate Transformations Conjecture, this is a reflection across the *x*-axis.

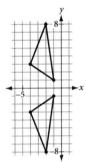

3. Reflection. By the Coordinate Transformations Conjecture, this is a reflection across the line *y* = *x*.

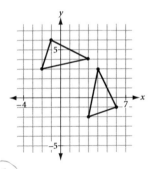

4. Reflection. Use the given rule to find the image of each vertex of the given quadrilateral, and then connect these image points to form the translated quadrilateral. The image of (2, 1) is (6, 1), the image of (6, 2) is (2, 2), the image of (5, 5) is (3, 5), and the image of (3, 4) is (5, 4).

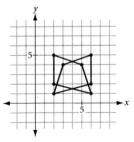

From this drawing, you can see that the transformation is a reflection across the vertical line *x* = 4. If you look at this transformation as −*x* + 8, you can see that this is a combination of a reflection across the *y*-axis followed by a translation right 8 units. For example, the reflection across the *y*-axis moves (2, 1) to (−2, 1), and then translation right 8 units moves this point to (6, 1).

5. Rotation. Use the given rule to find the image of each vertex of the original triangle, and then connect these image points to form the transformed triangle. The image of (−3, 1) is (3, −1), the image of (4, 3) is (−4, −3), and the image of (−1, −3) is (1, 3). The figure shows that the triangle has been rotated.

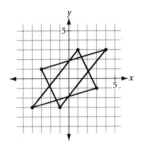

6. Rules that involve either *x* or *y* changing signs, or *x* and *y* switching places, produce reflections. If both *x* and *y* change signs, the rule produces a rotation. Rules that involve a constant being added to the *x* and/or *y* terms produce translations. The translation vector for Exercise 1 is ⟨5, 0⟩.

7. (*x*, *y*) → (*x*, −*y*). Compare the ordered pairs for *V* and *V'*, *R* and *R'*, and *Y* and *Y'*. In each case, the *x*-coordinates of the original point and its image are the same, whereas the *y*-coordinates of the original point and its image are opposites. Use this information to write the rule. This is a reflection across the *x*-axis. (You can also simply observe from the figure that the transformation is a reflection across the *x*-axis and use the Coordinate Transformations Conjecture to find the rule.)

8. (*x*, *y*) → (−*x*, −*y*). Compare the ordered pairs for *D* and *D'*, *H* and *H'*, and *R* and *R'*. In each case, the *x*-coordinates of the original point and its image are opposites, and the *y*-coordinates of the original point and its image are opposites. Use this information to write the rule. This is a rotation about the origin. (You can also simply observe from the figure that the transformation is a rotation about the origin and use the Coordinate Transformations Conjecture to find the rule.)

9.

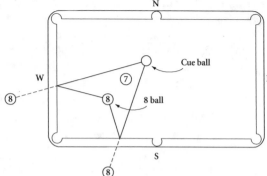

10. There are two possible points, one on the W wall and one on the N wall.

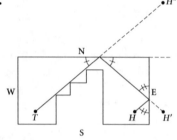

11.

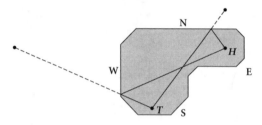

12. Possible answer: Use the Minimal Path Conjecture to draw $\overline{AB'}$ and find intersection point C.

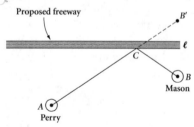

13. Notice that each figure is made up of a numeral attached to its "mirror image" (reflection across a vertical line), with the mirror image directly to the left of the numeral. Because the numerals are in increasing order, the next two figures will use the numerals 6 and 7.

14. The numbers in the corner square are the odd integers starting with 1, so the next two figures will

contain 11 and 13. Also, the numerals that form these odd integers are reflected in the following order after the first figure: reflection across vertical line (down center of figure), reflection across horizontal line (through center of figure), reflection across vertical line, and reflection across horizontal line to return to the original position. Therefore, in the fifth figure, 11 will be oriented like 3 in the second figure, and in the sixth figure, 13 will be oriented like 5 in the third figure. Also, the small square opposite the square containing the number is either shaded (in odd-numbered figures of the sequence) or contains a dot in the center of the square (in even-numbered figures of the sequence.) Therefore, the fifth figure will contain a dot in the lower left corner (like the second figure), and the sixth figure will have the upper-left corner square shaded (like the third figure).

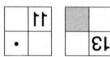

15. Possible answer: HIKED. There are many other possible answers. Some of these (with fewer than five letters) are HEED, HIDE, COD, DIED, BIKE, and DICE. Any words all of whose letters are on the following list will work: B, C, D, E, H, I, K, O, and X. These are all the letters that have a horizontal line of symmetry.

16. One unless it is equilateral, in which case it has three.

17. Two unless it is a square, in which case it has four.

18. This is the "mirror image" of the message that appears in the mirror:

YOUR TEE
SHIRT IS
INSIDE
OUT

19. Draw a diameter of the circle. Draw two radii that form noncongruent acute angles with the diameter, and reflect them across the diameter. Construct the lines perpendicular to the radii at the points where the radii intersect the circle. Each of these perpendicular lines is tangent to the circle (Tangent Conjecture). Extend the four tangent lines until they meet to form a quadrilateral. By the Tangent Segments Conjecture and addition, this quadrilateral has two pairs of adjacent congruent sides, so it is a kite.

Sample construction:

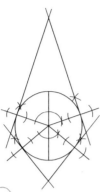

20. Pick a point on the circle and construct a tangent through it. Choose a point on the tangent: this will be one vertex of your rhombus. Draw a line through this point and the center of the circle. This is one diagonal of the rhombus. Construct another diameter perpendicular to the first one, and extend it outside the circle in both directions. This is the other diagonal. Mark the point where this line intersects the tangent line: This is the second vertex of the rhombus. Copy this length three times to construct the other three sides of the rhombus. (The other vertices are the intersections of this length and the diagonals.)

Sample construction:

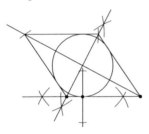

21. False. Possible counterexample: a trapezoid with two right angles.

22. False. Possible counterexample: an isosceles trapezoid.

IMPROVING YOUR REASONING SKILLS

Alphabet v. The third vowel of the alphabet is i, the second consonant after i is k, and the third letter before k is h. The twenty-sixth word of the puzzle is *the*, which contains the letter h. The fortieth word of the puzzle is *alphabet*. The twenty-second letter of the alphabet is v. Therefore, v should be printed directly after *alphabet*.

EXTENSIONS

A. Sample answer: Rules such as $(x, y) \rightarrow (3x, 3y)$, $(x, y) \rightarrow (-2x, -2y)$, $(x, y) \rightarrow \left(\frac{1}{2}x, \frac{1}{2}y\right)$, $(x, y) \rightarrow$

$(-x, 2y)$, and $(x, y) \rightarrow (2x, 3y)$ create nonrigid transformations. Either x or y or both x and y must be multiplied by constants other than 1 or -1. The same constant or different constants can be used as multipliers for x and y.

B. The minimal path on a sphere is an arc of a great circle. Minimal paths on the lateral (curved) surface of a cylinder are lines (parallel to the axis of the cylinder), circles (perpendicular to the axis), and helixes. All of these, including the helix, can be found by unwrapping the lateral surface and laying it flat, and connecting two endpoints with a straight line. Minimal paths on the ends of the cylinder are lines, and minimal paths connecting points on the ends of the cylinder with points on the curved surface would vary.

C. H, I, O, and X are the only letters that typically have both reflectional and rotational symmetry, so a word with both types of symmetry would have to use only these letters and also be a palindrome. There aren't many; an example would be OHO.

LESSON 7.3

EXERCISES

1. $\langle 10, 10 \rangle$. The single translation can be represented by the rule $(x, y) \rightarrow (x + 2 - 5 + 13, y + 3 + 7 + 0)$, or $(x, y) \rightarrow (x + 10, y + 10)$. This is a translation by $\langle 10, 10 \rangle$.

2. A 180° rotation. If the centers of rotation differ, rotate 180° and add a translation. If the center is the same for all the rotations, simply add the angles of rotation: $45° + 50° + 85° = 180°$.

Now consider the case in which the centers of rotation differ. Example: Draw right triangle ABC on a coordinate grid. (In this figure, $m\angle A = 30°$, $m\angle B = 90°$, and $m\angle C = 60°$.) All of the rotations are assumed to be counterclockwise because the direction of rotation is not specified. Rotate the triangle three times, using a different center of rotation each time. First rotate 45° counterclockwise through B. Label the new triangle as $\triangle A'B'C'$, where $B' = B$. Now rotate $\triangle A'B'C'$ 50° clockwise through A'. Label the new triangle as $\triangle A''B''C''$, where $A'' = A'$. Finally, rotate $\triangle A''B''C''$ 85° counterclockwise through C''. Label the new triangle as $\triangle A'''B'''C'''$, where $C''' = C''$. Compare the final triangle, $\triangle A'''B'''C'''$, to the original, $\triangle ABC$. You will notice that the original triangle has been rotated 180° and also translated from its original position.

In this case, the translation is to the right and upward.

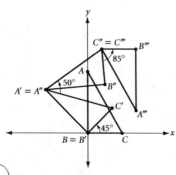

3. a. 20 cm. Use the Reflections across Parallel Lines Conjecture. The distance between the parallel lines is 10 cm, so $AA' = 20$ cm.

   b. 20 cm, but in the opposite direction. See the figure below. A' is the first image (after A is reflected across n), and A'' is the second image (after A' is reflected across m).

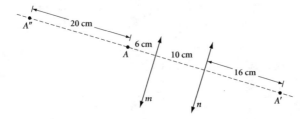

4. a. 80° counterclockwise. Use the Reflections across Intersecting Lines Conjecture.

   b. 80° clockwise. Here, B' is the reflection of B across line n, and B'' is the reflection of B' across line m. (You can find the images under these reflections by measuring, by using the Reflection Line Conjecture, or by folding patty paper on line m and then line n.) To find the angle of rotation (with center P) that rotates the second image, B'', back to B, draw $\overline{PB}$ and $\overline{PB''}$; then use a protractor to find that $m\angle B''PB = 80°$. From the figure, you can see that the rotation that rotates B'' back to B is 80° clockwise.

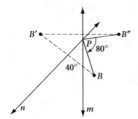

5. 180°. Fold the patty paper on $\overrightarrow{AP}$ and crease. Draw the image of the figure. Then fold the patty paper

on $\overrightarrow{AL}$, and crease again. Draw the image of the first image.

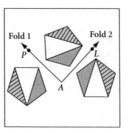

Notice that the final result is equivalent to rotating the original figure 180°. Because $m\angle PAL = 90°$, this result is consistent with the Reflections across Intersecting Lines Conjecture. (Because 180° is half the total angle measure of a circle, the results of clockwise and counterclockwise rotations of 180° are the same, so it is not necessary to specify the direction of rotation when the angle of rotation is 180°.)

6. About 3 cm. By the Reflections across Parallel Lines Conjecture, the length of the equivalent translation vector is twice the distance between the parallel lines. In the figure in your book, the distance between $\overrightarrow{PA}$ and $\overrightarrow{RL}$ is about 1.5 cm, so the length of the translation vector will be about 3 cm, which you can confirm by measuring the distance between corresponding points on the original figure and the image after two translations.

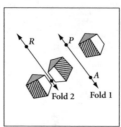

7. Connect a pair of corresponding points. Construct two perpendiculars to the segment connecting these points, with half the distance between the two given figures between them. There are many possible positions for the lines that will work, but the distance between them must be half the distance between corresponding points on the two figures.

Possible answer:

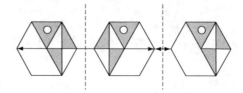

Discovering Geometry Solutions Manual
©2008 Key Curriculum Press

8. Possible answer:

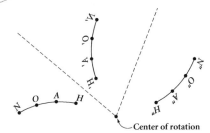

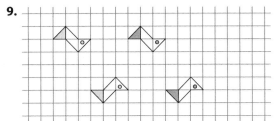

Center of rotation

Using segments to connect any point (for instance *N*) on the original figure to the center of rotation and then to its image (in this case *N'*) gives the angle of rotation. Bisecting this angle by folding the patty paper gives a half angle. This half angle can be duplicated anywhere between the original figure and its image, with its vertex at the center of rotation. The two rays can then be used as lines of reflection.

9.

10. Two reflections about intersecting lines yield a rotation. The measure of the angle of rotation is twice the measure of the angle between the lines of reflection, or twice 90°, which is 180°.

11. Answers may vary. Possible answer: reflection across the figure's horizontal axis and 60° clockwise rotation.

12. The letters that appear in the corners are every other capital letter in alphabetical order. In the first five figures, the letters are A, C, E, G, I, so the next two figures will contain K and M. Notice that the letters move counterclockwise through the four squares and also rotate through four different orientations. Therefore, in the sixth figure, K will be placed the same way that C is in the second figure, and in the seventh figure, M will be placed the same way as E is in the third figure. The numbers that appear in the squares are even numbers in order, starting with 2, so the sixth figure will contain 12 (positioned like 4 in the second figure) and the seventh figure will contain 14 (positioned like 6 in the third figure). Also, the shaded triangles and shaded sectors of circles in the sixth figure will match those in the second figure, while those in the seventh figure will match those in the third figure.

13. Notice that each figure is made up of a capital letter and reflections of that letter through a horizontal line, a vertical line, and both the horizontal and vertical lines. The figures shown use the letters A, B, C, D, and E in alphabetical order, so the next two figures will use F and G in the same way.

14. Sample answer: Draw a figure on an overhead transparency, and then project the image onto a screen.

15. Possible answers: rotational: playing card, ceiling fan, propeller blade; reflectional: human body, backpack

16. One: yes; two: no; three: yes. An isosceles triangle that is not equilateral (that is, a triangle with *exactly* two congruent sides) has exactly one line of symmetry, while an equilateral triangle has three lines of symmetry.

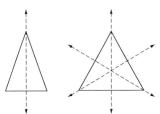

17. Label the two points *A* and *B*. Draw $\overline{AB}$. Find the midpoint of $\overline{AB}$, and label it *O*. Connect *O* to one of the endpoints (either *A* or *B*) with a curve. Copy the curve onto patty paper and rotate it about *O* to form the other half of the curve. Possible answer:

18. Each entry of the resulting matrix is the sum of the corresponding entries in the original matrices.

a. $\begin{bmatrix} -9 & 0 \\ 12 & -7 \end{bmatrix}$

b. $\begin{bmatrix} a + a & b + 2b & c + 3c \\ d + (-d) & e + (d - e) & f + 0 \end{bmatrix}$

$= \begin{bmatrix} 2a & 3b & 4c \\ 0 & d & f \end{bmatrix}$

IMPROVING YOUR VISUAL THINKING SKILLS

EXERCISES

1. Answers will vary. Possible answers include floor, ceiling, and wall tilings, and a checkerboard.

2. Answers will vary.

3. $3^3.4^2$. Each vertex is surrounded by three equilateral triangles and then two squares.

4. $3^4.6$. Each vertex is surrounded by four equilateral triangles and then one regular hexagon.

5. $3^2.4.3.4$. Each vertex is surrounded by two equilateral triangles, then a square, then another equilateral triangle, and then another square.

6. $3.4.6.4/3.4^2.6$. One type of vertex is surrounded by an equilateral triangle, then a square, then a regular hexagon, and then another square. The other type of vertex is surrounded by an equilateral triangle, two squares, and a regular hexagon.

7. $3^3.4^2/3^2.4.3.4$. One type of vertex is surrounded by three equilateral triangles and then two squares. The other type is surrounded by two equilateral triangles, then a square, then another equilateral triangle, and then another square.

8. $3^6/3^2.4.12$. One type of vertex is surrounded by six equilateral triangles. The other kind is surrounded by two equilateral triangles, then a square, then a regular dodecagon.

9. a. The dual of a square tessellation is a square tessellation.

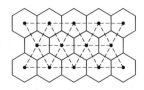

b. The dual of a hexagon tessellation is a triangle tessellation.

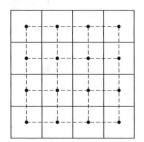

c. If tessellation A is the dual of tessellation B, then tessellation B is the dual of tessellation A.

10. The dual is a $3^4/3^8$ tessellation of isosceles right triangles.

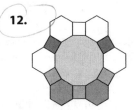

11.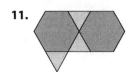

12.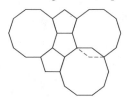

13. A ring of ten pentagons fits around a decagon, and another decagon can fit into any two of the pentagons. However, if two decagons fit into pairs of pentagons that share a common pentagon, then the decagons overlap.

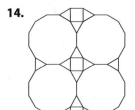

14.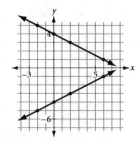

15. Answers will vary.

16. $y = -\frac{1}{2}x + 4$. From the graph, you can see that the reflected line has y-intercept 4 and slope $-\frac{1}{2}$, so its equation is $y = -\frac{1}{2}x + 4$.

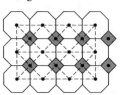

17. Possible answers: TOT, AHA. To fit the criteria, all the letters in the word need to have a vertical line of symmetry themselves or be the mirror image of another letter. The following list will work: A, H, I, M, O, T, U, V, W, X, and Y. These are all the letters that have a vertical line of symmetry.

There are no uppercase letters that are each other's reflections, but there are lowercase letters that are:

b and d, and p and q. (Note that b and p, and d and q, are each other's reflections across a horizontal line.)

18. Work backward. Reflect a point of the 8-ball across the S cushion. Then reflect this image across the N cushion. Aim at this second image.

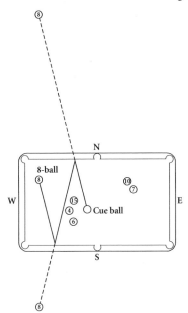

IMPROVING YOUR VISUAL THINKING SKILLS

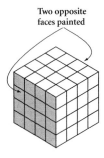

Two opposite faces painted

Inside every cube is a smaller cube with 2 fewer small cubes on each side; these will have no painted faces. The large cube has more than 3 cubes on each edge because 32 is more than $3^3 = 27$, and it doesn't have 6 cubes on each edge because then $4^3 = 64$ cubes in the middle would be completely unpainted. So, the only possibilities are that the large cube contain $4^3 = 64$ or $5^3 = 125$ small cubes.

In the latter case, there will be 27 small cubes, necessarily unpainted, in the interior, so the painting must avoid exactly 5 cubes in the outer layer. Even if only one face of the large cube is left unpainted, 9 cubes in the middle of that face will remain clear because the 16 cubes on the edges of that face will have paint on their other faces. So more than 32 small cubes altogether will be clear. Therefore, the large cube must be 4 by 4 by 4.

If one face of this large cube is painted, then 16 small cubes are painted on one face and 48 remain unpainted.

If two opposite faces are painted, then 32 small cubes are painted, so 32 remain unpainted.

Alternatively, you could consider the 8 interior cubes that are necessarily unpainted and see how to arrive at 24 unpainted small cubes in the outer layer.

LESSON 7.5

EXERCISES

1. Answers will vary.

2. To construct the dual tessellation, connect centers across the common side. The dual is a $5^3/5^4$ tessellation.

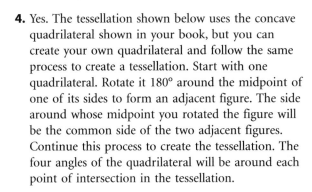

3.

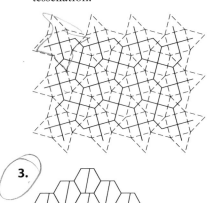

4. Yes. The tessellation shown below uses the concave quadrilateral shown in your book, but you can create your own quadrilateral and follow the same process to create a tessellation. Start with one quadrilateral. Rotate it 180° around the midpoint of one of its sides to form an adjacent figure. The side around whose midpoint you rotated the figure will be the common side of the two adjacent figures. Continue this process to create the tessellation. The four angles of the quadrilateral will be around each point of intersection in the tessellation.

You may find it helpful to draw one quadrilateral and then cut it out so that you can move it around and copy it in various positions. You may also find it helpful to label the sides, as in the figure below, to keep track of the location of each side of the original figure.

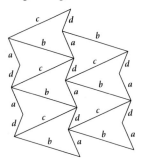

5. By the Triangle Sum Conjecture, $a + b + c = 180°$. Around each point, the sum of the angle measures is $2(a + b + c) = 2 \cdot 180° = 360°$. Therefore, a triangle will fill the plane edge-to-edge without gaps or overlaps. Thus, any triangle can be used to create monohedral tiling.

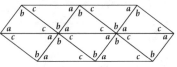

6. 3 ways

7.

8. $y = -2x + 3$. From the graph, you can see that the image line has y-intercept 3 and slope -2, so its equation is $y = -2x + 3$.

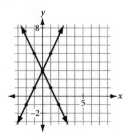

IMPROVING YOUR VISUAL THINKING SKILLS

There are several possible answers. Here is one answer for each of the two patterns.

1.

2.

PROJECT

Project should satisfy the following criteria:

• The tessellation has no gaps or overlaps.

• Dots are correctly placed so that the tiling is nonperiodic.

Extra credit

• Exceptional creativity and care are shown in the coloring.

EXTENSION

Research results will vary.

LESSON 7.6

EXERCISES

1. Answers will vary. You can add features to make this look like a bat.

2. Answers will vary. You can add an eye and feathers to make this look like a profile of a bird's head.

3. Answers will vary. You can add an eye and feathers to make this look like a profile of a bird.

4. Regular hexagons

5. Squares or parallelograms

6. Squares or parallelograms

7. Repeat the shape over and over so that the shapes fit together and fill the grid.

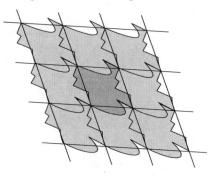

8. Repeat the shape over and over so that the shapes fit together and fill the grid.

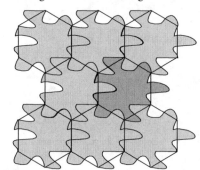

9. Answers will vary.

10. Answers will vary.

11.

12. $y = -\frac{2}{3}x - 3$. The lines have the same y-intercept and slopes of the opposite sign. Therefore, the image line has slope $-\frac{2}{3}$, and its equation is $y = -\frac{2}{3}x - 3$.

Discovering Geometry Solutions Manual
©2008 Key Curriculum Press

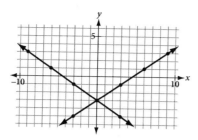

13. 3.4.6.4/4.6.12. One type of vertex is surrounded by an equilateral triangle, then a square, then a regular hexagon, and then another square. The other type of vertex is surrounded by a square, then a regular hexagon, and then a regular dodecagon.

14. $\dfrac{440 \text{ rev}}{1 \text{ min}} \cdot \dfrac{2\pi \cdot 28 \text{ ft}}{1 \text{ rev}} \cdot \dfrac{1 \text{ min}}{60 \text{ s}} \approx 1290 \text{ ft/s}$

15. a. True. Possible explanation: The kite diagonal between vertex angles is the perpendicular bisector of the other diagonal; in a square, diagonals bisect each other.

   b. False. It could be an isosceles trapezoid.

   c. False. It could be a rectangle.

   d. True. Parallel lines cut off congruent arcs of a circle, so inscribed angles (the base angles of the trapezoid) are congruent.

PROJECT

Project should satisfy the following criteria:

- A kaleidoscope is carefully constructed.

- The report shows an understanding of the relationship between angle measurement and the number of images created. A 60° angle shows six mirrors and five images, plus the original object; a 45° angle shows eight mirrors and the seven images, plus the original object.

EXTENSION

Tessellations will vary.

LESSON 7.7

EXERCISES

1. Equilateral triangles

2. Regular hexagons

3.

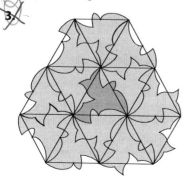

4.

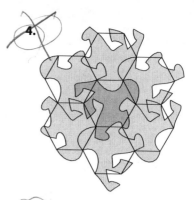

5. Answers will vary.

6. Answers will vary.

7. Sample design:

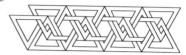

The first design by Roelofs actually uses two copies of a tessellation superimposed with a third, different tessellation. You might give extra credit if students match this feat.

8. False. If the diagonals of a quadrilateral bisect each other, the quadrilateral is a parallelogram. The diagonals of a parallelogram are congruent only if the quadrilateral is a rectangle.

9. True

10. True

11. False. Possible counterexamples: isosceles trapezoid, kite

12. Approximately 6280 miles, which will take 126 hours, or around $5\frac{1}{4}$ days.

13. a. By the Reflection Line Conjecture, the line of reflection is the perpendicular bisector of $\overline{AA'}$ and $\overline{BB'}$. Because these segments are both perpendicular to the reflection line, they are parallel to each other. Note that if $\overline{AB}$ is parallel to the reflection line, quadrilateral $AA'B'B$ will be a rectangle instead of a trapezoid.

   b. Yes. It has reflectional symmetry, so legs and base angles are congruent.

   c. Greatest: near each of the acute vertices; least: at the intersection of the diagonals (where both A, C, and B' become collinear and A', C, and B become collinear).

14. a.
$$\begin{bmatrix} 3 \cdot 8 + 5 \cdot 6 + -6 \cdot -9 & 3 \cdot 7 + 5 \cdot 0 + -6 \cdot 2 \\ 1 \cdot 8 + 0 \cdot 6 + 4 \cdot -9 & 1 \cdot 7 + 0 \cdot 0 + 4 \cdot 2 \end{bmatrix}$$
$$= \begin{bmatrix} 108 & 9 \\ -28 & 15 \end{bmatrix}$$

b. $\begin{bmatrix} 8 & 3 \\ 12 & -5 \end{bmatrix} \cdot \begin{bmatrix} 2 & 0 \\ -1 & 10 \end{bmatrix} = \begin{bmatrix} 13 & 30 \\ 29 & -50 \end{bmatrix}$. First

rewrite the equation with variables in the blank spaces. Then you can write equations to solve for the variables.

$$\begin{bmatrix} 8 & 3 \\ 12 & -5 \end{bmatrix} \cdot \begin{bmatrix} 2 & a \\ b & c \end{bmatrix} = \begin{bmatrix} 13 & 30 \\ d & -50 \end{bmatrix}$$

Multiply the first row of the first matrix by the first column of the second matrix to get $8 \cdot 2 + 3b = 13$, so $3b = -3$ and $b = -1$. Multiply the second row of the first matrix by the first column of the second matrix to get $12 \cdot 2 + -5b = d$. Substitute -1 for b in this equation to get $d = 24 + 5 = 29$. To find a and c, write a system of equations based on multiplying the first and second rows of the first matrix by the second column of the second matrix.

$$\begin{cases} 8a + 3c = 30 \\ 12a + -5c = -50 \end{cases}$$

Multiply the first equation by 3 and the second equation by -2, and then add them to eliminate a.

$$\begin{array}{r} 24a + 9c = 90 \\ -24a + 10c = 100 \\ \hline 19c = 190 \end{array}$$

Therefore, $c = 10$. Substitute 10 for c into the first equation in the system, and solve for a. $8a + 3 \cdot 10 = 30$, hence $8a = 0$ and $a = 0$. Now substitute all of the values for the variables in the original matrix equation to find the solution.

IMPROVING YOUR REASONING SKILLS

Here's a sample of the kind of reasoning required: Both Denise and Charles claim to be second, so at least one of them is lying; therefore, Kai must be either first or third. Kai claims to have been last and that Leyton was best; because Kai can't be last, Leyton was best.

Continue with this kind of reasoning. Frances claims that Kai was second; because Kai must be first or third, Frances was fourth. Leyton said that he was third, but you already know that he was best, so Charles was last. Charles claims that he came in second, but you know that he was last, so Kai was third. There is only one student, Denise, and one position, second, left, so Denise must be second. You can check this by checking Denise's statements: She claimed that Kai won, but you know that Kai was third, so Denise was second. From first to last, the order of finish was Leyton, Denise, Kai, Frances, and Charles.

EXERCISES

1. Parallelograms

2. Parallelograms

3.

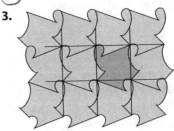

4.

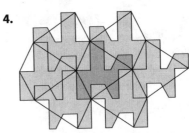

5. Answers will vary. Use a grid of kites like the one below. Notice that in this grid, rows of kites alternate between those with "long sides down" and those with "long sides up."

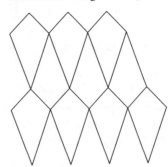

6. Answers will vary. Use a grid of parallelograms like the one in the example on page 411 in your book.

7. Circumcenter is (3, 4); orthocenter is (10, 8).

8.

9.

10.

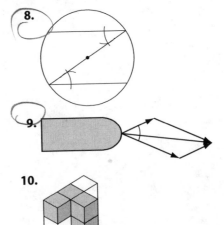

$x = \pm 15$. Apply the definitions of the two new functions: $a \triangle b = a^2 + b^2$ and $a \circ b = a^b$. $8 \triangle x = 8^2 + x^2$ and $17 \circ 2 = 17^2$. Therefore the equation $8 \triangle x = 17 \circ 2$ means $8^2 + x^2 = 17^2$. Then $64 + x^2 = 289$, so $x^2 = 225$, and $x = \pm 15$.

USING YOUR ALGEBRA SKILLS 7

EXERCISES

1. $y = -\frac{1}{6}x$. The median from R to $\overline{ES}$ is the segment whose endpoints are R and the midpoint of $\overline{ES}$. The midpoint of $\overline{ES}$ is $\left(\frac{4+8}{2}, \frac{-6+4}{2}\right) = (6, -1)$. To find the equation of the line through $R(0, 0)$ and $(6, -1)$, first find its slope: $\frac{-1-0}{6-0} = -\frac{1}{6}$. The line containing the median from R to $\overline{ES}$ goes through the origin, so its y-intercept is 0. Therefore, the equation of this line is $y = -\frac{1}{6}x$.

2. $y = -2x + 2$. First find the slope of $\overline{RS}$, and then use this slope to find the slope of the altitude from E to $\overline{RS}$. The slope of $\overline{RS}$ is $\frac{4-0}{8-0} = \frac{4}{8} = \frac{1}{2}$, so the slope of the altitude to $\overline{RS}$ is -2, the opposite reciprocal of $\frac{1}{2}$. Find the equation in the form $y = mx + b$ of the line through $E(4, -6)$ with slope -2.

$$\frac{y - (-6)}{x - 4} = -2$$
$$y + 6 = -2(x - 4)$$
$$y + 6 = -2x + 8$$
$$y = -2x + 2$$

3. Centroid is $\left(2, \frac{2}{3}\right)$; orthocenter is $(0, 5)$. There are two methods for finding the centroid.

Method 1: Find the equations of the lines containing two of the medians, and solve a system of equations to find their point of intersection, which will be the centroid.

Midpoint of $\overline{MO} = \left(\frac{-4 + 10}{2}, \frac{0 + (-3)}{2}\right)$
$$= \left(3, -\frac{3}{2}\right)$$

Find the equation of the line through $N(0, 5)$ and $\left(3, -\frac{3}{2}\right)$. The slope of this line is

$$\frac{5 - \left(-\frac{3}{2}\right)}{0 - 3} = \frac{\frac{13}{2}}{-3} = -\frac{13}{6}$$

Any line through $N(0, 5)$ has y-intercept 5, so an equation of the line containing the median from R to $\overline{RO}$ is $y = -\frac{13}{6}x + 5$.

Midpoint of $\overline{NO} = \left(\frac{0 + 10}{2}, \frac{5 + (-3)}{2}\right) = (5, 1)$

Find the equation of the line through $M(-4, 0)$ and $(5, 1)$. The slope of this line is $\frac{1 - 0}{5 - (-4)} = \frac{1}{9}$. Find the equation of the line passing through $(-4, 0)$ with slope $\frac{1}{9}$.

$$\frac{y - 0}{x - (-4)} = \frac{1}{9}$$
$$\frac{y}{x + 4} = \frac{1}{9}$$
$$9y = x + 4$$
$$y = \frac{1}{9}x + \frac{4}{9}$$

Solve the system formed by the equations of the line containing the two medians.

$$\begin{cases} y = \frac{1}{9}x + \frac{4}{9} \\ y = -\frac{13}{6}x + 5 \end{cases}$$

To eliminate fractions, multiply both sides of the first equation by 9 and both sides of the second equation by 6.

$$\begin{cases} 9y = x + 4 \\ 6y = -13x + 30 \end{cases}$$

To solve this system by substitution, solve the first equation for x; then substitute the resulting expression in the second equation and solve for y.

$$x = 9y - 4$$
$$6y = -13(9y - 4) + 30$$
$$6y = -117y + 52 + 30$$
$$123y = 82$$
$$y = \frac{82}{123} = \frac{2}{3}$$

Now substitute $\frac{2}{3}$ for y in the equation $x = 9y - 4$ and solve for x.

$$x = 9\left(\frac{2}{3}\right) - 4 = 2$$

Therefore, the coordinates of the centroid are $\left(2, \frac{2}{3}\right)$.

Method 2: Find the mean of the x-coordinates and the mean of the y-coordinates of the three vertices of the triangle.

The mean of the x-coordinates is $\frac{-4 + 0 + 10}{3} = 2$.

The mean of the y-coordinates is $\frac{0 + 5 + (-3)}{3} = \frac{2}{3}$.

Therefore, the coordinates of the centroid are $\left(2, \frac{2}{3}\right)$.

Now find the orthocenter. Because the legs of a right triangle are perpendicular to each other (to form the right angle), they are two of the altitudes of the triangle. This means that the orthocenter of a right triangle is the right-angle vertex. From the figure or by computing slopes, you can see that $\angle N$ is the right angle in $\triangle MON$. Therefore, the orthocenter is $N(0, 5)$.

4. Centroid is (4, 0); orthocenter is (3, 0). First use the means of the coordinates of the vertices of $\triangle CDE$ to find the centroid.

Mean of x-coordinates $= \dfrac{0 + 12 + 0}{3} = 4$

Mean of y-coordinates $= \dfrac{6 + 0 + (-6)}{3} = 0$

The centroid is (4, 0).

To find the orthocenter, find the equations of two of the altitudes of $\triangle CDE$, and then solve a system of equations to find their intersection.

In an isosceles triangle, the median to the base is also an altitude. The figure shows that the median from E to $\overline{CD}$ is the x-axis, which is the line $y = 0$. Now find an equation for the altitude from D to $\overline{CE}$. The slope of $\overline{CE}$ is $\frac{0-6}{12-0} = -\frac{1}{2}$, so the slope of the altitude to $\overline{CE}$ is 2, the opposite reciprocal of $-\frac{1}{2}$. The y-intercept of any line through $C(0, -6)$ is -6, so the equation of the altitude from D to $\overline{CE}$ is $y = 2x - 6$. To solve the system $\begin{cases} y = 2x - 6 \\ y = 0 \end{cases}$, substitute 0 for y in the first equation to get $0 = 2x - 6$, or $x = 3$. Therefore, the orthocenter is (3, 0).

5. $\left(1, \frac{4}{3}\right)$. Sketch the triangle and find the coordinates of its vertices. Graph the line $12x + 9y = 36$ by finding its intercepts: If $x = 0$, $y = 4$, so the y-intercept is 4. If $y = 0$, $x = 3$, so the x-intercept is 3.

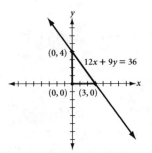

From the graph, you can see that the vertices of the triangle are (0, 0), (0, 4), and (3, 0). The mean of the x-coordinates is $\frac{0 + 3 + 0}{3} = 1$, and the mean of the y-coordinates is $\frac{4 + 0 + 0}{3} = \frac{4}{3}$. Therefore, the centroid of the triangle is $\left(1, \frac{4}{3}\right)$.

6. $(-1, -1)$. Find the vertices of the triangle by solving three systems of equations, each made up of two of the three equations. First solve the system formed by the first and second equations:
$$\begin{cases} 8x + 3y = 12 \\ 6y - 7x = 24 \end{cases}$$

To solve this system by elimination, rewrite the second equation as $-7x + 6y = 24$, multiply the first equation by 2, and then subtract one resulting equation from the other.

$$16x + 6y = 24$$
$$\underline{-7x + 6y = 24}$$
$$23x = 0$$
$$x = 0$$

Substitute 0 for x in the first original equation, and solve for y.

$$8(0) + 3y = 12$$
$$y = 4$$

One vertex is (0, 4).

Now solve the system formed by the first and third equations.

$$\begin{cases} 8x + 3y = 12 \\ x + 9y + 33 = 0 \end{cases}$$

Multiply the first equation by 3, and rewrite the second equation by subtracting 33 from both sides. Then one resulting equation from the other.

$$24x + 9y = 36$$
$$\underline{x + 9y = -33}$$
$$23x = 69$$
$$x = 3$$

Substitute 3 for x in the equation $x + 9y + 33 = 0$, and solve for y.

$$(3) + 9y + 33 = 0$$
$$9y = -36$$
$$y = -4$$

The second vertex is (3, -4).

Now solve the system formed by the second and third equations, with both of them rewritten in the same ways as before.

$$\begin{cases} -7x + 6y = 24 \\ x + 9y = -33 \end{cases}$$

Multiply the second equation by 7, and add the result to the first equation.

$$-7x + 6y = 24$$
$$\underline{7x + 63y = -231}$$
$$69y = -207$$
$$y = -3$$

Discovering Geometry Solutions Manual
©2008 Key Curriculum Press

Substitute -3 for y in the equation $x + 9y = -33$, and solve for x.

$$x + 9(-3) = -33$$
$$x - 27 = -33$$
$$x = -6$$

The third vertex is $(-6, -3)$.

Finally, use the coordinates of the three vertices, $(0, 4)$, $(3, -4)$, and $(-6, -3)$, to find the coordinates of the centroid.

$$\text{Mean of } x\text{-coordinates} = \frac{0 + 3 + (-6)}{3}$$
$$= \frac{-3}{3} = -1$$

$$\text{Mean of } y\text{-coordinates} = \frac{4 + (-4) + (-3)}{3}$$
$$= \frac{-3}{3} = -1$$

The centroid is $(-1, -1)$.

7. $(5, -8)$. Find equations for $\overleftrightarrow{AB}$ and $\overleftrightarrow{QB}$, and then find the coordinates of their intersection, which is point B.

Slope of $\overline{AP} = \dfrac{-2 - (-6)}{-3 - (-6)} = \dfrac{4}{3}$

Because $\overleftrightarrow{AB} \perp \overline{AP}$ (Tangent Conjecture), the slope of $\overleftrightarrow{AB}$ is $-\frac{3}{4}$. Find the equation in the form $y = mx + b$ of $\overleftrightarrow{AB}$, which is the line with slope $-\frac{3}{4}$ that passes through $A(-3, -2)$.

$$\frac{y - (-2)}{x - (-3)} = -\frac{3}{4}$$
$$\frac{y + 2}{x + 3} = \frac{-3}{4}$$
$$4(y + 2) = -3(x + 3)$$
$$4y + 8 = -3x - 9$$
$$4y = -3x - 17$$
$$y = -\frac{3}{4}x - \frac{17}{4}$$

$\overline{QB}$ and $\overline{PA}$ lie on parallel lines because both are perpendicular to $\overleftrightarrow{AB}$, so slope of $\overline{QB}$ = slope of $\overline{PA} = \frac{4}{3}$. Find the equation of $\overleftrightarrow{QB}$, which is the line with slope $\frac{4}{3}$ passing through $Q(11, 0)$.

$$\frac{y - 0}{x - 11} = \frac{4}{3}$$
$$3y = 4(x - 11)$$
$$3y = 4x - 44$$
$$y = \frac{4}{3}x - \frac{44}{3}$$

Now solve the system formed by the equations of $\overleftrightarrow{AB}$ and $\overleftrightarrow{QB}$.

$$\begin{cases} y = -\dfrac{3}{4}x - \dfrac{17}{4} \\ y = \dfrac{4}{3}x - \dfrac{44}{3} \end{cases}$$

Solve this system by substitution:

$$\frac{4}{3}x - \frac{44}{3} = -\frac{3}{4}x - \frac{17}{4}$$
$$12\left(\frac{4}{3}x - \frac{44}{3}\right) = 12\left(-\frac{3}{4}x - \frac{17}{4}\right)$$
$$16x - 176 = -9x - 51$$
$$25x = 125$$
$$x = 5$$

Substitute 5 for x in the first equation of the system.

$$y = -\frac{3}{4}(5) - \frac{17}{4} = -\frac{15}{4} - \frac{17}{4} = -\frac{32}{4} = -8$$

Therefore, B has coordinates $(5, -8)$.

CHAPTER 7 REVIEW

EXERCISES

1. True

2. True

3. True

4. True

5. True

6. True

7. False. A regular pentagon does not create a monohedral tessellation, whereas a regular hexagon does.

8. True

9. True

10. False. Several counterexamples are given in Lesson 7.5.

11. False. Any hexagon with one pair of opposite sides parallel and congruent will create a monohedral tessellation.

12. This statement can be either true or false. Among Exercises 1–11, 8 of the statements are true and 3 are false. If the statement in Exercise 12 is true, then there are 9 true and 3 false statements, so there are at least three times as many true statements as false ones. So, the statement in Exercise 12 is true. If the statement in Exercise 11 is false, then there are 8 true and 4 false statements, so there are not at least three times as many true statements as false ones. So, the statement in Exercise 11 is false. Therefore, if the statement is true, it's true, and if it's false, it's false.

13. 6-fold rotational symmetry

14. Translational symmetry

15. Reflectional. Color arrangements will vary, but the white candle must be in the middle. Notice that there is only one white candle, while there are two candles of each of the other colors. One way to make the colors symmetrical is to move the white candle to the middle, leave the four candles to the right of the middle where they are, and arrange the candles on the left in the following order (left to right): blue, pink, green, yellow.

16. The two towers are not the reflection (or even the translation) of each other. Each tower individually has bilateral symmetry. The center portion of the façade has bilateral symmetry.

Left tower   Center   Right tower

17. Answers will vary.

18. Answers will vary.

19. $3^6/3^2.4.3.4$; 2-uniform. One kind of vertex is surrounded by six equilateral triangles. The second kind is surrounded by two equilateral triangles, then a square, then an equilateral triangle, and then a square.

20. 4.8^2; semiregular. All vertices have the same arrangement. Each is surrounded by a square and two regular octagons.

21. $y = \frac{1}{2}x$. Make and label a diagram as shown.

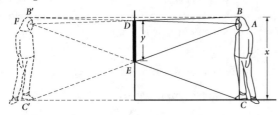

The minimal path from A (the person's eyes) to B (the top of her head), which are on the same side of line ℓ (the mirror), is found by reflecting point B across line ℓ, drawing $\overline{AB'}$, and then drawing $\overline{AD}$ and $\overline{DB}$, where D is the point of intersection of $\overline{AB'}$ and line ℓ. Likewise, reflect C, find intersection E, and draw $\overline{AE}$ and $\overline{EC}$ to find the minimal path from her eyes to B (her feet). Draw $\overline{AF} \parallel \overline{BB'} \parallel \overline{CC'}$, with F on

$\overline{B'C'}$. You can easily show that $BCC'B'$, $ABB'F$, and $ACC'F$ are rectangles. In rectangle $BCC'B'$, $\overline{B'C'} \cong \overline{BC}$. In rectangle $ABB'F$, diagonal $\overline{AB'}$ is bisected by diagonal $\overline{BF}$ (Rectangle Diagonals Conjecture), so $\overline{AD} \cong \overline{DB'}$. Similarly, in rectangle $ACC'F$, $\overline{AE} \cong \overline{EC'}$. Therefore, $\overline{DE}$ is the midsegment of $\triangle AB'C'$, so $DE = \frac{1}{2}B'C' = \frac{1}{2}BC$ by the Triangle Midsegment Conjecture.

22. Use the Minimal Path Conjecture. The path will involve three bounces. Start at the hole, and work backward from the hole. This problem is similar to Example B on pages 379–380 of your book, but here there are three bounces rather than two.

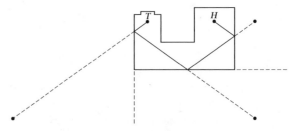

23. Use a grid of squares. Tessellate by translation.

24. Use a grid of equilateral triangles. Tessellate by rotation.

25. Use a grid of parallelograms. Tessellate by glide reflection.

26. Yes. It is a glide reflection for one pair of sides and midpoint rotation for the other two sides.

27. No. Because the shape is suitable for glide reflection, the rows of parallelograms should alternate the direction in which they lean (row 1 leans right, row 2 leans left, row 3 leans right, and so on).

28.

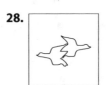

TAKE ANOTHER LOOK

1. There are eight different solutions.

Two solutions are N-W-S and S-W-N.

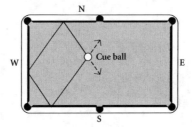

Two solutions are N-E-S and S-E-N.

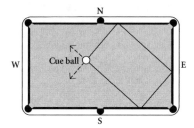

Two solutions are W-N-E and E-N-W.

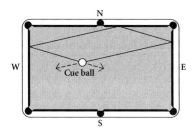

Two solutions are W-S-E and E-S-W.

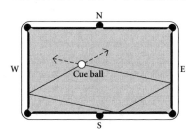

2. Answers will vary.

3. Answers will vary.

4. $\begin{bmatrix} 0 & 6 & 7 & 2 & 0 \\ 0 & 0 & 3 & 7 & 5 \end{bmatrix} + \begin{bmatrix} -5 & -5 & -5 & -5 & -5 \\ -3 & -3 & -3 & -3 & -3 \end{bmatrix}$

$= \begin{bmatrix} -5 & 1 & 2 & -3 & -5 \\ -3 & -3 & 0 & 4 & 2 \end{bmatrix}$

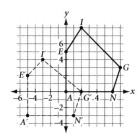

5. a. $\begin{bmatrix} 1 & 0 \\ 0 & -1 \end{bmatrix}\begin{bmatrix} -4 & -3 & 0 \\ 3 & 1 & 5 \end{bmatrix} = \begin{bmatrix} -4 & -3 & 0 \\ -3 & -1 & -5 \end{bmatrix}$

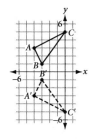

The transformation is a reflection across the *x*-axis.

b. $\begin{bmatrix} -1 & 0 \\ 0 & -1 \end{bmatrix}\begin{bmatrix} -4 & -3 & 0 \\ 3 & 1 & 5 \end{bmatrix} = \begin{bmatrix} 4 & 3 & 0 \\ -3 & -1 & -5 \end{bmatrix}$

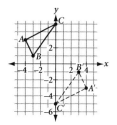

The transformation is a reflection across both the *x*-axis and *y*-axis, or a rotation by 180° clockwise or 180° counterclockwise about the origin.

c. $\begin{bmatrix} 0 & -1 \\ 1 & 0 \end{bmatrix}\begin{bmatrix} -4 & -3 & 0 \\ 3 & 1 & 5 \end{bmatrix} = \begin{bmatrix} -3 & -1 & -5 \\ -4 & -3 & 0 \end{bmatrix}$

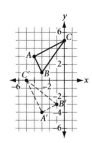

The transformation is a rotation by 90° counterclockwise about the origin or a rotation by 270° clockwise about the origin.

d. $\begin{bmatrix} 0 & 1 \\ -1 & 0 \end{bmatrix}\begin{bmatrix} -4 & -3 & 0 \\ 3 & 1 & 5 \end{bmatrix} = \begin{bmatrix} 3 & 1 & 5 \\ 4 & 3 & 0 \end{bmatrix}$

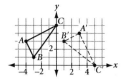

The transformation is a rotation by 90° clockwise about the origin or a rotation by 270° counterclockwise about the origin.

e. $\begin{bmatrix} 2 & 0 \\ 0 & 2 \end{bmatrix}\begin{bmatrix} -4 & -3 & 0 \\ 3 & 1 & 5 \end{bmatrix} = \begin{bmatrix} -8 & -6 & 0 \\ 6 & 2 & 10 \end{bmatrix}$

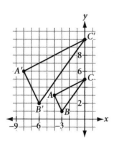

The image has sides that are twice as long. This is a nonrigid transformation.

CHAPTER 8

LESSON 8.1

EXERCISES

1. 228 m². Use the Rectangle Area Conjecture.
$A = bh = (19)(12) = 228$ m².

2. 41.85 cm². $A = bh = (9.3)(4.5) = 41.85$ cm².

3. 8 yd. $A = bh$, so 96 yd² $= b \cdot 12$. $\frac{96}{12} = 8$,
so $b = 8$ yd.

4. 21 cm. $A = bh$, so $273 = 13h$. $\frac{273}{13} = 21$,
so $h = 21$ cm.

5. 91 ft². First use the given perimeter and height
to find the length of the base. $P = 2b + 2h$,
so $40 = 2b + 2(7) = 2b + 14$. Therefore, $2b = 26$,
and $b = 13$ ft. Now use the length of the base and
the height to find the area of the rectangle:
$A = bh = (13)(7) = 91$ ft².

6. 182 m². The shaded area is the difference between
the area of the large rectangle, which has base
length 21 m and height 12 m, and the area of the
small (unshaded) rectangle, which has base length
$21 - 11 = 10$ m and height $12 - 5 = 7$ m. Then
the shaded area is $(21)(12) - (10)(7) = 252 - 70 = 182$ m².

7. 96 in.². Use the Parallelogram Area Conjecture.
$A = bh = (12)(8) = 96$ in².

8. 210 cm. First use the given area and height to find
the length of the base, and then use the length of
the base and the height to find the perimeter.

$$A = bh$$
$$2508 = b \cdot 44$$
$$b = 57$$
$$P = 2b + 2h$$
$$P = 2(57) + 2(48) = 210 \text{ cm}$$

9. $A = 42$ ft². The shaded region is one of two
congruent triangles that make up a parallelogram.
Area of shaded region $= \frac{1}{2}$(area of parallelogram)
$= \frac{1}{2}bh = \frac{1}{2}(12)(7) = 42$ ft².

10. Factor 48 in two different ways. For example,
$48 = 4 \cdot 12$ and $48 = 8 \cdot 6$. (Other factorizations
are possible.) Sample answer:

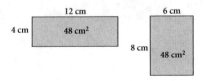

11. 3 square units. The shaded triangle is half of a
parallelogram with base length 3 units and height
2 units, so its area is $\frac{1}{2}(3)(2) = 3$ square units.

12. 10 square units. The shaded
triangle can be divided into two
right triangles, each of which is half
a rectangle.

Area of triangle on left $= \frac{1}{2}(3)(4) = 6$ square units

Area of triangle on right $= \frac{1}{2}(2)(4) = 4$ square
units

Shaded area $= 6 + 4 = 10$ square units

13. $7\frac{1}{2}$ square units. The trapezoid
can be subdivided into two right
triangles and a rectangle. Each
of the triangles is half of a
rectangle.

Area of triangle on left $= \frac{1}{2}(2)(3) = 3$ square units

Area of rectangle $= (1)(3) = 3$ square units

Area of triangle on right $= \frac{1}{2}(1)(3) = \frac{3}{2} = 1\frac{1}{2}$ square units

Area of trapezoid $= \left(3 + 3 + 1\frac{1}{2}\right) = 7\frac{1}{2}$ square units

14. Look for ways to factor 64. Use one factor for the
length of the base and the other for the height.
Sample answer:

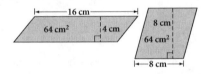

15. There are many possible solutions. Sample answer:

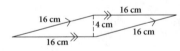

16. 23.1 m². The area of each panel is $(1)(0.7) = 0.7$ m²,
and there are $(11)(3) = 33$ panels, so the total area
of the arch is $33(0.7) = 23.1$ m².

17. 57 m². Two of the walls will be rectangles with
dimensions 4 m by 3 m, and the other two walls
will be rectangles with dimensions 5.5 m by 3 m.
Therefore, the total area of the four walls is
$2(4)(3) + 2(5.5)(3) = 57$ m².

18. 625 m². For a constant perimeter, the rectangle of
maximum area is a square. This can be found by
experimentation, as in the Project Maximizing Area.
Therefore, the length of each side of the pen
will be $100 \div 4 = 25$ m, and the area will be
$(25)(25) = 625$ m².

Discovering Geometry Solutions Manual
©2008 Key Curriculum Press

19. $\frac{1}{530}$. First find the area of the football field: $A = (53)(100) = 5300$ yd^2. The area of each square is 1 yd^2, so the probability that the math club wins is $\frac{10 \text{ yd}^2}{5300 \text{ yd}^2} = \frac{1}{530}$.

20. 112 tiles. First convert the dimensions of the wall from feet to inches: 4 ft = 4(12 in.) = 48 in., 7 ft = 7(12 in.) = 84 in. The area of the wall is $(48)(84) = 4032$ in^2, and the area of each tile is $(6)(6) = 36$ in^2, so the number of tiles required is $\frac{4032 \text{ in}^2}{36 \text{ in}^2} = 112$.

21. 96 square units. Draw quadrilateral *ABCD* on graph paper.

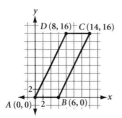

From the graph, observe that *ABCD* is a parallelogram with base 6 units and height 16 units. Area of $ABCD = bh = (6)(16) = 96$ square units.

22. 32 square units. Draw quadrilateral *EFGH* on graph paper.

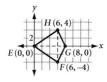

From the graph, observe that *EFGH* is a kite. Draw diagonals $\overline{HF}$ and $\overline{EG}$ to divide *EFGH* into four right triangles, each of which is half of a rectangle. The area of *EFGH* is the sum of the areas of these four triangles.

Area of $EFGH = \frac{1}{2}(6)(4) + \frac{1}{2}(6)(4) + \frac{1}{2}(2)(4) + \frac{1}{2}(2)(4) = 12 + 12 + 4 + 4 = 32$ square units

23. 500 cm^2. The dashed segments show that the trapezoid can be subdivided into two right triangles and a rectangle, where each of the right triangles is half of a rectangle.

Area of trapezoid $= \frac{1}{2}(5)(20) + (12)(20) + \frac{1}{2}(21)(20) = 50 + 240 + 210 = 500$ cm^2

24. a. Smallest: 191.88 cm^2, largest: 194.68 cm^2. To find the smallest possible area, use the smaller measurement for both base and height: $A = bh = (15.6 \text{ cm})(12.3 \text{ cm}) = 191.88$ cm^2. To find the largest possible area, use the larger measurement for both base and height: $A = bh = (15.7 \text{ cm})(12.4 \text{ cm}) = 194.68$ cm^2.

b. Answers will vary. Sample answer: about 193 cm^2. This is about halfway between the smallest and largest possible areas.

c. Answers will vary. The smallest and largest area values differ at the ones' place, so the digits after the decimal point are insignificant compared to the effect of the limit of precision in the measurements.

25. a. In one Ohio Star block, the sum of the areas of the red patches is 36 in^2, the sum of the areas of the blue patches is 72 in^2, and the area of the yellow patch is 36 in^2.

b. The complete quilt requires 42 blocks. The area of the quilt is $(72)(84) = 6048$ in^2, and the area of each square is $(12)(12) = 144$ in^2, so the number of squares is $\frac{6048 \text{ in}^2}{144 \text{ in}^2} = 42$. Notice that each dimension of the quilt is a multiple of 12 in, so 42 squares will cover the area exactly. $\left(\frac{72}{12} = 6; \frac{84}{12} = 7; 6 \cdot 7 = 42\right)$

c. About 1814 in^2 of red fabric, about 3629 in^2 of blue fabric, and about 1814 in^2 of yellow fabric. The border requires 5580 in^2 (if it does not need the extra 20%).

Red fabric: There are 42 quilt squares, each with 36 in^2 of red fabric; also, multiply by 1.2 (120%) to allow for the extra 20%: $42(36)(1.2) \approx 1814$ in^2.

Blue fabric: There are 42 quilt squares, each with 72 in^2 of blue fabric; also, multiply by 1.2 (120%) to allow for the extra 20%: $42(72)(1.2) \approx 3629$ in^2.

Yellow fabric: The same amount of yellow fabric is needed as red, so the amount of yellow fabric is also about 1814 in^2.

Border: From the diagram, you can see that the area of the border can be calculated by adding the areas of two rectangles with dimensions 114 in. by 15 in. and two rectangles with dimensions 72 in. by 15 in. Therefore, the area of the border is $2(15)(114) + 2(72)(15) = 3420 + 2160 = 5580$ in^2.

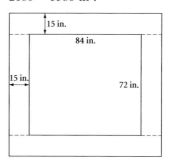

26. 100 cm^2; (36 + 64) cm^2. The area of the large square equals the sum of the areas of the small squares.

27. $a = 76°$, $b = 52°$, $c = 104°$, $d = 52°$, $e = 76°$, $f = 47°$, $g = 90°$, $h = 43°$, $k = 104°$, and $m = 86°$. For reference, let P be the center of the circle. First, $m\angle DBC = 90°$ (Angles Inscribed in a Semicircle Conjecture), and also $m\angle PBA = 90°$ (Tangent Conjecture). Therefore, both $\angle DBP$ and $\angle ABC$ are complements of $\angle PBC$, so $b = 52°$. Next, $AB = AC$ (Tangent Segments Conjecture), so $\triangle ABC$ is isosceles with $\angle BAC$ as the vertex angle. Then $a + 2b = a + 2(52°) = 180°$ (Triangle Sum Conjecture), so $a = 76°$. Next, $\triangle DPB$ is isosceles with vertex angle DPB because two of its sides are radii, so $d = 52°$ (Isosceles Triangle Conjecture). Then $e + 2(52°) = 180°$ (Triangle Sum Conjecture), so $e = 76°$, and $c = d + 52° = 52° + 52° = 104°$ (Triangle Exterior Angle Conjecture); or $c + e = c + 76° = 180°$ (Linear Pair Conjecture), so $c = 104°$. Also, $k = 104°$ because this arc is intercepted by the central angle of measure c (definition of the measure of an arc). Next, $f = \frac{1}{2}(94°) = 47°$ (Inscribed Angle Conjecture), and $g = 90°$ (Angles Inscribed in a Semicircle Conjecture). Then $h + f + g = 180°$ (Triangle Sum Conjecture), so $h = 43°$, and $m = 2(43°) = 86°$ (Inscribed Angle Conjecture). (Also, $m = 180° - 94° = 86°$ because $\overset{\frown}{DEC}$ is a semicircle.)

28. Copy $\overline{AM}$. Construct a line perpendicular to $\overline{AM}$ at M. Construct a 60° angle (an angle of any equilateral triangle), and bisect it to form a 30° angle that has $\overrightarrow{AM}$ as one of its sides. Copy this angle on the other side of $\overline{AM}$. Extend the other sides of these angles to intersect the perpendicular through M. The two intersection points will be the other two vertices of the required equilateral triangle. Sample construction:

29. a.

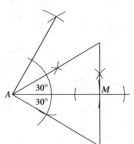

b.

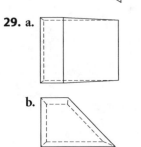

c.

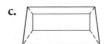

PROJECT

Project should satisfy the following criteria:

- Student provides clear descriptions, constraints, explanations, and predictions.

- Student includes graphs similar to these:

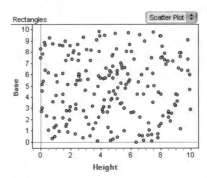

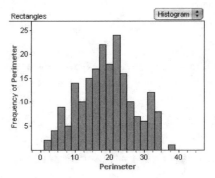

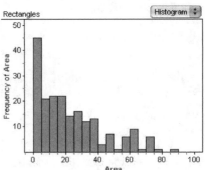

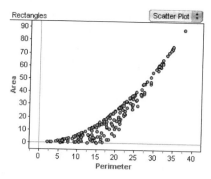

Extra credit

• Other graphs and relationships are presented.

EXTENSIONS

A. Results will vary.

B. There are two answers: 4 by 4 and 3 by 6. Possible explanation: For the perimeter to be equal to the area, there must be the same number of unit squares in the rectangle as there are unit lengths on the sides. If you count one square of area for each unit of length, you will count each square on the corner twice, for a total of four extra squares. The perimeter will be equal to the area only if the area of these four extra squares equals the area of the internal squares—the squares not counted in the perimeter. This happens only in rectangles that are 4 by 4 or 3 by 6.

C. Approximate areas: Tennessee: 42,000 mi²; Utah: 85,000 mi²; Wyoming: 98,000 mi².

LESSON 8.2

EXERCISES

1. 20 cm². Use the Triangle Area Conjecture. $A = \frac{1}{2}bh = \frac{1}{2}(8)(5) = 20$ cm².

2. 49.5 m². $A = \frac{1}{2}bh = \frac{1}{2}(11)(9) = 49.5$ m².

3. 300 square units. Use the Kite Area Conjecture with $d_1 = 9 + 16 = 25$ and $d_2 = 12 + 12 = 24$. $A = \frac{1}{2}d_1d_2 = \frac{1}{2}(25)(24) = 300$ square units.

You can also find the area of the kite by adding the areas of the four right triangles that are formed by the diagonals. If you use this method, the area of the kite is $2\left(\frac{1}{2}\right)(12)(9) + 2\left(\frac{1}{2}\right)(12)(16) = 108 + 192 = 300$ square units.

4. 60 cm². Use the Trapezoid Area Conjecture with $b_1 = 14$ cm and $b_2 = 6$ cm. $A = \frac{1}{2}h(b_1 + b_2) = \frac{1}{2}(6)(14 + 6) = 60$ cm².

5. 6 cm. Use the Triangle Area Conjecture.

$$A = \frac{1}{2}bh$$
$$39 = \frac{1}{2}(13)h$$
$$78 = (13)h$$
$$h = \frac{78}{13} = 6 \text{ cm}$$

6. 9 ft. Use the Triangle Area Conjecture.

$$A = \frac{1}{2}bh$$
$$31.5 = \frac{1}{2}(b)(7)$$
$$63 = b(7)$$
$$b = 9 \text{ ft}$$

7. 30 ft. Use the Kite Area Conjecture with $d_1 = BU = 20 + 8 = 28$ ft and $d_2 = LE$.

$$A = \frac{1}{2}d_1d_2$$
$$420 = \frac{1}{2}(28)d_2$$
$$420 = (14)d_2$$
$$d_2 = LE = 30 \text{ ft}$$

8. 5 cm. Use the Trapezoid Area Conjecture with $b_1 = 13$ cm and $b_2 = 7$ cm.

$$A = \frac{1}{2}h(b_1 + b_2)$$
$$50 = \frac{1}{2}h(13 + 7)$$
$$50 = 10h$$
$$h = 5 \text{ cm}$$

9. 16 m. Use the Trapezoid Area Conjecture with $b_1 = 24$ m and $b_2 = b$.

$$A = \frac{1}{2}h(b_1 + b_2)$$
$$180 = \frac{1}{2}(9)(24 + b)$$
$$360 = (9)(24 + b)$$
$$40 = 24 + b$$
$$b = 16 \text{ m}$$

10. 168 cm. Let b represent the unmarked side of the triangle. The height to this side is 24 cm. Find b, and then use this side length to find the perimeter of the triangle.

$$A = \frac{1}{2}bh$$
$$924 = \frac{1}{2}b(24)$$
$$924 = b(12)$$
$$b = 77 \text{ cm}$$
$$P = 51 + 40 + 77 = 168 \text{ cm}$$

11. 12 cm. Let $b_1 = 10$ cm and let b_2 represent the length of the unmarked base of the trapezoid. First use the perimeter and the known side lengths to find b_2.

$$P = 15 + 10 + 13 + b_2$$

$$62 = 38 + b_2$$

$$b_2 = 24 \text{ cm}$$

Now use the Trapezoid Area Conjecture to find h.

$$A = \frac{1}{2}h(b_1 + b_2)$$

$$204 = \frac{1}{2}h(10 + 24)$$

$$204 = h(17)$$

$$h = 12 \text{ cm}$$

12. $x = 3.6$ ft, $y = 10.8$ ft. The area of the triangle can be calculated in three different ways (using each base and its corresponding altitude), but all of them must give the same area. Notice that two of the altitudes lie outside the triangle.

$$A = \frac{1}{2}(15)(x) = \frac{1}{2}(5)(y) = \frac{1}{2}(6)(9) = 27$$

$$\frac{1}{2}(15)(x) = 27 \qquad \frac{1}{2}(5)(y) = 27$$

$$(15)(x) = 54 \qquad (5)(y) = 54$$

$$x = \frac{54}{15} \qquad y = \frac{54}{5}$$

$$= 3.6 \text{ ft} \qquad = 10.8 \text{ ft}$$

13. Find two positive integers whose product is 2 times 54, or 108. Two such integers are 9 and 12. In the pair of triangles shown below, one uses 9 cm as the length of the base and 12 cm as the height, while the other uses 12 cm as the length of the base and 9 cm as the height. Sample answer:

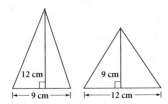

14. Choose a factor of 56 for the height. Divide 56 by that number to get the average of the lengths of the two bases. For example, if you choose 8 cm for the height, the average of the lengths of the bases will be 7 cm, and one possibility is to make the bases have lengths 10 cm and 4 cm. Sample answer:

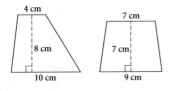

15. Because half the product of the two diagonals is 1092, choose two numbers whose product is twice 1092, or 2184, to be the two diagonals. One possible choice is 24 and 91. You can use 24 cm as the length of the diagonal that is bisected by the other diagonal. You can split the length of 91 cm in many ways, corresponding to different positions where the diagonals intersect. The figures below show two ways to do this. Sample answer:

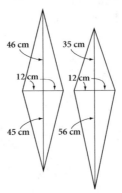

16. The length of the base of the triangle equals the sum of the lengths of both bases of the trapezoid.

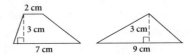

17. $\frac{1}{2}$. Draw altitude $\overline{PQ}$ of $\triangle TPR$. Then the area of $\triangle TPR = \frac{1}{2}(TR)(PQ) = \frac{1}{2}(TR)(AR) = \frac{1}{2}$(area of rectangle $ARTY$). Notice that this result does not depend on the position of P, which can be any point on $\overline{AY}$.

18. More than half, because the top card completely covers one corner of the bottom card. Notice that this is like the figure in Exercise 17, but the covered area of the card here is a larger fraction of the rectangle (or card) than in Exercise 17, so the top card covers more than half the bottom card.

19. a. 86 in. of balsa wood and 960 in² of Mylar. Find the sum of the lengths of the diagonals to find the amount of balsa wood, and the total area of the kite and flaps to find the amount of Mylar. The sum of the lengths of the diagonals is $2(15) + 20 + 36 = 86$ in. To find the area of the kite, substitute 30 for d_1 and $20 + 36 = 56$ for d_2 in the kite area formula, $A = \frac{1}{2}d_1d_2$. $A = \frac{1}{2}(30)(56) = 840$, so the area of the kite is 840 in². Each of the four flaps is a trapezoid with height 1 in.; two have bases of lengths 21 in. and 25 in., while the other two have bases of lengths 35 in. and 39 in. Find the total area of all the flaps: $2\left[\frac{1}{2} \cdot 1(21 + 25)\right] + 2\left[\frac{1}{2} \cdot 1(35 + 39)\right] = 46 + 74 = 120$, so the area is 120 in². The total amount of Mylar needed is $840 + 120 = 960$ in².

b. 56 in. (or less, if he tilts the kite). Because the length of the shorter diagonal is 30 in., the easiest way to cut the kite out of a 36-inch-wide piece of Mylar is to place the shorter diagonal along the width of the unrolled Mylar. Then the length of Mylar needed would simply be the length of the longer diagonal of the kite, which is 56 in.

20. 3600 shingles (to cover an area of 900 ft^2). To find the total area to be covered with shingles, add the areas of the two congruent trapezoids and the two congruent triangles.

Area of two trapezoids: $2\left[\frac{1}{2} \cdot 15(20 + 30)\right] = 750$, so the sum of the areas of the two trapezoids is 750 ft^2.

Area of two triangles: $2\left(\frac{1}{2} \cdot 10 \cdot 15\right) = 150$, so the sum of the areas of the two triangles is 150 ft^2.

Therefore, the total area of the roof is $750 + 150 = 900$ ft^2. Because each shingle covers 0.25 ft^2, Crystal should buy $\frac{900 \text{ ft}^2}{0.25 \text{ ft}^2} = 3600$ shingles.

21. The isosceles triangle is a right triangle because the angles on either side of the right angle are complementary. If you use the trapezoid area formula, the area of the trapezoid is $\frac{1}{2}(a + b)(a + b)$. If you add the areas of the three triangles, the area of the trapezoid is $\frac{1}{2}ab + \frac{1}{2}c^2 + \frac{1}{2}ba = \frac{1}{2}c^2 + ab$.

22. Given: trapezoid $ABCD$ with height h. Area of $\triangle ABD = \frac{1}{2}hb_1$. Area of $\triangle BCD = \frac{1}{2}hb_2$. Area of trapezoid = sum of areas of two triangles $= \frac{1}{2}hb_1 + \frac{1}{2}hb_2 = \frac{1}{2}h(b_1 + b_2)$.

23. $11\frac{1}{4}$ square units. Count the complete and fractional squares inside the figure. There are 7 whole squares, 7 half-squares, and 1 three-quarter square. Add these to get the area of the figure: $A = 7(1) + 7\left(\frac{1}{2}\right) + 1\left(\frac{3}{4}\right) = 7 + 3\frac{1}{2} + \frac{3}{4} = 11\frac{1}{4}$, so the area of the figure is $11\frac{1}{4}$ square units.

24. 7 square units. Enclose the triangle in a square. Find the area of the original triangle by subtracting the areas of the three surrounding right triangles from the area of the square.

Area of square $= 4^2 = 16$

Area of triangle I $= \frac{1}{2}(4)(2) = 4$

Area of triangle II $= \frac{1}{2}(2)(3) = 3$

Area of triangle III $= \frac{1}{2}(4)(1) = 2$

Therefore, the area of the original triangle is $16 - (4 + 3 + 2) = 16 - 9 = 7$ square units.

25. 70 m. First find the length of the base of the rectangle. Let b represent the length of the base.

$A = bh$, so $264 = b(24)$, and $b = 11$ m. Now find the perimeter of the rectangle: $P = 2b + 2h = 2(11) + 2(24) = 70$ m.

26. 144 cm^2. The parallelogram has two sides of length 10 cm. Let b represent the length of each of the other two sides. Using the given perimeter, $2b + 2(10) = 52$ cm. Then $b = 16$ cm, and $A = bh = (16)(9) = 144$ cm^2.

27. $A = 828$ ft^2, $P = 144$ ft. Divide the figure into two rectangles and use subtraction to find the unmarked side lengths.

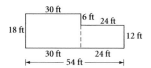

Area of larger rectangle $= bh = (30)(18) = 540$ ft^2

Area of smaller rectangle $= bh = (24)(12) = 288$ ft^2

Area of shaded figure $= 540$ ft^2 $+ 288$ ft^2 $= 828$ ft^2

In calculating the perimeter, note that the dashed segment is not part of the original figure, and its length should not be included.

Perimeter of shaded figure $= 54 + 18 + 30 + 6 + 24 + 12 = 144$ ft

28. $A = 1440$ cm^2, $P = 220$ cm. Divide the figure into two parallelograms and use subtraction to find the unmarked side lengths.

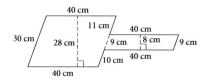

Area of larger parallelogram $= bh = (40)(28) = 1120$ ft^2

Area of smaller parallelogram $= bh = (40)(8) = 320$ ft^2

Area of shaded figure $= 1120$ ft^2 $+ 320$ ft^2 $= 1440$ ft^2

In calculating the perimeter, note that the dashed segment separating the two parallelograms is not part of the original figure, and its length should not be included.

Perimeter of shaded figure $= 40 + 30 + 40 + 11 + 40 + 9 + 40 + 10 = 220$ cm

29. a. Incenter. The construction marks show that this is the point of concurrency of the angle bisectors.

b. Orthocenter. The construction marks show that this is the point of concurrency of the altitudes.

c. Centroid. The construction marks show that this is the point of concurrency of the medians.

30. $a = 34°$, $b = 68°$, $c = 68°$, $d = 56°$, $e = 56°$, $f = 90°$, $g = 34°$, $h = 56°$, $m = 56°$, $n = 90°$, and $p = 34°$. For reference, let O be the center of the circle. First, $m\overset{\frown}{BC} = 2(56°) = 112°$ (Inscribed Angle Conjecture). Because $\overset{\frown}{DBC}$ is a semicircle, $b = 180° - 112° = 68°$. Next, $a = \frac{1}{2}b$ (Inscribed Angle Conjecture), so $a = 34°$. By the definition of the measure of an arc, $c = b$, so $c = 68°$. Now look at $\triangle BAO$ and $\triangle CAO$. Notice that $\overline{OB} \cong \overline{OC}$ (all radii of a circle are congruent), $\overline{AB} \cong \overline{AC}$ (Tangent Segments Conjecture), and $\overline{AO} \cong \overline{AO}$ (same segment), so $\triangle BOA \cong \triangle COA$ by SSS. Therefore, $d = e$ by CPCTC. Observe that $c + d + e = 180°$, so $68° + 2d = 180°$. Then $2d = 112°$, so $d = 56°$, and also $e = 56°$. By the Tangent Conjecture, $\overline{OC} \perp \overrightarrow{AC}$, so $f = 90°$. Next, $g + e + f = 180°$ (Triangle Sum Conjecture), so $g + 56° + 90° = 180°$, and $g = 34°$. Next, $h = \frac{1}{2}(112°) = 56°$ (Inscribed Angle Conjecture) and $m = \frac{1}{2}(112°) = 56°$ (Inscribed Angle Conjecture). Now, by the Intersecting Chords Conjecture (see Lesson 6.5, Exercise 16), $n = \frac{1}{2}(b + 112°) = \frac{1}{2}(68° + 112°) = \frac{1}{2}(180°) = 90°$. Finally, $p + n + 56° = 180°$ (Triangle Sum Conjecture), so $p = 180° - 90° - 56° = 34°$.

31. $3^2.6^2/3.6.3.6$. There are two types of vertices. One type of vertex is surrounded by two equilateral triangles, then two regular hexagons. The other type of vertex is surrounded by an equilateral triangle, then a regular hexagon, then another equilateral triangle, and then another regular hexagon.

PROJECT

You might gather some data points and use quadratic regression rather than finding and graphing a function expression. Projects should satisfy the following criteria:

- The expression and equation are equivalent to $A = x(10 - 2x)$.

- The graph shows the maximum area at $x = 2.5$.

Extra credit

- The project includes an explanation of why the maximum area is 12.5 m². One reason, not using the graph, is that if there were twice as much fencing available and no barn, then the region of maximum area would be a square (as discovered in Exercise 18 in Lesson 8.1); the barn wall can be considered a line of symmetry, cutting the amount of fencing in half but making the shape half a square, with width $\frac{1}{4}$ the total amount of fencing.

EXTENSIONS

A. In a triangle, each midsegment is one-half the length of a side. If you consider one side as the base and label its length as b, then length of midsegment $= \frac{1}{2}b$. Then area of triangle $= \frac{1}{2}bh =$ (midsegment)(height).

In a trapezoid, there is one midsegment, and its length is half the sum of the lengths of the bases, that is, length of midsegment $= \frac{1}{2}(b_1 + b_2)$. Then area of trapezoid $= \frac{1}{2}h(b_1 + b_2) = \frac{1}{2}(b_1 + b_2)h =$ (midsegment)(height).

B. Possible answers (all use trapezoid $ABCD$ with long base $\overline{AB}$, short base $\overline{CD}$, $b_1 = AB$, $b_2 = CD$, and h as the perpendicular height between the bases):

Area of trapezoid $=$ area$(\triangle ABC) +$ area$(\triangle CDA)$
$$= \frac{1}{2}b_1h + \frac{1}{2}b_2h = \frac{1}{2}h(b_1 + b_2)$$

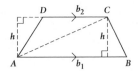

Construct point E on $\overline{AB}$ so that $\overline{ED}$ is parallel to $\overline{BC}$. Therefore, area of trapezoid $=$ area$(\triangle AED) +$ area(parallelogram $EBCD$) $= \frac{1}{2}h(b_1 - b_2) + hb_2 = \frac{1}{2}h(b_1 + b_2)$.

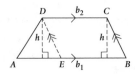

Construct $\overline{DE} \perp \overline{AB}$, with points E and F on $\overline{AB}$. Let $c = AE$. Then $FB = b_1 - b_2 - c$. Therefore, area of trapezoid $=$ area$(\triangle AED) +$ area(rectangle $EFCD$) $+$ area$(\triangle FBC) = \frac{1}{2}ch + b_2h + \frac{1}{2}(b_1 - b_2 - c)h = \frac{1}{2}h(b_1 + b_2)$.

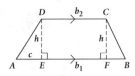

Start as you did in the previous method, then duplicate $\triangle AED$ as $\triangle DE'A$ and $\triangle FBC$ as $\triangle F'CB$, forming rectangle $ABF'E'$. Therefore, area of trapezoid $=$ area(rectangle $ABF'E'$) $-$ area$(\triangle DE'A) -$ area$(\triangle CF'B) = b_1h - \frac{1}{2}ch - \frac{1}{2}(b_1 - b_2 - c)h = \frac{1}{2}h(b_1 + b_2)$.

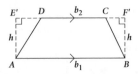

C. Approximate areas: California: 164,000 mi²; Texas: 269,000 mi²; Nevada: 111,000 mi².

Discovering Geometry Solutions Manual
©2008 Key Curriculum Press

LESSON 8.3

EXERCISES

1. a. 121,952 ft². Each room has two walls with dimensions 14 ft by 10 ft and two walls with dimensions 16 ft by 10 ft, while the ceiling is 14 ft by 16 ft. Find the sum of the areas of these rectangles: $2(14)(10) + 2(16)(10) + (14)(16) = 824$, so the total area to be painted for one room is 824 ft², and the total for 148 rooms is $148(824) = 121,952$ ft².

b. 244 gallons of base paint and 488 gallons of finishing paint. Find the number of gallons of each kind of paint separately.

Base paint: $121,952 \text{ ft}^2 \cdot \frac{1 \text{ gal}}{500 \text{ ft}^2} \approx 243.9$ gal; round up to 244 gal.

Finishing paint: $121,952 \text{ ft}^2 \cdot \frac{1 \text{ gal}}{250 \text{ ft}^2} \approx 487.8$ gal; round up to 488 gal.

2. He should buy at least four rolls of wallpaper. Two walls are rectangles with dimensions 11 ft by 10 ft. The other two walls are rectangles with dimensions 13 ft by 10 ft. Find the sum of the areas of these rectangles: $2 \cdot 11 \cdot 10 + 2 \cdot 13 \cdot 10 = 480$ ft², so the total surface area to be papered is 480 ft². Now find the area of each roll: $(2.5)(50) = 125$, so the area of each roll is 125 ft². Finally, find the number of rolls of wallpaper that is needed: $480 \text{ ft}^2 \cdot \frac{1 \text{ roll}}{125 \text{ ft}^2} \approx 3.84$ rolls; round up to 4 rolls.

If paper cut off at the corners is wasted, he'll need 5 rolls. Each 11-ft wall requires $11/2.5 = 4.4$ 10-ft strips, rounded up to 5 strips. Each 13-ft wall requires $13/2.5 = 5.2$ 10-ft strips, rounded up to 6 strips. The total needed is $2(5 \cdot 10) + 2(6 \cdot 10) = 220$ ft, which requires 4.4 50-ft rolls, rounded up to 5 rolls.

3. 1552 ft²; 776 ft² more surface area. First find the area of 65,000 rectangular cells: $65,000(1.25)(2.75) = 223,437.5$, so the total area of the cells is 223,437.5 in². Convert this area to square feet. There are 12 in. in a foot, so there are $12(12) = 144$ in² in a square foot. $223,437.5 \text{ in}^2 \cdot \frac{1 \text{ ft}^2}{144 \text{ in}^2} \approx 1552$ ft². If the cells are only 12% efficient, 50% more area will be needed than if they are 18% efficient, so the additional surface area that would need to be covered would be $0.5(1552) = 776$ ft².

4. 21. First find the area of the kite. The lengths of the diagonals are 40 ft and 70 ft, so the area of the kite is $\frac{1}{2}(40)(70) = 1400$ ft². Find the amount of sealant needed for one application: $1400 \text{ ft}^2 \cdot \frac{1 \text{ gal}}{400 \text{ ft}^2} = 3.5$ gal. Harold will make 6 applications of sealant (twice a year for three years), so he will need $6(3.5) = 21$ gal of sealant. Therefore, he should buy 21 one-gallon containers.

5. 336 ft²; $1,780. First find the area of one flowerbed. Each flowerbed is a trapezoid with height 7 ft and bases of lengths 12 ft and 20 ft, so its area is $\frac{1}{2}(7)(12 + 20) = 112$ ft². Then the total area of the three flowerbeds is $3(112) = 336$ ft², and the cost will be $100 + 336($5) = $1,780$.

6. $760. The easiest way to find the total area to be carpeted is to find the area of the complete rectangle at the top of the figure and then subtract the areas of the bathrooms. This way, you don't have to figure out the dimensions of the hallway.

Length of rectangle $= 10 + 10 + 7 = 27$ ft

Width of rectangle $= 9 + 8 = 17$ ft

Total area to be carpeted
= total area of three bedrooms and hallway
$= (27 \cdot 17) - (6 \cdot 10 + 7 \cdot 9) = 336$ ft²

Convert to square yards. There are 3 ft in a yard, so there are $3(3) = 9$ square feet in a square yard. $336 \text{ ft}^2 \cdot \frac{1 \text{ yd}^2}{9 \text{ ft}^2} = 37\frac{1}{3}$ yd²; round up to 38 yd² because carpeting, padding, and installation are priced per square yard.

The cost for carpeting, padding, and installation is $14 + $3 + $3 = $20 per square yard, so the cost for 38 yd² will be $38($20) = 760.

7. 220 terra cotta tiles, 1107 blue tiles; $1,598.15. First find the total area of the entryway and kitchen. Look at the rectangle that contains the entryway, kitchen, living room, and dining room, and at the two smaller rectangles containing the entryway and kitchen (on the left) and living room and dining room (on the right). From the dimensions of these rooms, you can see the total area of the entryway and kitchen is $(10)(22) = 220$ ft². Because 1-foot-square tiles are to be used for the entryway and kitchen, 220 tiles will be needed.

The dimensions of the bathrooms are 6 ft by 10 ft and 7 ft by 9 ft, so the total area of the two bathrooms is $60 + 63 = 123$ ft². The tiles for the bathroom floors are 4-inch-square tiles, so there are 9 of these tiles per square foot: $\frac{12}{4} = 3$; $3 \cdot 3 = 9$. Find the number of blue tiles needed: $123 \text{ ft}^2 \cdot \frac{9 \text{ tiles}}{1 \text{ ft}^2} = 1107$ tiles.

Finally, find the cost of the tiles.

Terra cotta tiles: $220($5) = $1,100$

Blue tiles: $1107($0.45) = 498.15

Total cost: $1,100 + $498.15 = $1,598.15$

8. 72 cm². Move the small shaded wedge from the upper right square to fit with the shaded quarter circle in the lower right square, completing a second shaded square. The new shaded region is a rectangle with base 12 cm and height 6 cm, so $A = bh = 12 \cdot 6 = 72$ cm².

9. $AB \approx 16.5$ cm, $BD \approx 15.3$ cm. First calculate the area of $\triangle ABC$ using $\overline{BC}$ as the base and $\overline{AF}$ as the corresponding altitude.

Area of $\triangle ABC = \frac{1}{2}bh = \frac{1}{2}(BC)(AF)\ \frac{1}{2}(16.0)(10.5)$
$= 84.0$ cm^2

The area of the triangle is the same for any choice of base, so we can use this result to find AB and BD.

First find AB. Notice that $\overline{CE}$ is the altitude to $\overline{AB}$.

$A = \frac{1}{2}bh$

$A = \frac{1}{2}(AB)(CE)$ Substitute AB for b and CE for h.

$84.0 = \frac{1}{2}(AB)(10.2)$ Substitute 84 for A and 10.2 for CE.

$168.0 = (AB)(10.2)$ Multiply by 2.

$AB \approx 16.5$ cm   Divide by 10.2 and round to the nearest tenth.

Now find BD. Notice that $\overline{BD}$ is the altitude to $\overline{AC}$.

$A = \frac{1}{2}bh$

$A = \frac{1}{2}(AC)(BD)$ Substitute AC for b and BD for h.

$84.0 = \frac{1}{2}(11.0)(BD)$ Substitute 84 for A and 11.0 for AC.

$168.0 = (11.0)(BD)$ Multiply by 2.

$BD \approx 15.3$ cm   Divide by 11.0 and round to the nearest tenth.

10. 60 cm^2 by either method. The first step in using Hero's formula is to find the semiperimeter.
$s = \frac{a+b+c}{2} = \frac{8+15+17}{2} = 20$.
Then substitute into Hero's formula:
$A = \sqrt{s(s-a)(s-b)(s-c)} =$
$\sqrt{20(20-8)(20-15)(20-17)} =$
$\sqrt{20 \cdot 12 \cdot 5 \cdot 3} = \sqrt{3600} = 60$, so the area of the triangle is 60 cm^2.

Using the standard triangle area formula,
$A = \frac{1}{2}bh = \frac{1}{2}(15)(8) = 60$, so by this formula, the area is 60 cm^2.

11. $\overline{AO} \cong \overline{BO}$ because all radii of a circle are congruent, so $\triangle AOB$ is isosceles. Therefore, $m\angle A = 20°$ and $m\angle AOB = 140°$. $m\overset{\frown}{AB} = 140°$ and $m\overset{\frown}{CD} = 82°$ (definition of arc measure). $m\overset{\frown}{AC} = m\overset{\frown}{BD}$ because parallel lines intercept congruent arcs on a circle.
$x = \frac{360° - 140° - 82°}{2} = 69°$.

12. E. None of the values change.

   A. Moving P doesn't change the height of $\triangle ABP$, so the area of $\triangle ABP$ won't change.

   B. Moving P doesn't change the height of $\triangle PDC$ or the length of $\overline{DC}$, so the area of $\triangle PDC$ won't change.

   C. Moving P doesn't change the length of $\overline{DC}$, so the area of the trapezoid doesn't change.

   D. $m\angle PCD = m\angle B$ (CA Conjecture), so $m\angle A + m\angle PCD + m\angle CPD = 180°$, regardless of the position of P.

IMPROVING YOUR VISUAL THINKING SKILLS

This problem can be done in hundreds of ways. One unusual way, if disconnected pieces are allowed, is to rearrange pieces of the triangle to make a parallelogram or rectangle of the same area, divide the resulting rectangle into four pieces, and then rearrange those pieces back into a triangle.

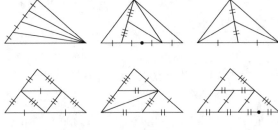

EXTENSIONS

   A. Results will vary. Divide the figure into more and more pieces and add the resulting areas. The areas will approach some number (the actual area) as the number of pieces increases.

   B. Results will vary.

USING YOUR ALGEBRA SKILLS 8

1. $x^2 + 6x + 5$

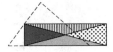

Combine the areas of the pieces to find the area of the large rectangle, which gives the product.

$(x + 5)(x + 1) = x^2 + 5x + 1x + 5$

$= x^2 + 6x + 5$

Discovering Geometry Solutions Manual
©2008 Key Curriculum Press

2. $2x^2 + 7x$

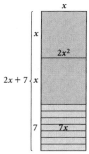

Combine the areas of the pieces to find the area of the large rectangle, which gives the product.

$$(x)(2x + 7) = 2x^2 + 7x$$

3. $6x^2 + 19x + 10$

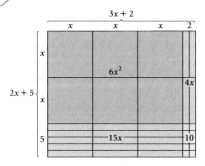

Combine the areas of the pieces to find the area of the large rectangle, which gives the product.

$$(3x + 2)(2x + 5) = 6x^2 + 4x + 15x + 10$$
$$= 6x^2 + 19x + 10$$

4. $(3)(2x + 1)$

Here is a way to arrange the pieces to make a rectangle.

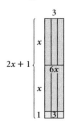

The base and height of the rectangle give the factors, so $6x + 3 = (3)(2x + 1)$.

5. $(x + 5)(x + 3)$

Here is a way to arrange the pieces to make a rectangle.

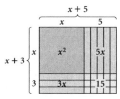

The base and height of the rectangle give the factors, so $x^2 + 8x + 15 = (x + 5)(x + 3)$.

6. $(2x + 3)(x + 4)$

Here is a way to arrange the pieces to make a rectangle.

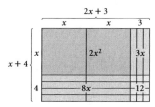

The base and height of the rectangle give the factors, so $2x^2 + 11x + 12 = (2x + 3)(x + 4)$.

7. $x^2 - 26x + 165$

Add the areas of the four small rectangles to find the area of the large rectangle, which gives the product.

$$(x - 15)(x - 11) = x^2 - 15x - 11x + 165$$
$$= x^2 - 26x + 165$$

8. $12x^2 - 13x - 35$

Add the areas of the four small rectangles to find the area of the large rectangle, which gives the product.

$$(3x - 7)(4x + 5) = 12x^2 - 28x + 15x - 35$$
$$= 12x^2 - 13x - 35$$

9. $x^2 + 8x + 16$

Add the areas of the four small rectangles to find the area of the large rectangle, which gives the product.

$$(x + 4)^2 = x^2 + 4x + 4x + 16$$
$$= x^2 + 8x + 16$$

10. $(2x + 5)(2x - 5) = 4x^2 - 25$

Add the areas of the four small rectangles to find the area of the large rectangle, which gives the product.

$$(2x + 5)(2x - 5) = 4x^2 + 10x - 10x - 25$$
$$= 4x^2 - 25$$

11. $(a + b)^2 = a^2 + 2ab + b^2$

$$(a + b)^2 = a^2 + ab + ab + b^2$$
$$= a^2 + 2ab + b^2$$

12. $a^2 - b^2$

$$(a + b)(a - b) = a^2 + ab - ab - b^2 = a^2 - b^2$$

13. $(x + 15)(x + 4)$. Draw a rectangle diagram with x^2 in the upper left region and 60 in the lower right region. The remaining two values must multiply to 60 because they are the dimensions of the lower right region. They must also add to 19 in order to get a sum of $19x$ from the other two regions. Both of these numbers must be positive because their product is positive and their sum is positive. The two numbers that work are 15 and 4.

The factors are the base and height of the rectangle, so $x^2 + 19x + 60 = (x + 15)(x + 4)$.

14. $(x - 12)(x + 2)$. Draw a rectangle diagram with x^2 in the upper left region and -24 in the lower right region. The remaining two values must multiply to -24 because they are the dimensions

of the lower right region. They must also add to -10 in order to get a sum of $-10x$ from the other two regions. One of these numbers must be negative and the other positive because their product is negative. The two numbers that work are -12 and 2.

The factors are the base and height of the rectangle, so $x^2 - 10x - 24 = (x - 12)(x + 2)$.

15. $(x + 5)(x - 4)$. Draw a rectangle diagram with x^2 in the upper left region and -20 in the lower right region. The remaining two values must multiply to -20 because they are the dimensions of the lower right region. They must also add to 1 in order to get a sum of x (or $1x$) from the other two regions. One of these numbers must be negative and the other positive because their product is negative. The two numbers that work are 5 and -4.

The factors are the base and height of the rectangle, so $x^2 + x - 20 = (x + 5)(x - 4)$.

16. $(x - 3)^2$. Here we need to find two numbers whose product is 9 and whose sum is -6. The numbers that work are -3 and -3.

$x^2 - 6x + 9 = (x - 3)(x - 3)$ or $(x - 3)^2$

17. $(x + 6)(x - 6)$. Here we need to find two numbers whose product is 36 and whose sum is 0. The numbers that work are 6 and -6.

$x^2 - 36 = (x + 6)(x - 6)$

Discovering Geometry Solutions Manual
©2008 Key Curriculum Press

18. $(2x + 7)(2x - 7)$. The upper left region will have an area of $4x^2$ and the lower right region an area of -49, while the sum of the areas of the other two regions must be 0.

$$4x^2 - 49 = (2x + 7)(2x - 7)$$

19.

$x^2 + 5x + 4 = 0$	Original equation.
$(x + 4)(x + 1) = 0$	Factor the left-hand side.
$x + 4 = 0$ or $x + 1 = 0$	Use the zero product property.
$x = -4$ or $x = -1$	Solve for x.

Check:

$$(-4)^2 + 5(-4) + 4 \overset{?}{=} 0$$
$$16 - 20 + 4 \overset{?}{=} 0$$
$$0 = 0$$
$$(-1)^2 + 5(-1) + 4 \overset{?}{=} 0$$
$$1 - 5 + 4 \overset{?}{=} 0$$
$$0 = 0$$

20.

$x^2 + 7x = 30$	Original equation.
$x^2 + 7x - 30 = 0$	Subtract 30 to get 0 on the right-hand side.
$(x + 10)(x - 3) = 0$	Factor the left-hand side.
$x + 10 = 0$ or $x - 3 = 0$	Use the zero product property.
$x = -10$ or $x = 3$	Solve for x.

Check:

$$(-10)^2 + 7(-10) \overset{?}{=} 30$$
$$100 - 70 \overset{?}{=} 30$$
$$30 = 30$$
$$(3)^2 + 7(3) \overset{?}{=} 30$$
$$9 + 21 \overset{?}{=} 30$$
$$30 = 30$$

21.

$x(x - 6) = 5x - 24$	Original equation.
$x^2 - 6x = 5x - 24$	Multiply on the left-hand side.
$x^2 - 11x + 24 = 0$	Add $(-5x + 24)$ to both sides.
$(x - 8)(x - 3) = 0$	Factor the left-hand side.
$x - 8 = 0$ or $x - 3 = 0$	Use the zero product property.
$x = 8$ or $x = 3$	Solve for x.

Check:

$$(8)[(8) - 6] \overset{?}{=} 5(8) - 24$$
$$8 \cdot 2 \overset{?}{=} 40 - 24$$
$$16 = 16$$
$$(3)[(3) - 6] \overset{?}{=} 5(3) - 24$$
$$8(-3) \overset{?}{=} 15 - 24$$
$$-9 = -9$$

22.

$(x + 2)(x - 2) = -x^2 - 9x - 8$	Original equation.
$x^2 - 4 = -x^2 - 9x - 8$	Multiply on the left-hand side.
$2x^2 + 9x + 4 = 0$	Add $(x^2 + 9x + 8)$ to both sides.
$(2x + 1)(x + 4) = 0$	Factor the left-hand side.
$2x + 1 = 0$ or $x + 4 = 0$	Use the zero product property.
$2x = -1$ or $x = -4$	Subtract 1 from both sides of the first equation.
$x = -\frac{1}{2}$ or $x = -4$	Solve for x.

Check:

$$\left[\left(-\frac{1}{2}\right) + 2\right]\left[\left(-\frac{1}{2}\right) - 2\right] \overset{?}{=} -\left(-\frac{1}{2}\right)^2 - 9\left(-\frac{1}{2}\right) - 8$$
$$\frac{3}{2}\left(-\frac{5}{2}\right) \overset{?}{=} -\frac{1}{4} + \frac{9}{2} - 8$$
$$-\frac{15}{4} = -\frac{15}{4}$$
$$[(-4) + 2][(-4) - 2] \overset{?}{=} -(-4)^2 - 9(-4) - 8$$
$$-2(-6) \overset{?}{=} -16 + 36 - 8$$
$$12 = 12$$

b. $b_1 = h$; $b_2 = h + 4$

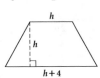

c. $\frac{1}{2}[h + (h + 4)]h = 48$

d.
$$\frac{1}{2}[h + (h + 4)]h = 48$$
$$\frac{1}{2}(2h + 4)h = 48$$
$$\frac{1}{2}(2h^2 + 4h) = 48$$
$$h^2 + 2h = 48$$
$$h^2 + 2h - 48 = 0$$
$$(h + 8)(h - 6) = 0$$
$$h + 8 = 0 \quad \text{or} \quad h - 6 = 0$$
$$h = -8 \quad \text{or} \quad h = 6$$

The height cannot be -8 feet, so the only valid solution is $h = 6$ and $h + 4 = 10$. The height is 6 feet, one base is 6 feet, and the other base is 10 feet.

Check: $\frac{1}{2}(6 + 10) \cdot 6 = \frac{1}{2} \cdot 16 \cdot 6 = 48$.

IMPROVING YOUR REASONING SKILLS

1. O should play in b1, to block X from getting the square b1-a4-d5-e2.

2. The last move forces X to play in c4. This creates two square options for X, c4-d2-b1-a3 and c4-c2-a2-a4. O can't block both of these in one move, so X will win.

3. b2; c1. O_5 in b2 will force X_6 in b3. Then O_7 in c1 will create two square options for O, c1-b2-c3-d2 and c1-b1-b2-c2, so O will win.

4. X_7, X_9, O_{10}, X_{11}, X_{13}, and O_{14} were forced; X will win. X_7 was forced by O in c3-c4-d4; X_9 was forced by O in d2-c3-d4; O_{10} was forced by X in e3-c2-b4; X_{11} was forced by O in d5-d4-c4; X_{13} was forced by O in b2-c3-d2; O_{14} was forced by X in c5-e3-c1. Now with O in a3-c4-d2, X is forced to play X_{15} in b1. That will create two square options for X, a2-b3-c2-b1 and d1-b1-b3-d3, so X will win.

LESSON 8.4

EXERCISES

1. 2092 cm². The figure is a heptagon, so $n = 7$.
$$A = \frac{1}{2}asn \approx \frac{1}{2}(24.9)(24)(7) \approx 2092 \text{ cm}^2$$

2. 74 cm. The figure is a pentagon, so $n = 5$.
$$A = \frac{1}{2}asn$$
$$19{,}887.5 \approx \frac{1}{2}a(107.5)(5)$$
$$39{,}775 \approx a(537.5)$$
$$a \approx \frac{39{,}775}{537.5} = 74 \text{ cm}$$

3. 256 cm. Use the formula $A = \frac{1}{2}aP$.
$$4940.8 \approx \frac{1}{2}(38.6)P$$
$$9881.6 \approx 38.6P$$
$$P \approx \frac{9881.6}{38.6} = 256 \text{ cm}$$

4. 33 cm². $A = \frac{1}{2}asn \approx \frac{1}{2}(3)(4.4)(5) = 33 \text{ cm}^2$

5. 63 cm. Use the formula $A = \frac{1}{2}aP$.
$$302.4 \approx \frac{1}{2}(9.6)P$$
$$604.8 \approx 9.6P$$
$$P \approx 63 \text{ cm}$$

6. 490 cm². $A = \frac{1}{2}aP \approx \frac{1}{2}(12)(81.6) \approx 490 \text{ cm}^2$

7. 57.6 m. Use the formula $A = \frac{1}{2}aP$.
$$259.2 \approx \frac{1}{2}(9)P$$
$$P \approx 57.6.$$

The perimeter is about 57.6 m.

8. 25 ft. Use the formula $A = \frac{1}{2}asn$ to find the value of s.
$$20{,}000 \approx \frac{1}{2}(80)s(20)$$
$$20{,}000 \approx 800s$$
$$s \approx 25 \text{ ft.}$$

The length of each side is about 25 ft.

9. ≈ 42 cm². Construct a circle with radius 4 cm. Mark six 4-centimeter chords around the circle.

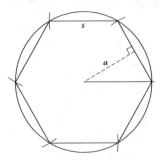

Use the formula $A = \frac{1}{2}asn$ to approximate the area of the hexagon. By construction, $s = 4$ cm. Measure the apothem with a ruler: $a \approx 3.5$ cm. Therefore, $A = \frac{1}{2}asn \approx \frac{1}{2}(3.5)(4)(6) \approx 42 \text{ cm}^2$.

10. ≈ 58 cm². Draw a circle with radius 4 cm, and use your protractor to form five congruent central angles, each of measure $\frac{360°}{5} = 72°$. Use the sides of these angles to form five radii of the circle. Use a protractor and the Tangent Conjecture to draw tangents to the circle at each of the points where the five radii touch the circle. The tangent segments form a regular pentagon circumscribed about the circle.

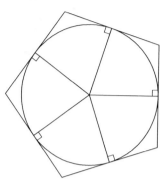

Because each radius is perpendicular to a tangent, the radii form apothems of the pentagon, so $a = 4$ cm, as required. Measure one of the tangent segments to find the length of a side of the pentagon: $s \approx 5.8$ cm. Then $A = \frac{1}{2}asn \approx \frac{1}{2}(4)(5.8)(5) \approx 58$ cm².

11. When a square with side s is divided into four isosceles triangles with vertices at the center of the square, the base of each triangle is s and the apothem is $a = \frac{s}{2}$ and $n = 4$, so $A = \frac{1}{2}asn = \frac{1}{2}\left(\frac{1}{2}s\right)s(4) = s²$.

12. It is impossible to increase its area because a regular pentagon maximizes the area. Any dragging of the vertices decreases the area. (Subsequent dragging to space them out more evenly can increase the area again, but never beyond that of the regular pentagon.)

13. ≈ 996 cm². First find the area of the complete octagon.

$A = \frac{1}{2}asn \approx \frac{1}{2}(20)(16.6)(8) = 1328$ cm²

The shaded area is $\frac{6}{8}$, or $\frac{3}{4}$, of the octagon, so its area is $\frac{3}{4}$ of the area of the octagon: $\frac{3}{4}(1328) = 996$ cm². Because the given measurements for the octagon are approximate, the shaded area is approximately 996 cm².

14. ≈ 497 cm². The area of the hexagonal donut is the difference between the area of the large hexagon and the area of the smaller hexagon. In a regular hexagon, the distance from the center to each vertex is equal to the length of each side, so in the small hexagon, $s = r \approx 8$ cm, and in the large hexagon, $s = 2r \approx 16$ cm. The given measurements are

approximate, so the areas calculated from these measurements will also be approximate.

Area of large hexagon $= \frac{1}{2}asn \approx \frac{1}{2}(2 \cdot 6.9)(16)(6) \approx 662.4$ cm²

Area of small hexagon $= \frac{1}{2}asn \approx \frac{1}{2}(6.9)(8)(6) \approx 165.6$ cm²

Area of donut $=$ (area of large hexagon) $-$ (area of small hexagon) ≈ 497 cm²

15. Total surface area $= 13{,}680$ in² $= 95$ ft²; cost $= \$8{,}075$. To find the total surface area, divide the lower portion of the kitchen floor plan into three rectangles and the upper portion into two rectangles and one regular octagon.

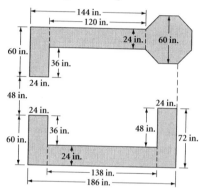

In the octagon, $s = 24$ in., $a = \frac{1}{2}(60) = 30$ in., and $n = 8$.

Lower portion: $(24)(60) + (24)(138) + (24)(72) = 6480$ in²

Upper portion: $(24)(60) + (120)(24) + \left(\frac{1}{2}\right)(30)(24)(8) = 7200$ in²

The total surface area of the countertops is $6{,}480 + 7{,}200 = 13{,}680$ in².

Convert to square feet: $13{,}680$ in² $\cdot \frac{1 \text{ ft}²}{144 \text{ in}²} = 95$ ft². The cost of the countertop will be $95(\$85) = \$8{,}075$.

16. 20 square units. Divide the quadrilateral into two triangles, A and B, as shown in this figure. Find the areas of each of these triangles, and add to find the area of the quadrilateral.

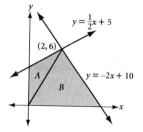

To find the area of triangle A, use the side along the y-axis as the base. Because the y-intercept of line

$y = \frac{1}{2}x + 5$ is 5, the length of this base is 5 units. The two lines intersect at $(2, 6)$, so the length of the altitude to this base is 2 units. (This altitude will fall outside the triangle.) Therefore, area(triangle A) = $\frac{1}{2}bh = \frac{1}{2}(5)(2) = 5$ square units.

To find the area of triangle B, use the side along the x-axis as the base. Because the x-intercept of the line $y = -2x + 10$ is 5, the length of this base is 5 units. The two lines intersect at $(2, 6)$, so the length of the altitude to this base is 6 units. Therefore, area(triangle B) = $\frac{1}{2}bh = \frac{1}{2}(5)(6) = 15$ square units. Thus, the total area of the quadrilateral is $5 + 15 = 20$ square units.

17. 36 square units. As in Exercise 16, divide the quadrilateral into two triangles, A and B, by connecting the origin to the point where the two lines intersect, which is $(6, 4)$ in this case.

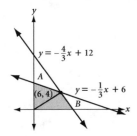

Let A be the upper triangle. The y-intercept of the line $y = -\frac{1}{3}x + 6$ is 6, so the vertices of this triangle are $(0, 0)$, $(0, 6)$, and $(6, 4)$. Use the side along the y-axis as the base. The length of the altitude to this base is 6, so area(triangle A) = $\frac{1}{2}(6)(6) = 18$ square units. Let B be the lower triangle. The x-intercept of the line $y = -\frac{4}{3}x + 12$ is 9, so the vertices of this triangle are $(0, 0)$, $(9, 0)$, and $(6, 4)$. The length of the altitude to this base is 4, so area(triangle B) = $\frac{1}{2}(9)(4) = 18$ square units. Thus, the total area of the quadrilateral is $18 + 18 = 36$ square units.

18. Conjecture: The three medians of a triangle divide the triangle into six triangles of equal area. Argument: Triangles 1 and 2 have equal area because they have equal bases and the same height. Because the centroid divides each median into thirds, you can show that the height of triangles 1 and 2 is $\frac{1}{3}$ the height of the whole triangle. Each has an area $\frac{1}{6}$ the area of the whole triangle. By the same argument, the other small triangles also have areas of $\frac{1}{6}$ the area of the whole triangle.

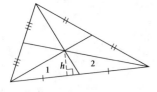

19. $nw + ny + 2x$. Write the expressions for the perimeter of the first few figures and look for a pattern. Each figure has two sides of length x, and the number of sides of lengths w and y increases by 1 each time, so the perimeter of the nth figure is $nw + ny + 2x$.

20. 504 cm². The area of pentagon $GHIJK$ is the sum of the areas of rectangle $KGHI$ and triangle HIJ:

Area of rectangle $KGHI = bh = (30)(15) = 450$ cm²

Area of $\triangle HIJ = \frac{1}{2}bh = \frac{1}{2}(9)(12) = 54$ cm²

Area of pentagon $GHIJK = 450$ cm² $+ 54$ cm² $= 504$ cm²

21. 840 cm². The area of the shaded region is the difference between the area of parallelogram $FELA$ and parallelogram $CDLB$. By subtraction, $BL = 44$ cm $- 32$ cm $= 12$ cm. $\overline{BL}$ is a base of the parallelogram.

Area of parallelogram $FELA = bh = (44)(24) = 1056$ cm²

Area of parallelogram $CDLB = bh = (12)(18) = 216$ cm²

Area of shaded region $= 1056$ cm² $- 216$ cm² $= 840$ cm²

IMPROVING YOUR VISUAL THINKING SKILLS

A: $29^2 = 841$; B: $33^2 = 1089$; C: $37^2 = 1369$; D: $42^2 = 1764$; E: $25^2 = 625$; F: $16^2 = 256$; G: $18^2 = 324$; H: $24^2 = 576$; I: $9^2 = 81$; J: $7^2 = 49$; K: $15^2 = 225$; L: $2^2 = 4$; M: $17^2 = 289$; N: $6^2 = 36$; O: $11^2 = 121$; P: $19^2 = 361$; Q: $35^2 = 1225$; R: $8^2 = 64$; S: $27^2 = 729$.

EXTENSIONS

A. Possible answer: Consider a regular polygon with a point at the center and divided into triangles with each side of the polygon as a base, where a is the apothem, s is the length of each side, and n is the number of sides in the regular polygon. If the polygon has an odd number of sides, the triangles can be arranged into a trapezoid with long base $\frac{n+1}{2}s$, short base $\frac{n-1}{2}s$, height a, and area

$$\left(\frac{\frac{n+1}{2}s + \frac{n-1}{2}s}{2}\right)a = \frac{1}{2}nas$$

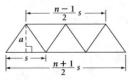

Odd number of sides
Regular pentagon
$(n = 5)$

If the polygon has an even number of sides, the triangles can be arranged into a parallelogram with base $\frac{n}{2}s$, height a, and area $\frac{1}{2}nas$.

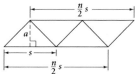

Even number of sides
Square
($n = 4$)

B. Results will vary.

LESSON 8.5

EXERCISES

1. 9π in². $A = \pi r^2 = \pi(3)^2 = 9\pi$ in².

2. 49π cm². $A = \pi r^2 = \pi(7)^2 = 49\pi$ cm².

3. 0.79 m². $A = \pi r^2 = \pi(0.5)^2 = 0.25\pi$ m² ≈ 0.79 m².

4. 3 cm. $A = \pi r^2 = 9\pi$ cm², so $r^2 = 9$, and $r = 3$ cm. (Note that r must be positive because it represents the length of a segment; the negative square root of 9, which is -3, is not relevant in this situation.)

5. $\sqrt{3}$ in. $A = \pi r^2 = 3\pi$ in², so $r^2 = 3$, and $r = \sqrt{3}$ in.

6. 0.5 m. $A = \pi r^2 = 0.785$ m², so $r = \sqrt{\frac{0.785}{\pi}} \approx 0.5$ m.

7. 36π in². $C = 2\pi r = 12\pi$ in, so $r = 6$ in. Then, $A = \pi r^2 = \pi(6)^2 = 36\pi$ in².

8. 7846 m². $C = 2\pi r = 314$ m, so $r = \frac{314}{2\pi}$ m. (Keep this number stored in your calculator.) Then $A = \pi r^2 = \pi\left(\frac{314}{2\pi}\right)^2 \approx 7846$ m².

9. $(25\pi - 48) \approx 30.5$ square units. The area of the shaded region is the difference between the area of the circle and the area of the rectangle. Circle: $r = 5$, so $A = 25\pi$. Rectangle: The dimensions are $2(3) = 6$ by $2(4) = 8$, so $A = 6 \cdot 8 = 48$. The area of the shaded region is $(25\pi - 48)$ square units.

10. $(100\pi - 128) \approx 186$ square units. The area of the shaded region is the difference between the area of the circle and the area of the triangle. Circle: $r = 10$, so $A = 100\pi$. Triangle: Use the horizontal segment at the top of the triangle as the base. Its length is $2(8) = 16$, and the corresponding height is $6 + 10 = 16$. Therefore, $A = \frac{1}{2}(16)(16) = 128$. The area of the shaded region is $(100\pi - 128)$ square units.

11. $A = \pi r^2 = 324\pi$ cm², so $r = \sqrt{324} = 18$ cm.

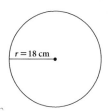

$r = 18$ cm

12. 804 m². $A = \pi r^2 = \pi(16)^2 = 256\pi \approx 804$ m².

13. 11,310 km². $A = \pi r^2 = \pi(60)^2 = 3,600\pi \approx$ 11,310 km².

14. 154 m². $A = \pi r^2 = \pi(7)^2 = 49\pi \approx 154$ m².

15. 4 times. Find the areas of the two circular regions and then compare the areas.

Muscle with radius of 3 cm: $A = 9\pi$ cm²

Muscle with radius of 6 cm: $A = 36\pi$ cm²

Ratio: $\frac{\text{strength of second muscle}}{\text{strength of first muscle}} = \frac{36\pi \text{ cm}^2}{9\pi \text{ cm}^2} = 4$

Therefore, the second (larger) muscle is 4 times as strong as the first (smaller) muscle.

16. $A \approx \pi r^2$ because the 100-gon almost completely fills the circle. Observe how, as the number of sides of a regular polygon increases, more and more of the circle is filled.

Hexagon   Dodecagon

17. 456 cm². The figure is a rhombus, so use the Parallelogram Area Conjecture: $A = bh = (24)(19) = 456$ cm².

18. 36 ft². Use the Triangle Area Conjecture. The segment of length 9 ft is the altitude to the side of the triangle with length 8 ft. $A = \frac{1}{2}bh = \frac{1}{2}(8)(9) = 36$ ft².

19. The triangles have equal area when the point is at the intersection of the two diagonals. There is no other location at which all four triangles have equal area.

20. $m\widehat{DE} = 2 \cdot 24° = 48°$ (Inscribed Angle Conjecture). $x = m\widehat{DE} = 48°$ (Parallel Lines Intercepted Arcs Conjecture).

21. $90° + 38° + 28° + 28° \neq 180°$. The measure of the unmarked base angle of the isosceles triangle is 28° (Isosceles Triangle Conjecture). Add the angle measures of the large right triangle: $90° + (38° + 28°) + 28° = 184°$, but this is impossible because the sum of the angles of any triangle must be 180° (Triangle Sum Conjecture).

22.

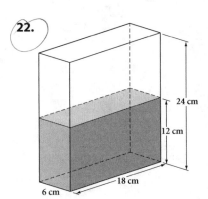

24 cm

12 cm

18 cm

6 cm

IMPROVING YOUR VISUAL THINKING SKILLS

$\frac{3}{7}$. There are 3 isosceles triangles with vertex angle at each corner, 4 with vertex angle at each side midpoint, and 8 with vertex angle in the center: $3 \cdot 4 + 4 \cdot 4 + 8 = 36$. There are 84 possible ways to select three points from the grid: $\frac{9 \cdot 8 \cdot 7}{2 \cdot 3} = 84$. 36 out of 84 gives a probability of $\frac{36}{84} = \frac{3}{7}$.

LESSON 8.6

EXERCISES

1. 6π cm². The shaded region is a sector of the circle with $a = 60°$. $A_{\text{sector}} = \frac{a}{360°} \cdot \pi r^2 = \frac{60°}{360°} \cdot \pi(6)^2 = \frac{1}{6} \cdot 36\pi = 6\pi$. The area of the shaded region is 6π cm².

2. $\frac{64\pi}{3}$ cm². The shaded region is a sector of the circle with $a = 360° - 240° = 120°$. $A_{\text{sector}} = \frac{a}{360°} \cdot \pi r^2 = \frac{120°}{360°} \cdot \pi(8)^2 = \frac{1}{3} \cdot 64\pi = \frac{64\pi}{3}$. The area of the shaded region is $\frac{64\pi}{3}$ cm².

3. 192π cm². The shaded region is a sector of the circle with $a = 360° - 90° = 270°$. $A_{\text{sector}} = \frac{a}{360°} \cdot \pi r^2 = \frac{270°}{360°} \cdot \pi(16)^2 = \frac{3}{4} \cdot 256\pi = 192\pi$. The area of the shaded region is 192π cm².

4. $(\pi - 2)$ cm². The shaded region is a segment of the circle with $a = 90°$. The area of the segment is the area of the sector minus the area of the triangle. $A_{\text{segment}} = \frac{a}{360°} \cdot \pi r^2 - \frac{1}{2}bh = \frac{90°}{360°} \cdot \pi(2)^2 - \frac{1}{2} \cdot 2 \cdot 2 = \frac{1}{4} \cdot 4\pi - 2 = \pi - 2$. The area of the shaded region is $(\pi - 2)$ cm².

5. $(48\pi + 32)$ cm². The area of the shaded region is the sum of the areas of the sector, which is $\frac{3}{4}$ of the circle, and the triangle, so $A = \frac{3}{4} \cdot 64\pi + \frac{1}{2} \cdot 8 \cdot 8 = 48\pi + 32$. The area of the shaded region is $(48\pi + 32)$ cm².

6. 33π cm². The shaded region is an annulus of the circle. $A_{\text{annulus}} = \pi R^2 - \pi r^2 = \pi(7)^2 - \pi(4)^2 = 49\pi - 16\pi = 33\pi$. The area of the shaded region is 33π cm².

7. 21π cm². The shaded region is an annulus of the circle. The radius of the larger circle is $\frac{1}{2}(10) = 5$ cm. $A_{\text{annulus}} = \pi R^2 - \pi r^2 = \pi(5)^2 - \pi(2)^2 = 25\pi - 4\pi = 21\pi$. The area of the shaded region is 21π cm².

8. $\frac{105\pi}{2}$ cm². The shaded region is $\frac{300°}{360°} = \frac{5}{6}$ of an annulus of the circle. $A = \frac{5}{6}\left[\pi(12)^2 - \pi(9)^2\right] = \frac{5}{6}(144\pi - 81\pi) = \frac{5}{6}(63\pi) = \frac{105\pi}{2}$. The area of the shaded region is $\frac{105\pi}{2}$ cm².

9. $r = 6$ cm. The shaded region is a sector of the circle with $a = 120°$.

$$A_{\text{sector}} = \frac{a}{360°} \cdot \pi r^2$$

$$12\pi = \frac{1}{3}\pi r^2$$

$$36 = r^2$$

$$r = 6$$

The radius is 6 cm.

10. $r = 7$ cm. The shaded region is an annulus of the circle. The radius of the larger circle is $\frac{1}{2}(18) = 9$ cm.

$$A_{\text{annulus}} = \pi R^2 - \pi r^2$$

$$32\pi = 81\pi - \pi r^2$$

$$\pi r^2 = 49\pi$$

$$r = 7 \text{ cm}$$

11. $x = 75°$. The shaded region is a sector of the circle with $a = x$ and $r = 24$ cm.

$$A_{\text{sector}} = \frac{a}{360°} \cdot \pi r^2$$

$$120\pi = \frac{x}{360°} \cdot \pi(24)^2$$

$$\frac{x}{360°} = \frac{120\pi}{576\pi} = \frac{5}{24}$$

$$x = \frac{5}{24} \cdot 360°$$

$$x = 75°$$

12. $x = 100°$. The shaded region is $\frac{x}{360°}$ of an annulus of the circle.

$$A = \frac{x}{360°} \cdot \pi(10^2 - 8^2)$$

$$10\pi = \frac{x}{360°} \cdot 36\pi$$

$$\frac{10\pi}{36\pi} = \frac{x}{360°}$$

$$\frac{10}{36} = \frac{x}{360°}$$

$$x = \frac{10}{36} \cdot 360°$$

$$x = 100°$$

13. 42 cans. The pizza slice is a sector of the circle. Area of slice $= \frac{36°}{360°} \cdot \pi(20)^2 = \frac{1}{10}\pi \cdot 400 = 40\pi$. The area of the pizza slice is 40π ft^2. Now find the number of cans of tomato sauce needed to cover this slice: 40π ft$^2 \cdot \frac{1 \text{ can}}{3 \text{ ft}^2} = \frac{40\pi}{3} \approx 41.9$ cans. Round up to 42 cans.

14. \$448. The path around the circular fountain can be considered an annulus of a larger circle. The radius of the smaller circle is $\frac{1}{2} \cdot 8 = 4$ m, and the radius of the larger circle is $4 + 1.5 = 5.5$ m. Area of path $= \pi(5.5)^2 - \pi(4)^2 = 30.25\pi - 16\pi = 14.25\pi$. The area of the path is 14.25π m^2. Now find the cost to pave this path: 14.25π m$^2 \cdot \frac{\$10}{1 \text{ m}^2} = \$142.5\pi \approx \$448$.

15. a.

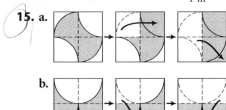

b.

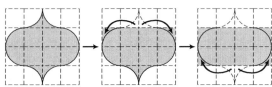

c.

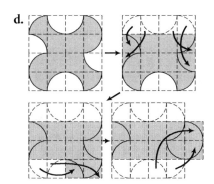

d.

16. Sample answer:

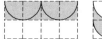

17. The area of each square is $12 \cdot 12 = 144$ cm^2. Subtract the area of the circle or circles from the area of the square to find the area of the shaded region.

a. $(144 - 36\pi)$ cm^2; 78.54%. The radius of the circle is 6 cm, so its area is 36π cm, and the area of the shaded region is $(144 - 36\pi)$ cm^2. Now compare the area of the circle to the area of the square.

$$\frac{\text{area of circle}}{\text{area of square}} = \frac{36\pi \text{ cm}^2}{144 \text{ cm}^2} \approx 78.54\%$$

b. $(144 - 36\pi)$ cm^2; 78.54%. The radius of each circle is $\frac{1}{4} \cdot 12 = 3$ cm, so the area of the four circles is $4\pi \cdot (3)^2 = 4\pi \cdot 9 = 36\pi$ cm^2. Therefore, as in 17a, the area of the shaded region is $(144 - 36\pi)$ cm^2, and the area of the circles is about 78.54% of the area of the square.

c. $(144 - 36\pi)$ cm^2; 78.54%. The radius of each circle is $\frac{1}{6} \cdot 12 = 2$ cm, so the area of the nine circles is $9\pi(2)^2 = 9\pi \cdot 4 = 36\pi$ cm^2. Therefore, as in 17a, the area of the shaded region is $(144 - 36\pi)$ cm^2, and the area of the circles is about 78.54% of the area of the square.

d. $(144 - 36\pi)$ cm^2; 78.54%. The radius of each circle is $\frac{1}{8} \cdot 12 = \frac{12}{8} = 1.5$ cm, so the area of the sixteen circles is $16\pi(1.5)^2 = 16\pi \cdot 2.25 = 36\pi$ cm^2. Therefore, as in 17a, the area of the shaded region is $(144 - 36\pi)$ cm^2, and the area of the circles is about 78.54% of the area of the square.

18. 480 m^2. Combine two conjectures about trapezoids to find an alternate formula for the area of a trapezoid. By the Trapezoid Area Conjecture, $A = \frac{1}{2}h(b_1 + b_2)$. By the Trapezoid Midsegment Conjecture, the length of the midsegment is $\frac{1}{2}(b_1 + b_2)$. Therefore, by substitution, $A = (\text{midsegment})(\text{height})$. Thus, the area of a trapezoid with height 15 m and midsegment with length 32 m is $(32)(15) = 480$ m^2.

19. $AB \approx 17.0$ cm, $AG \approx 6.6$ cm. First calculate the area of $\triangle ABC$ using $\overline{AC}$ as the base and $\overline{BH}$ as the corresponding altitude.

Area of $\triangle ABC = \frac{1}{2}bh = \frac{1}{2}(7.1)(12.0) = 42.6$ cm^2

The area of the triangle is the same for any choice of base, so we can use this result to find AB and AG. First find AB. Notice that $\overline{CE}$ is the altitude to $\overline{AB}$.

$A = \frac{1}{2}bh$	
$A = \frac{1}{2}(AB)(CE)$	Substitute AB for b and CE for h.
$42.6 = \frac{1}{2}AB \cdot 5.0$	Substitute 42.6 for A and 5.0 for h.
$85.2 = AB \cdot 5.0$	Multiply by 2.
$AB \approx 17.0$ cm	Divide by 5.0.

Now find AG. Notice that $\overline{AG}$ is the altitude to $\overline{BC}$.

$A = \frac{1}{2}bh$	
$A = \frac{1}{2}(BC)(AG)$	Substitute BC for b and AG for h.
$42.6 = \frac{1}{2}(13.0)AG$	Substitute 42.6 for A and 13.0 for BC.

$85.2 = 13.0 \cdot AG$ Multiply by 2.

$AG \approx 6.6$ cm   Divide by 13.0 and round to the nearest tenth.

20. True. If $24\pi = \frac{90°}{360°} \cdot 2\pi r$, then $r = 48$ cm.

21. True. If $\frac{360°}{n} = 24°$, then $n = 15$.

22. False. It could be a rhombus.

23. True. Triangle Inequality Conjecture.

IMPROVING YOUR REASONING SKILLS

1. 45 Degrees in an Acute Angle of an Isosceles Right Triangle

2. 7 Sides of a Heptagon

3. 90 Degrees in each Angle of a Rectangle

4. 5 Diagonals in a Pentagon

EXTENSIONS

A. Research results will vary.

B. This method works because $\frac{2\pi R + 2\pi r}{2}(R - r) = \pi(R + r)(R - r) = \pi(R^2 - r^2) = \pi R^2 - \pi r^2$.

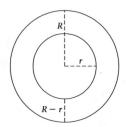

C. $\frac{2\pi R + 2\pi r}{2}$ is the average of the two circumferences.

EXPLORATION · GEOMETRIC PROBABILITY II

PROJECT

Project should satisfy the following criteria:

• Predictions mention possible outcomes and most likely outcomes.

• Irregularities in weight and shape of dice are minimized.

• The histogram's range reflects the minimum and maximum possible outcomes and has the approximate correct shape.

• Simulation results roughly match the theoretical probability.

• Report makes a connection between the number of trials and how closely the outcomes match the expected values.

Extra credit

• Unusual dice are explored.

• Report compares theoretical outcomes for several kinds of dice.

EXERCISES

1. 150 cm². The solid is a cube. Each of the six faces is a square with area $(5)(5) = 25$ cm², so the surface area of the cube is $6(25) = 150$ cm².

2. 4070 cm². The solid is a rectangular prism, so it has six faces: two squares with sides of length 37 cm, and four rectangles, each with dimensions 37 cm by 9 cm. To find the surface area of the prism, add the areas of the six faces: $2(37 \cdot 37) + 4(37 \cdot 9) = 2738 + 1332 = 4070$, so the surface area of the rectangular prism is 4070 cm².

3. 216 cm². The solid is a triangular prism, so it has five faces: one rectangle with base of length 6 cm and height 7 cm, one rectangle with base of length 8 cm and height 7 cm, one rectangle with base of length 10 cm and height 7 cm, and two triangles, each with base of length 8 cm and height 6 cm. To find the surface area of the prism, add the areas of the five faces: $(6)(7) + (8)(7) + (10)(7) + 2(\frac{1}{2} \cdot 8 \cdot 6) = 42 + 56 + 70 + 48 = 216$, so the surface area of the triangular prism is 216 cm².

4. 340 cm². The solid is a square pyramid. Use one of the formulas from Investigation 1 on page 464 of your book. Here $a = 5$ (the apothem connects the center of the square to the midpoint of its side), $l = 12$, and $P = nb = 4(10) = 40$. Substitute these values in the formula $SA = \frac{1}{2}P(l + a)$ to obtain $SA = \frac{1}{2} \cdot 40(12 + 5) = 340$. Thus, the surface area of the square pyramid is 340 cm².

5. ≈ 103.7 cm². The solid is a cone. To find its surface area, use the formula from Investigation 2 on page 465 of your book. Substitute 3 for r and 8 for l in the formula $SA = \pi r l + \pi r^2$ to obtain $SA = \pi(3)(8) + \pi(3)^2 = 24\pi + 9\pi = 33\pi \approx 103.7$. Thus, the surface area of the cone is approximately 103.7 cm².

6. ≈ 1187.5 cm². The solid is a cylinder. To find its surface area, use the formula from Example B on pages 462–463 of your book. Substitute 7 for r and 20 for h in the formula $SA = 2 \cdot \pi r^2 + (2\pi r)h = 2 \cdot \pi \cdot 7^2 + 2 \cdot \pi \cdot 7 \cdot 20 = 98\pi + 280\pi = 378\pi \approx 1187.5$. Thus, the surface area of the cylinder is approximately 1187.5 cm².

7. ≈ 1604.4 cm². The solid is a hexagonal prism, so it has eight faces: two hexagonal faces (the bases) and six congruent rectangular lateral faces with sides of length 14 cm and height 7 cm. To find the sum of the areas of the two hexagonal bases, substitute 12.1 for a, 14 for s, and 6 for n in the formula $A = \frac{1}{2}asn$, and multiply by 2 to obtain $2 \cdot \frac{1}{2}(12.1)(14)(6) = 1016.4$. Because 12.1 is an approximate value, the total area of the hexagons is approximately

1016.4 cm². Now find the sum of the areas of the six rectangular lateral faces: 6(14)(7) = 588, so the total area of the lateral faces is 588 cm². (Another way to think of this is to imagine unwrapping the six rectangles into one rectangle. The lateral area of this "unwrapped" rectangle is the height times the perimeter, which gives the same result.) Therefore, the surface area of the hexagonal prism is about 1016.4 + 588 = 1604.4 cm².

8. ≈ 1040 cm². The solid is a pyramid whose base is a regular pentagon, so it has six faces: the pentagonal base and the five triangular lateral faces. To find the area of the base, substitute 11 for a, 16 for s, and 5 for n in the formula for the area of a regular polygon: $A = \frac{1}{2}asn \approx \frac{1}{2}(11)(16)(5) = 440$. Therefore, the area of the base is approximately 440 cm². Find the area of each triangular lateral face: $\frac{1}{2}sl = \frac{1}{2}(16)(15) = 120$, so the area of each lateral face is 120 cm², and the total area of the five lateral faces is 5 · 120 = 600 cm². Thus, the surface area of the pyramid is approximately 440 + 600 = 1040 cm².

9. ≈ 414.7 cm². Draw and label all the faces of this solid.

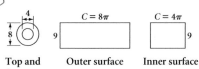

Top and bottom   Outer surface   Inner surface

To find the area of the bottom surface, find the area of an annulus with outer radius 4 and inner radius 2: $\pi(4)^2 - \pi(2)^2 = 16\pi - 4\pi = 12\pi$. The area of the top surface is the same, so the sum of the areas of the top and bottom surfaces is 24π. The area of the outer lateral surface is $8\pi \cdot 9 = 72\pi$, and the area of the inner lateral surface is $4\pi \cdot 9 = 36\pi$. Therefore, the surface area of the solid is $24\pi + 72\pi + 36\pi = 132\pi \approx 414.7$ cm².

10. ≈ 329.1 cm². The solid is a rectangular prism with a hole through its center. First find the areas of the rectangular faces. The top and bottom faces each have area lw, so the sum of the areas of these two faces is 2(8)(4) = 64 cm². The side faces each have area hw, so the sum of the areas of these two faces is 2(10)(4) = 80 cm². Next find the areas of the front and back faces by subtracting the area of a circle with radius 2 cm from that of a rectangle with area lh. The sum of the areas of these two faces is $2(lh - \pi r^2) = 2[(8)(10) - \pi(2)^2] = 160 - 8\pi$. Now find the surface area of the hole. Notice that the hole is a cylinder with radius 2 cm and height 4 cm. The lateral surface area of this cylinder is $2\pi rh = 2\pi(2)(4) = 16\pi$. Add all the areas that you have found to obtain the total surface area of the solid: $64 + 80 + (160 - 8\pi) + 16\pi =$

$304 + 8\pi \approx 329.1$. The surface area of the solid is approximately 329.1 cm².

11. Area of square + 4 · area of trapezoid + 4 · area of triangle

12. $1,570. Find the cost of the paint and then the cost of the shingles. Paint: Use the measurements given in the end view to find the area of each end wall. The area of each end wall is the sum of the areas of a rectangle, a trapezoid, and a triangle: $(30)(24) + \frac{1}{2}(12)(12 + 30) + \frac{1}{2}(2.5)(12) = 720 + 252 + 15 = 987$ ft². There are two end walls, so the sum of the areas is 2(987) = 1974 ft². Each of the side walls is a rectangle with $b = 40$ ft and $h = 24$ ft, so each side wall has an area of (40)(24) = 960 ft², and the sum of the areas of these two walls is 2 · 960 = 1920 ft². Therefore, the total surface area of all the walls is 1974 + 1920 = 3894 ft². Find the number of gallons of paint needed to paint these walls: $3894 \text{ ft}^2 \cdot \frac{1 \text{ gal}}{250 \text{ ft}^2} \approx 15.6$ gal. Because the paint must be purchased in gallons, round up to 16 gal. The cost of 16 gal of paint at $25 per gallon is 16 · $25 = $400.

Shingles: Find the total surface area of the roof, which is made up of two rectangles with dimensions 40 ft by 15 ft and two rectangles with dimensions 40 ft by 6.5 ft. 2(40)(15) + 2(40)(6.5) = 1200 + 520 = 1720, so the total surface area of the roof is 1720 ft². Find the number of bundles of shingles needed for the roof: $1720 \text{ ft}^2 \cdot \frac{1 \text{ bundle}}{100 \text{ ft}^2} = 17.2$ bundles. Because the shingles must be purchased in complete bundles, round up to 18 bundles. The cost of 18 bundles of shingles at $65 per bundle is 18($65) = $1,170.

The total cost for painting the walls and putting new shingles on the roof is $400 + $1,170 = $1,570.

13. Sample answer:

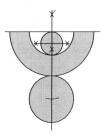

14. Sample tiling:

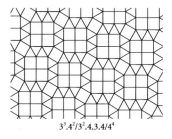

$3^3.4^2/3^2.4.3.4/4^4$

15. $a = 75°$, $b = 75°$, $c = 30°$, $d = 60°$, $e = 150°$, and $f = 30°$. First, $a = \frac{1}{2}(150°) = 75°$ (Inscribed Angle Conjecture). Then $b = a = 75°$ (Isosceles Triangle Conjecture). Next, $c = 180° - 2(75°) = 30°$ (Triangle Sum Conjecture), and $d = 2(30°) = 60°$ (Inscribed Angle Conjecture). Also, $e = 2b = 150°$ (Inscribed Angle Conjecture). Finally, $f = \frac{1}{2}[(150° + d) - e] = \frac{1}{2}(210° - 150°) = \frac{1}{2}(60°) = 30°$ by the Intersecting Tangents Conjecture. (See Lesson 6.2, Exercise 23.)

16. About 23 days. Each sector is about 1.767 km². The number of days that the cattle will graze on each sector is $\frac{365}{16} \approx 23$. The area of each sector is $\frac{1}{16}\pi r^2 = \frac{1}{16}\pi(3)^2 = \frac{9}{16}\pi \approx 1.767$ km².

17. $a = 50°$, $b = 50°$, $c = 80°$, $d = 100°$, $e = 80°$, $f = 100°$, $g = 80°$, $h = 80°$, $k = 80°$, $m = 20°$, and $n = 80°$. First, $a = 50°$ (AIA Conjecture), and $b = a$, so $b = 50°$. $a + b + c = 180°$, so $c = 180° - 2(50°) = 80°$. The angle with measure d forms a linear pair with the corresponding angle of the angle with measure c, so $d = 180° - c = 100°$. Likewise, the angle with measure e forms a linear pair with the corresponding angle of the angle of measure d, so $e = 180° - d = 80°$. By the same reasoning, $f = 180° - e = 100°$, and $g = 180° - f = 80°$. Also, $h = g$ (AIA Conjecture), so $h = 80°$, and $k = g = 80°$ (Isosceles Triangle Conjecture). Next, $m + g + k = 180°$ (Triangle Sum Conjecture), so $m = 180° - 2(80°) = 20°$. Finally, $n = k$ (AIA Conjecture), so $n = 80°$.

18. 398 square units. Find the surface area of each of the first four solids and look for a pattern.

Solid number (n)	1	2	3	4
Surface area	6	14	22	30

The surface area of the first solid in this pattern is 6, and each number after the first is found by adding 8 to the previous one, so the surface area of the nth solid will be $6 + (n - 1)(8) = 6 + 8n - 8 = 8n - 2$. Therefore, the surface area of the 50th solid will be $8(50) - 2 = 400 - 2 = 398$ square units.

Another way to find the expression $6 + (n - 1)(8)$ is to observe that the first solid, which is a single cube, has a surface area of 6, and that each solid after that adds 2 more cubes, each of which increases the surface area by 4. Each additional cube adds 5 units to the surface area, but subtracts 1 because one face of a cube in the previous solid is covered. Therefore, the number of cubes added in each solid after the first is $2(4) = 8$.

IMPROVING YOUR VISUAL THINKING SKILLS

Move g and j to the second row, and move a to make a new bottom row:

EXTENSION

Prism: $2lw + 2lh + 2wh$ or $2(lw + lh + wh)$. Square-based pyramid: $b^2 + 2bl$ or $b(b + 2l)$. Cylinder: $2\pi r^2 + 2\pi rh$ or $2\pi r(r + h)$. Cone: $\pi r^2 + \pi rl$ or $\pi r(r + l)$.

EXPLORATION · ALTERNATIVE AREA FORMULAS

IMPROVING YOUR VISUAL THINKING SKILLS

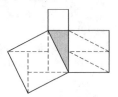
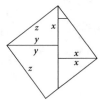
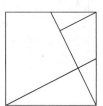

CHAPTER 8 REVIEW

EXERCISES

1. Parallelogram (B) **2.** Triangle (A)

3. Trapezoid (C) **4.** Kite (E)

5. Regular polygon (F) **6.** Circle (D)

7. Sector (J) **8.** Annulus (I)

9. Cylinder (G) **10.** Cone (H)

11.

Apothem

12.
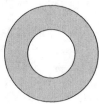

13.
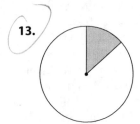

14. Sample answer: Construct an altitude from the vertex of an obtuse angle to the base. Cut off the right triangle and move it to the opposite side, forming a rectangle. Because the parallelogram's area hasn't changed, its area equals the area of the rectangle. Because the area of the rectangle is given by the formula $A = bh$, the area of the parallelogram is also given by $A = bh$.

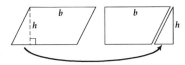

15. Sample answer: Make a copy of the trapezoid and put the two copies together to form a parallelogram with base $(b_1 + b_2)$ and height h. Thus, the area of one trapezoid is given by the formula $A = \frac{1}{2}(b_1 + b_2)h$, or $A = \frac{1}{2}h(b_1 + b_2)$.

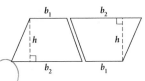

16. Sample answer: Cut a circular region into a large number of wedges and arrange them into a shape that resembles a rectangle. The base length of this "rectangle" is πr and the height is r, so its area is πr^2. Thus, the area of a circle is given by the formula $A = \pi r^2$.

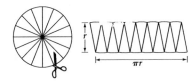

17. 800 cm^2. Use the midsegment formula for the area of a trapezoid: $A = (\text{midsegment})(\text{height}) = (40)(20) = 800$ cm^2.

18. 5990.4 cm^2. The figure is a regular octagon, so use the formula for the area of a regular polygon. $A = \frac{1}{2}asn \approx \frac{1}{2}(36)(41.6)(8) = 5990.4$ cm^2.

19. $60\pi \approx 188.5$ cm^2. The shaded region is an annulus. $A_{\text{annulus}} = \pi R^2 - \pi r^2 = \pi(8)^2 - \pi(2)^2 = 64\pi - 4\pi = 60\pi \approx 188.5$ cm^2.

20. 32 cm. Use the formula $A = \frac{1}{2}bh$. Here $576 = \frac{1}{2} \cdot 36 \cdot h$, so $576 = 18h$, and $h = 32$ cm.

21. 32 cm. The figure is a kite, so use the formula $A = \frac{1}{2}d_1d_2$. Here $576 = \frac{1}{2} \cdot d_1 \cdot 36$, so $576 = 18d_1$, and $d_1 = 32$ cm.

22. 15 cm. The figure is a trapezoid, so use the formula $A = \frac{1}{2}h(b_1 + b_2)$.

$126 = \frac{1}{2}(9)(13 + b)$

$252 = 9(13 + b)$

$28 = 13 + b$

$b = 15$ cm

23. 81π cm^2. Find the radius of the circle and then use the radius to find the area. $C = 2\pi r$, so $18\pi = 2\pi r$, and $r = 9$ cm. Then $A = \pi r^2 = \pi(9)^2 = 81\pi$ cm^2.

24. 48π cm. Find the radius of the circle and then use the radius to find the circumference. $A = \pi r^2$, so $576\pi = \pi r^2$, $r^2 = 576$, and $r = 24$ cm. Then $C = 2\pi r = 2\pi(24) = 48\pi$ cm.

25. 40°. The shaded region is a sector of a circle with radius 12 cm. The area of the sector is 16π cm^2 and the area of the complete circle is 144π cm^2, so

$$\frac{A_{\text{sector}}}{A_{\text{circle}}} = \frac{16\pi \text{ cm}^2}{144\pi \text{ cm}^2} = \frac{1}{9}$$

Therefore, the sector is $\frac{1}{9}$ of the circle, so $m\angle FAN = \frac{1}{9}(360°) = 40°$.

26. 153.9 cm^2. To find the area of the shaded region, subtract the areas of the two small semicircles from the area of the large semicircle.

Large semicircle: $r = 14$ cm; $A = \frac{1}{2}\pi r^2 = \frac{1}{2}\pi(14)^2 = 98\pi$ cm^2

Two small semicircles: $r = 7$ cm; $A = 2\left(\frac{1}{2}\pi r^2\right) = \pi(7)^2 = 49\pi$ cm^2

Therefore, the area of the shaded region is $98\pi - 49\pi = 49\pi \approx 153.9$ cm^2.

27. 72 cm^2. By rearranging this figure into a rectangle, you can show that its area is one-half the area of the square. (See Lesson 8.6, Exercise 15a. The figure here is the same, except that it has been rotated 90°, which does not affect its area.) Because the arcs in this figure are arcs of a circle with radius 6 cm, the square has sides of length 12 cm. Therefore, the area of the square is 144 cm^2, and the area of the shaded region is $\frac{1}{2}(144) = 72$ cm^2.

28. 30.9 cm^2. To find the area of the shaded region, subtract the combined area of the four quarter-circles from the area of the square. As in Exercise 27, the area of the square is 144 cm^2. The area of the four quarter-circles is $4\left(\frac{1}{4}\right)\pi(6)^2 = 36\pi$ cm^2. Therefore, the area of the shaded region is $(144 - 36\pi) \approx 30.9$ cm^2.

29. 300 cm^2. The solid is a triangular prism, so it has five faces: one rectangle with dimensions 8 cm by 12 cm, one rectangle with dimensions 8 cm by 5 cm, one rectangle (the slanted face) with dimensions 8 cm by 13 cm, and two right triangles, each with base of length 12 cm and height 5 cm. To find the surface area of the prism, add the areas of the five faces: $(8 \cdot 12) + (8 \cdot 5) + (8 \cdot 13) + 2\left(\frac{1}{2} \cdot 12 \cdot 5\right) = 96 + 40 + 104 + 60 = 300$, so the surface area of the triangular prism is 300 cm².

30. 940 cm². To find the surface area of the prism, add the areas of its six faces.

Area of two trapezoids: $2\left[\frac{1}{2} \cdot 12(35 + 10)\right] = 12(45) = 540$ cm²

Area of four rectangles: $15 \cdot 5 + 10 \cdot 5 + 20 \cdot 5 + 35 \cdot 5 = 75 + 50 + 100 + 175 = 400$ cm²

Surface area of prism $= 540 + 400 = 940$ cm²

31. 1356 cm². The solid is a pyramid with a rectangular base. To find the surface area of the pyramid, add the areas of its five faces.

Area of rectangular base $= 30 \cdot 14 = 420$ cm²

Area of two triangles with base length 30 cm and height 20 cm: $2\left(\frac{1}{2} \cdot 30 \cdot 20\right) = 600$ cm²

Area of two triangles with base length 14 cm and height 24 cm: $2\left(\frac{1}{2} \cdot 14 \cdot 24\right) = 336$ cm²

Surface area of pyramid $= 420 + 600 + 336 = 1356$ cm²

32. $A = 112$ square units. The figure is a parallelogram with base length 14 units and height 8 units, so its area is $14 \cdot 8 = 112$ square units.

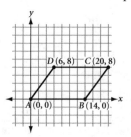

33. $A = 81$ square units. Draw $\overline{RO}$ to divide quadrilateral $FOUR$ into $\triangle RFO$ and $\triangle RUO$. Find the areas of these two triangles, using $\overline{RO}$ as the base for both triangles. Notice that $15 - (-3) = 18$.

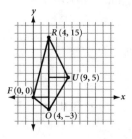

Area of $\triangle RFO = \frac{1}{2}(18)(4) = 36$ square units

Area of $\triangle RUO = \frac{1}{2}(18)(5) = 45$ square units

Area of quadrilateral $FOUR = 36 + 45 = 81$ square units

34. 6 cm. Use the formula $A = \frac{1}{2}h(b_1 + b_2)$. Notice that although the values of b_1 and b_2 are not given individually, the value of $b_1 + b_2$ is provided.

$$A = \frac{1}{2}h(b_1 + b_2)$$
$$66 = \frac{1}{2}h(22)$$
$$66 = 11h$$
$$h = 6$$

The height of the trapezoid is 6 cm.

35. 172.5 cm². Use the formula $A = \frac{1}{2}asn$. The apothem length given in this exercise is approximate, so $A \approx \frac{1}{2}(6.9)(10)(5) = 172.5$, and the area of the pentagon is approximately 172.5 cm².

36. Sample answers:

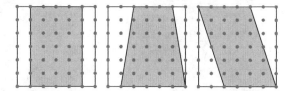

37. 1250 m². This problem was investigated in the Maximizing Area project at the end of Lesson 8.2 (see page 433 in your book). The only difference is that here there are 100 m of fencing rather than 10 m. If you completed that project, apply your result to this problem. If not, work through the project with your graphing calculator, but use 100 rather than 10. The rectangle with maximum area has the following shape.

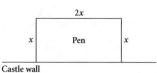

38. The circle gives the maximum area. For the square, $100 = 4s$, $s = 25$ ft, $A = 25^2 = 625$ ft². For the circle, $100 = 2\pi r$ and $r \approx 15.9$, so $A \approx \pi(15.9)^2 \approx 794$ ft².

39. A round peg in a square hole. Draw two circles with the same radius, r, one with the circle inscribed in a square and the other with a square inscribed in the circle.

For each of these figures, find the fraction of the hole that is covered by a cross section of the peg.

Round peg in square hole: Area of circle $= \pi r^2$. The length of a side of this square is $2r$, so area of square $= (2r)^2 = 4r^2$. Fraction of square hole filled by round peg:

$$\frac{\text{area of circle}}{\text{area of square}} = \frac{\pi r^2}{4r^2} = \frac{\pi}{4}$$

Square peg in round hole: Area of circle $= \pi r^2$. The diagonals of the square are diameters of the circle, so they each have length $2r$. Look at the four triangles formed by the diagonals. Each has area

$$\frac{1}{2}bh = \frac{1}{2}r^2$$

so the area of the whole square is $4\left(\frac{1}{2}\right)r^2 = 2r^2$. Fraction of round hole filled by square peg:

$$\frac{\text{area of square}}{\text{area of hole}} = \frac{2r^2}{\pi r^2} = \frac{2}{\pi}$$

Now compare $\frac{\pi}{4}$ and $\frac{2}{\pi}$. $\frac{\pi}{4} \approx 0.785$ and $\frac{2}{\pi} \approx 0.637$, so $\frac{\pi}{4} > \frac{2}{\pi}$. Therefore, the round peg fills a larger fraction of the square hole (78.5%) than the square peg fills in a round hole (63.7%). This means that the round peg in the square hole is the better fit.

40. Giant. From the drawing, the giant slice is $\frac{1}{4}$ of the pizza, the large slice is $\frac{1}{6}$ of the pizza, and the regular slice is $\frac{1}{8}$ of the pizza. An easy way to figure out the best deal is to find the cost for the whole pizza based on the cost per slice.

Giant slice: 4($2.85) = $11.40

Large slice: 6($2.25) = $13.50

Regular slice: 8($1.75) = $14.00

Because the cost of a whole pizza is smallest for the giant slice, the giant slice is the best deal.

An equivalent approach is to find the amount of pizza per dollar that you get with each kind of slice.

Giant slice: $\frac{\frac{1}{4}}{\$2.85} \approx 0.088$ pizza/dollar

Large slice: $\frac{\frac{1}{6}}{\$2.25} \approx 0.074$ pizza/dollar

Regular slice: $\frac{\frac{1}{8}}{\$1.75} \approx 0.071$ pizza/dollar

Because the amount of pizza per dollar is greatest for the giant slice, the giant slice is the best deal.

41. About 14 oz. Compare the areas of the two pizzas. For the 12-inch-diameter pizza, $r = 6$ in, so $A = 36\pi$ in². For the 16-inch-diameter pizza, $r = 8$ in, so $A = 64\pi$ in². The amount of dough that is needed for the larger pizza can be found by solving a proportion. Let x represent the number of ounces of dough needed for the 16-inch-diameter pizza.

$$\frac{8 \text{ oz}}{x} = \frac{36\pi \text{ in}^2}{64\pi \text{ in}^2} = \frac{9}{16}$$

$$9x = 8(16)$$

$$9x = 128$$

$$x = \frac{128}{9} \approx 14.2$$

About 14 oz of dough will be needed to make the 16-inch-diameter pizza.

42. Biggest slice: one-eighth of a 12-inch-diameter pie. Most crust: One-fourth of a 6-inch pie and one-eighth of a 12-inch pie both have the same length of crust, and more than one-sixth of an 8-inch pie.

To find the biggest slice, compare the areas of the slices, which are sectors of a circle.

One-fourth of 6-inch-diameter pizza: $r = 3$ in; $A = \frac{1}{4}(9\pi) = \frac{9\pi}{4}$ in²

One-sixth of 8-inch-diameter pizza: $r = 4$ in; $A = \frac{1}{6}(16\pi) = \frac{8\pi}{3}$ in²

One-eighth of 12-inch-diameter pizza: $r = 6$ in; $A = \frac{1}{8}(36\pi) = \frac{9\pi}{2}$ in²

Because $\frac{9}{2} > \frac{8}{3} > \frac{9}{4}$, one-eighth of a 12-inch-diameter pizza is the largest slice. To find out which slice has the most crust around its edge, compare the outer circumferences of the pizzas (sectors) by finding the appropriate fraction of the circumference of each pizza.

One-fourth of 6-inch-diameter pizza: $\frac{1}{4}C = \frac{1}{4}\pi d = \frac{1}{4}\pi(6) = \frac{3\pi}{2}$ in.

One-sixth of 8-inch-diameter pizza: $\frac{1}{6}C = \frac{1}{6}\pi d = \frac{1}{6}\pi(8) = \frac{4\pi}{3}$ in.

One-eighth of 12-inch-diameter pizza: $\frac{1}{8}C = \frac{1}{8}\pi d = \frac{1}{8}\pi(12) = \frac{3\pi}{2}$ in.

Because $\frac{3}{2} > \frac{4}{3}$, the slice of the 6-inch-diameter pizza and the slice of the 12-inch-diameter pizza have the same length of crust around the edge, and this is more than the amount of crust around the edge of the 8-inch-diameter pizza.

43. a. Perimeter at widest part = 96 ft. Perimeter at bottom = 40 ft. The widest part of the balloon is at the bottom of the top row of trapezoids. Here the perimeter is $8 \cdot 12 = 96$ ft. The perimeter at the bottom of the balloon is $8 \cdot 5 = 40$ ft.

b. 3290 ft². This figure may help you see the panels that make up the balloon more clearly.

Find the surface area of the balloon by adding the areas of all the panels.

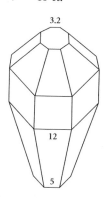

Octagon: $A = \frac{1}{2}asn = \frac{1}{2}(3.8)(3.2)(8) = 48.64$ ft²

8 small trapezoids: $A = 8\left[\frac{1}{2}h(b_1 + b_2)\right] = 8\left[\frac{1}{2} \cdot 12(3.2 + 12)\right] = 729.6$ ft²

8 squares: $A = 8s^2 = 8(12)^2 = 1152$ ft²

8 large trapezoids: $A = 8\left[\frac{1}{2}h(b_1 + b_2)\right] =$
$8\left[\frac{1}{2} \cdot 20(12 + 5)\right] = 1360$ ft²

Total surface area of balloon = 48.64 + 729.6 + 1152 + 1360 = 3290.24. To the nearest square foot, the total surface area of the balloon is 3290 ft².

44. $3,000. First find the surface area of one wedge, which is a triangular prism, so it has 5 faces: two triangular bases that are right triangles with base length 6 cm and height 8 cm, one rectangle with dimensions 6 cm by 0.5 cm, one rectangle with dimensions 8 cm by 0.5 cm, and one rectangle with dimensions 10 cm by 0.5 cm.

Area of two triangles = $2\left(\frac{1}{2} \cdot 6 \cdot 8\right) = 48$ cm²

Sum of areas of three rectangles = $6(0.5) + 8(0.5) + 10(0.5) = 12$ cm²

Surface area of wedge = 48 + 12 = 60 cm²

The total surface area of 10,000 metal wedges is $10,000(60) = 600,000$ cm².

Find the cost for the silver to electroplate these wedges.

$600,000$ cm² $\cdot \dfrac{\$1}{200 \text{ cm}^2} = \$3,000$

45. $4,160. First find the surface area of the top and lateral faces of the cylinder, which has radius 3.5 m and height 10 m. Because the bottom faces will not be painted, there is only one circular face, so use πr^2 rather than $2\pi r^2$ in computing the surface area.

$SA = \pi r^2 + 2\pi rh = \pi(3.5)^2 + 2\pi(3.5)(10) = 12.25\pi + 70\pi = 82.25\pi$ m²

There are nine containers to be painted, so the total surface area to be painted is $9(82.25\pi) = 740.25\pi$ m². Next find the number of gallons of sealant that is needed.

740.25π m² $\cdot \dfrac{1 \text{ gal}}{18 \text{ m}^2} \approx 129.2$ gal

Because the sealant is sold in gallon containers, round up to 130 gal. The cost for 130 gal of sealant is $130(\$32) = \$4,160$.

46. It's a bad deal. $2\pi r_1 = 44$ cm. $2\pi r_2 = 22$ cm, which implies $4\pi r_2 = 44$ cm. Therefore, $r_1 = 2r_2$. The area of the large bundle is $4\pi(r_2)^2$ cm². The combined area of the two small bundle is $2\pi(r_2)^2$ cm. Thus, he is getting half as much for the same price.

47. $2,002. First find the lateral surface area of one cone, which has radius 24 in. and slant height 51 in.

Lateral surface area of one cone $= \pi rl = \pi(24)(51) = 1,224\pi$ in²

Lateral surface area of 100 cones $= 100(1,224\pi) = 122,400\pi$ in²

Now find the number of pints of oxidizer that is needed to cover 100 cones.

$122,400\pi$ in² $\cdot \dfrac{1 \text{ pt}}{5,000 \text{ in}^2} \approx 76.9$ pt

The oxidizer is sold in pints, so round up to 77 pt. The cost for 77 pt of oxidizer is $77(\$26) = \$2,002$.

48. $384 (16 gal). Add the areas of all the walls to be painted.

Front rectangle: $10 \cdot 40 = 400$ ft²

2 rectangles of front portion: $2 \cdot 28 \cdot 10 = 560$ ft²

2 rectangles of back portion: $2 \cdot 18 \cdot 10 = 360$ ft²

Far-back rectangle: $24 \cdot 10 = 240$ ft²

Rectangle at back of front portion: $16 \cdot 10 = 160$ ft²

Front triangle: $\frac{1}{2} \cdot 40 \cdot 16 = 320$ ft²

Back triangle: $\frac{1}{2} \cdot 24 \cdot 10 = 120$ ft²

Partially covered triangle at back of front portion: $\frac{1}{2} \cdot 40 \cdot 16 - \frac{1}{2} \cdot 24 \cdot 10 = 320 - 120 = 200$ ft²

Total surface area of walls = 2360 ft²

Find the number of gallons of paint required. 2360 ft² $\cdot \dfrac{1 \text{ gal}}{150 \text{ ft}^2} \approx 15.7$ gal; round up to 16 gal.

The cost of 16 gal of paint is $16(\$24) = \$384$.

TAKE ANOTHER LOOK

1. a. Possible approach: To make a base of constant length, construct line j between points A and B. Mark vector AB. Construct point C on line j. Translate point C to C' by the marked vector. Then CC' will be constant. To create a constant altitude, construct point D not on line j. Construct line k through point D parallel to line j. Construct point E on line k. Construct segments to form $\triangle CC'E$ of constant base and height. Then hide points A, B, and D and lines j and k.

b. For the parallelogram, follow the same steps as for the triangle, through constructing point E. Then translate E to E' by the marked vector AB. Connect points to form parallelogram $CC'E'E$.

2. True. Given $\triangle ABC$ with inscribed circle O touching $\overline{BC}$ at point D, $\overline{CA}$ at point E, and $\overline{AB}$ at point F, let $a = AF = AE$, $b = BF = BD$, $c = CD = CE$, and $r = OD = OE = OF$. The triangle is composed of three pairs of congruent right triangles. Its area is therefore $\frac{1}{2}r(a + b + b + c + c + a) = \frac{1}{2}Pr$.

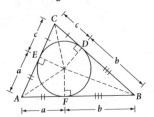

3. Yes. Proposed area of dart $= \frac{1}{2} \cdot d_1 \cdot d_2 = \frac{1}{2} \cdot x \cdot 2y = xy$; area of two triangles $= 2 \cdot \frac{1}{2} \cdot x \cdot y = xy$.

4. See Lesson 8.5, Exercise 16. As $n \to \infty$, $a \to r$. Therefore, $A = \frac{1}{2}aP \to A = \frac{1}{2}r \cdot 2\pi r = \pi r^2$.

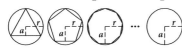

5. Area of two bases $= 2 \cdot \frac{1}{2} \cdot a \cdot P = aP$; area of n rectangular sides $= n \cdot$ side length of polygon $\cdot h = Ph$; total surface area $= Ph + aP = P(h + a)$.

6. As the number of sides of the base gets larger, the prism approaches a cylinder, and a becomes r. Or use the method used in activity 5, except with C and r:

Area of two bases $= 2 \cdot \pi r^2$

Area of side $= Ch$

Total surface area $= Ch + 2\pi r^2$

$\qquad\qquad\qquad = Ch + 2\pi r \cdot r$

$\qquad\qquad\qquad = Ch + Cr$

$\qquad\qquad\qquad = C(h + r)$

7. The Trapezoid Area Conjecture tells you that $A = \frac{1}{2}(b_1 + b_2)h$. But the Trapezoid Midsegment Conjecture tells you that $m = \frac{1}{2}(b_1 + b_2)$. Thus, if $A = \frac{1}{2}(b_1 + b_2)h$ and $m = \frac{1}{2}(b_1 + b_2)$, then $A = mh$.

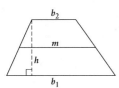

Similarly, the Triangle Area Conjecture says that the formula for the area of a triangle is $A = \frac{1}{2}bh$. But the Triangle Midsegment Conjecture tells us that the length of the midsegment is half the length of the third side, or $m = \frac{1}{2}b$. By substitution $A = mh$.

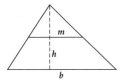

8. Let the sides of the quadrilateral be k, l, m, and j. Let the diagonal be n. Divide the quadrilateral along the diagonal into two triangles.

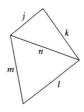

Find the semiperimeter of each triangle: $s_1 = \frac{1}{2}(k + n + j)$ and $s_2 = \frac{1}{2}(l + m + n)$. Find the area of each triangle, using Hero's formula, and add them: Area $= \sqrt{s_1(s_1 - k)(s_1 - n)(s_1 - j)} + \sqrt{s_2(s_2 - l)(s_2 - m)(s_2 - n)}$.

9. True. If the diagonal of length b divides the diagonal of length a into pieces of lengths a_1 and a_2, then the area of the quadrilateral is the sum of the areas of two triangles with base of length b and heights a_1 and a_2. Using algebra, $\frac{1}{2}a_1b + \frac{1}{2}a_2b = \frac{1}{2}(a_1 + a_2)b = \frac{1}{2}ab$.

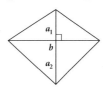

10. Yes, it is always true. Possible proof: Suppose there are n circles of radius r in each of n rows in a square. This gives n^2 circles, each with area πr^2, so the sum of the areas of the circles is $n^2(\pi r^2)$, or $\pi r^2 n^2$. The length of each side of the square equals n circle diameters, or $2rn$, so the area of the square is $(2rn)^2$, or $4r^2n^2$. Therefore, the ratio of the sum of the areas of the circles to the area of the square is $\frac{\pi r^2 n^2}{4n^2 r^2} = \frac{\pi}{4}$.

CHAPTER 9

LESSON 9.1

EXERCISES

1. $c \approx 19.2$ cm. Use the Pythagorean Theorem to find c, the length of the hypotenuse of the right triangle.

$$a^2 + b^2 = c^2$$

$$(12)^2 + (15)^2 = c^2$$

$$144 + 225 = c^2$$

$$369 = c^2$$

$$c = \sqrt{369}$$

$$c \approx 19.2 \text{ cm}$$

2. $a = 12$ cm. Use the Pythagorean Theorem to find a, the length of one of the legs of the right triangle.

$$a^2 + b^2 = c^2$$
$$a^2 + (5)^2 = (13)^2$$
$$a^2 + 25 = 169$$
$$a^2 = 144$$
$$a = \sqrt{144}$$
$$a = 12 \text{ cm}$$

3. $b \approx 5.3$ cm. Use the Pythagorean Theorem to find b, the length of one of the legs of the right triangle.

$$a^2 + b^2 = c^2$$
$$(6)^2 + b^2 = (8)^2$$
$$36 + b^2 = 64$$
$$b^2 = 28$$
$$b = \sqrt{28}$$
$$b \approx 5.3 \text{ cm}$$

4. $d = 10$ cm. The diagonal of the rectangle is the hypotenuse of two congruent right triangles. $(6)^2 + (8)^2 = d^2$, so $36 + 64 = d^2$. Then $d^2 = 100$, so $d = \sqrt{100} = 10$ cm.

5. $s = 26$ cm. The solid is a prism whose bases are right triangles, so the Pythagorean Theorem can be applied to either of the congruent triangular bases to find s: $(10)^2 + (24)^2 = s^2$, so $100 + 576 = s^2$. Then $s^2 = 676$, so $s = \sqrt{676} = 26$ cm.

6. $c \approx 8.5$ cm. This is an isosceles triangle, so each leg has length 6 cm. $(6)^2 + (6)^2 = c^2$, so $36 + 36 = c^2$, or $72 = c^2$. Then $c = \sqrt{72} \approx 8.5$ cm.

7. $b = 24$ cm. The solid is a rectangular prism. Apply the Pythagorean Theorem to one of the right triangles formed by the diagonal of the front face of the prism.

$$(7)^2 + b^2 = (25)^2$$
$$49 + b^2 = 625$$
$$b^2 = 576$$
$$b = \sqrt{576} = 24 \text{ cm}$$

8. $x = 3.6$ cm. The solid is a pyramid. Apply the Pythagorean Theorem to one of the triangular lateral faces to find x. Notice that the edge of the pyramid with length 3.9 cm is the hypotenuse of the right triangle.

$$x^2 + (1.5)^2 = (3.9)^2$$
$$x^2 + 2.25 = 15.21$$
$$x^2 = 12.96$$
$$x = \sqrt{12.96} = 3.6 \text{ cm}$$

9. $x = 40$ cm. The solid is a cone. Apply the Pythagorean Theorem to one of the right triangles; the lengths of the legs are the radius and height of the cone, and the length of the hypotenuse is the slant height.

$$(9)^2 + x^2 = (41)^2$$
$$81 + x^2 = 1681$$
$$x^2 = 1600$$
$$x = \sqrt{1600} = 40 \text{ cm}$$

10. $s \approx 3.5$ cm. Apply the Pythagorean Theorem to either of the isosceles triangles formed by the diagonal of the square.

$$s^2 + s^2 = (5)^2$$
$$2s^2 = 25$$
$$s^2 = 12.5$$
$$s = \sqrt{12.5} \approx 3.5 \text{ cm}$$

11. $r = 13$ cm. The radius of the circle is the hypotenuse of the right triangle. The dashed segment, which is perpendicular to the x-axis, has endpoints with coordinates $(5, 0)$ and $(5, 12)$, so the lengths of the legs of the right triangle are 5 cm and 12 cm. Then $(5)^2 + (12)^2 = r^2$, so $25 + 144 = 169 = r^2$, or $r = \sqrt{169} = 13$ cm.

12. 127 ft. Let s represent the length of the side of the square and d represent the distance from home plate to second base.

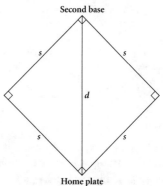

Notice that d is the length of a diagonal of the square and is also the hypotenuse of the two isosceles right triangles into which the diagonal divides the square.

$$s^2 + s^2 = d^2$$
$$(90)^2 + (90)^2 = d^2$$
$$8{,}100 + 8{,}100 = d^2$$
$$16{,}200 = d^2$$
$$d = \sqrt{16{,}200} \approx 127$$

The distance from home plate to second base is about 127 ft.

Discovering Geometry Solutions Manual
©2008 Key Curriculum Press

13. 512 m². Let s represent the length of the side of the square. Then $s^2 + s^2 = (32)^2$, so $2s^2 = 1024$, and $s^2 = 512$. The area of the square is s^2, so the area is 512 m².

14. ≈ 11.3 cm. Let s represent the length of the side of the square and d represent the length of the diagonal. $s^2 + s^2 = d^2$, so $2s^2 = d^2$. The area of the square is s^2, which is 64 cm², so substitute 64 for s^2 in the equation $2s^2 = d^2$: $2(64) = d^2$, so $d^2 = 128$, and $d = \sqrt{128} \approx 11.3$. The length of the diagonal of the square is about 11.3 cm.

15. 3, 4, 5. Because these numbers are small integers, you may be able to find them by trial and error: $(3)^2 + (4)^2 = 9 + 16 = 25 = (5)^2$.

To solve this problem algebraically, let n, $n + 1$, and $n + 2$ represent the three consecutive integers. The three integers represent the lengths of the three sides of a right triangle, so the Pythagorean Theorem applies. $n + 2$ is the largest of the three integers, so it must represent the length of the hypotenuse. Substitute n for a, $n + 1$ for b, and $n + 2$ for c; then use algebra to solve for n.

$$a^2 + b^2 = c^2 \qquad \text{The Pythagorean Theorem.}$$

$$n^2 + (n + 1)^2 = (n + 2)^2 \qquad \text{Substitute the known values.}$$

$$n^2 + n^2 + 2n + 1 = n^2 + 4n + 4$$
$$\text{Expand the binomials.}$$

$$n^2 - 2n - 3 = 0 \qquad \text{Rewrite equation with 0 on one side.}$$

$$(n - 3)(n + 1) = 0 \qquad \text{Factor the equation.}$$

$$n - 3 = 0 \quad \text{or} \quad n + 1 = 0 \qquad \text{Zero Product Property.}$$

$$n = 3 \quad \text{or} \quad n = -1 \qquad \text{Solve the linear equations.}$$

Reject -1 as a possible solution because n represents the length of a side of a triangle, which cannot be negative. Therefore, $n = 3$, $n + 1 = 4$, and $n + 2 = 5$, so the integers are 3, 4, 5.

16. 28 m. A sketch of this situation will be the same as the figure for Exercise 4 in your book, except that now $d = 10$ m is given and the length of the rectangle is not given. From Exercise 4 or by applying the Pythagorean Theorem, you can see that the length of the garden is 8 m. Then $P = 2(8) + 2(6) = 16 + 12 = 28$ m.

17. The area of the large square is $4 \cdot$ area of triangle $+$ area of small square.

$$c^2 = 4 \cdot \frac{1}{2}ab + (b - a)^2$$
$$c^2 = 2ab + b^2 - 2ab + a^2$$
$$c^2 = a^2 + b^2$$

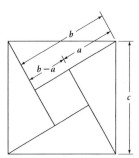

18. Sample answer: Yes, $\triangle ABC \cong \triangle XYZ$ by SSS. Both triangles are right triangles, so you can use the Pythagorean Theorem to find that $CB = ZY = 3$ cm.

19. 54 cm². Because $\sqrt{225} = 15$, the side length of the larger square is 15 cm, and because $\sqrt{36} = 6$, the side length of the smaller square is 6 cm. The bottom side of the shaded rectangle is a side of the smaller square, so its length is also 6 cm. By subtraction, the length of the longer side of the rectangle is $15 - 6 = 9$ cm. Use these dimensions to find the area of the shaded rectangle: $A = bh = (6)(9) = 54$ cm².

20. $3^6/3^2.4.3.4$. There are two types of vertices. One type is surrounded by six equilateral triangles. The other type is surrounded by two equilateral triangles, then a square, then another equilateral triangle, and then another square.

21. Mark the unnamed angles as shown in the figure below. By the Linear Pair Conjecture, $p + 120° = 180°$. Therefore, $p = 60°$. By the AIA Conjecture, $m = q$. By the Triangle Sum Conjecture, $q + p + n = 180°$. Substitute $m = q$ and $p = 60°$ to get $m + 60° + n = 180°$. Therefore, $m + n = 120°$.

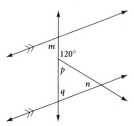

22. $a = 122°$, $b = 74°$, $c = 106°$, $d = 16°$, $e = 90°$, $f = 74°$, $g = 74°$, $h = 74°$, $n = 74°$, $r = 32°$, $s = 74°$, $t = 74°$, $u = 32°$, and $v = 74°$. First, by the Linear Pair Conjecture, $a = 180° - 58° = 122°$ and $b = 180° - 106° = 74°$. By the Vertical Angles Conjecture, $c = 106°$. Now look at the large triangle that has angle measures c, d, and 58° (by the Vertical Angles Conjecture). $c + d + 58° = 180°$, so $d = 16°$. By the Tangent Conjecture, $e = 90°$. Now look at the triangle containing the angle measures d and f. The third angle of this triangle is a right angle (Linear Pair Conjecture), so $d + f = 90°$, and $f = 74°$. Next look at the quadrilateral whose angle measures include c, e, and g. The fourth angle of this quadrilateral is a right angle (Tangent Conjecture), so $e + g + 90° + c = 360°$ (Quadrilateral Sum Conjecture); thus, $g = 74°$. Because h is the measure of the arc intercepted by the central angle of measure g, by the definition of the measure of an arc, $h = g$, so $h = 74°$. Now look at the triangle that contains the angle between the angles with measures g and n, a right angle (where the radius intersects ℓ_1), and a 58° angle (by the Vertical Angles Conjecture). The measure of the unknown angle, which is a central angle of the circle, is $180° - 58° - 90° = 32°$. Then, $n + 32° + g = 180°$, or $n + 32° + 74° = 180°$, so $n = 74°$. The arc with measure r is intercepted by the central angle of measure 32°, so $r = 32°$ by the definition of the measure of an arc. Next look at the arcs with measures s and t. The arc with measure t is intercepted by the central angle with measure n, and the arc with measure s is intercepted by the central angle that is the vertical angle of the angle with measure n. So, by the definition of the measure of an arc, $s = 74°$, and also $t = n = 74°$. $f + e +$ (measure of the angle that intercepts the arc with measure u) $= 180°$, so the unknown angle measure is 16°; therefore, $u = 2(16°) = 32°$ (Inscribed Angle Conjecture). Finally, look at the arc with measure v. Because the arc with measure $(v + u + t)$ is a semicircle, $v + u + t = 180°$, so $v = 180° - 32° - 74° = 74°$.

23.

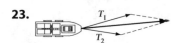

PROJECT

Project should satisfy the following criteria:

- Movement in the flip book is smooth.

- The student can explain the dissection used.

Extra credit

- The student adds other animation, for example, drawing a hand flipping the pages of a flip book, thus creating a flip book of a flip book!

- An animation is created using geometry software.

EXTENSIONS

A. Research results will vary.

B. See the solutions to Take Another Look activities 1, 2, and 3 on pages 202–203.

LESSON 9.2

EXERCISES

1. Yes. $(8)^2 + (15)^2 = 64 + 225 = 289 = (17)^2$, so this is a right triangle. Also, notice that 8-15-17 is on the list of Pythagorean triples in the Investigation Is the Converse True? on page 484 of your book.

2. Yes. 50-120-130 is a multiple of the Pythagorean triple 5-12-13, so this is a right triangle.

3. No. $(12)^2 + (35)^2 = 144 + 1225 = 1369$, while $(36)^2 = 1296$. Because $(12)^2 + (35)^2 \neq (36)^2$, this is not a right triangle.

4. No. $(12)^2 + (18)^2 = 144 + 324 = 468$, while $(22)^2 = 484$. Because $(12)^2 + (18)^2 \neq (22)^2$, this is not a right triangle.

5. No. $(10)^2 + (20)^2 = 100 + 400 = 500$, while $(24)^2 = 576$. Because $(10)^2 + (20)^2 \neq (24)^2$, this is not a right triangle.

6. No. $(1.73)^2 + (1.41)^2 = 2.9929 + 1.9881 = 4.981$, while $(2.23)^2 = 4.9729$, so this is not a right triangle. Notice that for this triangle, $a^2 + b^2$ is close to c^2, so a triangle drawn accurately with these measurements may appear to be a right triangle. However, in order to be a right triangle, $a^2 + b^2$ must be *exactly* equal to c^2.

7. No. $(9)^2 + (12)^2 = 81 + 144 = 225$, while $(18)^2 = 324$, so this is not a right triangle. Another way to look at this is to observe that because 9-12-15 is a Pythagorean triple (because it is a multiple of 3-4-5), it is not possible for 9-12-18 to be a Pythagorean triple.

8. No, the window frame is not rectangular. $(408)^2 + (306)^2 = 166,464 + 93,636 = 260,100$, while $(525)^2 = 275,625$, so the diagonal does not form right triangles. Therefore, the window frame is not rectangular.

9. $y = 25$ cm. Look at the large right triangle in which y is the length of the hypotenuse. The smaller square has area 25 cm², so each side has length 5 cm. Therefore, the length of the longer leg of the large right triangle is $15 + 5 = 20$ cm. The shorter leg is a side of the larger square, so its length is 15 cm. Multiplying 3-4-5 by 5 gives the Pythagorean triple 15-20-25, so $y = 25$ cm.

10. $y = 24$ units. Drop a perpendicular from the point $(-7, y)$ to the x-axis to form a right triangle. The point where the perpendicular touches the axis is $(-7, 0)$, so the triangle has one leg of length 7 units and hypotenuse of length 25 units. Because 7-24-25 is a Pythagorean triple, $y = 24$ units.

11. $y = \sqrt{301}$ m, or $y \approx 17.3$ m. $y^2 + (18)^2 = (25)^2$, so $y^2 = (25)^2 - (18)^2 = 625 - 324 = 301$. Thus, $y = \sqrt{301} \approx 17.3$ m.

12. 6, 8, 10. Check the list of Pythagorean triples in this lesson to find a triple made up of three consecutive even integers. Another way to find this triple is to start with the triple 3-4-5, which is made up of consecutive integers (which differ by 1) and then multiply by 2 to get 6-8-10, three consecutive even integers (which differ by 2).

13. 60 cm². Because 8-15-17 is a Pythagorean triple, the length of the other leg is 8 cm. The legs of a right triangle are perpendicular, so the area of any right triangle is half the product of the lengths of the legs. Thus, $A = \frac{1}{2}(8)(15) = 60$ cm².

14. About 14.1 ft. Let h represent the height that the ladder reaches on the building and make a sketch.

In this right triangle, $(5)^2 + h^2 = (15)^2$, so $h^2 = (15)^2 - (5)^2 = 225 - 25 = 200$. Then $h = \sqrt{200} \approx 14.1$, so the ladder will touch the wall about 14.1 ft up from the ground.

15. About 17.9 cm². Recall that the altitude from the vertex angle to the base of an isosceles triangle is also a median. Make a sketch.

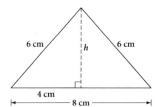

Use the Pythagorean Theorem to find h: $h^2 + (4)^2 = (6)^2$, so $h^2 = (6)^2 - (4)^2 = 36 - 16 = 20$. Thus, $h = \sqrt{20}$, so the height of the triangle is $\sqrt{20}$ cm. Then $A = \frac{1}{2}bh = \frac{1}{2}(8)\sqrt{20} = 4\sqrt{20} \approx 17.9$ cm².

16. 102 m. Let w represent the width of the rectangle. Make a sketch.

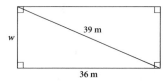

$36 = 3(12)$ and $39 = 3(13)$; the sides of this triangle are a multiple of the Pythagorean triple 5-12-13, so $w = 3(5) = 15$ m. Then $P = 2(36) + 2(15) = 72 + 30 = 102$, so the perimeter of the rectangular lot is 102 m. This means that 102 m of fencing will be needed.

17. a. About 1442.2 cm². First find the length of the diagonal of the rectangular base of the box. Let l represent this length. Apply the Pythagorean Theorem to one of the right triangles that make up the rectangular base: $l^2 = (40)^2 + (60)^2 = 1600 + 3600 = 5200$, so $l = \sqrt{5200}$ cm. The cardboard rectangle has base length $\sqrt{5200}$ cm and height 20 cm, so $A = bh = \sqrt{5200} \cdot 20 \approx 1442.2$ cm².

b. About 74.8 cm. Let d represent the diagonal of the cardboard rectangle. This diagonal divides the rectangle into two right triangles, each with base length $\sqrt{5200}$ cm and height 20 cm, so $d^2 = (\sqrt{5200})^2 + (20)^2 = 5200 + 400 = 5600$. Therefore, $d = \sqrt{5600} \approx 74.8$ cm.

18. Sample answer: The numbers given satisfy the Pythagorean Theorem, so the triangle is a right triangle; but the right angle should be inscribed in an arc of 180°. Thus, the triangle is not a right triangle.

19. Sample answer: $(BD)^2 = 6^2 - 3^2 = 27$; $(BC)^2 = (BD)^2 + 9^2 = 108$; then $36 + 108 = 144$, so $(AB)^2 + (BC)^2 = (AC)^2$, and $\triangle ABC$ is a right triangle by the Converse of the Pythagorean Theorem.

20. Centroid. The construction marks show that this is the point of concurrency of the medians of the triangle.

21. $\frac{3}{10}$. The total number of ways to randomly choose 3 points from the 10 points on the grid is

$$\binom{10}{3} = \frac{10 \cdot 9 \cdot 8}{3 \cdot 2 \cdot 1} = 120$$

Use systematic counting or make an organized list to find the number of isosceles triangles that can be formed with 3 of these points as vertices. Remember to include the equilateral triangles because an equilateral triangle is a special kind of isosceles triangle. In order to make a list of all the isosceles triangles, label the points on the grid.

$$\begin{array}{ccccc} & & A & & \\ & J & & D & \\ F & & O & & G \\ C & H & & E & B \end{array}$$

This solution shows one of many ways to categorize the triangles. It is important to do this in an organized way so that you don't miss any triangles and don't list any of them more than once. In each triangle listed below, the vertices will be written in alphabetical order to avoid listing the same triangle more than once. In the system used below, all triangles within a subcategory (such as small equilateral triangles) are congruent.

Equilateral triangles:

Large: △ABC (1)

Medium-sized vertical: △AFG, △CEJ, △BDH (3)

Medium-sized on a "slant": △DEF, △GHJ (2)

Small: △ADJ, △FJO, △DOJ, △DGO, △CFH, △FHO, △EHO, △EGO, △BEG (9)

Total number of equilateral triangles: 15

Now count the isosceles triangles that are not equilateral.

"Tall and skinny": △AEH, △BFJ, △CDG (3)

Triangles formed by the longer diagonal of a rhombus: △AJO, △ADO, △BGO, △BEO, △CFO, △CHO, △FHJ, △HJO, △DFJ, △DFO, △DEO, △DEG, △EGH, △EFH, △EFO, △GHO, △GJO, △DGJ (18)

Total number of isosceles triangles that are not equilateral: 21

Total number of isosceles triangles: 15 + 21 = 36

Total number of ways to use 3 points from grid: 120

Probability that 3 points selected at random form an isosceles triangle: $\frac{36}{120} = \frac{3}{10}$

22. Because $m\angle DCF = 90°$ (Tangent Conjecture), $m\angle DCE = 90° - x$. Because $\angle DCE$ is isosceles (two sides are radii), $m\angle DEC = m\angle DCE$ (Isosceles Triangle Conjecture), so $m\angle DEC = 90° - x$. Therefore, $m\angle D = 180° - 2(90° - x) = 180° - 180° + 2x = 2x$. Because $\angle D$ is a central angle, $2x = a$ by the definition of the measure of an arc. Therefore, $x = \left(\frac{1}{2}\right)a$.

23. Draw the prism unfolded. The path from C to M to T lies on a straight line and therefore must be shorter than the path from C to A to T (Triangle Inequality Conjecture).

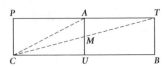

24. 790 square units. The first solid is made up of a single cube and has a surface area of 6 because a cube has 6 faces. Each solid after the first is formed by adding 4 more cubes, each one of the "arms" of the solid. Whenever a new cube is added, the surface area is increased by 5 (all but the face that is in contact with the previous solid), but decreased by 1 (because one face of the previous solid is

covered). Therefore, each new cube adds 4 to the surface area, and the 4 new cubes added at each stage add 4(4) = 16 to the surface area. Thus, a formula for the surface area of the nth solid is $6 + 16(n - 1) = 6 + 16n - 16 = 16n - 10$. Therefore, the surface area of the 50th solid is $16(50) - 10 = 800 - 10 = 790$.

25.

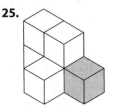

26. 19. An easy way to count the cubes is to count their tops. There are 9 cubes in the bottom layer, 7 in the middle layer, and 3 in the top layer, so the total number of cubes in the sculpture is 9 + 7 + 3 = 19.

IMPROVING YOUR REASONING SKILLS

One of many possible solutions: Fill the 4-liter container. Dump into the 9-liter container. Repeat. Then fill the 4-liter container and dump into the 9-liter container until the 9-liter container is full (1 liter). Three liters will be left in the 4-liter container.

EXTENSIONS

A. If the sum is less, the angle is obtuse. If the sum is greater, the angle is acute.

B. Results will vary.

USING YOUR ALGEBRA SKILLS 9

EXERCISES

1. $\sqrt{6}$. $\sqrt{3} \cdot \sqrt{2} = \sqrt{3 \cdot 2} = \sqrt{6}$.

2. 5. $(\sqrt{5})^2 = \sqrt{5} \cdot \sqrt{5} = \sqrt{25} = 5$. Also $(\sqrt{5})^2 = 5$ simply by the definition of square root.

3. $18\sqrt{2}$. $(3\sqrt{6})(2\sqrt{3}) = 3 \cdot 2 \cdot \sqrt{6 \cdot 3} = 6\sqrt{18} = 6\sqrt{9 \cdot 2} = 6\sqrt{9} \cdot \sqrt{2} = 6 \cdot 3 \cdot \sqrt{2} = 18\sqrt{2}$.

4. 147. $(7\sqrt{3})^2 = 7\sqrt{3} \cdot 7\sqrt{3} = 7 \cdot 7 \cdot \sqrt{3} \cdot \sqrt{3} = 49 \cdot 3 = 147$.

5. 8. $(2\sqrt{2})^2 = 2\sqrt{2} \cdot 2\sqrt{2} = 4 \cdot 2 = 8$.

6. $2\sqrt{3}$. The largest perfect square factor of 12 is 4. $\sqrt{12} = \sqrt{4 \cdot 3} = \sqrt{4} \cdot \sqrt{3} = 2\sqrt{3}$.

7. $3\sqrt{2}$. $\sqrt{18} = \sqrt{9 \cdot 2} = \sqrt{9} \cdot \sqrt{2} = 3\sqrt{2}$.

8. $2\sqrt{10}$. The largest perfect square factor of 40 is 4. $\sqrt{40} = \sqrt{4 \cdot 10} = \sqrt{4} \cdot \sqrt{10} = 2\sqrt{10}$.

9. $5\sqrt{3}$. $\sqrt{75} = \sqrt{25 \cdot 3} = \sqrt{25} \cdot \sqrt{3} = 5\sqrt{3}$.

10. $\sqrt{85}$. 85 has no perfect square factors other than 1, so $\sqrt{85}$ is already in its simplest form.

11. $4\sqrt{6}$. The largest perfect square factor of 96 is 16. $\sqrt{96} = \sqrt{16 \cdot 6} = \sqrt{16} \cdot \sqrt{6} = 4\sqrt{6}$.

12. 24. $24^2 = 576$, so $\sqrt{576} = 24$.

13. $12\sqrt{5}$. The largest perfect square factor of 720 is 144. $\sqrt{720} = \sqrt{144 \cdot 5} = \sqrt{144} \cdot \sqrt{5} = 12\sqrt{5}$.

14. 28. $28^2 = 784$, so $\sqrt{784} = 28$.

15. $6\sqrt{23}$. The largest perfect square factor of 828 is 36. $\sqrt{828} = \sqrt{36 \cdot 23} = \sqrt{36} \cdot \sqrt{23} = 6\sqrt{23}$.

16. Answers will vary. Possible answer: The length of the hypotenuse of an isosceles right triangle with legs of length 3 units is $\sqrt{18}$ units. This is the same as $\sqrt{18} = \sqrt{2} + \sqrt{2} + \sqrt{2}$, or $3\sqrt{2}$.

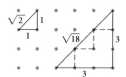

17. The hypotenuse represents $\sqrt{5}$ units. In the second right triangle, the legs have lengths 4 units and 2 units, so the hypotenuse has length $\sqrt{4^2 + 2^2} = \sqrt{20}$ units. The length of the hypotenuse is twice the length of the hypotenuse of the smaller triangle, so $\sqrt{20} = 2\sqrt{5}$.

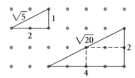

18. $1^2 + 3^2 = (\sqrt{10})^2$, so a right triangle with legs of lengths 1 unit and 3 units will have a hypotenuse of length $\sqrt{10}$ units.

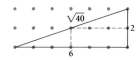

A right triangle with legs of lengths 2 units and 6 units has a hypotenuse of length $\sqrt{40}$ units. Using the triangle from above, $\sqrt{40} = \sqrt{10} + \sqrt{10} = 2\sqrt{10}$.

19. $2^2 + 3^2 = (\sqrt{13})^2$, so a right triangle with legs of lengths 2 units and 3 units will have a hypotenuse of length $\sqrt{13}$ units.

20. $x = \sqrt{3}$, $y = \sqrt{12}$. Apply the Pythagorean Theorem to the smaller right triangle to get $1^2 + x^2 = 2^2$ or $1 + x^2 = 4$, so $x = \sqrt{3}$. Apply the Pythagorean Theorem to the larger triangle to get $2^2 + y^2 = 4^2$ or $4 + y^2 = 16$, so $y = \sqrt{12}$. Because y is twice as long as x, $y = 2x$, so $\sqrt{12} = 2\sqrt{3}$.

21. $2^2 + (\sqrt{3})^2 = (\sqrt{7})^2$, so a right triangle with legs of length 2 units and $\sqrt{3}$ units will have a hypotenuse of length $\sqrt{7}$ units.

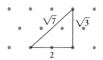

LESSON 9.3

EXERCISES

1. $72\sqrt{2}$ cm. The length of each of the legs of this isosceles right triangle is 72 cm, so by the Isosceles Right Triangle Conjecture, the length of the hypotenuse is $72\sqrt{2}$ cm, so $a = 72\sqrt{2}$ cm.

2. 13 cm. The length of the hypotenuse of this isosceles right triangle is $13\sqrt{2}$ cm, so by the Isosceles Right Triangle Conjecture, the length of each of the legs is 13 cm, so $b = 13$ cm. The length of the legs of an isosceles right triangle can be found by dividing the length of the hypotenuse by $\sqrt{2}$.

3. $a = 10$ cm, $b = 5\sqrt{3}$ cm. This is a 30°-60°-90° triangle in which the given length, 5 cm, is the length of the shorter leg (the side opposite the 30° angle). By the 30°-60°-90° Triangle Conjecture, the length of the hypotenuse is twice the length of the shorter leg, so $a = 2(5) = 10$ cm, and the length of the longer leg is the length of the shorter leg times $\sqrt{3}$, so $b = 5\sqrt{3}$ cm.

4. $c = 10\sqrt{3}$ cm, $d = 10$ cm. This is a 30°-60°-90° triangle in which the given length, 20 cm, is the length of the hypotenuse. By the 30°-60°-90° Triangle Conjecture, the length of the shorter leg is half the length of the hypotenuse, so $d = \frac{1}{2}(20) = 10$ cm, and the length of the longer leg is the length of the shorter leg times $\sqrt{3}$, so $c = 10\sqrt{3}$ cm.

5. $e = 34$ cm, $f = 17$ cm. This is a 30°-60°-90° triangle in which the given length, $17\sqrt{3}$ cm, is the length of the longer leg. By the 30°-60°-90° Triangle Conjecture, the length of the shorter leg is the length of the longer leg divided by $\sqrt{3}$, so $f = 17$ cm, and the length of the hypotenuse is twice the length of the shorter leg, so $e = 34$ cm.

6. 72 cm. Diagonal $\overline{EQ}$ divides the square into two congruent isosceles right triangles, and $\overline{EQ}$ is the hypotenuse of both triangles. Let s represent the length of a side of the square. By the Isosceles Right Triangle Conjecture, $s = 18$ cm. The perimeter of the square is $4s = 4(18) = 72$ cm.

7. $12\sqrt{3}$ cm. Draw $\overline{DB}$ to form two isosceles right triangles, $\triangle DAB$ and $\triangle CBD$, on the base of the cube, and right triangle HDB in the interior of the cube. In $\triangle DAB$, AB (the length of a leg) $= 12$ cm, so $DB = 12\sqrt{2}$ cm. Now look at $\triangle HDB$, in which $\angle HDB$ is a right angle and d is the length of the diagonal. Because $\overline{HD}$ is an edge of the cube, $HD = 12$ cm. Apply the Pythagorean Theorem to $\triangle HDB$ to find d:

$$(12)^2 + \left(12\sqrt{2}\right)^2 = d^2$$
$$144 + 12 \cdot 12 \cdot \sqrt{2} \cdot \sqrt{2} = d^2$$
$$144 + 144(2) = d^2$$
$$144 + 288 = d^2$$
$$432 = d^2$$
$$d = \sqrt{432}$$
$$= \sqrt{144} \cdot \sqrt{3}$$
$$= 12\sqrt{3} \text{ cm}$$

8. $g = 50$ cm, $h = 100$ cm. First look at the right triangle with sides of length g, 120 cm, and 130 cm. Because $120 = 10(12)$ and $130 = 10(13)$, the side lengths are a multiple of the 5-12-13 Pythagorean triple, so $g = 10(5) = 50$ cm. Now look at the small isosceles triangle in the lower left part of the figure. The angle between the congruent sides of this triangle is a right angle (Vertical Angles Conjecture), so this is an isosceles right triangle. Because the quadrilateral with sides of length 120 cm and $g = 50$ cm is a rectangle, the side of this rectangle opposite the side of length g also has length 50 cm. (Opposite sides of a rectangle, or any parallelogram, are congruent.) Therefore, both legs of the isosceles right triangle have length 50 cm. Finally, look at the triangle in the upper left in which h is the length of one side and 30° is the measure of one angle. This is a 30°-60°-90° triangle with a shorter leg of length 50 cm. Because h is the length of the hypotenuse, $h = 2(50) = 100$ cm.

9. 16 cm². Let s represent the length of a leg of the triangle. By the Isosceles Right Triangle Conjecture, $s = \frac{8}{\sqrt{2}}$ cm. Because this is an isosceles right triangle, use $\frac{8}{\sqrt{2}}$ as both the length of the base and the height to find the area of the triangle:

$$A = \frac{1}{2}bh = \frac{1}{2}\left(\frac{8}{\sqrt{2}} \cdot \frac{8}{\sqrt{2}}\right)$$
$$= \frac{1}{2} \cdot \frac{64}{2} = \frac{1}{2}(32) = 16 \text{ cm}^2$$

10. $\left(\frac{1}{\sqrt{2}}, \frac{1}{\sqrt{2}}\right)$. Draw a perpendicular segment from P to the x-axis to form an isosceles right triangle.

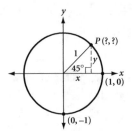

Let (x, y) be the coordinates of P. From the figure, you can see that x and y are also the lengths of the legs of the triangle; because it is isosceles, $x = y$. The radius of the circle is 1. From the figure, notice that the hypotenuse of the right triangle is a radius of the circle, so its length is 1. By the Isosceles Right Triangle Conjecture, $x = \frac{1}{\sqrt{2}}$ and $y = \frac{1}{\sqrt{2}}$.

11. A 30°-60°-90° triangle must have sides whose lengths are multiples of 1, 2, and $\sqrt{3}$. The triangle shown does not reflect this rule.

12. Possible answer:

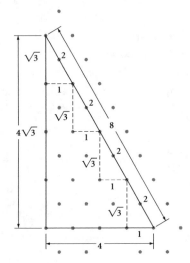

By the Pythagorean Theorem, the length of the longer leg of the large right triangle is $\sqrt{8^2 - 4^2} = \sqrt{64 - 16} = \sqrt{48}$. By the 30°-60°-90° Triangle Conjecture and the way in which the figure was drawn, the length of this segment is $4\sqrt{3}$. This illustrates that $\sqrt{48}$ is equivalent to $4\sqrt{3}$.

13. Possible answer:

By the Pythagorean Theorem, the length of the hypotenuse of the right triangle is $\sqrt{4^2 + 4^2} = \sqrt{32}$. By the Isosceles Right Triangle Conjecture and the way in which the figure was drawn, the length of this segment is $4\sqrt{2}$. This illustrates that $\sqrt{32}$ is equivalent to $4\sqrt{2}$.

14. $6^2 + 3^2 = (\sqrt{45})^2$, so a right triangle with legs of lengths 6 units and 3 units will have a hypotenuse of length $\sqrt{45}$ units.

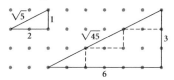

15. a. $\triangle CDA, \triangle AEC, \triangle AEB, \triangle BFA, \triangle BFC$

b. $\triangle MDB, \triangle MEB, \triangle MEC, \triangle MFC, \triangle MFA$

16. Apply the Pythagorean Theorem to the triangle.

$c^2 = x^2 + x^2$ The Pythagorean Theorem.

$c^2 = 2x^2$ Combine like terms.

$c = x\sqrt{2}$ Take the square root of both sides.

17. $169\sqrt{3}$ m² ≈ 292.7 m². Draw an altitude of the equilateral triangle to form two congruent 30°-60°-90° triangles. (Recall that every altitude of an equilateral triangle is also a median and an angle bisector.)

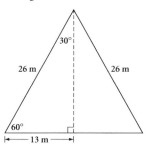

Apply the 30°-60°-90° Triangle Conjecture to the 30°-60°-90° triangle on the left. The hypotenuse of this triangle is one of the sides of the equilateral triangle, so its length is 26 m. So, the shorter leg has length 13 m and the longer leg has length $13\sqrt{3}$ m. The longer leg is the altitude of the equilateral triangle. Therefore, $A = \frac{1}{2}bh = \frac{1}{2}(26)(13\sqrt{3}) = (13)(13\sqrt{3}) = 169\sqrt{3}$, so the area of the equilateral triangle is $169\sqrt{3}$ m² ≈ 292.7 m².

18. 390 m². Make a sketch.

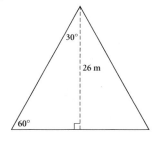

Look at the 30°-60°-90° triangle on the left. The altitude of the equilateral triangle is the longer leg of this triangle, so the length of the shorter leg is $\frac{26}{\sqrt{3}}$ m, and the length of the base (or any side of

the equilateral triangle) is $2\left(\frac{26}{\sqrt{3}}\right) = \frac{52}{\sqrt{3}}$ m. Now find the area:

$$A = \frac{1}{2}bh = \frac{1}{2}\left(\frac{52}{\sqrt{3}}\right)(26) = \frac{676}{\sqrt{3}} \approx 390$$

To the nearest square meter, the area of the triangle is 390 m².

19.

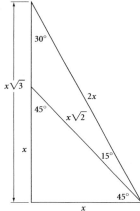

$\frac{\sqrt{3}}{1}$. Find the area of each triangle in terms of x and then find the ratio of the two areas.

Area of 30°-60°-90° triangle $= \frac{1}{2} \cdot x \cdot x\sqrt{3} = \frac{x^2 \cdot \sqrt{3}}{2}$

Area of 45°-45°-90° triangle $= \frac{1}{2} \cdot x \cdot x = \frac{x^2}{2}$

Ratio: $\dfrac{\text{area of } 30°\text{-}60°\text{-}90° \text{ triangle}}{\text{area of } 45°\text{-}45°\text{-}90° \text{ triangle}} = \dfrac{\frac{x^2 \cdot \sqrt{3}}{2}}{\frac{x^2}{2}}$

$$= \frac{x^2 \cdot \sqrt{3}}{2} \cdot \frac{2}{x^2}$$

$$= \frac{\sqrt{3}}{1}$$

20. Compass-and-straightedge construction: Construct an isosceles right triangle with legs of length a; construct a 30°-60°-90° triangle with legs of lengths a and $a\sqrt{3}$; and construct a right triangle with legs of lengths $a\sqrt{2}$ and $a\sqrt{3}$. If d is the length of the hypotenuse of the third right triangle, $d^2 = (a\sqrt{2})^2 + (a\sqrt{3})^2 = 2a^2 + 3a^2 = 5a^2$, so $d = \sqrt{5a^2} = a\sqrt{5}$.

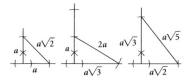

Another way to construct the segment of length $a\sqrt{3}$ is to construct a triangle with legs of length a and $a\sqrt{2}$ (copying the length $a\sqrt{2}$ from the isosceles right triangle). If c is the length of the hypotenuse of this new triangle (which replaces the middle triangle in the figure above), $c^2 = a^2 + (a\sqrt{2})^2 = a^2 + 2a^2 = 3a^2$, so $c = \sqrt{3a^2} = a\sqrt{3}$.

Patty-paper construction: Duplicate the given segment of length *a* onto a piece of patty paper. Construct a perpendicular at one of the endpoints of the segment by folding. Use a compass to duplicate length *a* along the perpendicular. Connect the endpoint where your arc intersects the perpendicular to the other endpoint of the original segment to form an isosceles right triangle. The length of its hypotenuse will be $a\sqrt{2}$. Now repeat the process to construct a right triangle in which the segment of length $a\sqrt{2}$ is used as one leg and length *a* is duplicated along a perpendicular to form the second leg. The length of the hypotenuse of the second triangle will be $a\sqrt{3}$. Finally, construct a third right triangle by using the segment of length $a\sqrt{3}$ as one leg and duplicating the segment of length $a\sqrt{2}$ along a perpendicular. The length of the hypotenuse of the third triangle will be $a\sqrt{5}$.

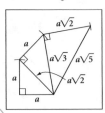

21. Areas: 4.5π cm², 8π cm², 12.5π cm². Notice that $4.5\pi + 8\pi = 12.5\pi$; that is, the sum of the areas of the semicircles on the two legs is equal to the area of the semicircle on the hypotenuse.

Compass-and-straightedge construction (with centimeter ruler): Use the ruler to draw a segment of length 8 cm and construct a segment perpendicular to the segment you have drawn at one of its endpoints. Use the ruler to draw the second segment with length 6 cm. Connect endpoints to form the hypotenuse, which will have length 10 cm by the Pythagorean Theorem. Use your compass and straightedge to bisect two of the legs of the triangle. These perpendicular bisectors will intersect at the midpoint of the hypotenuse. Use your compass to construct a semicircle on each side, using the midpoint as the center and half the length of the side as the radius.

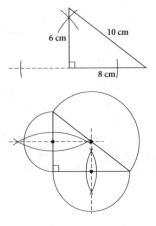

Patty-paper construction: Follow the same procedure, but use folding to construct the right angle and then to find the midpoints of the sides.

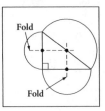

Using either method of construction, the radii of the three semicircles are 3 cm, 4 cm, and 5 cm, so their areas are $\frac{1}{2}(3)^2\pi = 4.5\pi$ cm², $\frac{1}{2}(4)^2\pi = 8\pi$ cm², and $\frac{1}{2}(5)^2\pi = 12.5\pi$ cm².

22. $\frac{73}{6}$ *chih* ≈ 12.2 *chih*. Make a sketch; form a triangle to show the situation where the rope is tightly stretched. Let *x* represent the length of the rope.

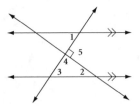

Apply the Pythagorean Theorem to this right triangle.

$$(x - 3)^2 + 8^2 = x^2$$
$$x^2 - 6x + 9 + 64 = x^2$$
$$73 = 6x$$
$$x = \frac{73}{6} \approx 12.2$$

The length of the rope is $\frac{73}{6}$ *chih* ≈ 12.2 *chih*.

23. Extend the rays that form the right angle. $m\angle 4 + m\angle 5 = 180°$ by the Linear Pair Conjecture, and it's given that $m\angle 5 = 90°$. Therefore, $m\angle 4 = 90°$. $m\angle 2 + m\angle 3 + m\angle 4 = m\angle 2 + m\angle 3 + 90° = 180°$. Therefore, $m\angle 2 + m\angle 3 = 90°$. $m\angle 3 = m\angle 1$ by the AIA Conjecture. Therefore, $m\angle 1 + m\angle 2 = 90°$.

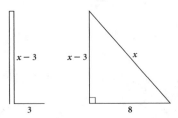

24. 80°. The lateral surface area of a cone is πrl, where *r* is the radius and *l* is the slant height, while the area of the sector of a circle is $\left(\frac{a}{360°}\right)\pi r^2$, where *a* is the number of degrees in the central angle and *r* is the radius. Because the lateral surface area of the cone is unwrapped to form the sector, the lateral

Discovering Geometry Solutions Manual
©2008 Key Curriculum Press

area of the cone is equal to the area of the sector. Notice also that the slant height of the cone becomes the radius of the sector. Use these two facts to find *a*.

$$\pi r_{cone} l = \left(\frac{a}{360°}\right)\pi (r_{sector})^2$$

$$\pi(6)(27) = \left(\frac{a}{360°}\right)\pi (27)^2$$

$$162\pi = \left(\frac{a}{360°}\right)\pi (729)$$

$$\frac{a}{360°} = \frac{162\pi}{729\pi} = \frac{2}{9}$$

$$9a = 2(360°) = 720°$$

$$a = 80°$$

The measure of the angle at the vertex of the sector is 80°.

IMPROVING YOUR VISUAL THINKING SKILLS

Each Monster visitor must go across alone. It makes no sense for one to return, so before each Monster crosses, the two Smallville players must cross, and one must stay on the other side to bring the boat back on the next trip. This will require 24 round trips for the 11 players and the coach (and the Smallville players will be left on the wrong side of the river). The team has enough money for 20 one-way trips. Even without seeing how to arrange the Smallville players to return the boat at least 11 times, the Monsters don't have enough money.

EXTENSION

See the solutions to Take Another Look activities 4, 5, and 6 on page 203.

LESSON 9.4

EXERCISES

1. No. The space diagonal of the box is about 33.5 in. Refer to the example on page 498 of your book. The situation here is the same, but with different measurements. As in the figure for the example, let *d* represent the length of the diagonal of the base (bottom of the box) and *x* represent the length of the space diagonal (the diagonal inside the box). Any of the three dimensions of the box can be used as the height; the result will be the same regardless of this choice. Here 12 in. is used as the height, so the dimensions of the base are 24 in. and 20 in. First apply the Pythagorean Theorem to either right triangle on the base to find d^2.

$$24^2 + 20^2 = d^2$$

$$576 + 400 = d^2$$

$$976 = d^2$$

Now apply the Pythagorean Theorem to the right triangle with legs of lengths *d* and 12 in. and hypotenuse of length *x*.

$$d^2 + 12^2 = x^2$$

$$976 + 144 = x^2$$

$$1120 = x^2$$

$$x \approx 33.5 \text{ in.}$$

The space diagonal is the longest segment inside the box. Because the bat is 34 in. long, it will not fit in the box.

2. 10 m. The tree was 36 m tall before it cracked, so the length of the hypotenuse is $(36 - x)$ m. Use the Pythagorean Theorem with $a = x$, $b = 24$, and $c = 36 - x$ to find *x*.

$$a^2 + b^2 = c^2$$

$$x^2 + (24)^2 = (36 - x)^2$$

$$x^2 + 576 = (36)^2 - 2(36)x + x^2$$

$$x^2 + 576 = 1296 - 72x + x^2$$

$$72x + 576 = 1296$$

$$72x = 720$$

$$x = 10$$

He would have to climb 10 m from the base of the tree.

3. 50 km/h. Draw a sketch that shows the distances involved.

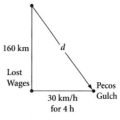

Paul traveled 4 hours at 30 km/h, a distance of $4(30) = 120$ km, so the lengths of the legs of the right triangle are 120 km and 160 km. Notice that $120 = 40(3)$ and $160 = 40(4)$, so these lengths are a multiple of 3-4-5. Therefore, $d = 40(5) = 200$ km. Rhaina must travel 200 km in 4 h, so her average speed must be $\frac{200 \text{ km}}{4 \text{ h}} = 50$ km/h.

4. 8 ft. Let *h* represent the height of the ladder on the building before it slips, and let *x* represent the number of feet that the bottom of the ladder slips out.

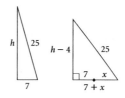

In the first right triangle, $h = 24$ ft because 7-24-25 is a Pythagorean triple. Then the height of the second right triangle is $h - 4 = 20$ ft. In this triangle, one leg has length 20 ft and the hypotenuse has length 25 ft. Because $20 = 5(4)$ and $25 = 5(5)$, these lengths are a multiple of 3-4-5, so the length of the other leg is $3(5) = 15$ ft. Then $7 + x = 15$ ft, so $x = 8$ ft.

5. $7,200. Make a sketch of the cabin and of its triangular front wall.

To find the area of the front wall, first find h, the height of the triangle. Notice that this altitude divides the isosceles triangle representing the wall into two congruent right triangles in which the length of the shorter leg is 5 m and the length of the hypotenuse is 13 m. Because 5-12-13 is a Pythagorean triple, $h = 12$ cm. Now find the area of the isosceles triangle: $A = \frac{1}{2}bh = \frac{1}{2}(10)(12) = 60$ m². The cost of the glass is $60 \text{ m}^2 \cdot \frac{\$120}{1 \text{ m}^2} = \$7,200$.

6. Surface area of prism $= (27\sqrt{3} + 180)$ cm² ≈ 226.8 cm²; surface area of cylinder $= 78\pi$ cm² ≈ 245.0 cm². First find the surface area of the prism, which has two congruent hexagonal faces (the bases) and six congruent rectangular faces (the lateral faces). To find the area of a hexagonal base, you need to find the length of its apothem. When a regular hexagon is inscribed in a circle, the length of each of its sides is equal to the radius of the circle. In this case, the diameter of the cylinder, and thus of the circular bases, is 6 cm, so the radius of the circular bases of the cylinder is 3 cm.

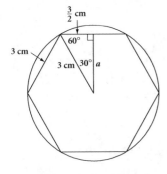

Notice that the apothem forms the larger leg of a 30°-60°-90° triangle in which the length of the hypotenuse is 3 cm and the length of the shorter leg is $\frac{3}{2}$ cm, so $a = \frac{3}{2} \cdot \sqrt{3}$. To find the area of one hexagonal base, use the formula for the area of a regular hexagon: $A = \frac{1}{2}asn = \frac{1}{2} \cdot \frac{3}{2}\sqrt{3} \cdot 3 \cdot 6 = \frac{27}{2}\sqrt{3}$ cm². Now find the area of one rectangular

(lateral) face. Each rectangle has a base of length 3 cm (a side of the hexagonal base) and height 10 cm (the height of the cylinder and prism), so each has area 30 cm². To find the total surface area of the prism, add the areas of the two hexagons and the six rectangles: $2\left(\frac{27}{2}\sqrt{3}\right) + 6(30) = 27\sqrt{3} + 180$, so the surface area of the prism is $(27\sqrt{3} + 180) \approx 226.8$ cm².

Now find the surface area of the cylinder by using a formula from Lesson 8.7: $SA = 2\pi r^2 + 2\pi rh = 2\pi(3)^2 + 2\pi(3)(10) = 18\pi + 60\pi = 78\pi \approx 245.0$ cm².

7. $\frac{36}{\sqrt{3}}$ cm ≈ 20.8 cm. Recall that any median of an equilateral triangle is also an altitude. This segment divides the equilateral triangle into two congruent 30°-60°-90° triangles. Let s represent the length of a side of the equilateral triangle.

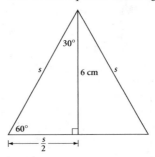

Look at the 30°-60°-90° triangle on the left. The median (and altitude) of the equilateral triangle is the longer leg of this triangle, so the length of the shorter leg is $\frac{6}{\sqrt{3}}$ cm. This is half the length of a side of the equilateral triangle, so $s = 2\left(\frac{6}{\sqrt{3}}\right) = \frac{12}{\sqrt{3}}$ cm, and the perimeter of the equilateral triangle is $3\left(\frac{12}{\sqrt{3}}\right) = \frac{36}{\sqrt{3}}$ cm ≈ 20.8 cm.

8. ≈ 48.2 ft; ≈ 16.6 lb. If the slope of the ramp is $\frac{1}{12}$, the ramp must cover a linear distance of 48 ft to gain a height of 4 ft: Slope $= \frac{rise}{run} = \frac{1}{12} = \frac{4}{48}$. Let l represent the length of the ramp.

The ramp forms the hypotenuse of a right triangle, and the lengths of the legs are known, so you can use the Pythagorean Theorem to find l: $l^2 = (4)^2 + (48)^2 = 16 + 2304 = 2320$, so $l = \sqrt{2320}$ ft ≈ 48.2 ft.

The work required to lift 200 lb by 4 ft is $(200 \text{ lb})(4 \text{ ft}) = 800$ ft-lb. Because the work is spread out by having the person and wheelchair go up a 48.2 ft ramp, the constant force required to go up the ramp is $\frac{800 \text{ ft-lb}}{48.2 \text{ ft}} \approx 16.6$ lb.

9. a. 160 ft-lb. Work $=$ force $\cdot$ distance $= (80 \text{ lb})(20 \text{ ft}) = 160$ ft-lb.

b. 40 lb. $\dfrac{160 \text{ ft-lb}}{4 \text{ ft}} = 40$ lb.

c. 20 lb. $\dfrac{160 \text{ ft-lb}}{8 \text{ ft}} = 20$ lb.

10. ≈ 4.6 ft. First find the work required: (160 lb)(2 ft) $= 320$ ft-lb. The equation work $=$ force $\cdot$ distance can be written as W $=$ fd, or d $= \frac{W}{f}$. In this case, $d = \dfrac{320 \text{ ft-lb}}{70 \text{ lb}} \approx 4.6$ ft.

11.

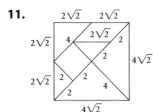

12.

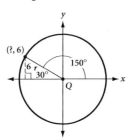

Swan   Horse with Rider

13. 12 units. Draw a perpendicular from the point in Quadrant II to the x-axis to form a 30°-60°-90° triangle.

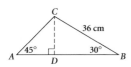

From the y-coordinate of the point, you know that the shorter leg of the triangle has length 6, so the length of the hypotenuse is 2(6) $= 12$. Because the hypotenuse is a radius of the circle, the radius of circle Q is 12.

14. $18\sqrt{2}$ cm. Draw the altitude from C to $\overline{AB}$ to form a 45°-45°-90° triangle on the left and a 30°-60°-90° triangle on the right. Let D be the point where the altitude meets $\overline{AB}$.

In $\triangle CDB$, $\overline{BC}$ is the hypotenuse and $\overline{CD}$ is the shorter leg (opposite the 30° angle), so $CD = \frac{1}{2}(BC)$ $= \frac{1}{2}(36) = 18$ cm. In $\triangle CDA$, $\overline{CD}$ is one of the legs and $\overline{AC}$ is the hypotenuse. This is an isosceles right triangle, so $AC = CD \cdot \sqrt{2} = 18\sqrt{2}$ cm.

15. Draw radii $\overline{CB}$ and $\overline{CD}$. By the Tangent Conjecture, $\overline{CB} \perp \overline{AB}$ and $\overline{CD} \perp \overline{AD}$, so $\angle ABC$ and $\angle ADC$ are right angles. Now apply the Quadrilateral Sum

Conjecture to quadrilateral $ABCD$: 54° $+$ 90° $+$ $m\angle BCD + 90° = 360°$, so $m\angle BCD = 126°$. But then the sum of the arc measures of the circle would be 226° $+$ 126° $= 352°$. This is impossible because the sum of the arc measures in any circle must be 360°.

16. $(4, 4\sqrt{3})$. Draw $\overline{AA'}$ and also $\overline{A'P}$, where $\overline{A'P}$ is the altitude from A' to $\overline{OA}$.

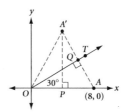

Because A' is the image of A after reflection across $\overrightarrow{OT}$, you know that $\overrightarrow{OT}$ is the perpendicular bisector of $\overline{AA'}$. Because $\overrightarrow{OT} \perp \overline{AA'}$, $\triangle OQA$ is a 30°-60°-90° triangle with hypotenuse $\overline{OA}$ with length 8, so $AQ = 4$. Also, because $\overrightarrow{OT}$ is the perpendicular bisector of $\overline{AA'}$, $A'Q = AQ = 4$, so $AA' = 8$. This makes $\triangle OAA'$ isosceles, but because the vertex angle QAO is a 60° angle, it must be equilateral. Now look at $\triangle OA'P$. Because $\triangle OAA'$ is equilateral, $OA' = 8$, and because every altitude of an equilateral triangle is a median, $OP = 4$. By the Pythagorean Theorem or by noticing that $\triangle OA'P$ is a 30°-60°-90° triangle with shorter leg of length 4 (and hypotenuse of length 8), you can tell that $A'P = 4\sqrt{3}$. Because $OP = 4$ and $A'P = 4\sqrt{3}$, the coordinates of A' are $(4, 4\sqrt{3})$.

17. SAA. Use the pair of vertical angles and the marked pairs of congruent angles and congruent segments.

18. Orthocenter. The construction marks show that this is the point of concurrency of the two altitudes.

19. 115°. When a polygon is named, the vertices are listed in consecutive order, so $\angle Q$ and $\angle U$ are consecutive angles of parallelogram $QUID$, and $\angle Q$ and $\angle I$ are opposite angles. Therefore, $\angle Q \cong \angle I$ (Parallelogram Opposite Angles Conjecture), so $2x + 5° = 4x - 55°$. Solve this equation.

$2x + 5° = 4x - 55°$

$60° = 2x$

$x = 30°$

Then $m\angle Q = 2x + 5° = 2(30°) + 5° = 65°$.

(As a check, you can find that $m\angle I = 4x - 55° = 4(30) - 55° = 65°$.)

By the Parallelogram Consecutive Angles Conjecture, $\angle Q$ and $\angle U$ are supplementary, so $m\angle U = 180° - 65° = 115°$.

20. $\overline{PO}$. In $\triangle PRO$, $\angle P$ is opposite $\overline{RO}$, $\angle R$ is opposite $\overline{PO}$, and $\angle O$ is opposite $\overline{PR}$. By the Triangle Sum Conjecture, $m\angle P + m\angle R + m\angle O = 180°$, so $m\angle O = 180° - 70° - 45° = 65°$. Therefore, $\angle R$ is the smallest angle in the triangle, so by the Side-Angle Inequality Conjecture, $\overline{PO}$ is the shortest side.

IMPROVING YOUR VISUAL THINKING SKILLS

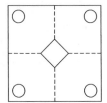

EXTENSION

See the solution for Exercise 15 in Lesson 9.1 on page 177.

LESSON 9.5

EXERCISES

1. 5 units. Label the points $A(10, 20)$ and $B(13, 16)$, and substitute their coordinates in the distance formula.

$(AB)^2 = (x_2 - x_1)^2 + (y_2 - y_1)^2$	The distance formula.
$= (13 - 10)^2 + (16 - 20)^2$	Substitute the given values.
$= (3)^2 + (-4)^2$	Subtract.
$= 9 + 16$	Square numbers.
$= 25$	Add.
$AB = \sqrt{25} = 5$	Take the positive square root of both sides.

2. 45 units. Label the points $A(15, 37)$ and $B(42, 73)$, and substitute their coordinates in the distance formula.

$$(AB)^2 = (x_2 - x_1)^2 + (y_2 - y_1)^2$$
$$= (42 - 15)^2 + (73 - 37)^2$$
$$= (27)^2 + (36)^2$$
$$= 729 + 1296$$
$$= 2025$$
$$AB = \sqrt{2025} = 45$$

3. 34 units. Label the points $A(-19, -16)$ and $B(-3, 14)$, and substitute their coordinates in the distance formula.

$$(AB)^2 = \left(x_2 - x_1\right)^2 + \left(y_2 - y_1\right)^2$$
$$= \left[(-3) - (-19)\right]^2 + \left[14 - (-16)\right]^2$$
$$= (16)^2 + (30)^2$$
$$= 256 + 900$$
$$= 1156$$
$$AB = \sqrt{1156} = 34$$

4. 354 m. Viki's and Scott's locations vary by 5 blocks vertically and 5 blocks horizontally. By the distance formula, the shortest distance between them is $\sqrt{5^2 + 5^2} = \sqrt{50}$ blocks. Because each block is approximately 50 m long, this distance is about $50\sqrt{50} \approx 354$ m.

You could also consider the distance between Viki and Scott as the hypotenuse of an isosceles right triangle with legs of length 5 blocks. The length of the hypotenuse is $5\sqrt{2}$ blocks, or $50(5\sqrt{2}) \approx 354$ m.

5. 52.4 units. Use the distance formula to find each side length in the triangle, and then add the lengths of the three sides to find the perimeter.

$(AB)^2 = (8 - 2)^2 + (12 - 4)^2 = (6)^2 + (8)^2 = 36 + 64 = 100$, so $AB = \sqrt{100} = 10$.

$(BC)^2 = (24 - 8)^2 + (0 - 12)^2 = (16)^2 + (-12)^2 = 256 + 144 = 400$, so $AB = \sqrt{400} = 20$.

$(AC)^2 = (24 - 2)^2 + (0 - 4)^2 = (22)^2 + (-4)^2 = 484 + 16 = 500$, so $AB = \sqrt{500}$.

Perimeter of $\triangle ABC = AB + BC + AC = 10 + 20 + \sqrt{500} \approx 52.4$.

6. Isosceles. Use the distance formula to find each side length in the triangle, and then see whether any of the lengths are equal.

$(DE)^2 = (39 - 6)^2 + \left[-12 - (-6)\right]^2 = (33)^2 + (-6)^2 = 1089 + 36 = 1125$, so $DE = \sqrt{1125}$.

$(EF)^2 = (24 - 39)^2 + \left[18 - (-12)\right]^2 = (-15)^2 + (30)^2 = 225 + 900 = 1125$, so $EF = \sqrt{1125}$.

$(DF)^2 = (24 - 6)^2 + \left[18 - (-6)\right]^2 = (18)^2 + (24)^2 = 324 + 576 = 900$, so $DF = \sqrt{900} = 30$.

Thus, $DE = EF \neq DF$, so the triangle has two congruent sides, but not three congruent sides. Therefore, $\triangle DEF$ is isosceles, but not equilateral.

7. Rectangle

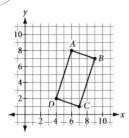

Use the slope formula, $m = \frac{y_2 - y_1}{x_2 - x_1}$, to find the slopes of the four sides of quadrilateral $ABCD$.

Slope of $\overline{AB} = \frac{7 - 8}{9 - 6} = \frac{-1}{3} = -\frac{1}{3}$

Slope of $\overline{BC} = \frac{1 - 7}{7 - 9} = \frac{-6}{-2} = 3$

Slope of $\overline{CD} = \frac{2 - 1}{4 - 7} = \frac{1}{-3} = -\frac{1}{3}$

Slope of $\overline{DA} = \frac{8 - 2}{6 - 4} = \frac{6}{2} = 3$

Because $\overline{AB}$ and $\overline{CD}$ have the same slope, $\overline{AB} \parallel \overline{CD}$ by the Parallel Slope Property. Likewise, $\overline{BC} \parallel \overline{DA}$, so $ABCD$ has two pairs of parallel sides, which makes it a parallelogram. Now determine whether it is a special kind of parallelogram. The slopes of $\overline{AB}$ and $\overline{BC}$ are opposite reciprocals of each other, so $\overline{AB} \perp \overline{BC}$ by the Perpendicular Slope Property, and therefore $\angle B$ is a right angle. Similarly, the other three angles are also right angles. Therefore, $ABCD$ is a rectangle. Now use the distance formula, $AB = \sqrt{(x_2 - x_1)^2 + (y_2 - y_1)^2}$, to determine whether it is a square.

$AB = \sqrt{(9 - 6)^2 + (7 - 8)^2} = \sqrt{3^2 + (-1)^2}$

$\quad = \sqrt{9 + 1} = \sqrt{10}$

$BC = \sqrt{(7 - 9)^2 + (1 - 7)^2} = \sqrt{(-2)^2 + (-6)^2}$

$\quad = \sqrt{4 + 36} = \sqrt{40}$

Because $AB \neq BC$, $ABCD$ is not equilateral, so it is not a square. Thus, the most specific name for quadrilateral $ABCD$ is a rectangle.

8. Parallelogram

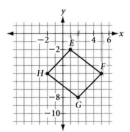

Find the slopes of the four sides of quadrilateral $EFGH$.

Slope of $\overline{EF} = \frac{-5 - (-2)}{5 - 1} = \frac{-3}{4} = -\frac{3}{4}$

Slope of $\overline{FG} = \frac{-8 - (-5)}{2 - 5} = \frac{-3}{-3} = 1$

Slope of $\overline{GH} = \frac{-5 - (-8)}{-2 - 2} = \frac{3}{-4} = -\frac{3}{4}$

Slope of $\overline{HE} = \frac{-2 - (-5)}{1 - (-2)} = \frac{3}{3} = 1$

Because opposite sides of $EFGH$ have the same slope, $\overline{EF} \parallel \overline{GH}$ and $\overline{FG} \parallel \overline{HE}$, so $EFGH$ is a parallelogram. The slopes of adjacent sides are not opposite reciprocals of each other, so $EFGH$ has no right angles and is not a rectangle, nor is it a square. Now use the distance formula to determine whether it is a rhombus.

$EF = \sqrt{(5 - 1)^2 + (-5 - (-2))^2}$

$\quad = \sqrt{4^2 + (-3)^2} = \sqrt{16 + 9} = \sqrt{25} = 5$

$FG = \sqrt{(2 - 5)^2 + (-8 - (-5))^2}$

$\quad = \sqrt{(-3)^2 + (-3)^2} = \sqrt{9 + 9} = \sqrt{18}$

Because $EF \neq FG$, $EFGH$ is not equilateral, so it is not a rhombus. Thus, the most specific name for quadrilateral $ABCD$ is a parallelogram.

9. Kite

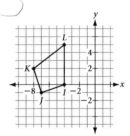

Find the slopes of the sides of quadrilateral $IJKL$.

Slope of $\overline{IJ} = \frac{-1 - 0}{-7 - (-4)} = \frac{-1}{-3} = \frac{1}{3}$

Slope of $\overline{JK} = \frac{2 - (-1)}{-8 - (-7)} = \frac{3}{-1} = -3$

Slope of $\overline{KL} = \frac{5 - 2}{4 - (-8)} = \frac{3}{12} = \frac{1}{4}$

$\overline{LI}$ is vertical, so its slope is undefined. Because $IJKL$ does not have any pair of parallel sides, it is neither a trapezoid nor a parallelogram. Now use the distance formula to determine whether it is a kite.

$IJ = \sqrt{(-7 - (-4))^2 + (-1 - 0)^2}$

$\quad = \sqrt{(-3)^2 + (-1)^2} = \sqrt{9 + 1} = \sqrt{10}$

$JK = \sqrt{(-8 - (-7))^2 + (2 - (-1))^2}$

$\quad = \sqrt{(-1)^2 + (3)^2} = \sqrt{1 + 9} = \sqrt{10}$

$$KL = \sqrt{(-4-(-8))^2 + (5-2)^2}$$
$$= \sqrt{(4)^2 + (3)^2} = \sqrt{16+9} = \sqrt{25} = 5$$
$$LI = \sqrt{(-4-(-4))^2 + (0-5)^2}$$
$$= \sqrt{(0)^2 + (-5)^2} = \sqrt{0+25} = \sqrt{25} = 5$$

Because quadrilateral *IJKL* has two distinct pairs of consecutive congruent sides, it is a kite.

10. Square

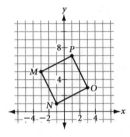

Find the slopes of the sides of quadrilateral *MNOP*.

Slope of $\overline{MN} = \dfrac{1-5}{-1-(-3)} = \dfrac{-4}{2} = -2$

Slope of $\overline{NO} = \dfrac{3-1}{3-(-1)} = \dfrac{2}{4} = \dfrac{1}{2}$

Slope of $\overline{OP} = \dfrac{7-3}{1-3} = \dfrac{4}{-2} = -2$

Slope of $\overline{PM} = \dfrac{5-7}{-3-1} = \dfrac{-2}{-4} = \dfrac{1}{2}$

Because opposite sides of *MNOP* have the same slope, $\overline{MN} \parallel \overline{OP}$ and $\overline{NO} \parallel \overline{PM}$, so *MNOP* is a parallelogram. The slopes of adjacent sides are opposite reciprocals of each other, so *MNOP* has four right angles and is a rectangle. Now use the distance formula with any pair of adjacent sides to determine whether it is a square.

$$MN = \sqrt{(-1-(-3))^2 + (1-5)^2}$$
$$= \sqrt{(2)^2 + (-4)^2} = \sqrt{4+16} = \sqrt{20}$$
$$NO = \sqrt{(3-(-1))^2 + (3-1)^2} = \sqrt{(4)^2 + (2)^2}$$
$$= \sqrt{16+4} = \sqrt{20}$$
$$OP = \sqrt{(1-3)^2 + (7-3)^2} = \sqrt{(-2)^2 + (4)^2}$$
$$= \sqrt{4+16} = \sqrt{20}$$
$$PM = \sqrt{(1-(-3))^2 + (5-7)^2}$$
$$= \sqrt{(4)^2 + (-2)^2} = \sqrt{16+4} = \sqrt{20}$$

Because quadrilateral *MNOP* is both equiangular (a rectangle) and equilateral (a rhombus), it is a square.

11. a. Circle A: Circle B:

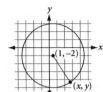

b. Circle A: $(x-1)^2 + (y+2)^2 = 64$; Circle B: $x^2 + (y-2)^2 = 36$.

For Circle A, use the distance formula in the form $r^2 = (x_2 - x_1)^2 + (y_2 - y_1)^2$ with $r = 8$, $(x_1, y_1) = (1, -2)$, and $(x_2, y_2) = (x, y)$.

$$r^2 = (x_2 - x_1)^2 + (y_2 - y_1)^2$$
$$8^2 = (x-1)^2 + (y-(-2))^2$$
$$64 = (x-1)^2 + (y+2)^2$$
$$\text{or} \quad (x-1)^2 + (y+2)^2 = 64$$

For Circle B, use the distance formula in the form $r^2 = (x_2 - x_1)^2 + (y_2 - y_1)^2$ with $r = 6$, $(x_1, y_1) = (0, 2)$, and $(x_2, y_2) = (x, y)$.

$$r^2 = (x_2 - x_1)^2 + (y_2 - y_1)^2$$
$$6^2 = (x-0)^2 + (y-2)^2$$
$$36 = x^2 + (y-2)^2 \quad \text{or} \quad x^2 + (y-2)^2 = 36$$

c. $(x-h)^2 + (y-k)^2 = (r)^2$. Possible patterns: The first term on the left is the difference between x and the x-coordinate of the center; the second term on the left is the difference between y and the y-coordinate of the center; and the term on the right side of the equation is the square of the radius.

Conjecture: The equation of a circle with radius r and center (h, k) is $(x-h)^2 + (y-k)^2 = (r)^2$.

12. $(x-2)^2 + y^2 = 25$. Substitute 2 for h, 0 for k, and 5 for r in the equation of a circle.

13. Center is $(0, 1)$, $r = 9$. The given equation can be rewritten as $(x-0)^2 + (y-1)^2 = 9^2$, so $h = 0$, $k = 1$, and $r = 9$.

14. $(x-3)^2 + (y+1)^2 = 18$. Use the distance formula to find the radius of the circle. The radius of a circle is the distance between the center and any point on the circle, so in this case, it is the distance between the center $(3, -1)$ and the point $(6, 2)$. Because the equation of a circle involves r^2, it is more convenient to find r^2: $r^2 = (6-3)^2 + (2-(-1))^2 = (3)^2 + (3)^2 = 18$. Now find the equation of the circle.

$$(x-h)^2 + (y-k)^2 = r^2 \quad \text{Equation of a circle.}$$
$$(x-3)^2 + (y-(-1))^2 = 18 \quad \text{Substitute 3 for } h, -1 \text{ for } k, \text{ and 18 for } r^2.$$
$$(x-3)^2 + (y+1)^2 = 18 \quad \text{Simplify.}$$

15. a. $\sqrt{14}$ units. This is the same as finding the space diagonal of a rectangular prism. Look at the "imaginary box" drawn on the figure. First find the diagonal of the base of the box in the x-y plane. In this plane, this segment has endpoints $(0, 0)$ and $(2, -1)$, so its length is $\sqrt{(2-0)^2 + (-1-0)^2} = \sqrt{4+1} = \sqrt{5}$. Find the length of the space diagonal with endpoints $(0, 0, 0)$ and $(2, -1, 3)$. Let d represent the length of this diagonal. This segment is the hypotenuse of a right triangle with legs of lengths $\sqrt{5}$ and 3, so $d^2 = (\sqrt{5})^2 + (3)^2 = 5 + 9 = 14$, and $d = \sqrt{14}$.

Another way to find the distance from the origin $(0, 0, 0)$ to $(2, -1, 3)$ is to extend the distance formula to three dimensions:
$d = \sqrt{(2-0)^2 + (-1-0)^2 + (3-0)^2} = \sqrt{4+1+9} = \sqrt{14}$.

b. $\sqrt{176} = 4\sqrt{11}$ units.

$PQ = \sqrt{(5-1)^2 + (6-2)^2 + (15-3)^2}$

$\quad = \sqrt{4^2 + 4^2 + 12^2}$

$\quad = \sqrt{16 + 16 + 144}$

$\quad = \sqrt{176}$

This radical can be simplified:
$\sqrt{176} = \sqrt{16} \cdot \sqrt{11} = 4\sqrt{11}$.

c. $\sqrt{(x_2 - x_1)^2 + (y_2 - y_1)^2 + (z_2 - z_1)^2}$ or $\sqrt{(x_1 - x_2)^2 + (y_1 - y_2)^2 + (z_1 - z_2)^2}$.

16. ≈ 86.5 units. Let $(x_1, y_1, z_1) = (-12, 9, -13)$ and $(x_2, y_2, z_2) = (25, 75, -52)$. Then the distance between the two given points is
$\sqrt{(x_2 - x_1)^2 + (y_2 - y_1)^2 + (z_2 - z_1)^2} = $
$\sqrt{(28 - (-12))^2 + (75 - 9)^2 + (-52 - (-13))^2} = $
$\sqrt{(40)^2 + (66)^2 + (-39)^2} = $
$\sqrt{1600 + 4356 + 1521} = \sqrt{7477} \approx 86.5$

17. 14 units. The longest possible diagonal in the prism will be a space diagonal. One space diagonal connects the origin, with three-dimensional coordinates $(0, 0, 0)$, with the point $(12, 6, 4)$. Use the three-dimensional distance formula to find the distance between $(x_1, y_1, z_1) = (0, 0, 0)$ and $(x_2, y_2, z_2) = (12, 6, 4)$. This distance is
$\sqrt{(x_2 - x_1)^2 + (y_2 - y_1)^2 + (z_2 - z_1)^2} = $
$\sqrt{(12 - 0)^2 + (6 - 0)^2 + (4 - 0)^2} = $
$\sqrt{12^2 + 6^2 + 4^2} = \sqrt{144 + 36 + 16} = \sqrt{196} = 14$,
so the length of the longest possible diagonal is 14 units.

18. Write a separate rule for each column of numbers and combine them: $n \cdot (n + 2) - 3 = (n + 3) \cdot (n - 1)$.

19. $\left(-\frac{\sqrt{3}}{2}, \frac{1}{2}\right)$. Draw a perpendicular segment from A to the x-axis to form a 30°-60°-90° triangle. (The measure of the angle that forms a linear pair with the 150° angle is 30°.) The hypotenuse of this triangle is a radius of the circle, so its length is 1. Therefore, the length of the shorter leg (opposite the 30° angle) is $\frac{1}{2}(1) = \frac{1}{2}$, and the length of the longer leg is $\frac{1}{2}(\sqrt{3}) = \frac{\sqrt{3}}{2}$. Because A is in Quadrant II, its x-coordinate is negative and its y-coordinate is positive, so the coordinates of A are $\left(-\frac{\sqrt{3}}{2}, \frac{1}{2}\right)$.

20. $k = \sqrt{2}$, $m = \sqrt{6}$. This figure includes both a 45°-45°-90° triangle and a 30°-60°-90° triangle. In the isosceles right triangle, the legs have length $\sqrt{3}$ and the hypotenuse has length m, so $m = \sqrt{3} \cdot \sqrt{2} = \sqrt{6}$. In the 30°-60°-90° triangle, k is the length of the shorter leg and m is the length of the longer leg, so $m = k \cdot \sqrt{3}$, or $k = \frac{m}{\sqrt{3}} = \frac{\sqrt{6}}{\sqrt{3}} = \sqrt{\frac{6}{3}} = \sqrt{2}$.

21. $x = \frac{6}{\sqrt{3}} = 2\sqrt{3}$, $y = \frac{12}{\sqrt{3}} = 4\sqrt{3}$. Because the large triangle is equilateral, the medians that are shown in the figure are also altitudes and angle bisectors. This means that the small triangle in the lower-left corner of the figure is a 30°-60°-90° triangle. (The 30° angle is half of a 60° angle of the equilateral triangle.)

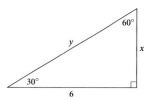

In this triangle, x is the length of the shorter leg, y is the length of the hypotenuse, and the length of the longer leg is 6 because this segment is half of a side of the equilateral triangle. Therefore, $x = \frac{6}{\sqrt{3}}$ and $y = 2x = 2\left(\frac{6}{\sqrt{3}}\right) = \frac{12}{\sqrt{3}}$.

22. 96 cm. Let x represent the depth of the water. Then $x + 8$ represents the length of the lily stem. Make a sketch.

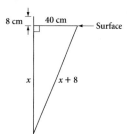

Apply the Pythagorean Theorem and solve for x.

$$x^2 + (40)^2 = (x + 8)^2$$

$$x^2 + 1600 = x^2 + 16x + 64$$

$$0 = 16x - 1536$$

$$16x = 1536$$

$$x = 96$$

The depth of the pond is 96 cm.

23. The angle of rotation is approximately 77°. Connect two pairs of corresponding points. Construct the perpendicular bisector of each segment. The point where the perpendicular bisectors meet is the center of rotation. This point is labeled as P in the diagram below. Measure the angle of rotation with a protractor. The rotation is counterclockwise, and the angle is approximately 77°.

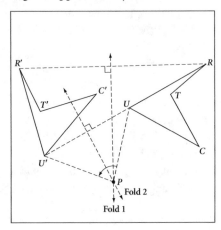

24. Any long diagonal of a regular hexagon divides it into two congruent quadrilaterals. Each angle of a regular hexagon is $\frac{(6 - 2) \cdot 180°}{6} = 120°$, and the diagonal divides two of the 120° angles into 60° angles. Look at the diagonal as a transversal. The alternate interior angles are congruent; thus, the opposite sides of a regular hexagon are parallel.

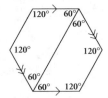

IMPROVING YOUR VISUAL THINKING SKILLS

Here are two routes that are shorter than 42 ft. The shortest path measures 40 ft.

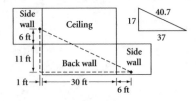

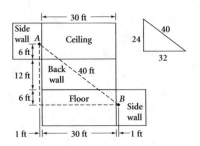

LESSON 9.6

EXERCISES

1. 18π cm² ≈ 56.5 cm². First find the length of the shorter leg of the right triangle. Because $16 = 4 \cdot 4$ and $20 = 5 \cdot 4$, the side lengths are a multiple of the 3-4-5 Pythagorean triple, and the length of the shorter leg is $3 \cdot 4 = 12$ cm. The shorter leg of the right triangle is also a diameter of the shaded semicircle, so the radius is $\frac{1}{2}(12) = 6$ cm. Therefore, the area of the shaded region is $\frac{1}{2}\pi r^2 = \frac{1}{2}\pi(6)^2 = \frac{1}{2}\pi(36) = 18\pi$ cm² ≈ 56.5 cm².

2. $(8\pi - 16)$ m² ≈ 9.1 cm². Draw diagonal $\overline{EQ}$ to divide square $SQRE$ into two isosceles right triangles, $\triangle ESQ$ and $\triangle ERQ$. Look at $\triangle ESQ$, which has legs $\overline{SE}$ and $\overline{SQ}$, each of length 4 m. By the Isosceles Right Triangle Conjecture (or the Pythagorean Theorem), the length of the hypotenuse, $\overline{EQ}$, is $4\sqrt{2}$ m. Segment EQ is also a diameter of the circle, so the radius is $\frac{1}{2}(4\sqrt{2}) = 2\sqrt{2}$ m. The area of a circle with radius $2\sqrt{2}$ m is $\pi(2\sqrt{2})^2 = \pi \cdot 4 \cdot 2 = 8\pi$ m², and the area of a square with side length 4 m is 16 m². The area of the shaded region is the difference between the area of the circle and the area of the square, $(8\pi - 16)$ m² ≈ 9.1 cm².

3. 456π cm² ≈ 1433 cm². Look at the angles in quadrilateral $BODY$. By the Tangent Conjecture, $\angle OBY$ and $\angle ODY$ are right angles, so by the Quadrilateral Sum Conjecture, $90° + 105° + 90° + m\angle DOB = 360°$, and $m\angle DOB = 75°$. Because $\angle DOB$ is the central angle that intercepts $\overarc{BD}$ (the minor arc), $m\overarc{BD} = 75°$, and the measure of major arc BD is $360° - 75° = 285°$. Now find the area of the shaded region, which is a sector of the circle.

$$A = \left(\frac{a}{360°}\right)\pi r^2 = \left(\frac{285°}{360°}\right)\pi(24)^2$$

$$= \frac{19}{24}\pi(24)^2 = (19 \cdot 24)\pi = 456\pi \text{ cm}^2$$

$$\approx 1433 \text{ cm}^2$$

4. 120π cm² ≈ 377.0 cm². $\overrightarrow{TA}$ is tangent to the circle N at A, so $\overrightarrow{TA} \perp \overline{NA}$ by the Tangent Conjecture. Then $\angle TAN$ is a right angle and $\triangle TAN$ is a 30°-60°-90° triangle. The length of the longer leg, $\overline{TA}$, is $12\sqrt{3}$ cm, so the length of the shorter leg, $\overline{NA}$, is 12 cm. Because $\overline{NA}$ is also a radius of the circle, the area of the circle is 144π cm². The area of the shaded region is $\frac{360-60}{360}$, or $\frac{5}{6}$, of the area of the circle. Therefore, the shaded area is $\frac{5}{6}(144\pi)$, or 120π cm² ≈ 377.0 cm².

5. $(32\pi - 32\sqrt{3})$ cm² ≈ 45.1 cm². The area of the shaded region is the difference between the area of the semicircle and the area of the triangle. $\angle T$ is a right angle (Angles Inscribed in a Semicircle Conjecture), so $\triangle RTH$ is a 30°-60°-90° triangle in which $\overline{HT}$ is the longer leg (opposite the 60° angle), $\overline{RT}$ is the shorter leg (opposite the 30° angle), and $\overline{RH}$ is the hypotenuse. Because $HT = 8\sqrt{3}$, $RT = 8$, and $RH = 2(8) = 16$ cm. $\overline{RH}$ is a diameter of the circle, so the radius is 8 cm.

Area of semicircle $= \frac{1}{2}\pi r^2 = \frac{1}{2}\pi(8)^2 = \frac{1}{2}\pi 64 = 32\pi$ cm²

Area of triangle $= \frac{1}{2}bh = \frac{1}{2}(8)(8\sqrt{3}) = 32\sqrt{3}$ cm²

Area of shaded region $= (32\pi - 32\sqrt{3})$ cm² ≈ 45.1 cm²

6. $(25\pi - 48)$ cm² ≈ 30.5 cm². The definition of a kite requires that $AD = 6$ cm and $DC = 8$ cm. Then, by the Chord Arcs Conjecture, $\overset{\frown}{AB} \cong \overset{\frown}{AD}$ and $\overset{\frown}{BC} \cong \overset{\frown}{DC}$. Next, $m\overset{\frown}{AB} + m\overset{\frown}{BC} = m\overset{\frown}{AD} + m\overset{\frown}{DC}$, so $m\overset{\frown}{ABC} = m\overset{\frown}{ADC}$. Therefore, $\overset{\frown}{ABC}$ and $\overset{\frown}{ADC}$ are semicircles, and $\overline{AC}$ is a diameter of the circle. By the Angles Inscribed in a Semicircle Conjecture, $\angle B$ and $\angle D$ are right angles, so $\triangle ABC$ and $\triangle ADC$ are right triangles, both with legs of lengths 6 cm and 8 cm and hypotenuse $\overline{AC}$. Then, by the Pythagorean Theorem, $AC = 10$ cm. Because $\overline{AC}$ is a diameter of the circle, the radius is 5 cm, so the area of the circle is 25π cm². The area of each right triangle is $\frac{1}{2} \cdot 6 \cdot 8 = 24$ cm², so the area of kite $ABCD$ is 48 cm². The area of the shaded region is the difference between the area of the circle and the area of the kite, $(25\pi - 48)$ cm² ≈ 30.5 cm².

7. $\left(\frac{64\pi}{3} - 16\sqrt{3}\right)$ cm² ≈ 39.3 cm². The area of the shaded region, which is a segment of the circle, is the difference between the area of the sector and the area of the triangle. Let P be the center of the circle. In the triangle, draw the altitude from the center to $\overline{OH}$. Let R be the point where the altitude meets the base, $\overline{OH}$. Because the original triangle is isosceles (two sides are radii), the altitude to the base is also a median and an angle bisector, so this segment divides the original triangle into two congruent 30°-60°-90° triangles.

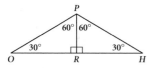

Because $OH = 8\sqrt{3}$ cm and $\overline{PR}$ is a median as well as an altitude, $OR = 4\sqrt{3}$ cm. Because $\overline{PR}$ is also

the bisector of the 120° angle, $m\angle OPR = 60°$. Therefore $\overline{OR}$ is the longer leg (opposite the 60° angle) in 30°-60°-90° triangle POR, $\overline{PR}$ is the shorter leg, and $\overline{PO}$ is the hypotenuse. Because $OR = 4\sqrt{3}$ cm, $PR = 4$ cm, and $PO = 2(4) = 8$ cm. Notice that $\overline{PO}$ is a radius of the circle, so $r = 8$ cm.

Area of sector $= \left(\frac{120°}{360°}\right)\pi r^2 = \frac{1}{3}\pi(8)^2 = \frac{64\pi}{3}$ cm²

Area of triangle $= \frac{1}{2}bh = \frac{1}{2}(8\sqrt{3})(4) = 16\sqrt{3}$ cm²

Area of shaded region $= \left(\frac{64\pi}{3} - 16\sqrt{3}\right)$ cm² ≈ 39.3 cm²

8. $(240 - 18\pi)$ square units ≈ 183.5 square units. In right triangle RGA, $RA = 34$ and $GA = 6 + 18 + 6 = 30$. Because $34 = 2 \cdot 17$ and $30 = 2 \cdot 15$, the side lengths are a multiple of the 8-15-17 Pythagorean triple, so $RG = 2 \cdot 8 = 16$. Use this information to find the area of $\triangle RGA$: $A = \frac{1}{2}bh = \frac{1}{2}(30)(16) = 240$. Now look at the sectors of circles centered at the three vertices of the triangle. By the Triangle Sum Conjecture, $m\angle R + m\angle G + m\angle A = 180°$. Because all three arcs have radius 6, this means that the total degree measure of the three sectors is 180°, so the three sectors together are equivalent to a semicircle with radius 6. Find the area of this semicircle. $A = \frac{1}{2}\pi r^2 = \frac{1}{2}\pi(6)^2 = \frac{1}{2}\pi(36) = 18\pi$. Therefore, the area of the shaded region is $(240 - 18\pi)$ square units ≈ 183.5 square units.

9. 102 cm. Let x be the distance from the center of the circle (the original pipe) to the chord. Then the radius of the pipe is $(x + 6)$ cm.

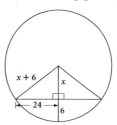

Notice that the segment of length x is the altitude of an isosceles triangle whose legs are radii of the circle, so it forms two congruent right triangles, each with legs of lengths 24 cm and x cm, and hypotenuse of length $(x + 6)$ cm. Apply the Pythagorean Theorem to one of these right triangles and solve for x.

$$x^2 + (24)^2 = (x + 6)^2$$

$$x^2 + 576 = x^2 + 12x + 36$$

$$540 = 12x$$

$$x = 45$$

$r = x + 6 = 51$ cm, so $d = 2r = 2(51) = 102$ cm. The pipe's original diameter was 102 cm.

10. Possible proof:

Given: Circle C with tangents $\overline{AM}$ and $\overline{AN}$

Show: $\overline{AM} \cong \overline{AN}$

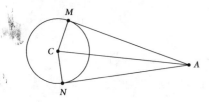

Add $\overline{MC}$, $\overline{NC}$, and $\overline{AC}$ to the diagram, as shown. By the Tangent Conjecture, $\angle M$ and $\angle N$ are right angles, so $\triangle AMC$ and $\triangle ANC$ are right triangles. Using the Pythagorean Theorem, $(AM)^2 + (MC)^2 = (AC)^2$ and $(AN)^2 + (NC)^2 = (AC)^2$. Solving for AM and AN, $AM = \sqrt{(AC)^2 - (MC)^2}$ and $AN = \sqrt{(AC)^2 - (NC)^2}$. Because $\overline{MC}$ and $\overline{NC}$ are both radii of the same circle, they have the same length. So, substitute MC for NC in the second equation: $AN = \sqrt{(AC)^2 - (MC)^2} = AM$. Therefore, $\overline{AM} \cong \overline{AN}$.

11. 18 m. Draw $\overline{OA}$, $\overline{OB}$, and $\overline{OT}$.

$\triangle OAB$ is isosceles because $\overline{OA}$ and $\overline{OB}$ are radii of the outer circle. Because $\overline{AB}$ is tangent to the inner circle, $\overline{OT} \perp \overline{AB}$ by the Tangent Conjecture, so $\angle OTA$ is a right angle, and $\triangle OTA$ is a right triangle with hypotenuse $\overline{OA}$. $\overline{OT}$ is a radius of the inner circle and $\overline{OA}$ is a radius of the outer circle, so $OT = 12$ m and $OA = 12 + 3 = 15$ m. Now apply the Pythagorean Theorem to $\triangle OTA$. Because $12 = 3(4)$ and $15 = 3(5)$, the side lengths in this triangle are a multiple of the Pythagorean triple 3-4-5. Therefore, $AT = 3(3) = 9$ m. Because $\triangle OAB$ is isosceles with base $\overline{AB}$, $\overline{OT}$ is a median as well as an altitude. Therefore, $BT = AT$, so $AB = 2(AT) = 2(9) = 18$ m.

12. 324π cm$^2 \approx 1018$ cm^2. Let x represent the radius of the inner circle.

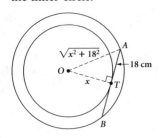

As in Exercise 11, the radius of the inner circle is perpendicular to the chord of the outer circle and also bisects that chord. Here $AT = \frac{1}{2}(AB) = \frac{1}{2}(36) = 18$ cm. Because $\overline{OT} \perp \overline{AT}$, $\triangle OAT$ is a right triangle with hypotenuse $\overline{OA}$. So, by the Pythagorean Theorem, $OA = \sqrt{x^2 + 18^2} = \sqrt{x^2 + 324}$ cm. Recall that the area of an annulus is the difference between the area of the outer circle and the area of the inner circle. Here the outer circle has radius $OA = \sqrt{x^2 + 324}$ and the inner circle has radius x.

$$
\begin{aligned}
A_{annulus} &= A_{outer\ circle} - A_{inner\ circle} \\
&= \pi \left(\sqrt{x^2 + 324} \right)^2 - \pi x^2 \\
&= \pi(x^2 + 324) - \pi x^2 \\
&= \pi x^2 + 324\pi - \pi x^2 \\
&= 324\pi \ \text{cm}^2 \approx 1018 \ \text{cm}^2
\end{aligned}
$$

13. ≈ 3931 cm^2. First find the area of the equilateral triangle. Because it is equilateral, the altitude to the horizontal base will form two congruent 30°-60°-90° triangles. In each of these triangles, the length of the shorter leg is 40 cm, so the length of the altitude, which is the longer leg, will be $40\sqrt{3}$ cm.

$$A_{triangle} = \frac{1}{2}bh = \frac{1}{2} \cdot 80 \cdot 40\sqrt{3} = 1600\sqrt{3} \ \text{cm}.$$

Now look at the outer edges of the arch. The line segment marked with length 80 cm in the center of the figure shows that the edge on the left is an arc of a circle with center in the lower right corner of the arch and radius 80 cm. By symmetry, the edge on the right of the arch is an arc of a circle with center in the lower left corner of the arch and radius 80 cm. (Notice that these are different circles because they have different centers, although they have the same radius.) This means that the parts of the interior of the arch that are outside the triangle are segments of the two circles described above. Each segment is formed with a 60° angle (from the equilateral triangle) and an 80 cm radius. Find the area of one of these segments, using the area of the equilateral triangle.

$$
\begin{aligned}
A_{segment} &= A_{sector} - A_{triangle} \\
&= \left(\frac{60°}{360°} \right) \pi(80)^2 - \left(1600\sqrt{3} \right) \\
&= \frac{1}{6}\pi(6400) - 1600\sqrt{3} \\
&= \left(\frac{3200\pi}{3} - 1600\sqrt{3} \right) \ \text{cm}^2
\end{aligned}
$$

$$
\begin{aligned}
A_{arch} &= 2A_{segment} + A_{triangle} \\
&= 2\left(\frac{3200\pi}{3} - 1600\sqrt{3} \right) + \left(1600\sqrt{3} \right) \\
&= \left(\frac{6400\pi}{3} - 1600\sqrt{3} \right) \ \text{cm}^2 \approx 3931 \ \text{cm}^2
\end{aligned}
$$

Discovering Geometry Solutions Manual
©2008 Key Curriculum Press

14. $(12 + 6\sqrt{3})$ cm $\approx$ 22.4 cm. Each side of the triangle in the center of the figure is made up of two radii, so this is an equilateral triangle with side length 12 cm. The altitude of this triangle divides the triangle into two congruent 30°-60°-90° triangles, each with shorter leg of length 6 cm. The altitude is the longer leg of this triangle, so its length is $6\sqrt{3}$ cm. If you transfer the lengths that you know to the left side of the rectangle, you will see that the height of the rectangle is $6 + 6\sqrt{3} + 6 = (12 + 6\sqrt{3})$ cm $\approx$ 22.4 cm.

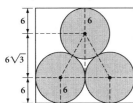

15. $\sqrt{77}$ cm $\approx$ 8.8 cm. The arc length of sector ABC is $\frac{80°}{360°}(2\pi r) = \frac{80°}{360°}(2 \cdot \pi \cdot 9) = \frac{2}{9} \cdot 18\pi = 4\pi$ cm. Therefore, the circumference of the base of the cone is 4π cm. Use this to find the radius of the circular base of the cone: $C = 2\pi r = 4\pi$, so $r = 2$ cm. The radius of the sector, which is 9 cm, becomes the slant height of the cone. Because the altitude of the cone is perpendicular to the base, the height of the cone, the radius of the base, and the slant height form a right triangle in which the slant height is the hypotenuse. Thus, $(2)^2 + h^2 = (9)^2$, so $4 + h^2 = 81$. Then $h^2 = 77$ and $h = \sqrt{77} \approx 8.8$ cm.

16. 76 cm. Use the circumference of the circular cross section to find its diameter: $C = \pi d$, so $d = \frac{C}{\pi} = \frac{336}{\pi}$ cm. The diagonals of the square are diameters of the circle. A diagonal of a square divides the square into two isosceles right triangles. By the Isosceles Right Triangle Conjecture, the length of a leg of an isosceles triangle can be found by dividing the hypotenuse by $\sqrt{2}$. Therefore, the side length of the largest square that can be cut from the cross section is

$$\frac{d}{\sqrt{2}} = \frac{\frac{336}{\pi}}{\sqrt{2}} \approx 76 \text{ cm}$$

17. Inscribed circle: 3π cm²; circumscribed circle: 12π cm². The area of the circumscribed circle is four times as great as the area of the inscribed circle. Draw a perpendicular segment from the center of the inscribed circle to $\overline{AB}$. Let O be the center of both circles and D be the point where the perpendicular segment meets $\overline{AB}$. Also draw $\overline{OA}$, which is a radius of the circumscribed circle.

$\overline{OA}$ bisects $\angle CAB$ and $m\angle CAB = 60°$ because $\triangle CAB$ is equilateral, so $\triangle AOD$ is a 30°-60°-90° triangle. $AB = 6$ cm, so $AD = 3$ cm. In the 30°-60°-90° triangle, $\overline{AD}$ is the longer leg (opposite the 60° angle), $\overline{OD}$ is the shorter leg, and $\overline{OA}$ is the hypotenuse. Because $AD = 3$ cm, $OD = \frac{3}{\sqrt{3}}$ cm and $OA = 2\left(\frac{3}{\sqrt{3}}\right) = \frac{6}{\sqrt{3}}$ cm. Now that you have found the radii of the two circles, you can find their areas.

Inscribed circle: $r = OD = \frac{3}{\sqrt{3}}$ cm

$A = \pi r^2 = \pi\left(\frac{3}{\sqrt{3}}\right)^2 = \pi \cdot \frac{9}{3} = 3\pi$ cm²

Circumscribed circle: $r = OA = \frac{6}{\sqrt{3}}$ cm

$A = \pi r^2 = \pi\left(\frac{6}{\sqrt{3}}\right)^2 = \pi \cdot \frac{36}{3} = 12\pi$ cm²

$12\pi = 4(3\pi)$, so the area of the circumscribed circle is four times the area of the inscribed circle.

18. 135°. Sketch a perpendicular segment, $\overline{MN}$, from M to the x-axis to form right triangle MNO.

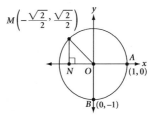

The legs of $\triangle MNO$ have lengths $MN = \frac{\sqrt{2}}{2}$ and $NO = \frac{\sqrt{2}}{2}$, so it is an isosceles right triangle, and $m\angle MON = 45°$. Then, by the Linear Pair Conjecture, $m\angle MOA = 180° - m\angle MON = 180° - 45° = 135°$.

19. $(x - 3)^2 + (y - 3)^2 = 36$. Substitute 3 for h, 3 for k, and 6 for r in the equation $(x - h)^2 + (y - k)^2 = r^2$.

20. Sample construction:

The diameter is the transversal, and the chords are parallel by the Converse of the Parallel Lines Conjecture. The chords are congruent because they can be shown to be the same distance from the center.

21. a. Because a carpenter's square has a right angle and both radii are perpendicular to the tangents, a square is formed. The radius is 10 in.; so, the diameter is 20 in.

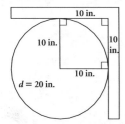

b. Possible answer: Measure the circumference with string and divide by π.

22. $\frac{5}{6}$. When a regular hexagon is inscribed in a circle, the length of each side of the hexagon (which is a chord of the circle) will be the radius of the circle. Make a sketch.

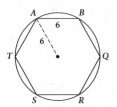

From this figure, you can see that $\triangle ABC$ will be an acute triangle if C is on $\overline{SR}$ and will be a right triangle if C is exactly at S or exactly at R. Therefore, if C is anywhere on major arc SAR (except exactly at A or exactly at B), $\triangle ABC$ will be an obtuse triangle. The measure of each of the six minor arcs of the circle is 60°, so $m\widehat{SAR} = 300°$. Therefore, the probability that $\triangle ABC$ will be an obtuse triangle if point C is selected randomly on the circle is $\frac{300°}{360°} = \frac{5}{6}$. (*Note:* If C coincides with A or B, there will be no triangle. Because there are infinitely many points on the circle, this can be ignored in calculating the probability.)

IMPROVING YOUR REASONING SKILLS

1. One approach: $A = 0$, and $C = 1$, so $B = 5$.

2. One approach: $D = 2$; $7F + 4$ ends in F, so F is 1 or 6. Trying each possibility leads to $J = 6$.

EXTENSION

Let c be the length of the hypotenuse of the right triangle.

Area of semicircle with diameter $c = \frac{1}{2}\pi\left(\frac{c}{2}\right)^2 = \frac{\pi c^2}{8}$

Area of right triangle $= \frac{1}{2}ab$

Area of semicircle with diameter $a = \frac{1}{2}\pi\left(\frac{a}{2}\right)^2 = \frac{\pi a^2}{8}$

Area of semicircle with diameter $b = \frac{1}{2}\pi\left(\frac{b}{2}\right)^2 = \frac{\pi b^2}{8}$

Total area of two segments of circle with diameter $c =$ area of semicircle with diameter c − area of triangle $= \frac{\pi c^2}{8} - \frac{1}{2}ab$

Total area of shaded regions = area of semicircle with diameter a + area of semicircle with diameter b − total area of two segments of circle with diameter c:

$$\left(\frac{\pi a^2}{8} + \frac{\pi b^2}{8}\right) - \left(\frac{\pi c^2}{8} - \frac{1}{2}ab\right)$$
$$= \frac{\pi a^2}{8} + \frac{\pi b^2}{8} - \frac{\pi c^2}{8} + \frac{1}{2}ab$$
$$= \frac{\pi}{8}(a^2 + b^2 - c^2) + \frac{1}{2}ab$$

By the Pythagorean Theorem, $a^2 + b^2 = c^2$, so $a^2 + b^2 - c^2 = 0$. Therefore, the area of the shaded region is $\frac{\pi}{8}(0) + \frac{1}{2}ab = \frac{1}{2}ab$, which is the area of the triangle.

CHAPTER 9 REVIEW

EXERCISES

1. 20 cm. $15 = 5(3)$ and $25 = 5(5)$. This is a multiple of the Pythagorean triple 3-4-5, so $x = 5(4) = 20$ cm.

2. 10 cm. The altitude from C to $\overline{AB}$ is also a median because C is the vertex angle of an isosceles triangle. This altitude divides the isosceles triangle into two congruent right triangles. Because 5-12-13 is a Pythagorean triple, the shorter leg of one of these right triangles has length 5 cm, so $AB = 2(5) = 10$ cm.

3. Obtuse. $(70)^2 + (240)^2 = 4{,}900 + 57{,}600 = 62{,}500$, and $(260)^2 = 67{,}600$. Because the sum of the squares of the two shorter sides is less than the square of the longest side, $\angle C$ is obtuse, and therefore the triangle is obtuse.

4. 26 cm. Find the diagonal of the base and then AB, the length of the space diagonal. The diagonal of the base (bottom rectangular face) is $\sqrt{8^2 + 24^2} = \sqrt{64 + 576} = \sqrt{640}$. Then $(AB)^2 = (\sqrt{640})^2 + (6)^2 = 640 + 36 = 676$, so $AB = \sqrt{676} = 26$ cm.

You could also find AB by extending the Pythagorean Theorem to three dimensions, which is similar to using the distance formula in three dimensions: $AB = \sqrt{(24)^2 + (8)^2 + (6)^2} = \sqrt{576 + 64 + 36} = \sqrt{676} = 26$ cm.

5. $\left(\frac{\sqrt{3}}{2}, \frac{1}{2}\right)$. Draw the perpendicular segment from U down to the x-axis to form a 30°-60°-90° triangle. The hypotenuse of this triangle is a radius of the circle. The circle has radius 1, so the length of the hypotenuse is also 1. Then, by the 30°-60°-90° Triangle Conjecture, the shorter (vertical) leg has length $\frac{1}{2}(1) = \frac{1}{2}$, and the length of the longer (horizontal) leg is $\frac{1}{2}(\sqrt{3}) = \frac{\sqrt{3}}{2}$. Because U is in Quadrant I, both of its coordinates are positive. Therefore, the coordinates of U are $\left(\frac{\sqrt{3}}{2}, \frac{1}{2}\right)$.

6. $\left(-\frac{1}{\sqrt{2}}, -\frac{1}{\sqrt{2}}\right)$. Draw the perpendicular from V to the x-axis. Because $225° - 180° = 45°$, the triangle that is formed is a 45°-45°-90° triangle. The hypotenuse of this triangle is a radius of the circle, and the circle has a radius of 1, so the length of the hypotenuse is also 1. Then, by the Isosceles Right Triangle Conjecture, the length of each leg is $\frac{1}{\sqrt{2}}$. Because V is in Quadrant III, both of its coordinates are negative. Therefore, the coordinates of V are $\left(-\frac{1}{\sqrt{2}}, -\frac{1}{\sqrt{2}}\right)$.

7. $200\sqrt{3}$ cm$^2 \approx 346.4$ cm^2. This is a 30°-60°-90° triangle with hypotenuse of length 40 cm. By the 30°-60°-90° Triangle Conjecture, the length of the shorter leg (opposite the 30° angle) is 20 cm, and the length of the longer leg is $20\sqrt{3}$ cm. Then the area of the triangle is $\frac{1}{2}(20)(20\sqrt{3}) = 200\sqrt{3}$ cm$^2 \approx 346.4$ cm^2.

8. $d = 12\sqrt{2}$ cm ≈ 17.0 cm^2. The diagonal divides the square into two congruent isosceles right triangles. From the given area, each side of the square has length 12 cm. Because the length of each leg of the isosceles right triangles is 12 cm, by the Isosceles Right Triangle Conjecture, $d = 12\sqrt{2}$ cm ≈ 17.0 cm^2.

9. 246 cm^2. Notice that the trapezoid is made up of two right triangles, so the Pythagorean Theorem can be used to find the lengths of its bases. In $\triangle ADC$, $\overline{DA}$ and $\overline{DC}$ are the legs and $\overline{AC}$ is the hypotenuse. Because $12 = 4(3)$ and $20 = 4(5)$, the side lengths in this triangle are a multiple of the Pythagorean triple 3-4-5, so $DC = 4(4) = 16$ cm. In $\triangle ABC$, $\overline{AC}$ and $\overline{BC}$ are the legs and $\overline{AB}$ is the hypotenuse. Because $15 = 5(3)$ and $20 = 5(4)$, the side lengths in this triangle are also a multiple of 3-4-5, so $AB = 5(5) = 25$ cm. You can now find the area of trapezoid $ABCD$ either by finding the areas of the two triangles separately and adding the results or by applying the Trapezoid Area Conjecture to find the area of the trapezoid directly. Both of these methods are shown here.

Method 1: Use the Triangle Area Conjecture:
$A = \frac{1}{2}bh$

Area of trapezoid $ABCD$ = area of $\triangle ADC$ + area of $\triangle ABC = \frac{1}{2}(16)(12) + \frac{1}{2}(20)(15) = 96 + 150 = 246$ cm^2

Method 2: Use the Trapezoid Area Conjecture:
$A = \frac{1}{2}h(b_1 + b_2)$

Area of trapezoid $ABCD = \frac{1}{2}(12)(25 + 16) = 246$ cm^2

10. 72π in$^2 \approx 226.2$ in^2. The diameter of the semicircle is the longer leg of the right triangle. Because 7-24-25 is a Pythagorean triple, the length of this

segment is 24 in., so the radius is 12 in. Then the area of the semicircle is $\frac{1}{2}\pi r^2 = \frac{1}{2}\pi(12)^2 = \frac{1}{2}\pi \cdot 144 = 72\pi$ in$^2 \approx 226.2$ in^2.

11. 24π cm$^2 \approx 75.4$ cm^2. The shaded region is a sector of the circle. In order to find its area, you need to know the radius of the circle. Draw $\overline{OT}$ to form two congruent 30°-60°-90° triangles. $m\angle OBT = 90°$ by the Tangent Conjecture, and $m\angle BOT = 60°$ because $\overline{OT}$ bisects the 120° angle, $\angle BOA$. Therefore, in $\triangle BOT$, $\overline{OB}$ is the shorter leg, $\overline{BT}$ is the longer leg, and $\overline{OT}$ is the hypotenuse. To find the radius of the circle, apply the 30°-60°-90° Triangle Conjecture to $\triangle BOT$: $BT = 6\sqrt{3}$ cm, so $OB = 6$ cm. Now find the area of the shaded sector. The angle for this sector is $360° - 120° = 240°$ and the radius is 6 cm.

$$A_{\text{sector}} = \left(\frac{a}{360°}\right)\pi r^2 = \left(\frac{240°}{360°}\right)\pi(6)^2$$
$$= \frac{2}{3}\pi(36) = 24\pi \text{ cm}^2 \approx 75.4 \text{ cm}^2$$

12. $(2\pi - 4)$ cm$^2 \approx 2.28$ cm^2. Because $SQRE$ is a square, $\triangle ESQ$ is an isosceles triangle with hypotenuse $\overline{QE}$. Because $QE = 2\sqrt{2}$ cm, the length of each side of the square is 2 cm. Use a compass to draw a circle with center S and radius SE.

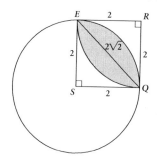

From the figure, you can see that each half of the shaded region is equal to the area of a segment of the circle in which the central angle is 90°. (The sector is a quarter-circle.) Notice that $\overline{SE}$ and $\overline{SQ}$ are radii of the circle, so $r = 2$ cm. Find the area of the segment.

$$A_{\text{segment}} = A_{\text{sector}} - A_{\text{triangle}}$$
$$= \frac{1}{4}\pi(2)^2 - \frac{1}{2}(2)(2) = (\pi - 2) \text{ cm}^2$$

Area of shaded region $= 2A_{\text{segment}}$
$$= 2(\pi - 2) = (2\pi - 4) \text{ cm}^2$$
$$\approx 2.28 \text{ cm}^2$$

13. 222.8 cm^2. From the figure, you can see that $\overline{BD}$ is both a diagonal of the square and a diameter of the circle. Use r and d to represent the radius and diameter of the circle, respectively. First use the given area of the circle to find the radius: $A = \pi r^2 = 350$ cm^2, so $r^2 = \frac{350}{\pi}$ and $r = \sqrt{\frac{350}{\pi}}$ cm. Then $d = 2r = 2\sqrt{\frac{350}{\pi}}$. The diameter is the hypotenuse of isosceles right triangle *BAD,* so by the Isosceles Right Triangle Conjecture,

$$AB = \frac{2\sqrt{\frac{350}{\pi}}}{\sqrt{2}}$$

$\overline{AB}$ and $\overline{AD}$ are sides of the square. Therefore, the area of square *ABCD* is

$$\left(\frac{2\sqrt{\frac{350}{\pi}}}{\sqrt{2}}\right)^2 = \frac{4\left(\frac{350}{\pi}\right)}{2}$$

$$= 2\left(\frac{350}{\pi}\right) = \frac{700}{\pi} \approx 222.8 \text{ cm}^2$$

Note: In order to get an accurate result, it is important that you do not round until the final step.

14. Isosceles right triangle. First use the distance formula to find the lengths of the three sides of the triangle.

$$AB = \sqrt{(11-3)^2 + (3-5)^2} = \sqrt{8^2 + (-2)^2}$$
$$= \sqrt{64 + 4} = \sqrt{68}$$
$$BC = \sqrt{(8-11)^2 + (8-3)^2} = \sqrt{(-3)^2 + 5^2}$$
$$= \sqrt{9 + 25} = \sqrt{34}$$
$$AC = \sqrt{(8-3)^2 + (8-5)^2} = \sqrt{5^2 + 3^2}$$
$$= \sqrt{25 + 9} = \sqrt{34}$$

Because $BC = AC$, $\triangle ABC$ is isosceles with legs $\overline{AB}$ and $\overline{BC}$. To determine whether this is an isosceles *right* triangle, see whether the side lengths satisfy the Pythagorean Theorem.

$$(BC)^2 + (AC)^2 = \left(\sqrt{34}\right)^2 + \left(\sqrt{34}\right)^2$$
$$= 34 + 34 = 68;$$
$$(AB)^2 = \left(\sqrt{68}\right)^2 = 68$$

Therefore, $\triangle ABC$ is an isosceles right triangle with hypotenuse $\overline{BC}$. (The slopes of $\overline{AC}$ and $\overline{BC}$ could also be used to show that $\angle C$ is a right angle, but since we've already calculated the three lengths, it's faster to just use them.)

15. No. The closest she can come to camp is 10 km. Let *d* represent the (direct) distance that Sally has traveled from camp. Make a sketch of the situation described in the exercise.

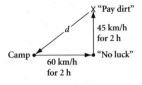

She has traveled 2(60) = 120 km east and 2(45) = 90 km north. The distances 120 km and 90 km form the legs of a right triangle in which *d* is the length of the hypotenuse. Thus, $(120)^2 + (90)^2 = d^2$. Notice that 120 = 30(4) and 90 = 30(3), so the

side lengths in this triangle are a multiple of 3-4-5, and therefore, *d* = 30(5) = 150 km. The distance back to camp is 150 km. Sally's complete trip covers a distance of 120 + 90 + 150 = 360 km, but she has enough gas to travel only 350 km, so she will fall 10 km short of making it back to camp.

16. No. The 15 cm diagonal is the longer diagonal. A diagonal of a rectangle divides the rectangle into two right triangles, each with the diagonal as a hypotenuse, so you can determine whether the parallelogram is a rectangle by seeing whether the given lengths 8.5 cm, 12 cm, and 15 cm satisfy the Pythagorean Theorem.

$(8.5)^2 + (12)^2 = 72.25 + 144 = 216.25$, while $(15)^2 = 225$, so the parallelogram is not a rectangle. Because $(8.5)^2 + (12)^2 < (15)^2$, the triangle formed by the two sides of the parallelogram and the diagonal of length 15 cm is an obtuse triangle, with the angle between the two sides of the parallelogram an obtuse angle. Every parallelogram that is not a rectangle has two congruent obtuse angles (a pair of opposite angles) and two acute angles (the other pair of opposite angles). The diagonal opposite an obtuse angle of a parallelogram is longer than the diagonal opposite an acute angle, so the 15 cm diagonal must be the longer diagonal of the parallelogram.

17. 1.4 km; 8.5 min. First find the distances that Peter and Paul walk before they stop. Peter walks 2 km/h for 30 min, or $\frac{1}{2}$ h, so he walks 1 km. Paul walks 3 km/h for 20 min, or $\frac{1}{3}$ h, so he also walks 1 km. Because their paths are at right angles to each other, the distance between them after they have both stopped walking is the length of the hypotenuse of an isosceles right triangle in which the length of each leg is 1 km. This distance is $\sqrt{2}$ km ≈ 1.4 km. If Peter and Paul start running straight toward each other with *both* of them running at 5 km/h, each of them will travel half this distance, or $\frac{\sqrt{2}}{2}$ km. The time required to travel $\frac{\sqrt{2}}{2}$ km at 5 km/h is

$$\frac{\frac{\sqrt{2}}{2} \text{ km}}{5 \text{ km/h}} = \frac{\sqrt{2}}{10} \text{ h}$$

Convert this time to minutes: $\frac{\sqrt{2}}{10}$ h $\cdot \frac{60 \text{ min}}{1 \text{ h}} = 6\sqrt{2}$ min ≈ 8.5 min.

Note: To get an accurate result for the time it will take Peter and Paul to reach each other, work with radicals as shown above, rather than rounding intermediate results. If you use the distance of 1.4 mi to calculate this time, you will get 8.4 min, rather than 8.5 min.

Discovering Geometry Solutions Manual
©2008 Key Curriculum Press

18. Yes. Find the length of the space diagonal of the box. Let d represent the length of the space diagonal. Use the second method shown in the solution for Exercise 4.

$$d = \sqrt{(12)^2 + (16)^2 + (14)^2}$$
$$= \sqrt{144 + 256 + 196} = \sqrt{596} \approx 24.4$$

Thus, the length of the space diagonal of the box is about 24.4 in., so the 24 in. long flute will fit in the box.

19. 29 ft. Make a sketch.

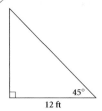

Because the flagpole makes a 45° angle with the ground, the triangle is an isosceles right triangle, so the vertical leg must also be 12 ft long, and the length of the diagonal will be $12\sqrt{2}$ ft ≈ 17 ft. The original height of the flagpole is the sum of the lengths of the vertical leg and the hypotenuse, or, to the nearest foot, $12 + 17 = 29$ ft.

20. ≈ 45 ft. By the Tangent Conjecture, the angle of the triangle whose vertex is the point of tangency is a right angle. Therefore, the triangle shown in the figure is a right triangle with legs of lengths r and 35 ft, and hypotenuse of length $(r + 12)^2$. Apply the Pythagorean Theorem to this triangle and solve for r.

$$r^2 + (35)^2 = (r + 12)^2$$
$$r^2 + 1225 = r^2 + 24r + 144$$
$$1081 = 24r$$
$$r = \frac{1081}{24} \approx 45$$

The radius of the tank is approximately 45 ft.

21. 50 mi. This is similar to Exercise 20, but you need to find the length of the tangent segment rather than the radius of the circle. Make a sketch.

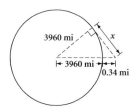

Apply the Pythagorean Theorem to the right triangle in the figure and solve for x.

$$(3960)^2 + x^2 = (3960 + 0.34)^2$$
$$(3960)^2 + x^2 = (3960.34)^2$$
$$x^2 = (3960.34)^2 - (3960)^2$$
$$x = \sqrt{(3960.34)^2 - (3960)^2} \approx 52$$

To the nearest 10 mi, the maximum broadcasting radius is 50 mi.

22. 225π m$^2 \approx 707$ m^2. Draw the radius of the circle to the feet of the diver to form a right triangle. The lengths of the legs of this triangle are 20 m and the radius, while the length of the hypotenuse is 25 m. Because $20 = 5(4)$ and $25 = 5(5)$, the side lengths in this triangle are a multiple of 3-4-5, so the length of the third side is $5(3) = 15$. Therefore, the radius of the circle is 15 m. Find the area of the circular region: $A = \pi r^2 = \pi(15)^2 = 225\pi \approx 707$ m^2.

23. $6\sqrt{3}$ and 18. By the 30°-60°-90° Triangle Conjecture, the length of the shorter leg is half the length of the hypotenuse and the length of the longer leg is the product of the length of the shorter leg and $\sqrt{3}$. In this triangle, the length of the shorter leg is $\frac{1}{2}(12\sqrt{3}) = 6\sqrt{3}$, and the length of the longer leg is $(6\sqrt{3})(\sqrt{3}) = (6)(3) = 18$.

24. 12 m. Let s represent the side length of the equilateral triangle. Draw an altitude (which is also a median and angle bisector) to form two congruent 30°-60°-90° triangles.

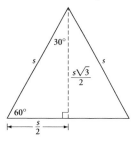

In each right triangle, s is the length of the hypotenuse, so by the 30°-60°-90° Triangle Conjecture, the length of the shorter leg is $\frac{s}{2}$ and the length of the longer leg is $\frac{s}{2} \cdot \sqrt{3} = \frac{s\sqrt{3}}{2}$. The longer leg is the altitude of the equilateral triangle. Use the Triangle Area Conjecture and the given area to find the value of s.

$$A = \frac{1}{2}bh$$
$$36\sqrt{3} = \frac{1}{2} \cdot s \cdot \frac{s\sqrt{3}}{2}$$
$$36\sqrt{3} = \frac{s^2\sqrt{3}}{4}$$
$$36 = \frac{s^2}{4}$$
$$s^2 = 144$$
$$s = 12 \text{ m}$$

25. 42. As in the solution for Exercise 24, let s represent the side length of the equilateral triangle. Refer to the sketch in the solution for Exercise 24. In this case, the height of the equilateral triangle, which is the longer leg of each 30°-60°-90° triangle, is $7\sqrt{3}$, so $\frac{s\sqrt{3}}{2} = 7\sqrt{3}$. Solve this equation to find s.

$$\frac{s\sqrt{3}}{2} = 7\sqrt{3}$$

$$s\sqrt{3} = 14\sqrt{3}$$

$$s = 14$$

$$P = 3s = 3(14) = 42$$

The perimeter is 42.

26. No. If you reflect one of the right triangles into the center piece, you'll see that the area of the kite is almost half again as large as the area of each of the triangles.

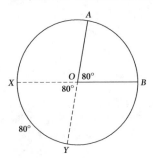

Or you might compare areas by assuming the short leg of the 30°-60°-90° triangle is 1. The area of each triangle is then $\frac{\sqrt{3}}{2} \approx 0.87$, and the area of the kite is $3 - \sqrt{3} \approx 1.27$.

27. $\frac{7}{9}$. Draw a circle with center O and points A and B on the circle so that $m\angle AOB = 80°$. Extend radii $\overline{OA}$ and $\overline{OB}$ to form diameters $\overline{AY}$ and $\overline{BX}$.

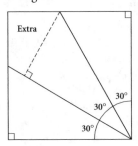

From the figure, you can see that $\triangle ABC$ will be an acute triangle if C is on $\overset{\frown}{XY}$ (between X and Y) and will be a right triangle if C is placed exactly at X or exactly at Y. Therefore, if C is placed anywhere on major arc XAY (except exactly at X or exactly at Y), $\triangle ABC$ will be an obtuse triangle. $m\angle XOY = 80°$ by the Vertical Angles Conjecture, so $m\overset{\frown}{XY} = 80°$ by the definition of the measure of an arc. Therefore, the measure of major arc $XAY = 360° - 80° = 280°$. Thus, the probability that $\triangle ABC$ will be an

obtuse triangle if C is selected randomly on the circle is $\frac{280°}{360°} = \frac{7}{9}$.

28. The quarter-circle gives the maximum area.
Triangle:

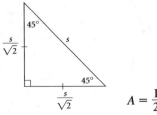

$$A = \frac{1}{2} \cdot \frac{s}{\sqrt{2}} \cdot \frac{s}{\sqrt{2}} = \frac{s^2}{4}$$

Square:

$$A = \frac{1}{2}s \cdot \frac{1}{2}s = \frac{s^2}{4}$$

Quarter-circle:

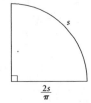

$$s = \frac{1}{4} \cdot 2\pi r$$

$$r = \frac{2s}{\pi}$$

$$A = \frac{1}{4}\pi\left(\frac{2s}{\pi}\right)^2 = \frac{s^2}{\pi}$$

For any value of s, $\frac{s^2}{\pi} > \frac{s^2}{4}$ because $\frac{1}{\pi} > \frac{1}{4}$. Thus, the quarter-circle gives the maximum area.

29. 1.6 m. For reference, redraw the figure in your book, label it as shown below, and draw $\overline{BD}$.

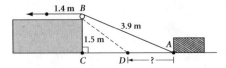

First look at right triangle BCA, which represents the situation before the wire is pulled over the pulley. Because $BC = 1.5 = 0.3(5)$ and $AB = 3.9 = 0.3(13)$, the side lengths of this triangle are a multiple of the Pythagorean triple 5-12-13, so $AC = 0.3(12) = 3.6$ m. After the wire is pulled 1.4 m in the direction of the arrow, the length of wire in the triangle will be shortened from 3.9 m to $3.9 - 1.4 = 2.5$ m. The new situation is represented by $\triangle BCD$, which is also a right triangle. Here $BC = 1.5 = 0.5(3)$ and $BD = 2.5 = 0.5(5)$, so the side lengths are a multiple of the 3-4-5 Pythagorean triple, and $CD = 0.5(4) = 2.0$. The distance that the block moves, labeled with a question mark in the figure, is $3.6 - 2.0 = 1.6$ m.

30. Draw a segment of any length for one of the legs. Its endpoints will be two of the vertices of the isosceles triangle. Bisect this leg to get the base length. Using one endpoint as center, draw an arc whose radius is the base length. Using the other endpoint as center, draw an arc whose radius is the length of the leg. The point where the two arcs intersect will be the third vertex of the triangle. Connect the endpoints of your segment to the third vertex to complete the triangle.

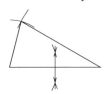

31. 4; 0; 10. The rule is $\frac{n}{2}$ if n is even, but 0 if n is odd. Draw a regular octagon and a regular nonagon.

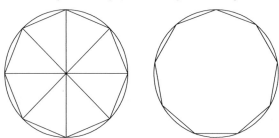

First look at the octagon. Any diagonal that passes through the center of the circle is a diameter that connects two opposite vertices of the octagon. Because there are 8 vertices equally spaced around the circle, there are 4 pairs of opposite vertices that are connected by diameters, so there are 4 diagonals that pass through the center.

Now look at the nonagon, which has 9 vertices equally spaced around the circle. Here, there are no pairs of opposite vertices, so none of the diagonals of the nonagon are diameters of the circle. Therefore, there are no diagonals that pass through the center of the circle.

For a 20-gon, the situation will be similar to the octagon. In the 20-gon, there are $\frac{20}{2} = 10$ pairs of

opposite vertices, so there are 10 diagonals that pass through the center of the circle.

For a general n-gon inscribed in a circle, if n is even, there are $\frac{n}{2}$ pairs of opposite vertices, so $\frac{n}{2}$ diagonals pass through the center. However, if n is odd, there are no pairs of opposite vertices, so 0 diagonals pass through the center of the circle.

32. 4π in./sec ≈ 12.6 in./sec. The fan makes one revolution per second, so the bug goes around a circle with radius 2 inches each second. The circumference of this circle is $2\pi r = 2\pi(2) = 4\pi$ in., so the bug travels at a velocity of 4π in./sec, or approximately 12.6 in./sec.

33. True

34. True

35. False. The hypotenuse has length $x\sqrt{2}$.

36. True

37. False. $AB = \sqrt{(x_2 - x_1)^2 + (y_2 - y_1)^2}$.

38. False. A glide reflection is a combination of a translation and a reflection.

39. False. Equilateral triangles, squares, and regular *hexagons* can be used to create monohedral tessellations.

40. True   **41.** D   **42.** B   **43.** A

44. C   **45.** C   **46.** D

47. (See figure at bottom of page.)

48. a., b. Use the Minimal Path Conjecture.

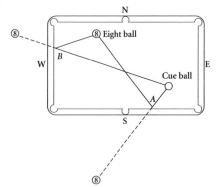

Chapter 9 Review, Exercise 47

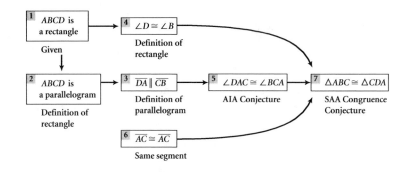

49. $A = 34$ cm^2. $P = (22 + 4\sqrt{2})$ cm ≈ 27.7 cm. First use the Trapezoid Area Conjecture to find the area.

$$A = \frac{1}{2}h(b_1 + b_2) = \frac{1}{2}(4)(12 + 5) = 2(17) = 34 \text{ cm}^2$$

In order to find the perimeter, you must find the length of the unmarked side of the trapezoid. Draw another perpendicular segment between the bases so that the trapezoid will be divided into two right triangles and a rectangle.

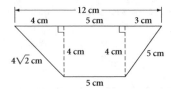

Because opposite sides of a rectangle are congruent, the length of the new segment will also be 4 cm. Now look at the top base of the trapezoid, which is divided into three parts. The triangle on the right is a right triangle with hypotenuse of length 5 cm and one leg of length 4 cm, so this is a 3-4-5 triangle, and the length of the other leg is 3 cm. This is the length of the right-hand section of the upper base. The middle section of the upper base is 5 cm because opposite sides of a rectangle are congruent. Because the total length of the upper base is 12 cm, the length of the left-hand section is $12 - 5 - 3 = 4$ cm. This section is one leg of the right triangle on the left, and the other leg also has length 4 cm, so this is an isosceles triangle. Therefore, by the Isosceles Right Triangle Conjecture, the hypotenuse of this triangle has length $4\sqrt{2}$ cm. This hypotenuse is the unmarked side of the trapezoid. Add the side lengths in the trapezoid to find its perimeter:

$$P = 5 + 5 + 12 + 4\sqrt{2} = \left(22 + 4\sqrt{2}\right)$$

$$\approx 27.7 \text{ cm}$$

50. $\frac{40\pi}{3}$ cm^2 ≈ 41.9 cm^2. The shaded region can be called "a sector of an annulus." Combine what you have learned about finding the area of an annulus of a circle with what you have learned about finding the area of a sector of a circle to find the area of the shaded region. Notice that the radius of the larger circle is $3 + 4 = 7$ cm.

$$A_{\text{annulus}} = A_{\text{outer circle}} - A_{\text{inner circle}}$$

$$= \pi(7)^2 - \pi(3)^2$$

$$= 49\pi - 9\pi = 40\pi \text{ cm}^2$$

$$A_{\text{sector of annulus}} = \left(\frac{120°}{360°}\right)(40\pi) = \left(\frac{1}{3}\right)(40\pi)$$

$$= \frac{40\pi}{3} \text{ cm}^2 \approx 41.9 \text{ cm}^2$$

51. $25\sqrt{5}$ m ≈ 55.9 m. Let d represent the diagonal distance across the pool. The pool is rectangular, so this diagonal divides the pool into two congruent right triangles. Apply the Pythagorean Theorem to one of these triangles to find d, the length of the hypotenuse of a right triangle whose legs have lengths 50 m and 25 m.

$$a^2 + b^2 = c^2$$

$$(50)^2 + (25)^2 = d^2$$

$$2500 + 625 = d^2$$

$$d^2 = 3125$$

$$d = \sqrt{3125} = \sqrt{625} \cdot \sqrt{5} = 25\sqrt{5}$$

The diagonal distance across the pool is $25\sqrt{5}$ m $\approx$ 55.9 m.

52. About 61.5 cm^2. Use the Regular Polygon Area Conjecture:

$$A = \frac{1}{2}asn \approx \frac{1}{2}(4.1)(6)(5) = 61.5$$

Because the length of the apothem is about 4.1 cm, the area of the pentagon is about 61.5 cm^2.

53. 48 cm. Let d represent the length of the diagonal of the base. Look at the triangle inside the box. The space diagonal of the box is the hypotenuse of this triangle; its legs have lengths 25 cm and d. Because $65 = 5(13)$ and $25 = 5(5)$, $d = 5(12) = 60$ cm. Now look at one of the right triangles on the bottom base of the box. In this triangle, the length of the hypotenuse is $d = 60$ cm, and the lengths of the legs are 36 cm and x. Because $60 = 12(5)$ and $36 = 12(3)$, $x = 12(4) = 48$ cm.

54. 322 ft^2. To find the surface area of a cylindrical container with an open top, add the area of one circular base and the lateral surface area, and then multiply by 2 for the other side of the container. You can use the formula for surface area of a cylinder given in Lesson 8.7 of your book if you modify it to reflect the fact that there is only one circular face in this case. The radius is $\frac{1}{2}(5) = 2.5$ ft, and the height is 9 ft.

$$SA = \pi r^2 + 2\pi rh = \pi(2.5)^2 + 2\pi(2.5)(9)$$

$$= 6.25\pi + 45\pi = 51.25\pi$$

The surface area of one side of the cylinder is 51.25π ft^2, so the surface area of both sides of the container is $2(51.25\pi) = 102.5\pi \approx 322$ ft^2.

TAKE ANOTHER LOOK

1. Demonstrations should include shapes other than a square. (Any regular polygon can be used. In fact, any three similar figures will work.)

2. Demonstrations will vary.

3. The small square in the center has sides with length $b - a$, the slanted square has area c^2, and the triangles each have area $\frac{ab}{2}$. The equation $c^2 = (b - a)^2 + 4\left(\frac{ab}{2}\right)$ simplifies to $c^2 = a^2 + b^2$.

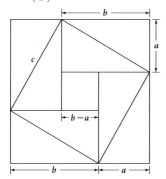

4. Possible proof: Given $\triangle ABC$ with $BC = x$, $AC = x\sqrt{3}$, and $AB = 2x$, construct 30°-60°-90° right triangle DEF with right angle F, 30° angle D, and $EF = x$. Then $DF = x\sqrt{3}$ and $DE = 2x$, by the 30°-60°-90° Triangle Conjecture. Then $\triangle ABC \cong \triangle DEF$ by SSS. Then $m\angle C = m\angle F = 90°$, $m\angle A = m\angle D = 30°$, and $m\angle B = m\angle E = 60°$.

5. Possible proof: Let $\triangle ABC$ and $\triangle DEF$ be right triangles with right angles B and E, $AB = DE = a$, and $AC = DF = c$.

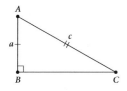 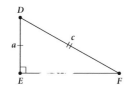

By the Pythagorean Theorem, $a^2 + (BC)^2 = c^2$, so $BC = \sqrt{c^2 - a^2}$. Using the same logic, $EF = \sqrt{c^2 - a^2}$, so $\overline{BC} \cong \overline{EF}$. Because $\overline{AB} \cong \overline{DE}$, $\overline{AC} \cong \overline{DF}$, and $\overline{BC} \cong \overline{EF}$, $\triangle ABC \cong \triangle DEF$ by SSS. Alternatively, because $\overline{AB} \cong \overline{DE}$, $\angle B \cong \angle E$ (all right angles are congruent), and $\overline{BC} \cong \overline{EF}$, $\triangle ABC \cong \triangle DEF$ by SAS.

6.

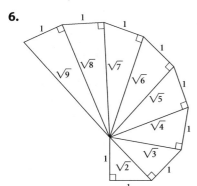

LESSON 10.1

EXERCISES

1. Polyhedron; polygonal; triangles

2. $\triangle PQR$, $\triangle TUS$ **3.** $PQUT$, $QRSU$, $RPTS$

4. $\overline{QU}$, $\overline{PT}$, $\overline{RS}$ **5.** 6 cm

6. $GYPTAN$ **7.** Point E

8. $\overline{GE}$, $\overline{YE}$, $\overline{PE}$, $\overline{TE}$, $\overline{AE}$, $\overline{NE}$

9. 13 cm   **10.** D (Square pyramid)

11. L (Hexagonal Prism)   **12.** C (Square Prism)

13. G (Octagonal Prism)   **14.** B (Cone)

15. H (Triangular Prism)   **16.** E (Sphere)

17. A (Cylinder)   **18.** J (Rectangular Prism)

19. J (Rectangular Prism)   **20.** M (Hemisphere)

21. H (Triangular Prism)   **22.** I (Trapezoidal Prism)

23.   **24.**

25.   **26.**

27. True

28. False. This statement is true only for a right prism.

29. True   **30.** True

31. False. It is a sector of a circle.

32. True

33. False. Counterexample:

34. True   **35.** True

36. *(See tables at bottom of next page.)*

Possible answer: The number of lateral faces of an antiprism is always twice the number for the related prism. The total number of faces is n more for the antiprism than for the related prism. The number of edges is n more for the antiprism than for the

---

related prism. The number of vertices is the same for each related prism and antiprism.

37. Sample answer: The painting "disappears" into the view out the window. Also, the cone-shaped tower appears similar to the road disappearing into the distance.

38. 8. You can fit two layers of blocks in the box with 4 blocks (2 · 2) in each layer, so the total number of blocks is 2(4) = 8.

39. 60. You can fit five layers of blocks in the box with 12 blocks (3 · 4) in each layer, so the total number of blocks is 5(12) = 60.

40. 30. Use one of the 3-by-5 rectangular faces of the large box as the base. You can fit 15 (3 · 5) small boxes on that base. Then the height of the large box will be 4 cm, so you can fit two layers of small blocks inside the large box. Therefore, the maximum number of small boxes that will fit inside the large box is 2(15) = 30.

41. a. Yes   **b.** Yes

c. No   **d.** Yes

IMPROVING YOUR VISUAL THINKING SKILLS

There are seven solids.

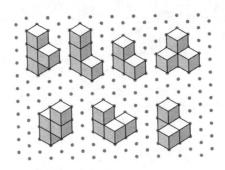

LESSON 10.2

EXERCISES

1. 72 cm³. Use $B = bh$ to find the area of the rectangular base.

$$V = BH = (bh)H = (4 \cdot 3) \cdot 6 = 12 \cdot 6 = 72$$

The volume of the rectangular prism is 72 cm³.

2. 24 cm³. Each base of the prism is a right triangle with hypotenuse of length 5 cm and shorter leg of length 3 cm, so each is a 3-4-5 triangle. Therefore, the length of the longer leg is 4 cm. Use $B = \frac{1}{2}bh$ to find the area of the triangular base.

$$V = BH = \left(\frac{1}{2}bh\right)H = \left(\frac{1}{2} \cdot 3 \cdot 4\right) \cdot 4 = 24$$

The volume of the triangular prism is 24 cm³.

Lesson 10.1, Exercise 36

	Triangular prism	Rectangular prism	Pentagonal prism	Hexagonal prism	*n*-gonal prism
Lateral faces	3	4	5	6	*n*
Total faces	5	6	7	8	*n* + 2
Edges	9	12	15	18	3*n*
Vertices	6	8	10	12	2*n*

	Triangular antiprism	Rectangular antiprism	Pentagonal antiprism	Hexagonal antiprism	*n*-gonal antiprism
Lateral faces	6	8	10	12	2*n*
Total faces	8	10	12	14	2*n* + 2
Edges	12	16	20	24	4*n*
Vertices	6	8	10	12	2*n*

Discovering Geometry Solutions Manual
©2008 Key Curriculum Press

3. 108 cm³. Notice that the top and bottom faces of the solid are not congruent, so these can't be the bases of the prisms. However, the front and back faces are congruent trapezoids, so these are the bases, and the height of the prism is 9 cm. Use $B = \frac{1}{2}h(b_1 + b_2)$ to find the area of the trapezoidal base.

$$V = BH = \left[\frac{1}{2}h(b_1 + b_2)\right]H = \left[\frac{1}{2} \cdot 3(3 + 5)\right] \cdot 9 = 108$$

The volume of the trapezoidal prism is 108 cm³.

4. 160π cm³ $\approx$ 502.65 cm³. Use $B = \pi r^2$ to find the area of the circular base.

$$V = BH = (\pi r^2)H = \pi(4)^2 \cdot 10 = 160\pi \approx 502.65$$

The volume of the cylinder is 160π cm³ $\approx$ 502.65 cm³.

5. 36π cm³ $\approx$ 113.10 cm³. The solid is half a cylinder, so each base is a semicircle with radius 3 cm. You can find its volume either by finding the volume of the complete cylinder and dividing by 2 or by using $B = \frac{1}{2}\pi r^2$ to find the area of the base and then multiplying by the height. These two methods are equivalent.

First method:

$$V_{cylinder} = \pi(3)^2(8) = 72\pi$$

$$V_{half\text{-}cylinder} = \frac{1}{2}(V_{cylinder}) = \frac{1}{2}(72\pi) = 36\pi$$

Second method:

$$V_{half\text{-}cylinder} = BH = \left(\frac{1}{2}\pi r^2\right)H = \left(\frac{1}{2}\pi \cdot 3^2\right) \cdot 8$$

$$= \frac{9}{2}\pi(8) = 36\pi$$

The volume of the half-cylinder is 36π cm³ $\approx$ 113.10 cm³.

6. 324π cm³ $\approx$ 1017.88 cm³. $\frac{90°}{360°} = \frac{1}{4}$ of the cylinder has been removed, so $\frac{3}{4}$ of the cylinder remains. As in Exercise 5, you can find the required volume in either of two equivalent ways.

First method: Find the volume of the complete cylinder and then multiply by $\frac{3}{4}$.

$$V_{cylinder} = \pi(6)^2(12) = 432\pi;$$

$$V_{three\text{-}quarter\ cylinder} = \frac{3}{4}(432)\pi = 324\pi$$

Second method: Use $B = \frac{3}{4}\pi r^2$ to find the area of the base and then multiply by the height.

$$V_{three\text{-}quarter\ cylinder} = BH = \left(\frac{3}{4}\pi r^2\right)H$$

$$= \left(\frac{3}{4}\pi \cdot 6^2\right) \cdot 12 = 27\pi(12)$$

$$= 324\pi$$

The volume of the three-quarter cylinder is 324π cm³ $\approx$ 1017.88 cm³.

7. a. 480 cm³; $V = BH = \left(\frac{1}{2}bh\right)H = \left(\frac{1}{2} \cdot 6 \cdot 8\right) \cdot 20 = 480$ cm³

b. 1080 cm³; $V = BH = \left(\frac{1}{2}bh\right)H = \left(\frac{1}{2} \cdot 9 \cdot 12\right) \cdot 20 = 1080$ cm³

c. 1656 cm³; $V = BH = \left(\frac{1}{2}bh\right)H = \left(\frac{1}{2} \cdot 8 \cdot 18\right) \cdot 23 = 1656$ cm³

d. 960 cm³; $V = BH = (bh)H = (6 \cdot 8) \cdot 20 = 960$ cm³

e. 2160 cm³; $V = BH = (bh)H = (9 \cdot 12) \cdot 20 = 2160$ cm³

f. 3312 cm³; $V = BH = (bh)H = (8 \cdot 18) \cdot 23 = 3312$ cm³

g. 1040 cm³; $V = BH = \left(\frac{1}{2}h(b_1 + b_2)\right) \cdot H = \left[\frac{1}{2} \cdot 8(6 + 7)\right] \cdot 20 = 1040$ cm³

h. 2520 cm³; $V = BH = \left(\frac{1}{2}h(b_1 + b_2)\right) \cdot H = \left[\frac{1}{2} \cdot 12(9 + 12)\right] \cdot 20 = 2520$ cm³

i. 5589 cm³; $V = BH = \left(\frac{1}{2}h(b_1 + b_2)\right) \cdot H = \left[\frac{1}{2} \cdot 18(8 + 19)\right] \cdot 23 = 5589$ cm³

j. 180π cm³ $\approx$ 565.5 cm³; $V = BH = (\pi r^2) \cdot H = \pi(3)^2 \cdot 20 = 180\pi$ cm³

k. 720π cm³ $\approx$ 2262 cm³; $V = BH = (\pi r^2) \cdot H = \pi(6)^2 \cdot 20 = 720\pi$ cm³

l. 1472π cm³ $\approx$ 4624 cm³; $V = BH = (\pi r^2) \cdot H = \pi(8)^2 \cdot 23 = 1472\pi$ cm³

8. 960 in³

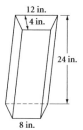

$$V = BH = \left[\frac{1}{2}h(b_1 + b_2)\right]H$$

$$= \left[\frac{1}{2} \cdot 4(8 + 12)\right] \cdot 24 = 960$$

The volume of the prism is 960 in³.

9. $QT\pi$ cubic units

$$V = BH = (\pi r^2) \cdot H = \pi(\sqrt{Q})^2 \cdot T = QT\pi$$

The volume of the cylinder is $QT\pi$ cubic units.

10. Possible answer:

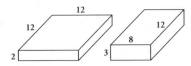

Prism on left: $V = BH = (bh)H = (12 \cdot 12) \cdot 2 = 288 \text{ cm}^3$

Prism on right: $V = BH = (bh)H = (12 \cdot 8) \cdot 3 = 288 \text{ cm}^3$

11. $2x^3$. $V = BH = (bh)H = (x \cdot x) \cdot 2x = 2x^3$.

12. $3\pi r^3$. $V = BH = (\pi r^2) \cdot H = \pi(r)^2 \cdot 3r = 3\pi r^3$.

13. $13x^3$. Subtract the volume of the hole from the volume of the prism.

$$V_{\text{prism}} = 3x \cdot 5x \cdot x = 15x^3$$
$$V_{\text{hole}} = x \cdot 2x \cdot x = 2x^3$$
$$V_{\text{solid}} = 15x^3 - 2x^3 = 13x^3$$

14. Margaretta has room for 0.5625 cord. She should order a half cord.

Volume of each box: $2 \cdot 3 \cdot 4 = 24 \text{ ft}^3$

Volume of 3 boxes: $3(24) = 72 \text{ ft}^3$

$72 \text{ft}^3 \cdot \dfrac{1 \text{ cord}}{128 \text{ ft}^3} = 0.5625$ cord

15. 170 yd^3. This is a triangular prism whose bases are right triangles with base length 17 yd and height 2 yd.

$V = BH = \left(\dfrac{1}{2}bh\right)H = \left(\dfrac{1}{2} \cdot 17 \cdot 2\right) \cdot 10 = 170 \text{ yd}^3$

16. 5100 lb. First find the volume of one block, which is a rectangular prism.

$V = (3)(4)(2.5) = 30 \text{ ft}^3$

Now find the weight of one block.

$30 \text{ ft}^3 \cdot \dfrac{170 \text{ lb}}{1 \text{ ft}^3} = 5100 \text{ lb}$

17. 11,140. First find the volume of one swimming pool, which is a rectangular prism.

$V = (20)(30)(5) = 3{,}000 \text{ ft}^3$

Convert 250 million gal to cubic feet.

$250{,}000{,}000 \text{ gal} \cdot \dfrac{0.13368 \text{ ft}^3}{1 \text{ gal}} = 33{,}420{,}000 \text{ ft}^3$

Now find the number of swimming pools that could be filled with 250 million gal of crude oil.

$\dfrac{33{,}420{,}000 \text{ ft}^3}{3{,}000 \text{ ft}^3} = 11{,}140$

Therefore, 250 million gal of crude oil could fill 11,140 swimming pools with the given dimensions.

18. The volume of the quilt in 1996 was 4000 ft^3. The quilt panels were stacked 2 ft 8 in. high.

Area of 3-by-6-foot panel $= 18 \text{ ft}^2$

Area of 12-by-12-foot panel $= 144 \text{ ft}^2$

$\dfrac{144 \text{ ft}^2}{18 \text{ ft}^2} = 8$, so eight 3-by-6-foot panels can fit in 1 ft^3 of storage space.

$\dfrac{32{,}000}{8} = 4{,}000$, so the quilt's volume was 4,000 ft^3.

$\dfrac{4{,}000 \text{ ft}^2}{1{,}500 \text{ ft}^2} = 2\dfrac{2}{3}$ ft, or 2 ft 8 in.

19. **20.**

21. True

22. False. If you cut off a corner, then the section is a triangle. If you cut through the midpoints of two adjacent edges of the six faces, then the section is a regular hexagon. The section can also be a pentagon.

23. **24.** Possible answer: prism

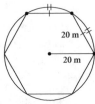

Salt crystal

25. Approximately 1.89 m. The six points on the circular track form the vertices of a regular hexagon inscribed in the circle.

20 m

20 m

The length of Ben's path is $\dfrac{2}{6} = \dfrac{1}{3}$ of the circumference of the circle, so this is an arc length on the circle: The length of Ben's path $= \dfrac{1}{3}C = \dfrac{1}{3}(2\pi r) = \dfrac{1}{3}(2\pi \cdot 20) = \dfrac{40\pi}{3}$ m.

The length of Al's path is the sum of the lengths of two sides of the hexagon. The side length of an inscribed hexagon is equal to the radius of the circle. The length of Al's path $= 2r = 2(20) = 40$ m.

Difference between length of Ben's path and length of Al's path $= \dfrac{40\pi}{3} - 40 \approx 1.89$ m.

26. $12 - 6\sqrt{2}$. Draw $\overline{OS}$, $\overline{OT}$, and $\overline{MT}$.

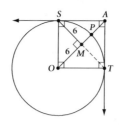

$\angle OSA$ and $\angle OTA$ are right angles by the Tangent Conjecture, so $SOTA$ is a rectangle because it is a quadrilateral with four right angles. Also, $OS = OT$ because $\overline{OS}$ and $\overline{OT}$ are radii of the same circle. Because opposite sides of a rectangle (or any parallelogram) are congruent, this means that $SOTA$ is a square because it has four congruent sides and four congruent (right) angles. Because $SOTA$ is a square, its diagonals, $\overline{ST}$ and $\overline{OA}$, are congruent and are perpendicular bisectors of each other. Thus, $OM = SM = 6$, and $\triangle SMO$ is an isosceles right triangle. By the Isosceles Right Triangle Conjecture, $OS = 6\sqrt{2}$. Then $OP = 6\sqrt{2}$ because $\overline{OS}$ and $\overline{OP}$ are both radii of the circle. Because the diagonals of the square bisect each other, $OA = 2(6) = 12$, so $PA = OA - OP = 12 - 6\sqrt{2}$.

PROJECT

Project should satisfy the following criteria:

- The seven unique pieces are built.

- The project shows at least one of the 240 distinct ways to arrange the seven pieces into a cube. (The number exceeds 1,000,000 if rotations are included.)

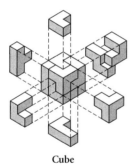

Cube

- Solutions are given for the four shapes pictured in the book.

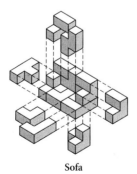

Sofa

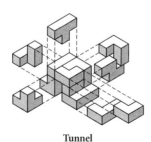

Tunnel

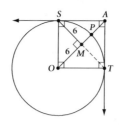

Castle   Aircraft Carrier

- An interesting shape is built and drawn.

Extra credit

- The student completes research on the number and strategies of solutions.

EXTENSIONS

A. Research results will vary.

B. Results will vary.

LESSON 10.3

EXERCISES

1. 192 cm³. Use the Pyramid-Cone Volume Conjecture.

$$V = \frac{1}{3}BH = \frac{1}{3}(8 \cdot 8) \cdot 9 = 192$$

The volume of the square pyramid is 192 cm³.

2. 84π cm³ ≈ 263.9 cm³. Use the Pyramid-Cone Volume Conjecture.

$$V = \frac{1}{3}BH = \frac{1}{3}(\pi r^2)H = \frac{1}{3}(\pi \cdot 6^2) \cdot 7 = 84\pi$$

The volume of the cone is 84π cm³.

3. 150 cm³. Use the Pyramid-Cone Volume Conjecture. Use the formula $B = \frac{1}{2}h(b_1 + b_2)$ to find the area of the trapezoidal base.

$$V = \frac{1}{3}BH = \frac{1}{3}\left[\frac{1}{2}h(b_1 + b_2)\right] \cdot H$$
$$= \frac{1}{3}\left[\frac{1}{2} \cdot 5(8 + 4)\right] \cdot 15 = 150$$

The volume of the trapezoidal pyramid is 150 cm³.

4. 60 cm³. The base of the pyramid is a right triangle with hypotenuse of length 13 cm and shorter leg of length 5 cm. Because 5-12-13 is a Pythagorean triple, the length of the longer leg is 12 cm.

$$V = \frac{1}{3}BH = \frac{1}{3}\left(\frac{1}{2}bh\right)H = \frac{1}{3}\left(\frac{1}{2} \cdot 5 \cdot 12\right) \cdot 6 = 60$$

The volume of the triangular pyramid is 60 cm³.

5. 84π cm³ ≈ 263.9 cm³. The volume of a semicircular cone is half the volume of a complete cone with the same radius and height.

$$V = \frac{1}{2}\left(\frac{1}{3}BH\right) = \frac{1}{2}\left[\frac{1}{3}(\pi r^2)H\right]$$

$$= \frac{1}{2}\left[\frac{1}{3}(\pi \cdot 6^2) \cdot 14\right] = 84\pi$$

The volume of the semicircular cone is 84π cm³.

6. 384π cm³ ≈ 1206 cm³. The volume of a cylinder with a cone removed is the difference between the volume of the cylinder and the volume of the cone. Notice that the cylinder and the cone have the same radius and the same height.

$$V_{solid} = V_{cylinder} - V_{cone} = BH - \frac{1}{3}BH = \frac{2}{3}BH$$

$$= \frac{2}{3}(\pi r^2)H = \frac{2}{3}(\pi \cdot 6^2) \cdot 16 = \frac{2}{3}(36\pi)(16)$$

$$= 384\pi$$

The volume of the solid is 384π cm³.

7. $\frac{m^3}{3}$ cm³. $V = \frac{1}{3}BH = \frac{1}{3} \cdot m^2 \cdot m = \frac{m^3}{3}$. The volume of the square pyramid is $\frac{m^3}{3}$ cm³.

8. $\frac{2}{3}\pi b^3$ cm³. $V = \frac{1}{3}BH = \frac{1}{3}(\pi r^2)H = \frac{1}{3}(\pi b^2)(2b) = \frac{2}{3}\pi b^3$. The volume of the cone is $\frac{2}{3}\pi b^3$ cm³.

9. $324\pi x^3$ cm³; 29.6%. First find the volume of the cone.

$$V = \frac{1}{3}BH = \frac{1}{3}(\pi r^2)H = \frac{1}{3}\pi(9x)^2(12x)$$

$$= \frac{1}{3}\pi(81x^2)(12x) = 324\pi x^3$$

The volume of the cone is $324\pi x^3$ cm³.

Now find the volume of the portion of the cone that is filled with the liquid. This portion forms a smaller cone with radius 6π cm and height $8x$.

$$V = \frac{1}{3}BH = \frac{1}{3}(\pi r^2)H = \frac{1}{3}\pi(6x)^2(8x)$$

$$= \frac{1}{3}\pi(36x^2)(8x) = 96\pi x^3$$

The volume of the portion of the cone filled with the liquid is $96\pi x^3$ cm³.

$$\frac{96\pi x^3}{324\pi x^3} = \frac{96}{324} = \frac{8}{27} \approx 0.296 \text{ or } 29.6\%$$

Therefore, about 29.6% of the volume of the cone is filled with liquid.

10. a. 120 cm³; $V = \frac{1}{3}BH = \frac{1}{3}\left(\frac{1}{2}bh\right)H = \frac{1}{3}\left(\frac{1}{2} \cdot 6 \cdot 6\right) \cdot 20 = 120$ cm³

b. 240 cm³; $V = \frac{1}{3}BH = \frac{1}{3}\left(\frac{1}{2}bh\right)H = \frac{1}{3}\left(\frac{1}{2} \cdot 9 \cdot 8\right) \cdot 20 = 240$ cm³

c. 884 cm³; $V = \frac{1}{3}BH = \frac{1}{3}\left(\frac{1}{2}bh\right)H = \frac{1}{3}\left(\frac{1}{2} \cdot 13 \cdot 17\right) \cdot 24 = 884$ cm³

d. 240 cm³; $V = \frac{1}{3}BH = \frac{1}{3}(bh)H = \frac{1}{3}(6 \cdot 6) \cdot 20 = 240$ cm³

e. 480 cm³; $V = \frac{1}{3}BH = \frac{1}{3}(bh)H = \frac{1}{3}(9 \cdot 8) \cdot 20 = 480$ cm³

f. 1768 cm³; $V = \frac{1}{3}BH = \frac{1}{3}(bh)H = \frac{1}{3}(13 \cdot 17) \cdot 24 = 1768$ cm³

g. 260 cm³; $V = \frac{1}{3}BH = \frac{1}{3}\left[\frac{1}{2}h(b_1 + b_2)\right]H = \frac{1}{3}\left[\frac{1}{2} \cdot 6(6 + 7)\right] \cdot 20 = 260$ cm³

h. $\frac{2480}{3}$ cm³ ≈ 826.7 cm³; $V = \frac{1}{3}BH = \frac{1}{3}\left[\frac{1}{2}h(b_1 + b_2)\right]H = \frac{1}{3}\left[\frac{1}{2} \cdot 8(9 + 22)\right] \cdot 20 = \frac{2480}{3}$ cm³

i. 2856 cm³; $V = \frac{1}{3}BH = \frac{1}{3}\left[\frac{1}{2}h(b_1 + b_2)\right]H = \frac{1}{3}\left[\frac{1}{2} \cdot 17(13 + 29)\right] \cdot 24 = 2856$ cm³

j. 60π cm³ ≈ 188.5 cm³; $V = \frac{1}{3}BH = \frac{1}{3}(\pi r^2)H = \frac{1}{3}(\pi \cdot 3^2) \cdot 20 = \frac{1}{3} \cdot 9\pi \cdot 20 = 60\pi$ cm³

k. 240π cm³ ≈ 754.0 cm³; $V = \frac{1}{3}BH = \frac{1}{3}(\pi r^2)H = \frac{1}{3}(\pi \cdot 6^2) \cdot 20 = \frac{1}{3} \cdot 36\pi \cdot 20 = 240\pi$ cm³

l. 512π cm³ ≈ 1608.5 cm³; $V = \frac{1}{3}BH = \frac{1}{3}(\pi r^2)H = \frac{1}{3}(\pi \cdot 8^2) \cdot 24 = \frac{1}{3} \cdot 64\pi \cdot 24 = 512\pi$ cm³

11. $V = \frac{1}{3}M^2H$ ft³

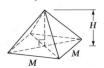

12. Possible answer:

Tall cone: $V = \frac{1}{3}BH = \frac{1}{3}(\pi r^2)H = \frac{1}{3}(\pi \cdot 16^2) \cdot 27 = 2304\pi$ cm³

Short cone: $V = \frac{1}{3}BH = \frac{1}{3}(\pi r^2)H = \frac{1}{3}(\pi \cdot 48^2) \cdot 3 = 2304\pi$ cm³

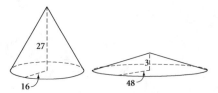

13. Mount Etna is larger. The volume of Mount Etna is approximately 2193 km³, and the volume of Mount Fuji is approximately 169 km³. First convert the heights of both volcanoes from meters to kilometers by dividing by 1000.

Height of Mount Fuji = 3776 m = 3.776 km

Height of Mount Etna = 3350 m = 3.35 km

Because Mount Fuji has a slope of 30°, you can find its radius by using the 30°-60°-90° Triangle Conjecture.

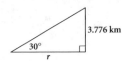

Discovering Geometry Solutions Manual
©2008 Key Curriculum Press

The height of the volcano is the shorter leg of the triangle (opposite the 30° angle), so the radius of the base of the volcano, which is the length of the longer leg, can be found by multiplying the length of the shorter leg by $\sqrt{3}$. Thus, for Mount Fuji, $r = 3.776\sqrt{3}$ km. For Mount Etna, the diameter is given as 50 km, so $r = 25$ km.

Find the volumes of the volcanoes, each of which is a cone.

$$V_{\text{Mount Fuji}} = \frac{1}{3}BH = \frac{1}{3}\pi r^2 H$$
$$= \frac{1}{3}\pi(3.776\sqrt{3})^2(3.776) \approx 169 \text{ km}^3$$
$$V_{\text{Mount Etna}} = \frac{1}{3}BH = \frac{1}{3}\pi r^2 H$$
$$= \frac{1}{3}\pi(25)^2(3.35) \approx 2193 \text{ km}^3$$

14. 78,375 grams. First use the formula for the area of a pentagon to find the area of the base.

$$B = \frac{1}{2}asn = \frac{1}{2}(27.5)(40)(5) = 2{,}750 \text{ cm}^2$$

Now find the volume of the pentagonal prism.

$$V = \frac{1}{3}BH = \frac{1}{3}(2{,}750)(30) = 27{,}500 \text{ cm}^3$$

Finally, find the weight of the sculpture.

$$27{,}500 \text{ cm}^3 \cdot \frac{2.85 \text{ g}}{1 \text{ cm}^2} = 78{,}375 \text{ g}$$

The weight of the sculpture is 78,375 grams.

15. 48 in³. Draw the solid for this net.

The solid is an oblique triangular prism.

$$V = \frac{1}{3}BH = \frac{1}{3}\left(\frac{1}{2}bh\right)H = \frac{1}{3}\left(\frac{1}{2} \cdot 6 \cdot 6\right) \cdot 8 = 48 \text{ in}^3$$

The volume is 48 in³, so the container will not hold 50 in³.

16. 4π units³. If the triangle is rotated about the x-axis, the side of the triangle that lies along the y-axis will sweep out a circle with radius 2 units, and the solid formed will be a cone with radius 2 units and height 3 units.

$$V = \frac{1}{3}\pi r^2 H = \frac{1}{3}\pi(2)^2 \cdot 3 = 4\pi \text{ units}^3$$

17. $144x^3$ cm³. The volume of the liquid is half the volume of the rectangular prism.

$$V = \frac{1}{2}BH = \frac{1}{2} \cdot 12x \cdot 4x \cdot 6x = 144x^3 \text{ cm}^3$$

18. 40,200 gal; 44 hr 40 min. The two congruent parallel faces are the pentagons at the front and back of the solid, so these are the faces and the

solid is a pentagonal prism. Notice that the pentagons are not regular, so you can't use the formula for the area of a regular polygon. Instead, subdivide one of these pentagons into a trapezoid and a rectangle.

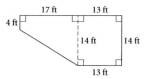

Area of trapezoid $= \frac{1}{2}h(b_1 + b_2)$
$$= \frac{1}{2} \cdot 17(4 + 14) = 153 \text{ ft}^2$$

Area of rectangle $= bh = 13 \cdot 14 = 182 \text{ ft}^2$

B = area of trapezoid + area of rectangle
$$= 153 + 182 = 335 \text{ ft}^2$$

$V = BH = 335 \cdot 16 = 5360 \text{ ft}^3$

Convert this volume from cubic feet to gallons.

$$5{,}360 \text{ ft}^3 \cdot \frac{7.5 \text{ gal}}{1 \text{ ft}^3} = 40{,}200 \text{ gal}$$

Now find how long it will take to fill the pool.

$$40{,}200 \text{ gal} \cdot \frac{1 \text{ min}}{15 \text{ gal}} = 2{,}680 \text{ min}$$

Finally, convert this time to hours and minutes.

$$2{,}680 \text{ min} \cdot \frac{1 \text{ hr}}{60 \text{ min}} = 44\frac{2}{3} \text{ hr, or } 44 \text{ hr } 40 \text{ min}$$

19. About 71 ft³. The retaining wall is a trapezoidal prism.

$$V = BH = \frac{1}{2}h(b_1 + b_2)H = \frac{1}{2} \cdot 31(18 + 48)(120)$$
$$= 122{,}760 \text{ in}^3$$

Convert this volume from cubic inches to cubic feet.

$$1 \text{ ft}^3 = (12 \text{ in.})(12 \text{ in.})(12 \text{ in.}) = 1{,}728 \text{ in}^3$$
$$122{,}760 \text{ in}^3 \cdot \frac{1 \text{ ft}^3}{1{,}728 \text{ in}^3} \approx 71 \text{ ft}^3$$

20. 403 barrels. First find the volume of one barrel in cubic feet.

$$V = \pi r^2 H = \pi(0.8)^2(2.8) = 1.792\pi \text{ ft}^3$$

Convert this volume to gallons.

$$1.792\pi \text{ ft}^3 \cdot \frac{7.5 \text{ gal}}{1 \text{ ft}^3} = 13.44\pi \text{ gal}$$

Therefore, one barrel holds 13.44π gal of oil sludge.

Now find the number of barrels needed to hold 17,000 gal of sludge.

$$17{,}000 \text{ gal} \cdot \frac{1 \text{ barrel}}{13.44\pi \text{ gal}} \approx 402.6$$

The number of barrels must be an integer, so round up to 403 barrels.

21. If you are not familiar with the polyhedrons described in 21a–c of this exercise, see the pictures on page 544 of your book.

a. $16\sqrt{3}$ cm$^2 \approx 27.71$ cm^3. A regular tetrahedron has four faces that are congruent equilateral triangles. The edges of the tetrahedron are the sides of the triangles. Sketch one of the faces.

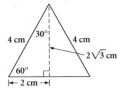

The area of one face is $\frac{1}{2}bh = \frac{1}{2}(4)(2\sqrt{3}) = 4\sqrt{3}$ cm^2, so the surface area of the tetrahedron is $4(4\sqrt{3}) = 16\sqrt{3}$ cm^2.

b. 96 cm^2. A regular hexahedron is a cube. Its six faces are congruent squares. The edges of the hexahedron are the sides of the squares, so the area of each face is 16 cm^2, and the surface area of the hexahedron is $6(16) = 96$ cm^2.

c. $80\sqrt{3}$ cm$^2 \approx 138.6$ cm^2. A regular icosahedron has 20 faces that are congruent equilateral triangles. From 21a, the area of an equilateral triangle with side length 4 is $4\sqrt{3}$ cm^2, so the surface area of the icosahedron is $20(4\sqrt{3}) = 80\sqrt{3}$ cm^2.

d. $(24\sqrt{13} + 120)$ cm$^2 \approx 206.5$ cm^2. Add the areas of the four congruent rectangular faces and the areas of the eight congruent triangular faces. The area of each rectangle is $5 \cdot 6 = 30$ cm^2. The triangular faces of this polyhedron are the lateral faces of two pyramids. Sketch a right triangle inside the solid whose right-angle vertex is at the center of the square, with one leg that is an altitude of the pyramid and with the other leg an apothem of the square.

By the Pythagorean Theorem, the length of the hypotenuse of this right triangle is $\sqrt{2^2 + 3^2} = \sqrt{13}$ cm. This length is the slant height of the pyramid and also an altitude of the triangular faces. Now find the area of each triangular face. The bases of these triangles are the edges that are sides of a square with side length 6 cm. Therefore, the area of each triangle is $\frac{1}{2}bh = \frac{1}{2}(6)(\sqrt{13}) = 3\sqrt{13}$ cm^2.

The total surface area of the polyhedron is $4(30) + 8(3\sqrt{13}) = (120 + 24\sqrt{13})$ cm^2.

22. Possible answer: From the properties of reflection, $\angle 1 \cong \angle 3$ and $\angle 2 \cong \angle 4$. $m\angle 1 + m\angle 2 = 90°$, so $m\angle 3 + m\angle 4 = 90°$, and $m\angle 1 + m\angle 2 + m\angle 3 + m\angle 4 = 180°$. Therefore, D', C, and D'' are collinear.

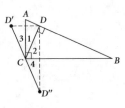

23. a. $Y(a + c, d)$

b. $Y(a + c, b + d)$

c. $Y(a + c - e, b + d - f)$

PROJECT

Project should satisfy the following criteria:

- The volume of the pyramid at Cholula: volume of bottom section $= 162,374,666\frac{2}{3}$ ft^3, volume of top section $= 14,511,100$ ft^3, total volume $= 176,885,666\frac{2}{3}$ ft$^3 \approx 6.6$ million yd^3.

- The volume of the Great Pyramid at Giza: $V = \frac{1}{3} \cdot 756^2 \cdot 481 = 91,636,272$ ft$^3 \approx 3.4$ million yd^3.

- Accurate models are built using the same scale for both pyramids.

EXTENSION

If the dimensions of the base are doubled, the volume will be multiplied by 4. If all the dimensions are doubled, the volume will be multiplied by 8.

LESSON 10.4

EXERCISES

1. 58.5 in^3. Make a sketch of the piece of paper with the corners cut out. When the paper is folded, the dimensions of the base will be 9 in. by 6.5 in. because 1 in. has been taken off both ends of both the length and the width. Because the paper is folded up along the dashed lines shown in the figure at right the height of the box is 1 in.

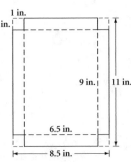

$V = BH = (9 \cdot 6.5)(1) = 58.5$ in^3

2. $32\sqrt{3}$ cm$^3 \approx 55.43$ cm^3. First find the area of the triangular base. The altitude divides the triangle into two congruent 30°-60°-90° right triangles.

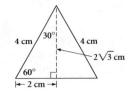

Area of base: $B = \frac{1}{2}bh = \frac{1}{2}(4)(2\sqrt{3}) = 4\sqrt{3}$ cm²

Now find the volume of the pyramid.

$V = BH = (4\sqrt{3})(8) = 32\sqrt{3}$ cm³

3. 15 cm. Let b represent the side length of the triangle to be found.

$$V = \frac{1}{3}\left(\frac{1}{2}b \cdot 6\right) \cdot 12$$

$$180 = 12b$$

$b = 15$, so the length of the side is 15 cm.

4. 11 cm. Let h represent the height of the trapezoidal base.

$$V = \frac{1}{3}BH = \frac{1}{3}\left[\frac{1}{2}h(b_1 + b_2)\right]H$$

$$3168 = \frac{1}{3}\left[\frac{1}{2}h(20 + 28)\right] \cdot 36$$

$$3168 = 288h$$

$$11 = h$$

The height of the trapezoidal base is 11 cm.

5. 5.0 cm. Substitute the given values in the formula for the volume of a cylinder.

$$V = BH = \pi r^2 H$$

$$628 = \pi r^2 \cdot 8$$

$$\pi r^2 = 78.5$$

$$r^2 = \frac{78.5}{\pi}$$

$$r = \sqrt{\frac{78.5}{\pi}} \approx 5.0$$

The radius of the base is about 5.0 cm.

6. Find the volumes of the two cylinders.
$\pi\left(\frac{8.5}{2\pi}\right)^2 \cdot 11 \approx 63.24$ in³; $\pi\left(\frac{11}{2\pi}\right)^2 \cdot 8.5 \approx$ 81.85 in³. Thus, the short, fat cylinder has greater volume.

7. 257 ft³. For the circular base, $C = 2\pi r = 44$ ft, so $r = \frac{44}{2\pi} = \frac{22}{\pi}$ ft.

$$V = \frac{1}{3}\pi r^2 H = \frac{1}{3}\pi\left(\frac{22}{\pi}\right)^2 \cdot 5 \approx 257 \text{ ft}^3$$

8. 4 cm. The smallest face measures 6 cm by 12 cm, so if the container sits on this face, its height will be 15 cm. If it is filled with water up to 5 cm from the top, then it is filled with water to a depth of 10 cm. Find the volume of the water.

$$V = BH = (6 \cdot 12) \cdot 10 = 720 \text{ cm}^3$$

The largest face of the container measures 12 cm by 15 cm. Use the volume that you have calculated to

find the height of the water if the container sits on the base.

$$V = BH$$

$$720 = (12 \cdot 15)H = 180H$$

$$H = 4$$

If the container sits on its largest face, the height of the water will be 4 cm.

9. He must refute the statement. To find the area of the base of each prism, use the formula $B = \frac{1}{2}aP$ for the area of a regular polygon.

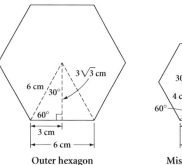

Outer hexagon   Missing hexagon

$$V_{\text{larger prism}} = BH = \left(\frac{1}{2}aP\right)H = \frac{1}{2}(3\sqrt{3}) \cdot 36 \cdot 2$$

$$= 108\sqrt{3} \text{ cm}^3$$

$$V_{\text{missing prism}} = BH = \left(\frac{1}{2}aP\right)H = \frac{1}{2}(2\sqrt{3}) \cdot 24 \cdot 2$$

$$= 48\sqrt{3} \text{ cm}^3$$

$$V_{\text{ring}} = V_{\text{larger prism}} - V_{\text{missing prism}}$$

$$= 108\sqrt{3} - 48\sqrt{3} = 60\sqrt{3} \text{ cm}^3$$

Therefore, the volume of the ring is not equal to the volume of the hole, so the claim is false.

10. 1502 lb. First convert 8 in. to $\frac{2}{3}$ ft and find the volume of the mattress in cubic feet.

$$V = BH = (5.5 \cdot 6.5)\left(\frac{2}{3}\right) = \frac{71.5}{3} \text{ ft}^3$$

Now find the weight of $\frac{71.5}{3}$ ft³ of water.

$$\frac{71.5}{3} \text{ ft}^3 \cdot \frac{63 \text{ lb}}{1 \text{ ft}^3} = 1501.5 \approx 1502$$

The water in the waterbed weighs about 1502 lb.

11. 192.4 gal. First convert 8 in. to $\frac{2}{3}$ ft and find the volume of the water in the wading pool in cubic feet. The pool is a cylinder with radius 3.5 ft and height $\frac{2}{3}$ ft.

$$V = \pi r^2 H = \pi(3.5)^2\left(\frac{2}{3}\right) = \frac{24.5\pi}{3} \text{ ft}^3$$

Convert this volume to gallons.

$$\frac{24.5\pi}{3} \text{ ft}^3 \cdot \frac{7.5 \text{ gal}}{1 \text{ ft}^3} \approx 192.4 \text{ gal}$$

To the nearest 0.1 gallon, the wading pool will hold 192.4 gal of water.

12. 13 min. First look at the base of the hot tub. The base is a regular hexagon with side length 3 ft.

By the 30°-60°-90° Triangle Conjecture, the length of the apothem is $\frac{3}{2}\sqrt{3}$ ft. The perimeter is $6(3) = 18$ ft.

$$V = BH = \left(\frac{1}{2}aP\right)H = \left(\frac{1}{2} \cdot \frac{3}{2}\sqrt{3} \cdot 18\right) \cdot 3$$
$$= \frac{81}{2}\sqrt{3} \text{ ft}^3$$

Convert this volume to gallons.

$$\frac{81}{2}\sqrt{3} \text{ ft}^3 \cdot \frac{7.5 \text{ gal}}{1 \text{ ft}^3} \approx 526 \text{ gal}$$

Because 526 is approximately halfway between 500 and 550, it will take about 13 min to raise the water temperature from 93°F to 103°F.

13. Any values of r and H such that $\pi r^2 H = 14.4$ in³. The volume of the juice box is

$$(8 \text{ oz})\left(\frac{1.8 \text{ in}^3}{1 \text{ oz}}\right) = 14.4 \text{ in}^3$$

so the volume of the can should be the same. Using the volume formula for a cylinder, this means that $\pi r^2 H = 14.4$ in³. Any values of r and H satisfying this equation will work. Choose a reasonable value for the can's height, such as 4 in., and solve the equation to find $r \approx 1.07$ in.

14. Approximately 38 in³. If you ignore the thickness of the plastic, the ice tray is two halves of a cylinder with radius 1 in. and height 12 in.

$$V = \pi r^2 H = \pi \cdot 1^2 \cdot 12 = 12\pi \text{ in}^3 \approx 38 \text{ in}^3$$

15. 100,000π m³, or about 314,159 m³; 16,528 loads. First change the length to meters: 2 km = 2000 m. The amount of dirt to be removed will be the volume of the tunnel. Because the tunnel is half of a cylinder, its volume will be $\frac{1}{2}\pi r^2 h = \frac{1}{2}\pi(10)^2(2000) = 100,000\pi$ m³, or about 314,159 m³. The volume of the dump truck is $2.2 \cdot 4.8 \cdot 1.8 = 19.008$ m³. To find the number of loads that will be needed to carry away the dirt, divide the volume of the tunnel by the volume of the dump truck: $\frac{100,000\pi}{19.008} \approx 16,527.7$, so 16,528 loads will be required.

16. $\overline{AB} \cong \overline{EC}$ because the opposite sides of a parallelogram are congruent. $\overline{EC} \cong \overline{BD}$ because the diagonals of a rectangle are congruent. So, $\overline{AB} \cong \overline{BD}$ because both are congruent to $\overline{EC}$. Therefore, $\triangle ABD$ is isosceles.

17. 8.2 cm. Connect the center of the square base to one of the vertices of the base. Let h represent the height of the pyramid and x represent the distance from the center to the vertex. The segment of length x is half of a diagonal of the square. By the Isosceles Right Triangle Conjecture, the length of the diagonal is $8\sqrt{2}$ cm, so $x = 4\sqrt{2}$ cm. The segments of lengths x and h are the legs of a right triangle with hypotenuse 10 cm. Apply the Pythagorean Theorem to this triangle and solve for h.

$$h^2 + x^2 = 10^2$$
$$h^2 + \left(4\sqrt{2}\right)^2 = 100$$
$$h^2 + 32 = 100$$
$$h^2 = 68$$
$$h = \sqrt{68} \approx 8.2$$

The height of the pyramid is about 8.2 cm.

18. $x = 96°$. By the Inscribed Angle Conjecture, $m\overset{\frown}{BCD} = 2m\angle BAD = 2(80°) = 160°$. Then $m\overset{\frown}{CD} = m\overset{\frown}{BCD} - m\overset{\frown}{BC} = 160° - 76° = 84°$. Now look at $\angle DEC$. By the Vertical Angles Conjecture, $m\angle DEC = x$. Draw radii $\overline{OC}$ and $\overline{OD}$.

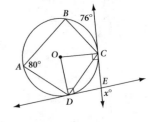

Look at quadrilateral $OCED$, which is a kite because $\overline{OC} \cong \overline{OD}$ (radii of the same circle) and $\overline{EC} \cong \overline{ED}$ (Tangent Segments Conjecture). Because $\overline{OC}$ and $\overline{OD}$ are radii drawn to points of tangency, $\overline{OD} \perp \overleftrightarrow{DE}$ and $\overline{OC} \perp \overleftrightarrow{CE}$ (Tangent Conjecture), so $\angle ODE$ and $\angle OCE$ are right angles. $\angle COD$ is a central angle of the circle, and $\overset{\frown}{CD}$ is its intercepted arc. You found earlier that $m\overset{\frown}{CD} = 84°$, so $m\angle COD = 84°$ (definition of the measure of an arc). Now apply the Quadrilateral Sum Conjecture to kite $OCED$: $90° + 84° + 90° + m\angle DEC = 360°$, so $m\angle DEC = 96°$. $m\angle DEC = x$, so $x = 96°$.

Another way to approach this exercise is to notice that $\angle DEC$ is formed by two tangents intersecting outside the circle. Therefore, by the Intersecting Tangents Conjecture,

$$x = m\angle DEC = \frac{1}{2}(m\overset{\frown}{DBC} - m\overset{\frown}{CD})$$
$$= \frac{1}{2}[(360° - 84°) - 84°] = \frac{1}{2}(276° - 84°)$$
$$= \frac{1}{2}(192°) = 96°$$

19. First construct an equilateral triangle. To find its circumcenter, construct the perpendicular bisectors of two sides of the triangle. The circumcenter is the point of intersection. Using this center and the distance from the center to any vertex as the radius, construct the circumscribed circle. The incenter (center of the inscribed circle) is the same point as the circumcenter. Using this center and the distance from the center to the point where the perpendicular bisector meets the circle as the radius, construct the inscribed circle.

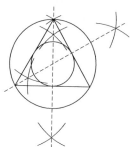

20. Possible construction:

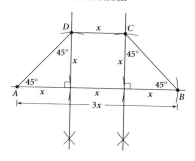

21. a. Always. If the diagonals of a quadrilateral bisect each other, then the quadrilateral is a parallelogram.

b. Sometimes. From 21a, *ABCD* is a parallelogram, and a rhombus is a parallelogram. There is not enough information to determine that all four sides of *ABCD* are congruent and also no information that would mean that all four sides are not congruent. Therefore, *ABCD might* be a rhombus but is not *necessarily* a rhombus.

c. Never. *ABCD* can't be a kite because two pairs of opposite sides of *ABCD* are congruent, while in a kite, two pairs of *consecutive* sides are congruent. Also, you know from 21a that *ABCD* is a parallelogram, and a kite is not a parallelogram.

d. Sometimes. $\triangle AMD \cong \triangle AMB$ only if $\angle AMD \cong \angle AMB$. Because these angles form a linear pair, they can be congruent only if they are right angles, which means that the diagonals would have to be perpendicular. This happens only when the parallelogram is a rhombus (which could be a square). From 21b, you know that

ABCD might be a rhombus but is not *necessarily* a rhombus.

e. Always. $\overline{DA} \parallel \overline{BC}$ because opposite sides of a parallelogram are congruent. $\overline{CA}$ is a transversal to these parallel lines, so $\angle DAM \cong \angle BCM$ by the AIA Conjecture.

IMPROVING YOUR REASONING SKILLS

From the fact that $A + B + 3 = B + 12 + 10$, you can find $A = 19$, so $A + 7 + 1 + 11$ gives the magic sum 38. Use the fact that each letter appears at least once in a sum with only numbers and itself to find the other values: $B = 16$, $C = 13$, $D = 15$, $E = 14$, $F = 18$, and $G = 17$.

EXTENSION

Results will vary.

LESSON 10.5

EXERCISES

1. 675 cm³. The new "slice" of water has a volume of $15 \cdot 15 \cdot 3 = 675$ cm³, so the volume of the rock is 675 cm³.

2. 36π cm³. The volume of the displaced water is equal to the volume of a cylinder with radius 6 cm and height 1 cm.

$$V = BH = \pi r^2 H = \pi(6)^2(1) = 36\pi \text{ cm}^3$$

3. ≈ 47 in.³. This situation is the reverse of displacement because the goldfish is removed from the tank. The decrease in volume when the fish is removed is equal to the volume of a rectangular prism with base 10 in. by 14 in. and height $\frac{1}{3}$ in.

$$V = BH = (10 \cdot 14)\left(\frac{1}{3}\right) \approx 47$$

Columbia's volume is about 47 in³.

4. 1798.4 g. First find the volume of the aluminum block, which is a rectangular prism.

$$V = BH = (4 \cdot 8) \cdot 20 = 640 \text{ cm}^3$$

From the table on page 551 in your book, the density of aluminum is 2.81 g/cm³.

$$\text{density} = \frac{\text{mass}}{\text{volume}}$$

$$\text{mass} = \text{volume} \cdot \text{density}$$

$$= 640 \text{ cm}^3 \cdot \frac{2.81 \text{ g}}{1 \text{ cm}^3} = 1798.4 \text{ g}$$

5. The solid cone of platinum has more mass. Find the volume and then the mass for the cylinder and the cone.

Gold cylinder:

$V = \pi r^2 H = \pi(3)^2(5) = 45\pi$ cm^3

mass = volume · density = 45π cm$^3 \cdot \dfrac{19.30 \text{ g}}{1 \text{ cm}^3} \approx$ 2728 g

Platinum cone:

$V = \frac{1}{3}\pi r^2 H = \frac{1}{3}\pi(4)^2(21) = 112\pi$ cm^3

mass = volume · density = 112π cm$^3 \cdot \dfrac{21.40 \text{ g}}{1 \text{ cm}^3} \approx$ 7530 g

The mass of the platinum cone is greater than that of the gold cylinder.

6. 1.5 cm. First find the volume of the displacement. From the table on page 551, the density of sodium is 0.97 g/cm^3.

density = $\dfrac{\text{mass}}{\text{volume}}$

volume = $\dfrac{\text{mass}}{\text{density}} = \dfrac{145.5 \text{ g}}{0.97 \text{ g/cm}^3} = 150$ cm^3

Also, $V = BH = (10 \cdot 10)H = 100H$. Therefore, $100H = 150$, or $H = 1.5$ cm.

7. 10.5 g/cm^3; silver. First find the volume of the displaced water.

$V = BH = (5 \cdot 5) \cdot 2 = 50$ cm^3

Now divide the mass by the volume to find the density.

density = $\dfrac{\text{mass}}{\text{volume}} = \dfrac{525 \text{ g}}{50 \text{ cm}^3} = 10.5$ g/cm^3

From the table, the metal is silver.

8. 8000 cm^3. First find the volume of the displaced water.

$V = BH = (35 \cdot 50) \cdot 4 = 7000$ cm^3

Because $\frac{7}{8}$ of the volume of the ice floats below the water level,

$V_{\text{displacement}} = \frac{7}{8}V_{\text{block of ice}}$

$V_{\text{block of ice}} = \frac{8}{7}V_{\text{displacement}} = \frac{8}{7}(7000) = 8000$ cm^3

9. The volume of the medallion is 160 cm^3. Yes, it is gold, and the Colonel is who he says he is.

$V_{\text{displacement}} = (10 \cdot 10)(54.6 - 53) = 100 \cdot 1.6$

$= 160$ cm^3

density = $\dfrac{\text{mass}}{\text{volume}} = \dfrac{3088 \text{ g}}{160 \text{ cm}^3} = 19.3$ g/cm^3

The table shows that the density of gold is 19.3 g/cm^3.

10. 679 cm^3. The slice removed is $\frac{60°}{360°} = \frac{1}{6}$ of the cylinder, so its volume will be $\frac{1}{6}$ of the volume of a cylinder with radius 6 cm and height 36 cm.

$V = \frac{1}{6}(\pi r^2 H) = \frac{1}{6} \cdot \pi \cdot 6^2 \cdot 36 \approx 679$

To the nearest cubic centimeter, the volume of the slice is 679 cm^3.

11. Approximately 193 lb; 22 fish. First find the volume of the aquarium. Look at one of its regular hexagonal bases.

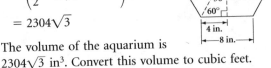

$V = BH = \left(\frac{1}{2}asn\right)H$

$= \left(\frac{1}{2} \cdot 4\sqrt{3} \cdot 8 \cdot 6\right) \cdot 24$

$= 2304\sqrt{3}$

The volume of the aquarium is $2304\sqrt{3}$ in^3. Convert this volume to cubic feet.

1 ft^3 = 12 in. · 12 in. · 12 in. = 1728 in^3

$2304\sqrt{3}$ in$^3 \cdot \dfrac{1 \text{ ft}^3}{1728 \text{ in}^3} = \frac{4}{3}\sqrt{3}$ ft^3

Now find the weight of the water.

$\frac{4}{3}\sqrt{3}$ ft$^3 \cdot \dfrac{63 \text{ lb}}{1 \text{ ft}^3} \approx 145$ lb

The aquarium itself weighs 48 lb, so its total weight when filled with water is about $145 + 48 = 193$ lb.

Finally, find the number of fish that this aquarium can house.

$2304\sqrt{3}$ in$^3 \cdot \dfrac{1 \text{ fish}}{180 \text{ in}^3} \approx 22$

The aquarium can house 22 fish.

12. $\frac{9}{2}\sqrt{3}$. Recall that the centroid is the point of concurrency of the three medians of a triangle. Because $\overline{AE}$ passes through M, $\overline{AE}$ is the median to $\overline{BC}$. In an equilateral triangle, every median is also an altitude. Look at $\triangle CEA$. $CB = AB$ because $\triangle ABC$ is equilateral, and $CE = \frac{1}{2}(CB)$ because $\overline{AE}$ is a median. Therefore, $CE = 3$. Because $\triangle CEA$ is a 30°-60°-90° triangle, AE (length of longer leg) = $3\sqrt{3}$. Because $\overline{AE} \perp \overline{CE}$, area of $\triangle CEA = \frac{1}{2}bh = \frac{1}{2}(3)(3\sqrt{3}) = \frac{9}{2}\sqrt{3}$.

13. Paragraph Proof: $\angle S \cong \angle R$ because $\overline{SP} \parallel \overline{RQ}$ (AIA Conjecture). $\overline{SM} \cong \overline{MR}$ because it is given. $\angle SMP \cong \angle RMQ$ because they are vertical angles. $\triangle SMP \cong \triangle RMQ$ by ASA. $\overline{MP} \cong \overline{MQ}$ because they are corresponding parts of congruent triangles. Thus, M is the midpoint of PQ because $\overline{MP} \cong \overline{MQ}$.

Discovering Geometry Solutions Manual
©2008 Key Curriculum Press

FLOWCHART PROOF

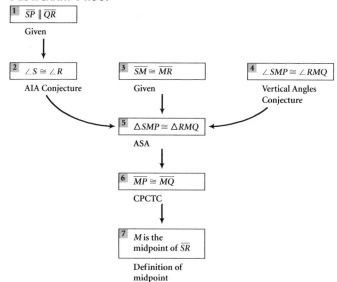

1	$\overline{SP} \parallel \overline{QR}$
	Given

2	$\angle S \cong \angle R$
	AIA Conjecture

3	$\overline{SM} \cong \overline{MR}$
	Given

4	$\angle SMP \cong \angle RMQ$
	Vertical Angles Conjecture

5	$\triangle SMP \cong \triangle RMQ$
	ASA

6	$\overline{MP} \cong \overline{MQ}$
	CPCTC

7	M is the midpoint of $\overline{SR}$
	Definition of midpoint

14. 15. Look at a vertex that is common to all three regular polygons. One of these polygons is a regular decagon and another is an equilateral triangle. Recall that the measure of each interior angle of a regular n-gon is $\frac{(n-2) \cdot 180°}{n}$, so the measure of each interior angle of the decagon is $\frac{8 \cdot 180°}{10} = 144°$. The measure of each interior angle of an equilateral triangle is 60°. Let x represent the angle measure of an interior angle in the red polygon. The sum of the angle measures around a vertex is always 360°, so $x = 360° - 144° - 60° = 156°$. Then find the number of sides in a regular polygon in which each interior angle measures 156°.

$$\frac{(n-2) \cdot 180°}{n} = 156°$$
$$(n-2) \cdot 180° = 156° \cdot n$$
$$180° \cdot n - 360° = 156° \cdot n$$
$$24° \cdot n = 360°$$
$$n = 15$$

Therefore, the red polygon has 15 sides.

15. a. (1, 3). Plot and label the three given points and sketch a circle passing through them. (You will not yet know exactly where the center is.) Connect the three points to form a triangle inscribed in the circle.

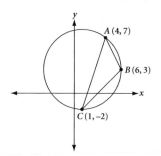

The center of the circumscribed circle is the circumcenter of the triangle. Recall that the circumcenter of a triangle is the point of concurrency of the three perpendicular bisectors of the sides of the triangle. Therefore, you can find the coordinates of the circumcenter by finding equations for any two of the three perpendicular bisectors and then solving a system of equations to find the intersection point of the two perpendicular bisectors.

First find the perpendicular bisector of $\overline{AB}$.

$$\text{Midpoint of } \overline{AB} = \left(\frac{x_1 + x_2}{2}, \frac{y_1 + y_1}{2}\right)$$
$$= \left(\frac{4 + 6}{2}, \frac{7 + 3}{2}\right) = (5, 5)$$
$$\text{Slope of } \overline{AB} = \frac{y_2 - y_1}{x_2 - x_1} = \frac{3 - 7}{6 - 4} = \frac{-4}{2} = -2$$

The slope of the perpendicular bisector of $\overline{AB}$ is the opposite reciprocal of -2, which is $\frac{1}{2}$, and it passes through the midpoint, (5, 5). Find the equation in the form $y = mx + b$ for this line.

$$\frac{y - 5}{x - 5} = \frac{1}{2}$$
$$2(y - 5) = 1(x - 5)$$
$$2y - 10 = x - 5$$
$$2y = x + 5$$
$$y = \frac{1}{2}x + \frac{5}{2}$$

Now follow the same steps to find the perpendicular bisector of $\overline{BC}$.

$$\text{Midpoint of } \overline{BC} = \left(\frac{6 + 1}{2}, \frac{3 + (-2)}{2}\right) = \left(\frac{7}{2}, \frac{1}{2}\right)$$
$$\text{Slope of } \overline{BC} = \frac{-2 - 3}{1 - 6} = \frac{-5}{-5} = 1$$

The slope of the perpendicular bisector of $\overline{BC}$ is the opposite reciprocal of 1, which is -1, and it passes through the midpoint, $\left(\frac{7}{2}, \frac{1}{2}\right)$. Find the equation in the form $y = mx + b$ for this line.

$$\frac{y - \frac{1}{2}}{x - \frac{7}{2}} = -1$$
$$\frac{2\left(y - \frac{1}{2}\right)}{2\left(x - \frac{7}{2}\right)} = -1$$
$$\frac{2y - 1}{2x - 7} = -1$$
$$2y - 1 = -1(2x - 7)$$
$$2y - 1 = -2x + 7$$
$$2y = -2x + 8$$
$$y = -x + 4$$

To find the intersection point of the two perpendicular bisectors, solve the system formed by the two equations that you have found.

$$\begin{cases} y = \frac{1}{2}x + \frac{5}{2} \\ y = -x + 4 \end{cases}$$

To solve this system by substitution, substitute $-x + 4$ for y in the first equation.

$$-x + 4 = \frac{1}{2}x + \frac{5}{2}$$

$$2(-x + 4) = 2\left(\frac{1}{2}x + \frac{5}{2}\right)$$

$$-2x + 8 = x + 5$$

$$-3x = -3$$

$$x = 1$$

Substitute 1 for x in the second equation of the system and solve for y.

$$y = -x + 4 = -1 + 4 = 3$$

Therefore, the center of the circle through A, B, and C is $(1, 3)$.

b. $(x - 1)^2 + (y - 3)^2 = 25$. To find the equation of a circle, you need to know its center and radius. You found that the center is $(1, 3)$ in 15a. The radius is the distance between the center and any point on the circle. Let P represent the center of the circle. Use the distance formula to find PA.

$$PA = \sqrt{(x_1 - x_2)^2 + (y_2 - y_1)^2}$$

$$= \sqrt{(4 - 1)^2 + (7 - 3)^2}$$

$$= \sqrt{3^2 + 4^2} = \sqrt{25} = 5$$

$\overline{PA}$ is a radius of the circle, so $r = PA = 5$.

Finally, substitute 1 for h, 3 for k, and 5 for r in the equation of a circle.

$$(x - h)^2 + (y - k)^2 = r^2$$

$$(x - 1)^2 + (y - 3)^2 = (5)^2$$

$$(x - 1)^2 + (y - 3)^2 = 25$$

16. 58; $3n - 2$. In each case, the function value is 2 less than 3 times the number, so $20 \to 3(20) - 2 = 58$, and $n \to 3n - 2$.

PROJECT

Project should satisfy the following criteria:

- The equation $y = x(10 - 2x)(10 - 2x)$ is graphed (on a calculator, in a window such as [0, 6, 1, 0, 80, 10]).

- An interpretation is given of the x-intercepts when the volume is zero.

- The maximum point at $(1.67, 74.07)$ is explained as representing a maximum volume of 74.07 in³ when the cut is 1.67 in.

Extra credit

- In general, the maximum volume occurs when the cut equals $\frac{1}{6}$ of the side length. For a 12-inch-square sheet, the cut should be 2 inches to maximize the volume.

LESSON 10.6

EXERCISES

1. 36π cm³. Use the Sphere Volume Conjecture with $r = 3$ cm.

$$V = \frac{4}{3}\pi r^3 = \frac{4}{3}\pi(3)^3 = \frac{4}{3}\pi \cdot 27 = 36\pi$$

The volume of the sphere is 36π cm³.

2. $\frac{\pi}{6}$ cm³. Use the Sphere Volume Conjecture with $r = \frac{1}{2}$ cm.

$$V = \frac{4}{3}\pi r^3 = \frac{4}{3}\pi\left(\frac{1}{2}\right)^3 = \frac{4}{3}\pi \cdot \frac{1}{8} = \frac{1}{6}\pi = \frac{\pi}{6}$$

The volume of the sphere is $\frac{\pi}{6}$ cm³.

3. $\frac{9\pi}{32}$ cm³. The solid is a hemisphere with $r = \frac{3}{4}$ cm.

$$V = \frac{2}{3}\pi r^3 = \frac{2}{3}\pi\left(\frac{3}{4}\right)^3 = \frac{2}{3}\pi \cdot \frac{27}{64} = \frac{9}{32}\pi = \frac{9\pi}{32}$$

The volume of the hemisphere is $\frac{9\pi}{32}$ cm³.

4. 720π cm³. This solid can be called a capsule. It is made up of a cylinder with a hemisphere attached to each base of the cylinder. The radius for both the cylinder and the hemispheres is 6 cm, and the height of the cylinder is 12 cm.

$$V_{\text{capsule}} = 2V_{\text{hemisphere}} + V_{\text{cylinder}}$$

$$= 2\left(\frac{2}{3} \cdot \pi \cdot 6^3\right) + (\pi \cdot 6^2 \cdot 12)$$

$$= \frac{4}{3}\pi \cdot 216 + \pi \cdot 36 \cdot 12$$

$$= 288\pi + 432\pi = 720\pi$$

The volume of the capsule is 720π cm³.

5. 30π cm³. The solid is made up of a hemisphere sitting on top of a cone. To find the volume of this solid, add the volume of the cone to the volume of the hemisphere. To find the height of the cone, look at the right triangle in which the length of the shorter leg is 3 cm (the radius of the cone) and the length of the hypotenuse is 5 cm (the slant height of the cone). This is a 3-4-5 triangle, so the length of the longer leg, which is the height of the cone, is 4 cm.

$$V_{\text{cone}} = \frac{1}{3}BH = \frac{1}{3}(\pi r^2)H = \frac{1}{3} \cdot \pi \cdot (3)^2 \cdot 4$$

$$= 12\pi \text{ cm}^3$$

$$V_{\text{hemisphere}} = \frac{2}{3}\pi r^3 = \frac{2}{3}\pi(3)^2 = \frac{2}{3} \cdot 27\pi = 18\pi \text{ cm}^3$$

The volume of the solid is $12\pi + 18\pi = 30\pi$ cm³.

6. 3456π cm^3. $\frac{40°}{360°} = \frac{1}{9}$ of the hemisphere is missing, so $\frac{8}{9}$ of the hemisphere remains.

$$V = \frac{8}{9}\left(\frac{2}{3}\pi r^3\right) = \frac{16}{27} \cdot \pi \cdot 18^3 = \frac{16}{27} \cdot \pi \cdot 5832$$

$$= 3456\pi$$

The volume of the solid is 3456π cm^3.

7. 18π m^3. The radius of the hemisphere can't exceed the smallest dimension of the block, which is 3 m, so find the volume of a hemisphere with radius 3 m.

$$V = \frac{2}{3}\pi r^3 = \frac{2}{3}\pi(3)^3 = \frac{2}{3} \cdot \pi \cdot 27 = 18\pi$$

The volume of the largest hemisphere that you could carve out of the block is 18π m^3.

8. No. The volume of the ice cream is $85.\overline{3}\pi$ cm^3, and the volume of the cone is 64π cm^3. The radius of both the cone and the sphere is 4 cm.

$$V_{\text{sphere}} = \frac{4}{3}\pi r^3 = \frac{4}{3}\pi(4)^3 = \frac{4}{3}\pi \cdot 64 = \frac{256\pi}{3}$$

$$= 85.\overline{3}\pi \text{ cm}^3$$

$$V_{\text{cone}} = \frac{1}{3}(\pi r^2)H = \frac{1}{3}(\pi \cdot 4^2) \cdot 12 = 64\pi \text{ cm}^3$$

9. Each container will hold only 20 scoops. Find the volume of the cylinder and the sphere. For the cylinder, $r = 3$ in. and $h = 10$ in. For the sphere, $r = \frac{3}{2}$ in.

$$V_{\text{cylinder}} = \pi r^2 H = \pi(3)^2(10) = 90\pi \text{ in}^3$$

$$V_{\text{sphere}} = \frac{4}{3}\pi r^3 = \frac{4}{3}\pi\left(\frac{3}{2}\right)^3 = \frac{4}{3}\pi \cdot \frac{27}{8} = \frac{9\pi}{2}$$

$$= 4.5\pi \text{ in}^3$$

To find out how many scoops of ice cream will fit in the container, divide the volume of the cylinder by the volume of the sphere.

$$\frac{V_{\text{cylinder}}}{V_{\text{sphere}}} = \frac{90\pi \text{ in}^3}{4.5\pi \text{ in}^3} = 20$$

20 scoops of ice cream will fit into the container.

10. $\frac{148\pi}{3}$ m^3 $\approx$ 155 m^3. To find the volume of the shell, find the difference between the volume of a sphere with diameter 8 m and a sphere with diameter 6 cm.

Sphere with $d = 8$ m ($r = 4$ m):

$$V = \frac{4}{3}\pi r^3 = \frac{4}{3}\pi(4)^3 = \frac{4}{3}\pi \cdot 64 = \frac{256\pi}{3} \text{ m}^3$$

Sphere with $d = 6$ m ($r = 3$ m):

$$V = \frac{4}{3}\pi r^3 = \frac{4}{3}\pi(3)^3 = \frac{4}{3}\pi \cdot 27 = 36\pi \text{ m}^3$$

$$V_{\text{shell}} = \frac{256\pi}{3} - 36\pi = \frac{256\pi}{3} - \frac{108\pi}{3} = \frac{148\pi}{3}$$

The volume of the shell is $\frac{148\pi}{3}$ m^3 $\approx$ 155 m^3.

11. They have the same volume.

$$V_{\text{hemisphere}} = \frac{2}{3}\pi r^3 = \frac{2}{3}\pi(2)^3 = \frac{16\pi}{3} \text{ cm}^3$$

$$V_{\text{cones}} = 2\left(\frac{1}{3}\pi r^2 H\right) = \frac{2}{3}\pi(2)^2 \cdot 2 = \frac{16\pi}{3} \text{ cm}^3$$

12. 9 in. Substitute 972π for V in the formula for the volume of a sphere and solve for r.

$$V = \frac{4}{3}\pi r^3$$

$$972\pi = \frac{4}{3}\pi r^3$$

$$972 = \frac{4}{3}r^3$$

$$\frac{3}{4}(972) = \frac{3}{4}\left(\frac{4}{3}r^3\right)$$

$$729 = r^3$$

$$r = \sqrt[3]{729} = 9$$

The radius of the sphere is 9 in.

13. 3 cm. Substitute 18π for V in the formula for the volume of a hemisphere and solve for r.

$$V = \frac{2}{3}\pi r^3$$

$$18\pi = \frac{2}{3}\pi r^3$$

$$18 = \frac{2}{3}r^3$$

$$\frac{3}{2}(18) = \frac{3}{2}\left(\frac{2}{3}r^3\right)$$

$$27 = r^3$$

$$r = \sqrt[3]{27} = 3$$

The radius of the hemisphere is 3 cm.

14. $\frac{8192\pi}{3}$ cm^3. Use the area of its circular base to find the radius of the hemisphere.

$$B = \pi r^2 = 256\pi$$

$$r^2 = 256$$

$$r = 16$$

Use the radius of 16 cm to find the volume of the hemisphere.

$$V_{\text{hemisphere}} = \frac{2}{3}\pi r^3 = \frac{2}{3}\pi(16)^3 = \frac{2}{3}\pi \cdot 4096$$

$$= \frac{8192\pi}{3}$$

The volume of the hemisphere is $\frac{8192\pi}{3}$ cm^3.

15. 18π in^3 $\approx$ 57 in^3. Find the volume of a hemisphere with $r = 3$ in.

$$V_{\text{hemisphere}} = \frac{2}{3}\pi r^3 = \frac{2}{3}\pi(3)^3 = 18\pi$$

The volume of the student's brain is 18π in^3 $\approx$ 57 in^3.

16. No. The unused volume is 16π cm^3, and the volume of the golf ball is $10.\overline{6}\pi$ cm^3.

First find the volume of a golf ball, which is a sphere with radius 2 cm.

$$V_{\text{sphere}} = \frac{4}{3}\pi r^3 = \frac{4}{3}\pi(2)^3 = \frac{32\pi}{3} \text{ cm}^3$$

The golf ball will displace $\frac{32\pi}{3}$ cm$^3 = 10.\overline{6}\pi$ cm^3 of water. Now find the unused volume of the cylinder, which is equal to the volume of a cylinder with radius 4 cm and height 1 cm.

$$V_{\text{unused}} = \pi r^2 H = \pi(4)^2 \cdot 1 = 16\pi \text{ cm}^3$$

The golf ball will displace a smaller volume of water than the unused volume of the glass, so the water will not overflow.

17. Approximately 15,704 gallons; approximately 53 days. The drawing shows two measurements. 9 ft is the diameter of both the hemispheres and the cylinder, so $r = \frac{9}{2}$ ft, while 36 ft is the sum of the height of the cylinder and one radius of each of the hemispheres. Therefore, $H = 36 - 2\left(\frac{9}{2}\right) = 36 - 9 = 27$ ft. Find the volume of the tank.

$$V_{\text{tank}} = V_{\text{cylinder}} + V_{\text{hemispheres}}$$

$$= \pi r^2 H + 2\left(\frac{2}{3}\pi r^3\right) = \pi r^2 H + \frac{4}{3}\pi r^3$$

$$= \pi\left(\frac{9}{2}\right)^2 \cdot 27 + \frac{4}{3}\pi\left(\frac{9}{2}\right)^3$$

$$= \pi \cdot \frac{81}{4} \cdot 27 + \frac{4}{3}\pi \cdot \frac{729}{8} = \frac{2187\pi}{4} + \frac{243\pi}{2}$$

$$= 546.75\pi + 121.5\pi = 668.25\pi \text{ ft}^3$$

Convert this volume from cubic feet to gallons.

$$668.25\pi \text{ ft}^3 \cdot \frac{1 \text{ gal}}{0.13368 \text{ ft}^3} \approx 15{,}704 \text{ gal}$$

The storage tank will hold approximately 15,704 gal of gasoline.

Each day, the service station fills twenty 15-gallon tanks from the storage tank, so the storage tank is emptied at a rate of 20(15 gal) = 300 gal per day.

$$15{,}704 \text{ gal} \cdot \frac{1 \text{ day}}{300 \text{ gal}} \approx 52.35 \text{ gal/day}$$

It will take approximately 53 days to completely empty the storage tank.

18. Lithium. First find the volume of displacement.

$$V_{\text{displacement}} = \pi r^2 H = \pi(4)^2 \cdot 2 = 32\pi \text{ cm}^3$$

$$\text{density} = \frac{\text{mass}}{\text{volume}} = \frac{54.3 \text{ g}}{32\pi \text{ cm}^3} \approx 0.54 \text{ g/cm}^3$$

From the table on page 551 of your book, the metal that has a density of 0.54 g/cm³ is lithium.

19. 31 ft. Let x represent the width of the parking lot. The floor area of the building is the area of a circle with radius 75 ft.

$$A = \pi r^2 = \pi(75)^2 = 5625\pi \text{ ft}^2$$

Parking lot: Find the area of the annulus of a circle with $R = (75 + x)$ ft and $r = 75$ ft, where R is the outer radius and r is the inner radius.

$$A_{\text{annulus}} = A_{\text{outer circle}} - A_{\text{inner circle}}$$

$$= \pi R^2 - \pi r^2$$

$$= \pi(75 + x)^2 - \pi(75)^2$$

$$= \pi(75 + x)^2 - 5625\pi$$

The parking lot will be equal in area to the floor of the building if $\pi(75 + x)^2 - 5625\pi = 5625\pi$. Solve this equation.

$$\pi(75 + x^2) - 5625\pi = 5625\pi$$

$$\pi(75 + x)^2 = 11{,}250\pi$$

$$(75 + x)^2 = 11{,}250$$

$$75 + x = \sqrt{11{,}250}$$

$$x = \sqrt{11{,}250} - 75 \approx 31$$

To the nearest foot, the parking lot should extend 31 ft from the building.

20. $ABCD$ is a parallelogram because the slopes of $\overline{CD}$ and $\overline{AB}$ are both 0 and the slopes of $\overline{BC}$ and $\overline{AD}$ are both $\frac{5}{3}$.

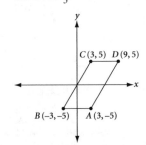

21. They trace two similar shapes, except that the one traced by C is smaller by a scale factor of 1:2.

22. The line traces an infinite hourglass shape. Or it traces the region between the two branches of a hyperbola.

23. $w = 110°$, $x = 115°$, $y = 80°$. The polygon is a non-regular pentagon. The two interior angles of the pentagon at the bottom of the figure both have measure x. The one in the lower right forms a linear pair with the exterior angle of measure 65°, so $x = 180° - 65° = 115°$. Similarly, the exterior angle of measure y forms a linear pair with a 100° angle, so $y = 180° - 100° = 80°$. The five interior angles of this pentagon include two angles each with measure $x = 115°$, two angles each with measure 100°, and one angle with measure w. The sum of the measures of the interior angles of any n-gon is $(n - 2) \cdot 180°$, so the sum of the interior angles of the pentagon is $(5 - 2) \cdot 180° = 3 \cdot 180° = 540°$. Therefore, $2(115°) + 2(100°) + w = 540°$, so $w = 110°$.

IMPROVING YOUR VISUAL THINKING SKILLS

The large cube has an odd number of small cubes. Because of the placement of pink cubes at the corners, there must be one more pink cube than blue cubes, so the single cube must be pink. You can imagine laying out the pairs so that the empty space occurs at a corner, at the middle of a face, or at the middle of a cube, so any of the pink cubes might be the single cube.

LESSON 10.7

EXERCISES

1. $V = 972\pi$ cm$^3 \approx 3054$ cm^3, $S = 324\pi$ cm$^2 \approx$ 1018 cm^2. Substitute 9 for r in the formulas for the volume and surface area of a sphere.

$$V = \frac{4}{3}\pi r^3 = \frac{4}{3}\pi(9)^3 = \frac{4}{3}\pi \cdot 729 = 972\pi \text{ cm}^3$$

$$S = 4\pi r^2 = 4\pi(9)^2 = 4\pi(81) = 324\pi \text{ cm}^2$$

2. $V = 0.972\pi$ cm$^3 \approx 3.054$ cm^3, $S = 3.24\pi$ cm$^2 \approx$ 10.18 cm^2. For this sphere, $d = 1.8$ cm, so $r = 0.9$ cm.

$$V = \frac{4}{3}\pi r^3 = \frac{4}{3}\pi(0.9)^3 = \frac{4}{3}\pi \cdot 0.729 = 0.972\pi \text{ cm}^3$$

$$S = 4\pi r^2 = 4\pi(0.9)^2 = 4\pi(0.81) = 3.24\pi \text{ cm}^2$$

3. $V = 1152\pi$ cm$^3 \approx 3619$ cm^3, $S = 432\pi$ cm$^2 \approx$ 1357 cm^2. For this hemisphere, $r = 12$ cm.

$$V = \frac{2}{3}\pi r^3 = \frac{2}{3}\pi(12)^3 = 1152\pi \text{ cm}^2$$

$$S = \frac{1}{2}(4\pi r^2) + \pi r^2 = 3\pi r^2 = 3\pi(12)^2 = 432\pi \text{ cm}^2$$

4. 160π cm$^2 \approx 502.7$ cm^2. Because the surface area formula contains πr^2, which is the area, it is most efficient to substitute the given area directly into the surface area formula.

$$S = 4\pi r^2 = 4\pi(40) = 160\pi$$

The surface area of the sphere is 160π cm^2.

5. $\frac{256\pi}{3}$ cm$^3 \approx 268.1$ cm^3. First use the given surface area to find the radius of the sphere. Then use the radius to find the volume.

$$S = 4\pi r^2$$
$$64\pi = 4\pi r^2$$
$$64 = 4r^2$$
$$r^2 = 16$$
$$r = 4$$
$$V = \frac{4}{3}\pi r^3 = \frac{4}{3}\pi(4)^3 = \frac{4}{3}\pi \cdot 64 = \frac{256\pi}{3}$$

The volume of the sphere is $\frac{256\pi}{3}$ cm^3.

6. 144π cm$^2 \approx 452.4$ cm^3. Use the given volume to find the radius of the sphere; then find the surface area.

$$V = \frac{4}{3}\pi r^3$$
$$288\pi = \frac{4}{3}\pi r^3$$
$$\frac{3}{4}(288) = \frac{3}{4}\left(\frac{4}{3}r^3\right)$$
$$r^3 = 216$$
$$r = \sqrt[3]{216} = 6$$
$$S = 4\pi r^2 = 4\pi(6)^2 = 144\pi$$

The surface area of the sphere is 144π cm^2.

7. Area of great circle $= \pi r^2$. Total surface area of hemisphere $= 3\pi r^2$. Total surface area of hemisphere is three times that of area of great circle. As in Exercise 3, the total area of the hemisphere includes the surface area of half a sphere ($2\pi r^2$) and the surface area of the circular bottom (πr^2).

8. 2 gal. The hemisphere and the circular floor will have the same radius. If r represents this radius, the surface area of the ceiling is $\frac{1}{2}(4\pi r^2) = 2\pi r^2$, and the area of the floor is πr^2, so the surface area of the ceiling is twice the area of the floor. Therefore, because it takes 4 gal of sealant to cover the ceiling, it will take 2 gal to cover the floor.

9. $V = 10.368\pi$ m$^3 \approx 32.57$ m^3; $S = 13.68\pi$ m^2 ≈ 42.98 m^2. Find the volume of the wigwam by adding the volume of the semicylinder and two half-hemispheres.

$$V_{\text{wigwam}} = V_{\text{semicylinder}} + V_{\text{hemisphere}}$$

Find the surface area using the same shape.

$$V = \frac{1}{2}\pi(1.8)^2(4.0) + \frac{1}{2} \cdot \frac{4}{3}\pi(1.8)^3$$
$$= 10.368\pi \text{ m}^3$$
$$S = \frac{1}{2} \cdot 2\pi(1.8)(4.0) + \frac{1}{2} \cdot 4\pi(1.8)^2 = 13.68\pi \text{ m}^2$$

10. a. Approximately 3082 ft^2. The total surface area that needs to be treated is the lateral surface area of the cylinder (walls) plus the surface area of the hemisphere (dome) plus the area of the circular floor. The height to the top of the dome is 50 ft, and the radius of both the hemisphere and the cylinder is 9 ft, so the height of the walls, which is the height of the cylinder, is $50 - 9 = 41$ ft.

$$S = 2\pi rh + 2\pi r^2 + \pi r^2 = 2\pi rh + 3\pi r^2$$
$$= 2\pi(9)(41) + 3\pi(9)^2 = 738\pi + 243\pi$$
$$= 981\pi \approx 3082$$

The surface area that needs to be treated is approximately 3082 ft^2.

b. 13 gal. $3082 \text{ ft}^2 \cdot \frac{1 \text{ gal}}{250 \text{ ft}^2} \approx 12.3$ gal. The farmer will need to purchase a whole number of gallons of resurfacing compound, so round up to 13 gal.

c. Approximately 9568 bushels. Find the volume of the silo, which is the sum of the volume of the cylinder and the volume of the hemisphere.

$$V_{\text{silo}} = \pi r^2 h + \frac{2}{3}\pi r^3 = \pi(9)^2(41) + \frac{2}{3}\pi(9)^3$$
$$= 3321\pi + 486\pi = 3807\pi$$

The volume of the silo is 3807π ft^3.

$$3807\pi \text{ ft}^3 \cdot \frac{0.8 \text{ bushel}}{1 \text{ ft}^3} \approx 9568 \text{ bushels}$$

The silo will hold about 9568 bushels of grain.

11. 153,200,000 km². The area not covered by water is 30%, or 0.3 times the surface area of a sphere with $r = \frac{1}{2}(12,750) = 6,375$ km.

$$S = 0.3(4\pi r^2) = 0.3(4\pi \cdot 6,375^2) \approx 153,211,547$$

To the nearest 100,000 km², the area of Earth's surface not covered by water is 153,200,000 km².

12. The total cost is $131.95. He will stay under budget.

Surface area of one hemisphere ($r = 3$ cm) without a base:

$$S = 2\pi r^2 = 2\pi(3)^2 = 18\pi \text{ cm}^2$$

Surface area of one sphere ($r = 4$ cm):

$$S = 4\pi r^2 = 4\pi(4)^2 = 64\pi \text{ cm}^2$$

Total surface area to be electroplated $= 6(18\pi) + 3(64\pi) = 108\pi + 192\pi = 300\pi$ cm² ≈ 942.5 cm².

$$942.5 \text{ cm}^2 \cdot \frac{\$0.14}{1 \text{ cm}^3} = \$131.95$$

It will cost $131.95 for the electroplating.

13. Approximately 1.13%. First write an expression for the volume of Earth. For this sphere, $d \approx 12,750$ km, so $r \approx 6,375$ km.

$$V = \frac{4}{3}\pi r^3 \approx \frac{4}{3}\pi(6,375)^3$$

Now write an expression for the volume of the "noncrust." For this sphere, $r \approx 6,375$ km $- 24$ km $\approx 6,351$ km.

$$V = \frac{4}{3}\pi r^3 \approx \frac{4}{3}\pi(6,351)^3$$

Compare the two volume expressions:

$$\frac{\text{volume of noncrust}}{\text{volume of Earth}} \approx \frac{\frac{4}{3}\pi(6,351)^3}{\frac{4}{3}\pi(6,375)^3} \approx 0.9887$$

The volume of the noncrust is about $0.9887 = 98.87\%$ of the volume of Earth, so the volume of the crust is about 1.13% of the volume of Earth.

14. 150π cm³ ≈ 471.2 cm³. Find the volume of the displaced water.

$$V_{\text{displacement}} = \pi r^2 H = \pi \cdot (5)^2 \cdot 3 = 75\pi \text{ cm}^3$$

Because this wood floats half out of the water and half under the surface, the displaced water represents only half its volume. The volume of the piece of wood is $2(75\pi) = 150\pi$ cm³.

15. $\frac{1}{4}$. Make a sketch. In the 30°-60°-90° triangle shown in this figure, the shorter leg is a radius of the inscribed circle, and the hypotenuse is a radius of the circumscribed circle. Let r represent the radius of the circumscribed circle. Then $\frac{1}{2}r$

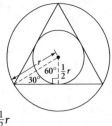

represents the radius of the inscribed circle because in a 30°-60°-90° triangle, the length of the shorter leg is half the length of the hypotenuse (30°-60°-90° Triangle Conjecture). Compare the areas of the two circles.

$$\frac{\text{area of inscribed circle}}{\text{area of circumscribed circle}} = \frac{\pi\left(\frac{1}{2}r\right)^2}{\pi r^2} = \frac{1}{4}$$

16. $\frac{1}{2}$. Make a sketch. In the 45°-45°-90° triangle shown in this figure, one of the legs is a radius of the inscribed circle, and the hypotenuse is a radius of the circumscribed circle. Let r represent the radius of the circumscribed circle. Then $\frac{r}{\sqrt{2}}$ represents the radius of the inscribed circle because in a 45°-45°-90° triangle, the length of each leg is the length of the hypotenuse divided by $\sqrt{2}$ (Isosceles Right Triangle Conjecture). Compare the areas of the two circles.

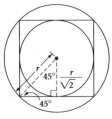

$$\frac{\text{area of inscribed circle}}{\text{area of circumscribed circle}} = \frac{\pi\left(\frac{r}{\sqrt{2}}\right)^2}{\pi r^2} = \frac{\frac{\pi r^2}{2}}{\pi r^2}$$
$$= \frac{\pi r^2}{2} \cdot \frac{1}{\pi r^2} = \frac{1}{2}$$

17. $\frac{3}{4}$. Make a sketch. In the 30°-60°-90° triangle shown in this figure, the longer leg is a radius of the inscribed circle and the hypotenuse is a radius of the circumscribed circle. Let r represent the radius of the circumscribed circle. Then, by the 30°-60°-90° Triangle Conjecture, the length of the shorter leg will be $\frac{r}{2}$ and the length of the longer leg will be $\frac{r\sqrt{3}}{2}$. Compare the areas of the two circles.

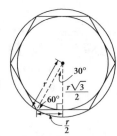

$$\frac{\text{area of inscribed circle}}{\text{area of circumscribed circle}} = \frac{\pi\left(\frac{r\sqrt{3}}{2}\right)^2}{\pi r^2} = \frac{\pi\left(\frac{3r^2}{4}\right)}{\pi r^2}$$
$$= \frac{3\pi r^2}{4} \cdot \frac{1}{\pi r^2} = \frac{3}{4}$$

18. The ratio gets closer to 1. From the figures shown for Exercises 15–17, you can see that as the number of sides increases, the areas of the inscribed and circumscribed circles get closer together because both circles get closer and closer to the polygon.

19. a.

n	1	2	3	4	5	6	n	200
$f(n)$	-2	1	4	7	10	13	$3n - 5$	595

The entries for $f(n)$ increase by 3 each time n increases by 1, so the entries for $n = 5$ and $n = 6$ are 10 and 13, respectively. This pattern tells you that $3n$ will be part of the general expression for $f(n)$. For each value of n, the corresponding value of $f(n)$ is 5 less than $3n$, so the general rule is $f(n) = 3n - 5$. Apply this rule when $n = 200$: $f(200) = 3(200) - 5 = 595$.

b.

n	1	2	3	4	5	6	n	200
$f(n)$	0	$\frac{1}{3}$	$\frac{1}{2}$	$\frac{3}{5}$	$\frac{2}{3}$	$\frac{5}{7}$	$\frac{n-1}{n+1}$	$\frac{199}{201}$

Here you find the value of $f(n)$ by taking each n and forming a fraction in which the numerator is one less than n and the denominator is one more than n, that is, $f(n) = \frac{n-1}{n+1}$, and you write this fraction in lowest terms. This pattern can be seen most clearly in the given entries for $n = 2$ and $n = 4$. It is less obvious for $n = 3$ because the original fraction obtained by the rule, $\frac{2}{4}$, has been changed to $\frac{1}{2}$.

20. $\overline{AB} \cong \overline{CB}$, $\overline{AD} \cong \overline{CD}$ (definition of rhombus), and $\overline{BD} \cong \overline{BD}$ (same segment), therefore $\triangle ABD \cong \triangle CBD$ (SSS). By CPCTC, $\angle 2 \cong \angle 3$ and $\angle 1 \cong \angle 4$, which shows that $\overline{BD}$ bisects both $\angle ABC$ and $\angle ADC$. This proof also applies to the other diagonal because $\overline{AB} \cong \overline{AD}$ and $\overline{CB} \cong \overline{CD}$ (definition of rhombus).

21. a. $\overline{AB} \cong \overline{CB}$ (definition of rhombus), $\angle 1 \cong \angle 2$ (Rhombus Angles Conjecture), $\overline{BE} \cong \overline{BE}$ (same segment). Therefore, by the SAS Conjecture, $\triangle AEB \cong \triangle CEB$.

   b. By 21a, $\triangle AEB \cong \triangle CEB$, therefore $\overline{AE} \cong \overline{CE}$ (CPCTC), which shows that $\overline{BD}$ bisects $\overline{AC}$.

   c. By 21a, $\triangle AEB \cong \triangle CEB$, therefore $\angle 3 \cong \angle 4$ (CPCTC). Furthermore, $\angle 3$ and $\angle 4$ form a linear pair. Therefore, $m\angle 3 = m\angle 4$ and $m\angle 3 + m\angle 4 = 180°$, so $m\angle 3 = m\angle 4 = 90°$.

   d. You still need to show that $\overline{AC}$ bisects $\overline{BD}$. Use a proof similar to that given in 21a to prove that $\triangle AEB \cong \triangle AED$. Then, by CPCTC, $\overline{BE} \cong \overline{DE}$, which shows that $\overline{AC}$ bisects $\overline{BD}$.

IMPROVING YOUR REASONING SKILLS

In Problem 3, note that each letter represents a different digit. In Problem 4, remember that 5 can be multiplied by numbers other than 0 to get 0 as the second digit.

   1. $C = 4$ **2.** $D = 4$ **3.** $K = 8$ **4.** $N = 8$

USING YOUR ALGEBRA SKILLS 10

1. $h = \dfrac{A}{b}$

$A = bh$	The original formula.
$\dfrac{A}{b} = h$	Divide both sides by b.

2. $b = \dfrac{P - 2h}{2}$ or $b = \dfrac{P}{2} - h$

$P = 2b + 2h$	The original formula.
$P - 2h = 2b$	Subtract $2h$ from both sides.
$\dfrac{P - 2h}{2} = b$	Divide both sides by 2.

An alternate form of the answer can be found by continuing with two more steps.

$\dfrac{P}{2} - \dfrac{2h}{2} = b$	Divide each term of the numerator.
$\dfrac{P}{2} - h = b$	Reduce.

3. $r = \sqrt{\dfrac{3V}{\pi H}}$

$V = \dfrac{1}{3}\pi r^2 H$	The original formula.
$3V = \pi r^2 H$	Multiply both sides by 3.
$\dfrac{3V}{\pi H} = r^2$	Divide both sides by πH.
$\sqrt{\dfrac{3V}{\pi H}} = r$	Take the positive square root of both sides.

4. $b = \sqrt{c^2 - a^2}$

$a^2 + b^2 = c^2$	The original formula.
$b^2 = c^2 - a^2$	Subtract a^2 from both sides.
$b = \sqrt{c^2 - a^2}$	Take the positive square root of both sides.

5. $a = \dfrac{2 \cdot SA}{P} - l$

$SA = \dfrac{1}{2}P(l + a)$	The original formula.
$2 \cdot SA = P(l + a)$	Multiply both sides by 2.
$\dfrac{2 \cdot SA}{P} = l + a$	Divide both sides by P.
$\dfrac{2 \cdot SA}{P} - l = a$	Subtract l from both sides.

6. $y_2 = m(x_2 - x_1) + y_1$ or $y_2 = mx_2 - mx_1 + y_1$

$m = \dfrac{y_2 - y_1}{x_2 - x_1}$	The original formula.
$m(x_2 - x_1) = y_2 - y_1$	Multiply both sides by $x_2 - x_1$.
$m(x_2 - x_1) + y_1 = y_2$	Add y_1 to both sides.

An alternate form of the answer can be found by continuing with one more step.

$mx_2 - mx_1 + y_1 = y_2$	Use the distributive property.

7. $v = \frac{d}{t}$; the original formula is the distance formula in terms of velocity and time.

$d = vt$	The original formula.
$\dfrac{d}{t} = v$	Divide both sides by t.

8. $F = \frac{9}{5}C + 32$; the original formula converts temperatures from degrees Fahrenheit to degrees Celsius.

$C = \dfrac{5}{9}(F - 32)$	Original formula.
$\dfrac{9}{5}C = F - 32$	Multiply both sides by $\frac{9}{5}$.
$\dfrac{9}{5}C + 32 = F$	Add 32 to both sides.

9. $L = g\left(\frac{T}{2}\right)^2$; the original formula gives the period of a pendulum (time of one complete swing) in terms of length and acceleration due to gravity.

$T = 2\sqrt{\dfrac{L}{g}}$	Original formula.
$\dfrac{T}{2} = \sqrt{\dfrac{L}{g}}$	Divide both sides by 2.
$\left(\dfrac{T}{2}\right)^2 = \dfrac{L}{g}$	Square both sides.
$g\left(\dfrac{T}{2}\right)^2 = L$	Multiply both sides by g.

10. a. $V = -F + E + 2$

$F = E - V + 2$	The original formula.
$F - E = -V + 2$	Subtract E from both sides.
$F - E - 2 = -V$	Subtract 2 from both sides.
$-F + E + 2 = V$	Multiply both sides by -1.

b. Substitute $F = 10$ (a decahedron has 10 faces) and $E = 16$: $V = -10 + 16 + 2 = 8$. The decahedron has 8 vertices.

11. a. Solve the formula for r:

$SA = \pi rl$	The original formula.
$\dfrac{SA}{\pi l} = r$	Divide both sides by πl.

l	$r = \dfrac{SA}{\pi l}$
10	$r = \dfrac{114}{\pi(10)} \approx 3.63$
11	$r = \dfrac{114}{\pi(11)} \approx 3.30$
12	$r = \dfrac{114}{\pi(12)} \approx 3.02$
13	$r = \dfrac{114}{\pi(13)} \approx 2.79$

The corresponding radii are approximately 3.63 cm, 3.30 cm, 3.02 cm, and 2.79 cm.

b. Solve the given formula for H:

$r^2 + H^2 = l^2$	The original formula.
$H^2 = l^2 - r^2$	Subtract r^2 from both sides.
$H = \sqrt{l^2 - r^2}$	Take the positive square root of both sides.

l	r	$H = \sqrt{l^2 - r^2}$
10	3.63	$H = \sqrt{(10)^2 - (3.63)^2} \approx 9.32$
11	3.30	$H = \sqrt{(11)^2 - (3.30)^2} \approx 10.49$
12	3.02	$H = \sqrt{(12)^2 - (3.02)^2} \approx 11.61$
13	2.79	$H = \sqrt{(13)^2 - (2.79)^2} \approx 12.70$

The corresponding heights are approximately 9.32 cm, 10.49 cm, 11.61 cm, and 12.70 cm.

c.

r	H	$V = \frac{1}{3}\pi r^2 H$
3.63	9.32	$V = \frac{1}{3}\pi(3.63)^2(9.32) \approx 129$
3.30	10.49	$V = \frac{1}{3}\pi(3.30)^2(10.49) \approx 120$
3.02	11.61	$V = \frac{1}{3}\pi(3.02)^2(11.61) \approx 111$
2.79	12.70	$V = \frac{1}{3}\pi(2.79)^2(12.70) \approx 104$

The corresponding volumes are approximately 129 cm³, 120 cm³, 111 cm³, and 104 cm³.

d. Answers will vary. Sample answer: The cone with slant height 10 cm has the widest radius, so a scoop of ice cream is least likely to fall off, and that cone also has the greatest volume.

e. Answers will vary. Sample answer: The cone with slant height 13 cm has the greatest height, so the cone appears bigger even though it has the same surface area as the other cones and would cost the same price; that cone also has the smallest radius and smallest volume, so it could hold smaller scoops of ice cream and still appear to be a bigger cone.

12. a. $A = \dfrac{m_1 + m_2 + m_3 + f + f}{5}$ or

$A = \dfrac{m_1 + m_2 + m_3 + 2f}{5}$

b. Average of 60: 31; average of 70: 56; average of 80: 81; average of 90: 106 (impossible).

Solve the formula for f:

$$A = \frac{m_1 + m_2 + m_3 + 2f}{5}$$ Original formula.

$$5A = m_1 + m_2 + m_3 + 2f$$ Multiply both sides by 5.

$$5A - (m_1 + m_2 + m_3) = 2f$$ Subtract the sum of m_1, m_2, and m_3 from both sides.

$$\frac{5A - (m_1 + m_2 + m_3)}{2} = f$$ Divide both sides by 2.

A	$f = \dfrac{5A - (m_1 + m_2 + m_3)}{2}$
60	$f = \dfrac{5(60) - (75 + 80 + 83)}{2} = 31$
70	$f = \dfrac{5(70) - (75 + 80 + 83)}{2} = 56$
80	$f = \dfrac{5(80) - (75 + 80 + 83)}{2} = 81$
90	$f = \dfrac{5(90) - (75 + 80 + 83)}{2} = 106$

Kara needs a score of 31 on the final exam in order to have an overall average of 60, a score of 56 on the final exam in order to have an overall average of 70, and a score of 81 on the final exam in order to have an overall average of 80. She would need a score of 106 on the final exam in order to have an overall average of 90, but that is impossible because the maximum score on each exam is 100.

CHAPTER 10 REVIEW

EXERCISES

1. They have the same formula for volume: $V = BH$.

2. They have the same formula for volume: $V = \frac{1}{3}BH$.

3. 6240 cm³. The solid is a rectangular prism.

$$V = BH = (bh)H = (12 \cdot 20) \cdot 26 = 6240 \text{ cm}^3$$

4. 1029π cm³ ≈ 3233 cm³. The solid is a cylinder with radius 7 cm.

$$V = BH = (\pi r^2)H = \pi(7)^2 \cdot 21 = 1029\pi \text{ cm}^3$$

5. 1200 cm³. The solid is a rectangular prism with a piece missing. First find the area of the base of the solid by subtracting the area of the base of the missing piece from the area of the complete prism. The base of the missing piece is a rectangle with dimensions $(12 - 6)$ cm by $(12 - 8)$ cm, or 6 cm by 4 cm. The base of the complete prism is a square

with side length 12 cm. Use these measurements to find the area of the base of the solid.

$$B = (12 \cdot 12) - (4 \cdot 6) = 144 - 24 = 120 \text{ cm}^2$$

$$V = BH = 120 \cdot 10 = 1200 \text{ cm}^3$$

6. 32 cm³. The solid is a square pyramid.

$$V = \frac{1}{3}BH = \frac{1}{3}(4 \cdot 4) \cdot 6 = 32 \text{ cm}^3$$

7. 100π cm³ ≈ 314.2 cm³. The solid is a cone. Its diameter is 10 cm, so its radius is 5 cm.

$$V = \frac{1}{3}BH = \frac{1}{3}(\pi r^2)H = \frac{1}{3}\pi \cdot (5)^2 \cdot 12 = 100\pi \text{ cm}^3$$

8. 2250π cm³ ≈ 7069 cm³. The solid is a hemisphere.

$$V = \frac{2}{3}\pi r^3 = \frac{2}{3}\pi \cdot (15)^3 = 2250\pi \text{ cm}^3$$

9. $H = 12.8$ cm. The solid is a triangular prism. Each base is a right triangle with shorter leg of length 8 cm and hypotenuse of length 17 cm. Because 8-15-17 is a Pythagorean triple, the length of the longer leg is 15 cm.

$$V = BH = \left(\frac{1}{2}bh\right)H$$

$$768 = \left(\frac{1}{2} \cdot 8 \cdot 15\right)H$$

$$768 = 60H$$

$$H = 12.8 \text{ cm}$$

10. $h = 7$ cm. The solid is a trapezoidal pyramid.

$$V = \frac{1}{3}BH = \frac{1}{3}\left[\frac{1}{2}h(b_1 + b_2)\right]H$$

$$896 = \frac{1}{3}\left[\frac{1}{2}h(20 + 12)\right] \cdot 24$$

$$896 = \frac{1}{6}h \cdot 32 \cdot 24$$

$$896 = 128h$$

$$h = 7 \text{ cm}$$

11. $r = 12$ cm. The solid is a cone.

$$V = \frac{1}{3}BH = \frac{1}{3}(\pi r^2)H$$

$$1728\pi = \frac{1}{3} \cdot \pi \cdot r^2 \cdot 36$$

$$1728\pi = 12\pi r^2$$

$$r^2 = 144$$

$$r = 12 \text{ cm}$$

12. $r = 8$ cm. One-fourth of the hemisphere is missing, so the solid is three-fourths of a hemisphere.

$$V = \frac{3}{4}\left(\frac{2}{3}\pi r^3\right) = \frac{1}{2}\pi r^3$$

$$256\pi = \frac{1}{2}\pi r^3$$

$$r^3 = 512$$

$$r = \sqrt[3]{512} = 8 \text{ cm}$$

13. 960 cm³. Let a, b, and c represent the three dimensions of a rectangular prism. Then the volume of the prism is abc. If each dimension is doubled, the result will be a larger rectangular prism with dimensions $2a$, $2b$, and $2c$, so the volume of the larger prism will be $(2a)(2b)(2c) = 8abc$, that is, eight times the volume of the original prism. In this case, the volume of the original rectangular prism is 120 cm³, so the volume of the prism obtained by doubling all three dimensions is $8(120) = 960$ cm³.

14. 9 m. Substitute the given volume and base area in the formula for the volume of a cone from the Pyramid-Cone Volume Conjecture and solve for H. Because the base area is given, it is not necessary to find the radius.

$$V = \frac{1}{3}BH$$

$$138\pi = \frac{1}{3}(46\pi)H$$

$$3(138\pi) = 3\left[\frac{1}{3}(46\pi)H\right]$$

$$414\pi = 46\pi H$$

$$414 = 46H$$

$$H = 9$$

The height of the cone is 9 m.

15. 851 cm³. Find B, the area of the base of the solid, by subtracting the area of the base of the cylinder (a circle) from the area of the base of the hexagonal prism (a regular hexagon). Make a sketch.

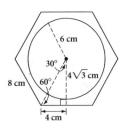

Area of hexagon $= \frac{1}{2}asn = \frac{1}{2} \cdot 4\sqrt{3} \cdot 8 \cdot 6$
$$= 96\sqrt{3}\ \text{cm}^2$$

Area of circle $= \pi r^2 = \pi \cdot (6)^2 = 36\pi\ \text{cm}^2$

$$B = \left(96\sqrt{3} - 36\pi\right)\ \text{cm}^2$$

$$V = BH = \left(96\sqrt{3} - 36\pi\right) \cdot 16 \approx 851$$

To the nearest cubic centimeter, the volume of the solid is 851 cm³.

16. Four times as great. First compare the areas of the rectangular bases of the two prisms. If the length and width of a rectangle are both doubled, the area will be multiplied by $2 \cdot 2 = 4$, so the area of the base of the larger prism is four times that of the smaller one. Because the heights are the same, the volume of the larger prism is also four times that of the smaller one.

17. a. $V_{\text{extra large}} = 3 \cdot 3 \cdot 6 = 54\ \text{in}^3$

$$V_{\text{jumbo}} = \frac{1}{3}\pi \cdot (4)^2 \cdot 12 = 64\pi\ \text{in}^3 \approx 201.1\ \text{in}^3$$

$$V_{\text{colossal}} = \pi \cdot (5)^2 \cdot 10 = 250\pi \approx 785.4\ \text{in}^3$$

b. 14.5 times. $\dfrac{V_{\text{colossal}}}{V_{\text{extra large}}} = \dfrac{250\pi\ \text{in}^3}{54\ \text{in}^3} \approx 14.5$

18. Cylinder B weighs $\frac{8}{3}$ times as much as cylinder A. Let x represent the radius of cylinder A and y represent the height of cylinder A. Then the radius of cylinder B is $4x$ and the height of cylinder B is $\frac{1}{6}y$.

$$V_A = \pi r^2 H = \pi(x)^2(y) = \pi x^2 y$$

$$V_B = \pi r^2 H = \pi(4x)^2\left(\frac{1}{6}y\right) = \pi(16x^2)\left(\frac{1}{6}y\right)$$

$$= \frac{16}{6}\pi x^2 y = \frac{8}{3}\pi x^2 y$$

$$\frac{V_B}{V_A} = \frac{\frac{8}{3}\pi x^2 y}{\pi x^2 y} = \frac{8}{3}$$

19. 2,129 kg; 9 loads. First find the volume of one pipe.

$$V_{\text{one pipe}} = V_{\text{outer cylinder}} - V_{\text{inner cylinder}}$$

$$= \pi \cdot (3)^2(160) - \pi \cdot (2.5)^2 \cdot 160$$

$$= 1,440\pi - 1,000\pi$$

$$= 440\pi$$

The volume of one pipe is 440π cm³, so the total volume of 200 pipes is $200(440\pi\ \text{cm}^3) = 88,000\pi$ cm³. Density $= \frac{\text{mass}}{\text{volume}}$, so mass $=$ volume $\cdot$ density $= 88,000\pi\ \text{cm}^3 \cdot \frac{7.7\ \text{g}}{1\ \text{cm}^3} = 677,600\pi$ g.

Convert the weight of 200 pipes from grams to kilograms. 1 kg $= 1,000$ g, so $677,600\pi$ g $= 677.6\pi$ kg $\approx 2,129$ kg.

Rosa's truck can handle a total weight of a quarter-tonne, which is $\frac{1}{4}(1,000\ \text{kg}) = 250$ kg. Find the number of loads needed to transport the 200 pipes.

$$\frac{2,129\ \text{kg}}{250\ \text{kg}} \approx 8.5$$

Round up to 9 loads.

20. 52.4% of the box is filled by the ball. $H = 2r$ because the height of the box is the diameter of the ball.

$$\frac{V_{\text{sphere}}}{V_{\text{box}}} = \frac{\frac{4}{3}\pi r^3}{(2r)^3} = \frac{\frac{4}{3}\pi r^3}{8r^3} \approx 0.524 = 52.4\%$$

21. Approximately 358 yd³. First find *B*, the area of the base of the slab floor. This is the area of a 70-by-50 ft rectangle minus the area of a 40-by-15 ft rectangle. (70 − 30 = 40; 50 − 35 = 15)

$$B = 70 \cdot 50 - 40 \cdot 15 = 3500 - 600 = 2900 \text{ ft}^2$$

Convert 4 in. to $\frac{1}{3}$ ft and find the volume of cement for one floor.

$$V = BH = 2900 \cdot \frac{1}{3} = \frac{2900}{3} \text{ ft}^3$$

The volume of ten identical floors is $10\left(\frac{2,900}{3} \text{ ft}^3\right) = \frac{29,000}{3}$ ft³.

Convert this volume from cubic feet to cubic yards.

1 yd = 3 ft, so 1 yd³ = (3 · 3 · 3) ft³ = 27 ft³

$$\frac{29,000}{3} \text{ ft}^3 \cdot \frac{1 \text{ yd}^3}{27 \text{ ft}^3} \approx 358 \text{ yd}^3$$

Approximately 358 yd³ of cement will be needed.

22. No. The unused volume is 98π in³, and the volume of the meatballs is 32π in³. First find the volume of one meatball. Each meatball has a 1-inch radius.

$$V_{\text{meatball}} = \frac{4}{3}\pi \cdot 1^2 = \frac{4}{3}\pi \text{ in}^3$$

The volume of 2 dozen meatballs is $24\left(\frac{4}{3}\pi\right) = 32\pi$ in³. The unused volume is equal to the volume of a cylinder with radius 7 in. and height 2 in., so $V_{\text{unused}} = \pi \cdot 7^2 \cdot 2 = 98\pi$ in³.

The unused volume in the pot is a lot more than the volume of the meatballs, which is the volume of the displaced sauce, so the sauce will not spill over.

23. The statue is composed of platinum. Find the volume of the displaced water. Sketch the hexagonal base of the prism. By the 30°-60°-90° Triangle Conjecture, the length of the apothem is $\frac{5}{2}\sqrt{3}$ cm. Use the formula for the area of a regular polygon to find the area of the hexagonal base.

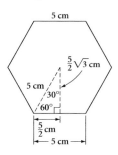

$$B = \frac{1}{2}asn = \frac{1}{2}\left(\frac{5}{2}\sqrt{3}\right)(5)(6) = \frac{150}{4}\sqrt{3}$$
$$= \frac{75}{2}\sqrt{3} \text{ cm}^2$$

$$V_{\text{displacement}} = BH = \left(\frac{75}{2}\sqrt{3}\right)(4) = 150\sqrt{3} \text{ cm}^3$$

Now find the density of the statue.

$$\text{density} = \frac{\text{mass}}{\text{volume}} = \frac{5560 \text{ g}}{150\sqrt{3} \text{ cm}^3} \approx 21.4 \text{ g/cm}^3$$

From the table, the metal that has density 21.40 is platinum, so the statue is composed of platinum.

24. No. The ball weighs 253 lb.

Volume of steel ball with radius 6 in.:

$$V = \frac{4}{3}\pi r^3 = \frac{4}{3}\pi(6)^3 = 288\pi \text{ in}^3$$

$$\text{weight} = \text{volume} \cdot \text{density} = 288\pi \text{ in}^3 \cdot \frac{0.28 \text{ lb}}{\text{in}^3}$$
$$\approx 253 \text{ lb}$$

To the nearest pound, the solid steel ball weighs 253 lb, so it is too heavy to lift.

25. 256 lb. Find the difference in volume between a sphere with radius 7 in. and a ball with radius 5 in.

$$V_{\text{hollow ball}} = \frac{4}{3}\pi(7)^3 - \frac{4}{3}\pi(5)^3$$
$$= \frac{4}{3}\pi \cdot 343 - \frac{4}{3}\pi \cdot 125$$
$$= \frac{4}{3}\pi(343 - 125)$$
$$= \frac{4}{3}\pi(218)$$
$$= \frac{872\pi}{3} \text{ in}^3$$

$$\text{weight} = \text{volume} \cdot \text{density} = \frac{872\pi}{3} \text{ in}^3 \cdot \frac{0.28 \text{ lb}}{\text{in}^3}$$
$$\approx 256 \text{ lb}$$

The weight of the hollow steel ball is about 256 lb.

26. Approximately 3 in. First find the volume of the hollow steel ball.

$$\text{density} = \frac{\text{weight}}{\text{volume}}$$

$$\text{volume} = \frac{\text{weight}}{\text{density}} = \frac{327.36 \text{ lb}}{0.28 \text{ lb/in}^3} \approx 1169 \text{ in}^3$$

Let *x* represent the thickness of the ball. Then $V_{\text{hollow ball}}$ = (volume of sphere with radius 7 in.) − (volume of sphere with radius (7 − *x*)).

$$1169 = \frac{4}{3}\pi \cdot 7^3 - \frac{4}{3}\pi \cdot (7 - x)^3$$
$$1169 = \frac{4}{3}\pi \cdot 343 - \frac{4}{3}\pi(7 - x)^3$$
$$\frac{4\pi}{3}(7 - x)^3 = \frac{1372\pi}{3} - 1169$$
$$\frac{3}{4\pi}\left[\frac{4\pi}{3}(7 - x)^3\right] = \frac{3}{4\pi}\left(\frac{1372\pi}{3} - 1169\right)$$
$$(7 - x)^3 = \frac{3}{4\pi} \cdot \frac{1372\pi}{3} - \frac{3}{4\pi} \cdot \frac{1169}{1}$$
$$(7 - x)^3 = \frac{1372}{4} - \frac{3507}{4\pi}$$
$$(7 - x)^3 = 343 - \frac{3507}{4\pi} \approx 64$$
$$7 - x \approx \sqrt[3]{64}$$
$$7 - x \approx 4$$
$$x \approx 3$$

The thickness of the ball is approximately 3 in.

27. $\left(\frac{\pi}{8} - \frac{3\sqrt{3}}{32}\right)$ m³ ≈ 0.23 m³. *Note:* To make the given measurements easier to work with, change them from decimals to fractions before solving the problem: 0.25 m = $\frac{1}{4}$ m and 1.5 m = $\frac{3}{2}$ m.

To find the volume of the water in the barrel, you must find the volume of a "solid" that is a portion of a cylinder. To find this volume, you need to find the area of its base. The base is a portion of one of the circular ends of the barrel, and the height is the same as the height of the cylinder, which is $\frac{3}{2}$ m.

The base of this portion of the cylinder is a segment of one of the circles of radius $\frac{1}{2}$ m that are bases for the complete cylinder. Sketch this segment and draw a triangle by connecting the center of the circle to the endpoints of the chord that cuts off the segment, as shown. Also draw a radius that passes through the midpoint of the chord.

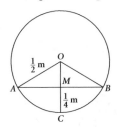

$\overline{OA}$, $\overline{OB}$, and $\overline{OC}$ are all radii of the circle, so because the diameter of the water barrel is 1 m, each radius has length $\frac{1}{2}$ m. $MC = \frac{1}{4}$ m, so $OM = OC - MC = \frac{1}{2} - \frac{1}{4} = \frac{1}{4}$ m. Now look at $\triangle AOB$ and $\triangle AOM$.

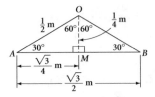

First, $\overline{OM} \perp \overline{AB}$ because M is the midpoint of $\overline{AB}$ and the median from the vertex angle to the base in an isosceles triangle is also an altitude. Thus, $\triangle OAM$ is a right triangle in which the length of the shorter leg (OM) is half the length of the hypotenuse (OA), so this is a 30°-60°-90° triangle. The shorter leg is opposite the 30° angle, so $m\angle OAM = 30°$ and $m\angle AOM = 60°$. By the 30°-60°-90° Triangle Conjecture, the length of the longer leg can be found by multiplying the length of the shorter leg by $\sqrt{3}$, so $AM = \frac{1}{4}\sqrt{3} = \frac{\sqrt{3}}{4}$ m.

Because M is the midpoint of $\overline{AB}$, $AB = 2\left(\frac{\sqrt{3}}{4}\right) = \frac{\sqrt{3}}{2}$ cm. Also, because the median from the vertex angle of an isosceles triangle is also an angle bisector, $m\angle AOB = 120°$.

Recall that the area of a segment of a circle is found by subtracting the area of a triangle from the area of a sector.

$$A_{\text{segment}} = A_{\text{sector}} - A_{\text{triangle}}$$
$$= \frac{120°}{360°}\pi r^2 - \frac{1}{2}bh$$
$$= \frac{1}{3}\pi\left(\frac{1}{2}\right)^2 - \frac{1}{2}\left(\frac{\sqrt{3}}{2}\right)\left(\frac{1}{4}\right)$$
$$= \frac{1}{3}\pi \cdot \frac{1}{4} - \frac{\sqrt{3}}{16}$$
$$= \frac{\pi}{12} - \frac{\sqrt{3}}{16}$$

The area of the segment is $\left(\frac{\pi}{12} - \frac{\sqrt{3}}{16}\right)$ cm². This is the area of the base of the portion of the cylinder. Let B represent this quantity.

The height of both the barrel and the portion filled with water is $\frac{3}{2}$ cm. Now use the Prism-Cylinder Volume Conjecture to find the volume of this portion of the barrel.

$$V = BH = \left(\frac{\pi}{12} - \frac{\sqrt{3}}{16}\right)\left(\frac{3}{2}\right) = \frac{3\pi}{24} - \frac{3\sqrt{3}}{32}$$
$$= \frac{\pi}{8} - \frac{3\sqrt{3}}{32}$$

The volume of the water in the barrel is $\left(\frac{\pi}{8} - \frac{3\sqrt{3}}{32}\right)$ m³ ≈ 0.23 m³.

28. 160π cubic units. The volume of the solid will be the difference between the volumes of two cylinders, with $R = 6$ units and $r = 2$ units, and each with height 5 units.

$$V = \pi R^2 H - \pi r^2 H = \pi \cdot (6)^2 \cdot 5 - \pi \cdot (2)^2 \cdot 5$$
$$= 180\pi - 20\pi = 160\pi$$

The volume of the solid is 160π cubic units.

TAKE ANOTHER LOOK

1. The models should have eight pieces. Volumes: one a^3, three a^2b, three ab^2, and one b^3; $(a + b)^3 = a^3 + 3a^2b + 3ab^2 + b^3$.

2. If you double all three dimensions of a rectangular prism, you get $V = (2l)(2w)(2h) = 8(lwh)$, but $S = 2(2l)(2w) + 2(2l)(2h) + 2(2w)(2h) = 4(2lw + 2lh + 2wh)$. Thus, the volume increases eightfold, but the surface area is increased only four times. Similarly, for a cylinder, $V = \pi(2r)^2(2h) = 8(\pi r^2 h)$, but $S = 2\pi(2r)^2 + 2\pi(2r)(2H) = 4(2\pi r^2 + 2\pi rH)$. Similarly, for a pyramid or a cone, $V = \frac{1}{3}(4B)(2H) = 8\left(\frac{1}{3}BH\right)$, but $S = 4(rl + 4r^2)$ for a cone and $S = 4\left(B + \frac{1}{2}bhn\right)$ for a pyramid.

3. Let r represent the radius of the sector and x represent the central angle. When the sector is rolled into a cone, the outside edge becomes the circumference of the base of the cone: $C = \frac{x}{360°}(2\pi r)$. Let R represent the radius of the base of the cone, and find the radius in terms of r: $2\pi R = \frac{x}{360°}(2\pi r)$, or $R = \frac{x}{360°} \cdot r$. When the sector is rolled into a cone, the radius of the sector becomes the slant height of the cone. Use the Pythagorean Theorem to find the perpendicular height, H, of the cone:

$$R^2 + H^2 = r^2$$

$$\left(\frac{x}{360°} \cdot r\right)^2 + H^2 = r^2$$

$$H = \sqrt{r^2 - \left(\frac{x}{360°}\right)^2 \cdot r^2}$$

$$= \sqrt{r^2\left(1 - \left(\frac{x}{360°}\right)^2\right)} = r\sqrt{1 - \left(\frac{x}{360°}\right)^2}$$

Now use the formula to find the volume of a cone:

$$V = \frac{1}{3}\pi R^2 H$$

$$= \frac{1}{3}\pi\left(\frac{x}{360°} \cdot r\right)^2\left(r\sqrt{1 - \left(\frac{x}{360°}\right)^2}\right)$$

$$= \frac{1}{3}\pi r^3 \left(\frac{x}{360°}\right)^2 \sqrt{1 - \left(\frac{x}{360°}\right)^2}$$

4. This example reveals the volume formula for one type of pyramid.

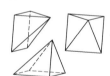

Use three congruent square pyramids, each with height equal to base length and with vertex over one vertex of the square base, and assemble them into a cube.

Here is another possible answer for a triangular prism, where the three triangular pyramids are of equal volume but not congruent.

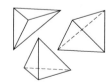

The first two of these pyramids have the same base and height as the prism, so the two pyramids have equal volumes. If you consider halves of the front face of the prism as the bases of the second and third pyramids, they also have equivalent bases and heights and hence equal volumes.

5. Answers will vary depending on the solid.

Sample: Almost four hemispheres of radius r fill a

cube of $s = 2r$. This is consistent with the Sphere Volume Conjecture, which predicts that

$$\frac{V_{cube}}{V_{hemisphere}} = \frac{(2r)^3}{\frac{1}{2} \cdot \frac{4}{3}\pi r^3} = \frac{8}{\frac{2}{3}\pi} = \frac{12}{\pi} \approx 3.82.$$

6. No. The spheres wouldn't have the same surface area. The surface area of the bumpy sphere would be greater because the pyramids add surface.

CHAPTER 11

USING YOUR ALGEBRA SKILLS 11

EXERCISES

1. $\frac{3}{8}$; $\frac{3}{5}$. There are $8 \cdot 4 = 32$ squares in the whole figure, of which 12 are shaded and $32 - 12$ are unshaded. Therefore, the ratio of the shaded area to the whole figure is $\frac{12}{32} = \frac{4 \cdot 3}{4 \cdot 8} = \frac{3}{8}$. The ratio of the shaded area to the unshaded area is $\frac{12}{20} = \frac{4 \cdot 3}{4 \cdot 5} = \frac{3}{5}$.

2. $\frac{AC}{CD} = \frac{3}{5}$, $\frac{CD}{BD} = \frac{5}{8}$, $\frac{BD}{BC} = \frac{8}{13}$

3. a. $\frac{3}{1}$. $\triangle RSH$ is a right triangle with $RH = 15 = 3 \cdot 5$ and $SH = 39 = 3 \cdot 13$, so the side lengths are a multiple of the Pythagorean triple 5-12-13, and $RS = 3 \cdot 12 = 36$. Therefore, the perimeter of $\triangle RSH$ is $15 + 36 + 39 = 90$. $\triangle MFL$ is a 5-12-13 triangle, so $MF = 12$, and the perimeter of $\triangle MFL$ is $5 + 12 + 13 = 30$.

$$\frac{\text{perimeter of } \triangle RSH}{\text{perimeter of } \triangle MFL} = \frac{90}{30} = \frac{3}{1}$$

b. $\frac{9}{1}$. Area of $\triangle RSH = \frac{1}{2}bh = \frac{1}{2}(36)(15) = 270$; area of $\triangle MFL = \frac{1}{2}bh = \frac{1}{2}(12)(5) = 30$.

$$\frac{\text{area of } \triangle RSH}{\text{area of } \triangle MFL} = \frac{270}{30} = \frac{9}{1}$$

4. $a = 6$. Solve the proportion:

$$\frac{7}{21} = \frac{a}{18} \qquad \text{Original proportion.}$$

$$18 \cdot \frac{7}{21} = 18 \cdot \frac{a}{18} \qquad \text{Multiply both sides by 18.}$$

$$6 = a$$

Another way to solve the given proportion is to observe that $\frac{7}{21} = \frac{1}{3}$, so $\frac{a}{18} = \frac{1}{3}$. Because $18 = 6 \cdot 3$, $a = 6 \cdot 1 = 6$.

5. $b = 16$. Solve the proportion:

$$\frac{10}{b} = \frac{15}{24} \qquad \text{Original proportion.}$$

$$24b \cdot \frac{10}{b} = 24b \cdot \frac{15}{24} \qquad \text{Multiply both sides by } 24b.$$

$$240 = 15b$$

$$\frac{240}{15} = \frac{15b}{15} \qquad \text{Divide both sides by 15.}$$

$$b = 16$$

6. $c = 39$. Rather than multiplying both sides by 13 and then by c, you can save steps by multiplying by their product, $13c$.

$$\frac{20}{13} = \frac{60}{c}$$

$$13c \cdot \frac{20}{13} = 13c \cdot \frac{60}{c}$$

$$20c = 780$$

$$c = \frac{780}{20} = 39$$

7. $x = 5.6$. Isolate x by multiplying both sides of the given proportion by 7.

$$\frac{4}{5} = \frac{x}{7}$$

$$7 \cdot \frac{4}{5} = 7 \cdot \frac{x}{7}$$

$$x = \frac{28}{5} = 5.6$$

8. $y = \pm 8$. Multiply both sides of the given proportion by $32y$, the product of y and 32.

$$\frac{2}{y} = \frac{y}{32}$$

$$32y \cdot \frac{2}{y} = 32y \cdot \frac{y}{32}$$

$$64 = y^2$$

$$y = \pm\sqrt{64} = \pm 8$$

9. $x = 12$. Multiply both sides by the least common denominator, which is 30.

$$\frac{14}{10} = \frac{x+9}{15}$$

$$30 \cdot \frac{14}{10} = 30 \cdot \frac{x+9}{15}$$

$$3 \cdot 14 = 2(x + 9)$$

$$42 = 2x + 18$$

$$24 = 2x$$

$$x = 12$$

10. $z = 6$. Reduce $\frac{35}{56}$ to $\frac{5}{8}$. Then multiply both sides of the given proportion by $8(10 + z)$, the least common denominator.

$$\frac{10}{10+z} = \frac{35}{56}$$

$$\frac{10}{10+z} = \frac{5}{8}$$

$$8(10 + z) \cdot \frac{10}{10+z} = 8(10 + z) \cdot \frac{5}{8}$$

$$80 = (10 + z) \cdot 5$$

$$80 = 50 + 5z$$

$$30 = 5z$$

$$6 = z$$

11. $d = 1$. Multiply both sides of the given proportion by the least common denominator, which is 20.

$$\frac{d}{5} = \frac{d+3}{20}$$

$$20 \cdot \frac{d}{5} = 20 \cdot \frac{d+3}{20}$$

$$4d = d + 3$$

$$3d = 3$$

$$d = 1$$

12. $y = 5$. Multiply both sides of the given proportion by $13(2y + 3)$, the least common denominator.

$$\frac{y-1}{2y+3} = \frac{4}{13}$$

$$13(2y + 3) \cdot \frac{y-1}{2y+3} = 13(2y + 3) \cdot \frac{4}{13}$$

$$13(y - 1) = (2y + 3) \cdot 4$$

$$13y - 13 = 8y + 12$$

$$5y = 25$$

$$y = 5$$

13. 318 mi. Let x represent the distance the car can go on 12 gallons of gas.

$$\frac{106 \text{ mi}}{4 \text{ gal}} = \frac{x \text{ mi}}{12 \text{ gal}}$$

$$\frac{106}{4} = \frac{x}{12}$$

Because $12 = 3(4)$, $x = 3(106) = 318$. The car can go 318 mi on a full tank of 12 gal.

14. 2.01. Let x represent Ernie's earned run average.

$$\frac{34 \text{ runs}}{152 \text{ innings}} = \frac{x \text{ runs}}{9 \text{ innings}}$$

$$\frac{34}{152} = \frac{x}{9}$$

Multiply both sides by 9 to isolate x.

$$9 \cdot \frac{34}{152} = 9 \cdot \frac{x}{9}$$

$$x = \frac{306}{152} \approx 2.01$$

Ernie's earned run average is 2.01.

15. 12 ft by 15 ft. Let w represent the width of the room and l represent the length of the room.

$$\frac{\frac{1}{4} \text{ in.}}{1 \text{ ft}} = \frac{3 \text{ in.}}{w \text{ ft}}$$

$$\frac{\frac{1}{4}}{1} = \frac{3}{w}$$

$$\frac{1}{4} = \frac{3}{w}$$

$$4w \cdot \frac{1}{4} = 4w \cdot \frac{3}{w}$$

$$w = 12 \text{ ft}$$

$$\frac{\frac{1}{4} \text{ in.}}{1 \text{ ft}} = \frac{3\frac{3}{4} \text{ in.}}{l \text{ ft}}$$

$$\frac{\frac{1}{4}}{1} = \frac{3\frac{3}{4}}{l}$$

$$\frac{1}{4} = \frac{\frac{15}{4}}{l}$$

$$4l \cdot \frac{1}{4} = 4l \cdot \frac{15}{4}$$

$$l = 15 \text{ ft}$$

Thus, the actual size of the room is 12 ft by 15 ft.

16. Almost 80 years old. Find the sum of the lengths of the antennae for both Altor and Zenor.

Altor: $8 + 10 + 13 + 16 + 14 + 12 = 73$ cm

Zenor: $7(17) = 119$ cm

Let A represent Altor's age.

$$\frac{73 \text{ cm}}{A \text{ yr}} = \frac{119 \text{ cm}}{130 \text{ yr}}$$

$$\frac{73}{A} = \frac{119}{130}$$

$$130A \cdot \frac{73}{A} = 130A \cdot \frac{119}{130}$$

$$9490 = 119A$$

$$A = \frac{9490}{119} \approx 79.7$$

Altor is almost 80 years old.

17. a. True

$$\frac{a}{b} = \frac{c}{d} \qquad \text{Given.}$$

$$bd\left(\frac{a}{b}\right) = bd\left(\frac{c}{d}\right) \qquad \text{Multiply by } bd.$$

$$\not{b}d \cdot \frac{a}{\not{b}} = b\not{d} \cdot \frac{c}{\not{d}} \qquad \text{Cancel common factors.}$$

$$ad = bc$$

b. False. Possible counterexample: $\frac{3}{6} = \frac{1}{2}$, but $3 \cdot 1 \neq 6 \cdot 2$.

c. True

$$\frac{a}{b} = \frac{c}{d} \qquad \text{Given.}$$

$$\frac{b}{c} \cdot \frac{a}{b} = \frac{b}{c} \cdot \frac{c}{d} \qquad \text{Multiply by } \frac{b}{c}.$$

$$\frac{\not{b}}{c} \cdot \frac{a}{\not{b}} = \frac{b}{\not{c}} \cdot \frac{\not{c}}{d} \qquad \text{Cancel common factors.}$$

$$\frac{a}{c} = \frac{b}{d}$$

d. True

$$ad = bc \qquad \text{From 17a.}$$

$$\frac{ad}{ac} = \frac{bc}{ac} \qquad \text{Divide by } ac.$$

$$\frac{\not{a}d}{\not{a}c} = \frac{b\not{c}}{a\not{c}} \qquad \text{Cancel common factors.}$$

$$\frac{b}{a} = \frac{d}{c}$$

e. False. Counterexample: $\frac{3}{6} = \frac{1}{2}$, but $\frac{3}{2} \neq \frac{1}{6}$.

f. True

$$ad = bc \qquad \text{From 17a.}$$

$$\frac{ad}{ab} = \frac{bc}{ab} \qquad \text{Divide by } ab.$$

$$\frac{a\not{d}}{\not{a}b} = \frac{\not{b}c}{a\not{b}} \qquad \text{Cancel common factors.}$$

$$\frac{d}{b} = \frac{c}{a}$$

18. a. Arithmetic: 10, 25, 40, 65; geometric: 10, 20, 40, 80 or 10, -20, 40, -80

b. Arithmetic: 2, 26, 50, 74; geometric: 2, 10, 50, 250 or 2, -10, 50, -250

c. Arithmetic: 4, 20, 36, 52; geometric: 4, 12, 36, 108 or 4, -12, 36, -108

19. a. Call the first number a and the second number b. Let c be the constant which is added to each previous number. Then $x = a + c$ and $b = x + c = (a + c) + c$, so $b = a + 2c$. Solve this for c.

$$b = a + 2c$$

$$b - a = 2c$$

$$\frac{b - a}{2} = c$$

Then $x = a + c = a + \frac{b - a}{2} = \frac{2a + b - a}{2} = \frac{a + b}{2}$. Add the numbers and divide by 2.

b. Call the first number a and the second number b, and let c be the constant that multiplies each previous number. Then $x = ac$ and $b = xc = (ac) \cdot c$, so $b = ac^2$. Solve this for c.

$$b = ac^2$$

$$\frac{b}{a} = c^2$$

$$\pm\sqrt{\frac{b}{a}} = c$$

Then $x = ac = a\left(\pm\sqrt{\frac{b}{a}}\right) = \sqrt{a^2}\left(\pm\sqrt{\frac{b}{a}}\right) = \pm\sqrt{a^2 \cdot \frac{b}{a}} = \pm\sqrt{ab}$. Because the geometric mean is defined to be positive, $x = \sqrt{ab}$. Multiply the numbers and take the positive square root of the result.

c.

$$\frac{a}{c} = \frac{c}{b}$$

$$bc\left(\frac{a}{c}\right) = bc\left(\frac{c}{b}\right)$$

$$ab = c^2$$

$$c = \sqrt{ab}$$

This formula holds for all positive values of a and b.

d. $\sqrt{2 \cdot 50} = \sqrt{100} = 10$;

$\sqrt{4 \cdot 36} = \sqrt{144} = 12$

EXTENSION

Results will vary.

LESSON 11.1

EXERCISES

1. A

2. B

3. Possible answer:

4. Possible answer:

5. Possible answer:

6. Figure A is similar to Figure C. Possible answer:

If $\triangle_A \sim \triangle_B$ and $\triangle_B \sim \triangle_C$,

then $\triangle_A \sim \triangle_C$.

7. $AL = 6$ cm, $RA = 10$ cm, $RG = 4$ cm, $KN = 6$ cm. Corresponding sides of similar polygons are proportional, so $\frac{TK}{LE} = \frac{KN}{EG} = \frac{NI}{RG} = \frac{IH}{RA} = \frac{HT}{AL}$. Substitute the given side lengths.

$$\frac{4}{8} = \frac{KN}{12} = \frac{2}{RG} = \frac{5}{RA} = \frac{3}{AL}$$

Because $\frac{TK}{LE} = \frac{4}{8} = \frac{1}{2}$, each side of the smaller pentagon is half as long as the corresponding side of the larger pentagon, so $KN = 6$ cm, $RG = 4$ cm, $RA = 10$ cm, and $AL = 6$ cm.

8. No; the corresponding angles are congruent, but the corresponding sides are not proportional. Three pairs of corresponding angles are marked as congruent, so the fourth pair of angles must also be congruent by the Quadrilateral Sum Conjecture. Compare ratios of corresponding sides.

$$\frac{150}{165} = \frac{10}{11} \text{ and } \frac{120}{128} = \frac{15}{16}$$

Because these two pairs of corresponding sides are not proportional, the pentagons are not similar. (It is not necessary to check the ratios of the other two pairs of corresponding sides because for polygons to be similar, *all* pairs of corresponding sides must be proportional.)

9. $NY = 21$ cm, $YC = 42$ cm, $CM = 27$ cm, $MB = 30$ cm

$$\frac{SP}{HN} = \frac{ER}{MB} = \frac{DE}{CM} = \frac{ID}{YC} = \frac{PI}{NY}$$

$$\frac{88}{66} = \frac{40}{MB} = \frac{36}{CM} = \frac{56}{YC} = \frac{28}{NY}$$

$$\frac{88}{66} = \frac{22 \cdot 4}{22 \cdot 3} = \frac{4}{3}, \text{ so } \frac{4}{3} = \frac{40}{MB} = \frac{36}{CM} = \frac{56}{YC} = \frac{28}{NY}$$

$28 = 4(7)$, so $NY = 3(7) = 21$ cm

$56 = 4(14)$, so $YC = 3(14) = 42$ cm

$36 = 4(9)$, so $CM = 3(9) = 27$ cm

$40 = 4(10)$, so $MB = 3(10) = 30$ cm

10. Yes; the corresponding angles are congruent, and the corresponding sides are proportional. Because four of the five pairs of corresponding angles are marked as congruent, the angles in the fifth pair must also be congruent because the sum of the measures of the angles of any pentagon is 540° by the Pentagon Sum Conjecture. Corresponding sides are proportional.

$$\frac{30}{20} = \frac{27}{18} = \frac{39}{26} = \frac{78}{52} = \frac{21}{14} = \frac{3}{2}$$

11. $x = 6$ cm, $y = 3.5$ cm. $\triangle ACE \sim \triangle IKS$, so $\frac{AC}{IK} = \frac{CE}{KS} = \frac{AE}{IS}$. Then $\frac{7}{y} = \frac{8}{4} = \frac{12}{x}$. Because $\frac{CE}{KS} = \frac{8}{4} = \frac{2}{1}$, each side of $\triangle ACE$ is twice as long as the corresponding side of $\triangle IKS$, so $x = 6$ cm and $y = 3.5$ cm.

12. $z = 10\frac{2}{3}$ cm. $\triangle RAM \sim \triangle XAE$, so corresponding sides are proportional.

$$\frac{RA}{XA} = \frac{AM}{AE} = \frac{RM}{XE}$$

$$\frac{4}{3} = \frac{AM}{AE} = \frac{z}{8}$$

$$8 \cdot \frac{4}{3} = 8 \cdot \frac{z}{8}$$

$$z = \frac{32}{3} = 10\frac{2}{3}$$

13. Yes, the corresponding angles are congruent. Yes, the corresponding sides are proportional. Yes, $\triangle AED \sim \triangle ABC$. Because $\overline{DE} \parallel \overline{BC}$, $\angle B \cong \angle AED$ and $\angle C \cong \angle ADE$ (CA Conjecture). Also, $\angle A \cong \angle A$ (same angle), so all pairs of corresponding angles are congruent. Now check the ratios of corresponding sides:

$$\frac{AE}{AB} = \frac{2}{4\frac{2}{3}} = \frac{2}{\frac{14}{3}} = \frac{2}{1} \cdot \frac{3}{14} = \frac{3}{7}$$

$$\frac{AD}{AC} = \frac{3}{7}$$

$$\frac{ED}{BC} = \frac{4}{9\frac{1}{3}} = \frac{4}{\frac{28}{3}} = \frac{4}{1} \cdot \frac{3}{28} = \frac{3}{7}$$

Discovering Geometry Solutions Manual
©2008 Key Curriculum Press

Therefore, all pairs of corresponding sides are proportional. Because corresponding angles are congruent and corresponding sides are proportional, $\triangle AED \sim \triangle ABC$.

14. $m = \frac{9}{2}$ cm = 4.5 cm, $n = \frac{9}{4}$ cm = 2.25 cm. $\triangle ABC \sim \triangle DBA$, so $\frac{AB}{DB} = \frac{BC}{BA} = \frac{AC}{DA}$. Then $\frac{3}{n} = \frac{4}{3} = \frac{6}{m}$. To find m and n, solve two proportions:

$$\frac{3}{n} = \frac{4}{3} \qquad\qquad \frac{4}{3} = \frac{6}{m}$$

$$3n \cdot \frac{3}{n} = 3n \cdot \frac{4}{3} \qquad 3m \cdot \frac{4}{3} = 3m \cdot \frac{6}{m}$$

$$9 = 4n \qquad\qquad 4m = 18$$

$$n = \frac{9}{4} = 2.25 \qquad m = \frac{18}{4} = \frac{9}{2} = 4.5$$

15. $\frac{3}{1}; \frac{9}{1}$. Let R', O', and Y' represent the coordinates of the dilation of $\triangle ROY$.

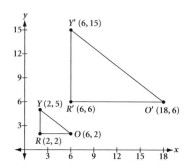

$\triangle ROY$ is a 3-4-5 triangle, so the perimeter of $\triangle ROY$ is $RO + OY + YR = 4 + 5 + 3 = 12$ units.

From the graph, you can see that the vertices of $\triangle R'O'Y'$ are $R'(6, 6)$, $O'(18, 6)$, and $Y'(6, 15)$. $\triangle R'O'Y'$ is a 9-12-15 triangle (a multiple of 3-4-5), so the perimeter of $\triangle R'O'Y'$ is $R'O' + O'Y' + Y'R' = 12 + 15 + 9 = 36$ units.

$$\frac{\text{perimeter of dilated triangle}}{\text{perimeter of original triangle}} = \frac{36 \text{ units}}{12 \text{ units}} = \frac{3}{1}$$

Area of $\triangle ROY = \frac{1}{2}bh = \frac{1}{2} \cdot 3 \cdot 4 = 6$ square units

Area of $\triangle R'O'Y' = \frac{1}{2}bh = \frac{1}{2} \cdot 9 \cdot 12 = 54$ square units

$$\frac{\text{area of dilated triangle}}{\text{area of original triangle}} = \frac{54 \text{ square units}}{6 \text{ square units}} = \frac{9}{1}$$

16.

Yes, they are similar.

17. Possible answer: Each arm would be about 260 ft. The actual sculpture will be similar to the scale model, so the ratio between the length of the arm

and the length of the face will be the same on the actual sculpture as on the scale model. In the model, the length of the arm appears to be about three times the height of the head. Therefore, the length of an arm on the sculpture will be about $3(87.5) = 262.5$ ft, or about 260 ft.

18. Possible answer: Not all isosceles triangles are similar because two isosceles triangles can have different angle measures. A counterexample is shown.

Not all right triangles are similar because they can have different side ratios, as in a triangle with side lengths 3, 4, and 5 and a triangle with side lengths 5, 12, and 13. All isosceles right triangles are similar because they have angle measures 45°, 45°, and 90°, and the side lengths have the ratio $1 : 1 : \sqrt{2}$.

19. $a = 36$. Solve the proportion:

$$\frac{15}{a} = \frac{20}{a + 12}$$

$$a(a + 12) \cdot \frac{15}{a} = a(a + 12) \cdot \frac{20}{a + 12}$$

$$(a + 12)(15) = 20a$$

$$15a + 180 = 20a$$

$$180 = 5a$$

$$a = 36$$

20. $ad = bc$. Solve the proportion for ad.

$$\frac{a}{b} = \frac{c}{d}$$

Multiply both sides by bd, to get ad on the left hand side.

$$bd\left(\frac{a}{b}\right) = bd\left(\frac{c}{d}\right)$$

$$da = bc, \text{ or } ad = bc$$

21. $\frac{b}{a} = \frac{d}{c}$. From Exercise 20, $\frac{a}{b} = \frac{c}{d}$ is equivalent to $ad = bc$. Divide both sides by ac.

$$ad = bc$$

$$\frac{ad}{ac} = \frac{bc}{ac}$$

$$\frac{d}{c} = \frac{b}{a}, \text{ or } \frac{b}{a} = \frac{d}{c}$$

22. Possible answers: Jade might get $\frac{1825}{4475}$ of the profits, or $2,773.18, and Omar might get $\frac{2650}{4475}$ of the profits, or $4,026.82. The total amount spent was $2,000 + $825 + $1,650 = $4,475. Jade contributed $1,000 + $825 = $1,825, and Omar contributed $1,000 + $1,650 = $2,650.

Jade's share: $\frac{1825}{4475}(\$6,800) = \$2,773.18$

Omar's share: $\frac{2650}{4475}(\$6,800) = \$4,026.82$

Or, they could first take out their investments, and then divide the profit equally. The profit is $6,800 − $2,000 − $825 − $1,650 = $2,325, so they should each get ($2,325)/2 = $1,162.50 on top of what they spent on supplies. Then Jade's share would be $1,825 + $1,162.50 = $2,987.50 and Omar's share would be $2,650 + $1,162.50 = $3,812.50. Either approach could be considered a fair division.

23. a.   **b.**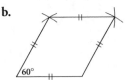

24. Approximately 92 gal. First, find the volume of the portion of the cylinder in cubic feet. The base of this solid is a segment of the base of the cylinder. Look at the figure at right.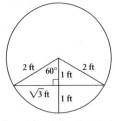

The length of the hypotenuse of each small triangle is twice the length of the shorter leg, so it is a 30°-60°-90° triangle, and the longer leg has length $\sqrt{3}$ ft. Because the large triangle is isosceles, this also means the arc measure of the segment is 2(60°) = 120°. Now find the volume of the solid using the area of the segment as the base.

$$V = BH = \left[\left(\frac{a}{360°}\right) \cdot \pi r^2 - \frac{1}{2}bh\right]H$$
$$= \left[\left(\frac{120°}{360°}\right) \cdot \pi(2)^2 - \frac{1}{2}(2\sqrt{3})(1)\right]5$$
$$= \left(\frac{4\pi}{3} - \sqrt{3}\right)5$$
$$= \frac{20\pi}{3} - 5\sqrt{3} \text{ ft}^3$$

Convert this volume from cubic feet to gallons.

$$\left(\frac{20\pi}{3} - 5\sqrt{3}\right) \text{ft}^3 \cdot \frac{7.5 \text{ gal}}{1 \text{ ft}^3} \approx 92 \text{ gal}$$

PROJECT

Project should satisfy the following criteria:

• The grid on the original image contains enough squares so that each square contains only a few lines.

• The mural accurately reproduces the original.

Extra credit

• A group of students produces a complex piece of art.

EXTENSIONS

A. Results will vary.

B. If you dilate by a scale factor less than 0, the result is a dilation plus a rotation of 180°.

C. See the solutions to Take Another Look activities 1 and 2 on page 254.

LESSON 11.2

EXERCISES

1. $g = 6$ cm. By the AA Similarity Conjecture, $\triangle LDI \sim \triangle CPA$, so corresponding sides are proportional.

$$\frac{LD}{CP} = \frac{DI}{PA} = \frac{LI}{CA}$$
$$\frac{4}{6} = \frac{g}{9} = \frac{7}{10\frac{1}{2}}$$

$\frac{4}{6} = \frac{2}{3}$, so each side of the smaller triangle is $\frac{2}{3}$ as long as the corresponding side of the larger triangle. Therefore, $g = \frac{2}{3}(9) = 6$ cm.

2. $h = 40$ cm, $k = 40$ cm. By the AA Similarity Conjecture, $\triangle GAS \sim \triangle JET$, so corresponding sides are proportional.

$$\frac{GA}{JE} = \frac{AS}{ET} = \frac{GS}{JT}$$
$$\frac{h}{50} = \frac{24}{30} = \frac{32}{k}$$

$\frac{24}{30} = \frac{4}{5}$, so $\frac{h}{50} = \frac{4}{5}$. 50 = 10 · 5, hence $h = 10 · 4 = 40$ cm.

$\frac{4}{5} = \frac{32}{k}$; 32 = 8 · 4, so $k = 8 · 5 = 40$ cm.

3. $m = 28$ cm. It may help to rotate $\triangle ARK$ so that you can see which sides correspond.

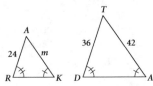

By the AA Similarity Conjecture, $\triangle DAT \sim \triangle RKA$.

$$\frac{AT}{KA} = \frac{DT}{RA}$$
$$\frac{42}{m} = \frac{36}{24}$$

$\frac{36}{24} = \frac{3}{2}$, so $\frac{42}{m} = \frac{3}{2}$. 42 = 14 · 3, hence $m = 14 · 2 = 28$ cm.

4. $n = 54$ cm, $s = 42$ cm. The two triangles are similar by the AA Similarity Conjecture (a pair of marked angles and a pair of vertical angles).

$$\frac{n}{36} = \frac{45}{30} = \frac{63}{s}$$

$\frac{45}{30} = \frac{3}{2}$, so $\frac{n}{36} = \frac{3}{2}$. 36 = 18 · 2, hence $n = 18 · 3 = 54$ cm.

Also, $\frac{63}{s} = \frac{3}{2}$. 63 = 21 · 3, so $s = 21 · 2 = 42$ cm.

5. No, $\frac{37}{30} \neq \frac{35}{28}$. Corresponding sides are not proportional, so the triangles are not similar. (If $\triangle AUL$ were similar to $\triangle MST$, $\overline{AU}$ and $\overline{MS}$, and $\overline{UL}$ and $\overline{ST}$, would be pairs of corresponding sides.)

6. Yes, $\triangle MOY \sim \triangle NOT$ by the SAS Similarity Conjecture. Compare the ratios of corresponding sides by writing each ratio in lowest terms. $\frac{104}{91} = \frac{13 \cdot 8}{13 \cdot 7} = \frac{8}{7}$ and $\frac{96}{84} = \frac{12 \cdot 8}{12 \cdot 7} = \frac{8}{7}$. The angles included between these two pairs of corresponding sides are marked as congruent, so the triangles are congruent by the SAS Similarity Conjecture.

7. Yes, $\triangle PHY \sim \triangle YHT$ because $\frac{20}{15} = \frac{16}{12} = \frac{12}{9}$ (SSS Similarity Conjecture). Yes, $\triangle PTY$ is a right triangle because $20^2 + 15^2 = 25^2$. In $\triangle PHY$, $YH = 12$. (12-16-20 is a Pythagorean triple.) In $\triangle YHT$, $HT = 9$. (9-12-15 is a Pythagorean triple.) In $\triangle PTY$, $PT = PH + HT = 25$ cm.

8. $\triangle TMR \sim \triangle THM \sim \triangle MHR$ by the AA Similarity Conjecture. $x \approx 15.1$ cm, $y \approx 52.9$ cm, $h \approx 28.2$ cm. Draw the three triangles separately and orient them so that corresponding vertices and sides are in the same relative position.

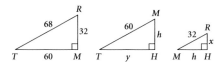

$\triangle TMR \sim \triangle THM$ by the AA Similarity Conjecture because each triangle has a right angle, and $\angle T$ is common to both triangles. $\triangle TMR \sim \triangle MHR$ by the AA Similarity Conjecture because each triangle has a right angle, and $\angle R$ is common to both triangles. Two triangles that are similar to the same triangle are similar to each other, so $\triangle TMR \sim \triangle THM \sim \triangle MHR$.

Use a pair of similar triangles to find each of the unknown side lengths. From $\triangle TMR \sim \triangle MHR$, $\frac{68}{32} = \frac{32}{x}$, or $\frac{17}{8} = \frac{32}{x}$.

$$8x \cdot \frac{17}{8} = 8x \cdot \frac{32}{x}$$
$$17x = 256$$
$$x = \frac{256}{17} \approx 15.1 \text{ cm}$$

From $\triangle TMR \sim \triangle THM$, $\frac{68}{60} = \frac{60}{y}$, or $\frac{17}{15} = \frac{60}{y}$.

$$15y \cdot \frac{17}{15} = 15y \cdot \frac{60}{y}$$
$$17y = 900$$
$$y = \frac{900}{17} \approx 52.9 \text{ cm}$$

Also, from $\triangle TMR \sim \triangle THM$, $\frac{68}{60} = \frac{32}{h}$, or $\frac{17}{15} = \frac{32}{h}$.

$$15h \cdot \frac{17}{15} = 15h \cdot \frac{32}{h}$$
$$17h = 480$$
$$h = \frac{480}{17} \approx 28.2 \text{ cm}$$

9. Yes, $\angle QTA \cong \angle TUR$ and $\angle QAT \cong \angle ARU$ by the CA Conjecture. $\triangle QTA \sim \triangle QUR$ by the AA Similarity Conjecture. $e = 6\frac{2}{3}$ cm. Use the similarity

statement to write a proportion that you can use to find e.

$$\frac{QT}{QU} = \frac{QA}{QR}$$
$$\frac{3}{8} = \frac{4}{4 + e}$$
$$8(4 + e) \cdot \frac{3}{8} = 8(4 + e) \cdot \frac{4}{4 + e}$$
$$(4 + e) \cdot 3 = 8 \cdot 4$$
$$12 + 3e = 32$$
$$3e = 20$$
$$e = \frac{20}{3} = 6\frac{2}{3} \text{ cm}$$

10. $f = 24$ cm, $g = 40$ cm. Look at triangles COR, CUE, and CNT. Because $\overline{OR} \parallel \overline{UE} \parallel \overline{NT}$, $\angle COR \cong \angle CUE \cong \angle CNT$ (CA Conjecture). All three triangles share $\angle C$. Therefore, $\triangle COR \sim \triangle CUE \sim \triangle CNT$ by the AA Similarity Conjecture. Use a pair of similar triangles to find each of the unknown side lengths. $\triangle COR \sim \triangle CUE$, so $\frac{CO}{CU} = \frac{CR}{CE}$.

$$\frac{36}{36 + f} = \frac{48}{48 + 32}$$
$$\frac{36}{36 + f} = \frac{48}{80} = \frac{3}{5}$$
$$5(36 + f) \cdot \frac{36}{36 + f} = 5(36 + f) \cdot \frac{3}{5}$$
$$5 \cdot 36 = (36 + f) \cdot 3$$
$$180 = 108 + 3f$$
$$72 = 3f, \text{ so } f = 24 \text{ cm}$$

$\triangle CUE \sim \triangle CNT$, so $\frac{CU}{CN} = \frac{CE}{CT}$.

$$\frac{36 + f}{(36 + f) + 30} = \frac{48 + 32}{(48 + 32) + g}$$
$$\frac{36 + 24}{66 + 24} = \frac{80}{80 + g}$$
$$\frac{60}{90} = \frac{80}{80 + g}$$
$$\frac{2}{3} = \frac{80}{80 + g}$$
$$3(80 + g) \cdot \frac{2}{3} = 3(80 + g) \cdot \frac{80}{80 + g}$$
$$(80 + g) \cdot 2 = 3 \cdot 80$$
$$160 + 2g = 240$$
$$2g = 80, \text{ so } g = 40 \text{ cm}$$

11. Yes, $\angle THU \cong \angle GDU$ and $\angle HTU \cong \angle DGU$. $p = 52$ cm, $q = 42$ cm. $\angle THU \cong \angle GDU$ and $\angle HTU \cong \angle DGU$ because in each case they are two angles inscribed in the same arc. Therefore, $\triangle HUT \sim \triangle DUG$ by the AA Similarity Conjecture. (You could also use the pair of vertical angles as one pair of corresponding congruent angles.) Use

the proportionality of corresponding sides of these similar triangles to find p and q.

$$\frac{HU}{DU} = \frac{HT}{DG} = \frac{UT}{UG}$$

$$\frac{p}{39} = \frac{60}{45} = \frac{56}{q}$$

$\frac{p}{39} = \frac{4}{3}$ and $\frac{56}{q} = \frac{4}{3}$. Solve these two proportions separately.

$$39 \cdot \frac{p}{39} = 39 \cdot \frac{4}{3} \qquad 3q \cdot \frac{56}{q} = 3q \cdot \frac{4}{3}$$
$$p = 52 \text{ cm} \qquad 168 = 4q$$
$$q = 42 \text{ cm}$$

12. $\triangle SUN \sim \triangle TAN$ by the AA Similarity Conjecture. $r = 13$ cm, $s = 20$ cm. Use the same reasoning as in Exercise 11.

$$\frac{SU}{TA} = \frac{UN}{AN} = \frac{SN}{TN}$$

$$\frac{s}{40} = \frac{r}{26} = \frac{18}{36}$$

$$\frac{s}{40} = \frac{r}{26} = \frac{1}{2}$$

Each side of the smaller triangle is half as long as the corresponding side of the larger triangle, so $r = 13$ cm and $s = 20$ cm.

13. Yes, $\angle RGO \cong \angle FRG$ and $\angle GOF \cong \angle RFO$. $\triangle GOS \sim \triangle RFS$ by the AA Similarity Conjecture. $t = 28$ cm, $s = 120$ cm. $\angle RGO$ and $\angle FRG$ are alternate interior angles formed when parallel lines $\overleftrightarrow{OG}$ and $\overleftrightarrow{RF}$ are cut by a transversal, $\overleftrightarrow{RG}$, so these angles are congruent by the AIA Conjecture. $\angle GOF \cong \angle RFO$ for a similar reason. Therefore, $\triangle GOS \sim \triangle RFS$ by the AA Similarity Conjecture.

$$\frac{GO}{RF} = \frac{OS}{FS} = \frac{GS}{RS}$$

$$\frac{48}{s} = \frac{t}{70} = \frac{36}{90}$$

$$\frac{48}{s} = \frac{t}{70} = \frac{2}{5}$$

$48 = 2 \cdot 24$, so $s = 5 \cdot 24 = 120$ cm.

$70 = 5 \cdot 14$, so $t = 2 \cdot 14 = 28$ cm.

14. $w = 20$ cm, $x = 21$ cm. Use the same reasoning as in Exercise 13 to show that $\triangle ADS \sim \triangle TOS$.

$$\frac{AD}{TO} = \frac{DS}{OS} = \frac{AS}{TS}$$

$$\frac{x}{35} = \frac{12}{w} = \frac{15}{25}$$

$$\frac{x}{35} = \frac{12}{w} = \frac{3}{5}$$

$35 = 7 \cdot 5$, so $x = 7 \cdot 3 = 21$ cm.

$12 = 4 \cdot 3$, so $w = 4 \cdot 5 = 20$ cm.

15. $x = 50$, $y = 9$. Draw a perpendicular segment from each of the three marked points in the first quadrant to the x-axis. Label the origin and the three points for reference.

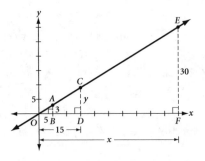

$\triangle OAB \sim \triangle OCD \sim \triangle OEF$ because all three triangles share $\angle O$ and each has a right angle. Therefore, the ratio of the length of the shorter leg to the length of the longer leg is the same in all three triangles.

$$\frac{AB}{OB} = \frac{CD}{OD} = \frac{EF}{OF}$$

$$\frac{3}{5} = \frac{y}{15} = \frac{30}{x}$$

$15 = 3 \cdot 5$, so $y = 3 \cdot 3 = 9$.

$30 = 10 \cdot 3$, so $x = 10 \cdot 5 = 50$.

16. $r = R\left(\frac{\sqrt{2} - 1}{\sqrt{2} + 1}\right)$, or $r = R\left(\sqrt{2} - 1\right)^2$. Look at a portion of the figure and apply the Isosceles Right Triangle Conjecture to find the lengths of the hypotenuses of the right triangles with legs of length R and legs of length r.

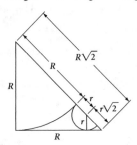

$$r\sqrt{2} + r + R = R\sqrt{2}$$
$$r\sqrt{2} + r = R\sqrt{2} - R$$
$$r\left(\sqrt{2} + 1\right) = R\left(\sqrt{2} - 1\right)$$
$$r = \frac{R\left(\sqrt{2} - 1\right)}{\sqrt{2} + 1}$$
$$r = R\left(\frac{\sqrt{2} - 1}{\sqrt{2} + 1}\right)$$

The expression $\frac{\sqrt{2} - 1}{\sqrt{2} + 1}$ can be rewritten by rationalizing the denominator:

$$\frac{\sqrt{2} - 1}{\sqrt{2} + 1} = \frac{\sqrt{2} - 1}{\sqrt{2} + 1} \cdot \frac{\sqrt{2} - 1}{\sqrt{2} - 1} = \frac{\left(\sqrt{2} - 1\right)^2}{\left(\sqrt{2}\right)^2 - 1^2}$$

$$= \frac{\left(\sqrt{2} - 1\right)^2}{2 - 1} = \left(\sqrt{2} - 1\right)^2$$

Therefore, another way to express the radius of the small circles in terms of the radius of the large circle is $r = R(\sqrt{2} - 1)^2$.

17. She should order approximately 919 lb, or 26 or 27 35-pound bags, every three months. Notice that the given information is about *two* months, but you are asked for the amount needed for *three* months. The amount of dog food that would be needed for 8 dogs for three months is $\frac{3}{2} \cdot 7 \cdot 35 = 367.5$ lb. Let x represent the number of pounds of dog food needed to feed 20 dogs for three months. Write a proportion and solve it to find x.

$$\frac{8}{367.5} = \frac{20}{x}$$
$$367.5x \cdot \frac{8}{367.5} = 367.5x \cdot \frac{20}{x}$$
$$8x = 7350$$
$$x = \frac{7350}{8} = 918.75 \text{ lb.}$$
$$\frac{918.75 \text{ lb}}{35 \text{ lb/bag}} = 26.25 \text{ bags}$$

Phoung must buy about 919 pounds of dog food every three months. If she is limited to buying 35-pound bags, she should buy 26 or 27 bags every three months.

18. 448 fish. Write a proportion.

$$\frac{\text{tagged fish in sample}}{\text{sample size}} = \frac{\text{fish previously tagged}}{\text{estimated population}}$$

Let x represent the estimate of the total population.

$$\frac{12}{64} = \frac{84}{x}$$
$$64x \cdot \frac{12}{64} = 64x \cdot \frac{84}{x}$$
$$12x = 5376$$
$$x = 448$$

19. The corresponding angles are congruent; the ratio of the corresponding side lengths is $\frac{3}{1}$; the dilated image is similar to the original.

20. Yes, $ABCD \sim A'B'C'D'$. The ratio of the perimeters is $\frac{2}{1}$. The ratio of the areas is $\frac{4}{1}$.

21. 118 square units. Finding the slopes of the sides or checking the side lengths in the Converse of the Pythagorean Theorem will show that this is not a right triangle, and the lengths of the altitudes are not known, so you can't use the usual area formula, $A = \frac{1}{2}bh$. So, graph the points on a coordinate grid and draw a rectangle around the triangle. Label the corners of the rectangle for reference and find their coordinates.

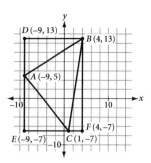

Now you can find the area of the triangle by subtracting the areas of the three right triangles from the area of the rectangle. To find the length and width of the rectangle, find the distance between the points.

Area of $DEFB = lw = [13 - (-7)][4 - (-9)]$
$$= 260 \text{ square units}$$

Area of $\triangle AEC = \frac{1}{2}bh = \frac{1}{2}[1 - (-9)][5 - (-7)]$
$$= 60 \text{ square units}$$

Area of $\triangle CFB = \frac{1}{2}bh = \frac{1}{2}(4 - 1)[13 - (-7)]$
$$= 30 \text{ square units}$$

Area of $\triangle DAB = \frac{1}{2}bh = \frac{1}{2}(13 - 5)[4 - (-9)]$
$$= 52 \text{ square units}$$

The area of $\triangle ABC = 260 - 60 - 30 - 52 = 118$ square units.

22. The statue was about 40 ft, or 12 m, tall. To estimate, approximate the height some part of a person in the picture, measure a part of the statue in the picture, calculate the approximate height of that statue piece, and assume that the statue has the same proportions as the average person.

IMPROVING YOUR VISUAL THINKING SKILLS

To create the tetrahedron, place the square faces together and rotate one solid until it completes the tetrahedron.

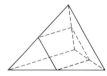

EXTENSIONS

A. See the solutions to Take Another Look activities 4 and 5 on page 254.

B. Draw the altitude to the hypotenuse.

$\triangle ABC \sim \triangle CBD \sim \triangle ACD$ by the AA Similarity Conjecture. (Each pair of triangles has one right angle and one common angle.) Set up proportions for the sides of the triangles. From the hypotenuse and longer legs, you get

$$\frac{b}{c-x} = \frac{c}{b}$$
$$b^2 = c^2 - cx$$

From the hypotenuses and shorter legs, you get

$$\frac{a}{x} = \frac{c}{a}$$
$$a^2 = cx$$

Substitute a^2 for cx in the equation above.

$$b^2 = c^2 - a^2$$
$$a^2 + b^2 = c^2$$

LESSON 11.3

EXERCISES

1. 16 m. Let h represent the height of the building.

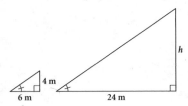

The triangles are similar by the AA Similarity Conjecture.

$$\frac{4}{6} = \frac{h}{24}$$

$24 = 4 \cdot 6$, so $h = 4 \cdot 4 = 16$.

The building is 16 m tall.

2. 4 ft 3 in. Let h represent the height of Melody's friend. 84 in. = 7 ft.

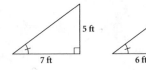

The triangles are similar by the AA Similarity Conjecture.

$$\frac{5}{7} = \frac{h}{6}$$
$$6 \cdot \frac{5}{7} = 6 \cdot \frac{h}{6}$$
$$h = \frac{30}{7} = 4\frac{2}{7} \text{ ft}$$

$\frac{2}{7}$ ft $= \frac{2}{7}(12 \text{ in.}) \approx 3$ in., so Melody's friend is approximately 4 ft 3 in. tall.

3. 30 ft. Let x represent the height of the flagpole and h represent the height of the goalpost.

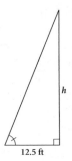
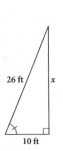

The light rays that create the shadow hit the ground at congruent angles. Assuming that the flagpole and the goalpost are perpendicular to the ground, the triangles are similar by the AA Similarity Conjecture. Set up a proportion that relates corresponding side lengths.

$$\frac{h}{x} = \frac{12.5}{10}$$

Find x, the height of the flagpole. The side lengths in the triangle on the left are doubles of the 5-12-13 Pythagorean triple, so $x = 2 \cdot 12 = 24$ ft. Now solve the proportion to find h, the height of the goalpost.

$$\frac{h}{24} = \frac{12.5}{10} \qquad \text{Substitute 24 for } x.$$

$$24 \cdot \frac{h}{24} = 24 \cdot \frac{12.5}{10} \qquad \begin{array}{l}\text{Multiply both sides by 24}\\ \text{to isolate } h.\end{array}$$

$$h = 30 \qquad \text{Simplify both sides.}$$

The height of the goalpost is 30 ft.

4. 10.92 m. Let h represent the height of the window.

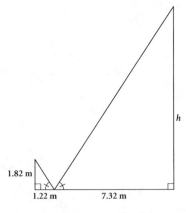

The triangles are similar by AA, so corresponding sides are proportional.

$$\frac{1.82}{1.22} = \frac{h}{7.32}$$
$$7.32 \cdot \frac{1.82}{1.22} = 7.32 \cdot \frac{h}{7.32}$$
$$h = \frac{13.3224}{1.22} = 10.92$$

The window is 10.92 m high.

5. 5.46 m. Let h represent the height of the tree. The two right triangles are similar by AA, so corresponding sides are proportional.

$$\frac{h}{1.82} = \frac{12.20 + 6.10}{6.10}$$

$$6.1 \cdot \frac{h}{1.82} = 6.1 \cdot \frac{18.3}{6.1}$$

$$h = \frac{33.306}{6.1} = 5.46$$

The tree is 5.46 m tall.

6. Thales used similar right triangles. The height of the pyramid and 240 m are the lengths of the legs of one triangle; 6.2 m and 10 m are the lengths of the corresponding legs of the other triangle. The height of the pyramid is 148.8 m.

$$\frac{6.2}{10} = \frac{H}{240}$$

$240 = 24 \cdot 10$, so $H = 24 \cdot 6.2 = 148.8$.

7. $PR = 90$ m. $\angle R$ and $\angle O$ are both right angles, and $\angle P$ is the same angle in both triangles, so $\triangle PRE \sim \triangle POC$ by AA. Thus, $\frac{PR}{PO} = \frac{RE}{OC}$. Let $x = PR$. Then $\frac{x}{x + 45} = \frac{60}{90} = \frac{2}{3}$. Solve this equation for x.

$$3(x + 45) \cdot \frac{x}{x + 45} = 3(x + 45) \cdot \frac{2}{3}$$

$$3x = 2(x + 45)$$

$$3x = 2x + 90$$

$$x = 90$$

The distance across the river is 90 m.

8. 300 cm. The diagram shows two similar rectangular pyramids, each lying on a lateral face. The base of the larger pyramid is the surface of the painting; its dimensions are 45 cm by 30 cm. The base of the smaller pyramid is an image of the painting; its dimensions are 3 cm by 2 cm. The ratio of corresponding sides of the bases (which are edges of the pyramid) is $\frac{45}{3} = \frac{30}{2} = \frac{15}{1}$. The ratio of heights of the pyramids will be the same, so $d = 15 \cdot 20 = 300$ cm.

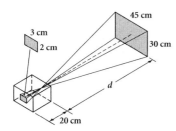

9. Possible answer: Walk to the point where the guy wire touches your head. Measure your height, h; the distance from you to the end of the guy wire, x; and the distance from the point on the ground directly below the top of the tower to the end of the guy wire, y. Solve a

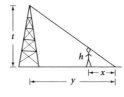

proportion to find the height of the tower, t: $\frac{h}{t} = \frac{x}{y}$. Finally, use the Pythagorean Theorem to find the length of the guy wire: $\sqrt{t^2 + y^2}$.

10. The triangles are similar by AA (because the ruler is parallel to the wall), so Kristin can use the length of string to the ruler, the length of string to the wall, and the length of the ruler to calculate the height of the wall. The height of the room is 144 in., or 12 ft.

Let h represent the height of the wall in inches.

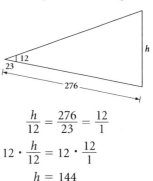

$$\frac{h}{12} = \frac{276}{23} = \frac{12}{1}$$

$$12 \cdot \frac{h}{12} = 12 \cdot \frac{12}{1}$$

$$h = 144$$

The height of the wall is 144 in., or 12 ft.

11. $\triangle MUN \sim \triangle MSA$ by AA; $x = 31\frac{2}{3}$. Draw the triangles separately to see the two triangles better. Because $\overline{UN} \parallel \overline{SA}$, $\angle MUN \cong \angle MSA$ (CA Conjecture), and $\angle M \cong \angle M$ (same angle), so $\triangle MUN \sim \triangle MSA$ by AA. Therefore, corresponding sides of these triangles are proportional.

$$\frac{MU}{MS} = \frac{UN}{SA}$$

$$\frac{9}{19} = \frac{15}{x}$$

$$19x \cdot \frac{9}{19} = 19x \cdot \frac{15}{x}$$

$$9x = 285$$

$$x = \frac{285}{9} = 31\frac{2}{3}$$

12. $\triangle BDC \sim \triangle AEC$ by AA; $y = 63$. $\angle DBC \cong \angle EAC$ because both angles are inscribed in the same arc, and $\angle BDC \cong \angle AEC$ for the same reason.

$$\frac{BD}{AE} = \frac{DC}{EC} = \frac{BC}{AC}$$

$$\frac{y}{91} = \frac{54}{78}$$

$$\frac{y}{91} = \frac{9}{13}$$

$91 = 7 \cdot 13$, so $y = 7 \cdot 9 = 63$.

13. $\triangle GHF \sim \triangle FHK \sim \triangle GFK$ by AA; $h = 18\frac{6}{13}$, $x = 7\frac{9}{13}$, $y = 44\frac{4}{13}$. Each pair of triangles shares one angle, and each triangle has one right angle, so the triangles are similar by AA. Draw the three triangles separately to see them more clearly.

To find *h*, use $\triangle GFK \sim \triangle FHK$ to write a proportion.

$$\frac{20}{h} = \frac{52}{48}$$

$$\frac{20}{h} = \frac{13}{12}$$

$$12h \cdot \frac{20}{h} = 12h \cdot \frac{13}{12}$$

$$240 = 13h$$

$$h = \frac{240}{13} = 18\frac{6}{13}$$

To find *x*, use $\triangle GFK \sim \triangle GHF$ to write a proportion.

$$\frac{20}{x} = \frac{52}{20}$$

$$\frac{20}{x} = \frac{13}{5}$$

$$5x \cdot \frac{20}{x} = 5x \cdot \frac{13}{5}$$

$$100 = 13x$$

$$x = \frac{100}{13} = 7\frac{9}{13}$$

To find *y*, use $\triangle GFK \sim \triangle FHK$ to write a proportion.

$$\frac{48}{y} = \frac{52}{48}$$

$$\frac{48}{y} = \frac{13}{12}$$

$$12y \cdot \frac{48}{y} = 12y \cdot \frac{13}{12}$$

$$576 = 13y$$

$$y = \frac{576}{13} = 44\frac{4}{13}$$

14.

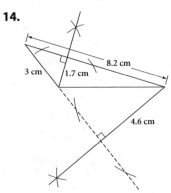

Sample answer:

$$A = \frac{1}{2} \cdot 8.2 \cdot 1.7 = 6.97 \text{ cm}^2$$

$$A = \frac{1}{2} \cdot 3 \cdot 4.6 = 6.9 \text{ cm}^2$$

The areas computed two different ways should be equal, but here the results vary slightly due to inexact measurements.

15. $5\frac{2}{3}$. Draw a radius of the circle to form a right triangle.

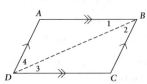

Apply the Pythagorean Theorem to the right triangle.

$$r^2 = 5^2 + (r - 3)^2$$

$$r^2 = 5^2 + r^2 - 6r + 9$$

$$0 = 34 - 6r$$

$$6r = 34$$

$$r = \frac{34}{6} = \frac{17}{3} = 5\frac{2}{3}$$

16.

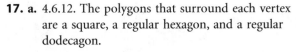

Given: Parallelogram *ABCD*

Show: $\overline{AB} \cong \overline{CD}$ and $\overline{AD} \cong \overline{BC}$

(See below)

17. a. 4.6.12. The polygons that surround each vertex are a square, a regular hexagon, and a regular dodecagon.

b. 3.12.12, or 3.12^2. The polygons that surround each vertex are an equilateral triangle and two regular dodecagons.

18. The golden ratio is $\frac{1 + \sqrt{5}}{2}$, or approximately 1.618. To find the golden ratio, solve the proportion $\frac{AB}{AX} = \frac{AX}{XB}$.

$$\frac{AB}{AX} = \frac{AX}{XB}$$

$$\frac{AX + XB}{AX} = \frac{AX}{XB}$$

$$AX \cdot XB \cdot \frac{AX + XB}{AX} = AX \cdot XB \cdot \frac{AX}{XB}$$

$$XB \cdot (AX + XB) = AX \cdot AX$$

$$XB \cdot AX + XB^2 = AX^2$$

$$AX^2 - XB \cdot AX - XB^2 = 0$$

Lesson 11.3, Exercise 16

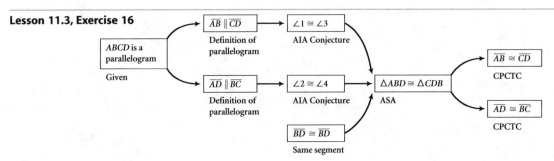

Discovering Geometry Solutions Manual
©2008 Key Curriculum Press

$$AX = \frac{-(-XB) \pm \sqrt{(-XB)^2 - 4(1)(-XB^2)}}{2(1)}$$

$$AX = \frac{XB \pm \sqrt{5 \cdot XB^2}}{2}$$

$$AX = \frac{XB \pm XB\sqrt{5}}{2}$$

$$AX = XB \cdot \frac{1 \pm \sqrt{5}}{2}$$

Because we want $AX > XB$, we must use $AX = XB \cdot \frac{1 + \sqrt{5}}{2}$, so the golden ratio is

$$\frac{AX}{XB} = \frac{XB \cdot \frac{1 + \sqrt{5}}{2}}{XB} = \frac{1 + \sqrt{5}}{2} \approx 1.618$$

Possible construction:

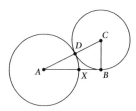

Construct $BC = \frac{1}{2}AB$, with $m\angle B = 90°$. Then $AC = \frac{\sqrt{5}}{2}AB$ by the Pythagorean Theorem. Using circles, construct $DC = BC$ and $AX = AD$. Then $AX = AD = AC - CD = \frac{\sqrt{5}}{2}AB - \frac{1}{2}AB = \frac{\sqrt{5} - 1}{2}AB$. So

$$\frac{AB}{AX} = \frac{2}{\sqrt{5} - 1} = \frac{2}{\sqrt{5} - 1} \cdot \frac{\sqrt{5} + 1}{\sqrt{5} + 1}$$

$$= \frac{2(1 + \sqrt{5})}{5 - 1} = \frac{2(1 + \sqrt{5})}{4} = \frac{1 + \sqrt{5}}{2}$$

Therefore, X is the golden cut.

19. a. Answers will vary.

b. Possible answer: The shape is an irregular curve.

c. Answers will vary. Possible answer: As the circular track becomes smaller, the curve becomes more circular; as the track becomes larger, the curve becomes more pointed near the fixed point. As the rod becomes shorter, the curve becomes more pointed near the fixed point; as the rod becomes longer, the curve becomes more like an oval. As the fixed point moves closer to the traced endpoint, the curve becomes more pointed near the fixed point; as the fixed point moves closer to the circular track, the curve begins to look like a crescent moon.

IMPROVING YOUR VISUAL THINKING SKILLS

The three unshaded squares must be arranged with one in each row and each column, and they must be arranged along one of the diagonals.

A. Research results will vary.

B. Results will vary.

LESSON 11.4

EXERCISES

1. 18 cm. Use the Proportional Parts Conjecture. The segments with lengths h and 12 cm are altitudes to corresponding sides $\overline{AG}$ and $\overline{IC}$ in the similar triangles, so $\frac{h}{12} = \frac{33}{22} = \frac{3}{2}$. $12 = 6 \cdot 2$, so $h = 6 \cdot 3 = 18$ cm.

2. 12 cm. Use the Proportional Parts Conjecture. The segments with lengths x and 16 cm are angle bisectors to corresponding sides $\overline{SK}$ and $\overline{JM}$ in the similar triangles, so $\frac{x}{16} = \frac{18}{24} = \frac{3}{4}$. $16 = 4 \cdot 4$, so $x = 4 \cdot 3 = 12$ cm.

3. 21 cm. In $\triangle PIE$, $\overline{ES}$ is the median to $\overline{PI}$, and in $\triangle SIC$, $\overline{CL}$ is the median to $\overline{SI}$, so by the Proportional Parts Conjecture, $\frac{SI}{PI} = \frac{CL}{ES}$. Because $\frac{SI}{PI} = \frac{1}{2}$, $\frac{CL}{ES} = \frac{1}{2}$, or $\frac{CL}{42} = \frac{1}{2}$, so $CL = 21$ cm.

4. 15 cm. Use the Proportional Parts Conjecture. $\overline{CL}$ is the angle bisector to $\overline{AP}$, and $\overline{DF}$ is the angle bisector to $\overline{AY}$. $\overline{AP}$ and $\overline{AY}$ are corresponding parts of the similar triangles, so they are in the same ratio as any pair of corresponding sides.

$$\frac{CL}{DF} = \frac{CA}{DA}$$

$$\frac{25}{FD} = \frac{35}{21} = \frac{5}{3}$$

$25 = 5 \cdot 5$, so $FD = 5 \cdot 3 = 15$ cm.

5. 2.0 cm. Use the Proportional Parts Conjecture. $\overline{DO}$ and $\overline{TE}$ are medians to corresponding sides $\overline{CL}$ and $\overline{HA}$ of the similar triangles. $CL = 2 \cdot 1.5 = 3.0$ cm and $HA = 2 \cdot 2.4 = 4.8$ cm. Use triangle similarity to write a proportion involving x.

$$\frac{DO}{TE} = \frac{CL}{HA}$$

$$\frac{x}{3.2} = \frac{3.0}{4.8}$$

$3.2 = \frac{2}{3} \cdot 4.8$, so $x = \frac{2}{3} \cdot 3.0 = 2.0$ cm.

6. Area of $\triangle ARM = 126$ cm², area of $\triangle LEG = 504$ cm². First, find the area of $\triangle ARM$.

Area of $\triangle ARM = \frac{1}{2}bh = \frac{1}{2}(18)(14) = 126$ cm²

To find the area of $\triangle LEG$, you need to know the length of the altitude to $\overline{LE}$. Let h represent this height and apply the Proportional Parts Conjecture.

$$\frac{14}{h} = \frac{18}{36} = \frac{1}{2}$$

$$h = 14 \cdot 2 = 28 \text{ cm}$$

Area of $\triangle LEG = \frac{1}{2}bh = \frac{1}{2}(36)(28) = 504$ cm²

7. 16 cm. Use the Angle Bisector/Opposite Side Conjecture.

$$\frac{v}{36} = \frac{20}{45} = \frac{4}{9}$$

$36 = 4 \cdot 9$, so $v = 4 \cdot 4 = 16$ cm.

8. 60 cm. Use the Angle Bisector/Opposite Side Conjecture.

$$\frac{40}{y} = \frac{34}{51} = \frac{2}{3}$$

$40 = 20 \cdot 2$, so $y = 20 \cdot 3 = 60$ cm.

9. $4\frac{4}{9}$ cm. Use the Angle Bisector/Opposite Side Conjecture. The angle bisector divides the opposite side into two segments with lengths x and $10 - x$.

$$\frac{x}{10 - x} = \frac{12}{15} = \frac{4}{5}$$

$$5(10 - x) \cdot \frac{x}{10 - x} = 5(10 - x) \cdot \frac{4}{5}$$

$$5x = 4(10 - x)$$

$$5x = 40 - 4x$$

$$9x = 40$$

$$x = \frac{40}{9} = 4\frac{4}{9} \text{ cm}$$

10. $\frac{a}{b} = \frac{p}{q}, \frac{a}{p} = \frac{b}{q}$. By the Angle Bisector/Opposite Side Conjecture, $\frac{a}{b} = \frac{p}{q}$. Rewrite this equation with $\frac{a}{p}$ on one side.

$$b \cdot \frac{a}{b} = b \cdot \frac{p}{q} \quad \text{Multiply both sides by } b.$$

$$a = \frac{bp}{q}$$

$$\frac{a}{p} = \frac{bp}{qp} \quad \text{Divide both sides by } p.$$

$$\frac{a}{p} = \frac{b}{q} \quad \text{Simplify.}$$

11. $6\sqrt{3}$ cm. There are several ways to solve this problem.

First solution: The large right triangle is a 30°-60°-90° triangle with shorter leg (opposite the 30° angle) of length 9 cm, so by the 30°-60°-90° Triangle Conjecture, the length of the hypotenuse is $2 \cdot 9 = 18$ cm. Use the Angle Bisector/Opposite Side Conjecture.

$$\frac{k}{3\sqrt{3}} = \frac{18}{9} = \frac{2}{1}, \text{ so } k = 6\sqrt{3} \text{ cm.}$$

Second solution: The large right triangle is a 30°-60°-90° triangle with shorter leg of length 9 cm, so by the 30°-60°-90° Triangle Conjecture, the length of the longer leg is $9\sqrt{3}$ cm. Then $k + 3\sqrt{3} = 9\sqrt{3}$, so $k = 6\sqrt{3}$ cm.

Third solution: The large right triangle is a 30°-60°-90° triangle, so the obtuse triangle is isosceles with two 30° angles. Then the angle bisector (which is a leg of the obtuse isosceles triangle and the hypotenuse of the small right triangle) has length k by the Converse of the

Isosceles Triangle Conjecture. Now apply the Pythagorean Theorem to the small right triangle.

$$k^2 = 9^2 + \left(3\sqrt{3}\right)^2 = 81 + 27 = 108$$

$$k = \sqrt{108} = \sqrt{36 \cdot 3} = 6\sqrt{3} \text{ cm}$$

12. 6 cm. You don't know the length of the third (unmarked) side of the large triangle, but by the Angle Bisector/Opposite Side Conjecture, you know that the ratio of its two parts (upper part to lower) is $\frac{15}{10} = \frac{3}{2}$, so these lengths can be represented by $3a$ and $2a$.

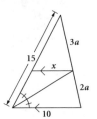

Using two pairs of corresponding angles formed when the parallel segments are cut by transversals (or using one of these pairs and the common angle at the top of the figure), the triangle with base of length x and the triangle with base of length 10 cm are similar. The ratio of the lengths of corresponding sides for these two triangles is $\frac{3a}{3a + 2a} = \frac{3a}{5a} = \frac{3}{5}$. Then $\frac{x}{10} = \frac{3}{5}$, so $x = 6$ cm.

13. $x = 3\frac{1}{3}$ cm, $y = \frac{5\sqrt{13}}{3}$ cm, $z = 8\frac{2}{3}$ cm. $\triangle ABC$ is a right triangle with hypotenuse $\overline{AB}$ of length 13 cm and shorter leg $\overline{BC}$ of length 5 cm, so this is a 5-12-13 triangle, and the length of the longer leg $\overline{AC}$ is 12 cm. Therefore, $x + z = 12$. Also, by the Angle Bisector/Opposite Sides Conjecture, $\frac{x}{z} = \frac{5}{13}$. These two equations form the system

$$\begin{cases} x + z = 12 \\ \dfrac{x}{z} = \dfrac{5}{13} \end{cases}$$

To solve this system by the substitution method, start by solving the second equation for x.

$$x = \frac{5}{13}z$$

Now substitute $\frac{5}{13}z$ for x in the first equation, and solve the resulting equation for z.

$$\frac{5}{13}z + z = 12$$

$$\frac{18}{13}z = 12$$

$$z = 12 \cdot \frac{13}{18} = \frac{26}{3} \text{ cm or, } 8\frac{2}{3} \text{ cm}$$

Substitute $\frac{26}{3}$ for z in the equation $x = \frac{5}{13}z$ and solve for x.

$$x = \frac{5}{13} \cdot \frac{26}{3} = \frac{10}{3} \text{ cm, or } 3\frac{1}{3} \text{ cm}$$

Discovering Geometry Solutions Manual
©2008 Key Curriculum Press

Now look at the small right triangle on the left. Its legs have lengths 5 cm and $x = \frac{10}{3}$ cm.

$$y^2 = 5^2 + \left(\frac{10}{3}\right)^2 = 25 + \frac{100}{9} = \frac{325}{9}$$

$$y = \sqrt{\frac{325}{9}} = \frac{\sqrt{325}}{\sqrt{9}} = \frac{\sqrt{13 \cdot 25}}{3} = \frac{5\sqrt{13}}{3} \text{ cm}$$

14. $B = (3, 5)$, $R = \left(1\frac{3}{4}, 7\right)$; $\frac{k}{h} = \frac{7}{4}$. By the Dilation Similarity Conjecture, $\triangle PQR \sim \triangle ABC$. By comparing the coordinates of A and P, you can see that each coordinate of P is $\frac{7}{4}$ of the corresponding coordinate of A, so this is the scale factor of the dilation. (The coordinates of each vertex of $\triangle PQR$ will be $\frac{7}{4}$ times the coordinates of the corresponding vertex of $\triangle ABC$, so the coordinates of each vertex in $\triangle ABC$ will be $\frac{4}{7}$ of the coordinates in the corresponding vertex of $\triangle PQR$.) Use this ratio to find the coordinates of B and R. For B, the corresponding vertex is Q.

x-coordinate of $B = \frac{4}{7}\left(5\frac{1}{4}\right) = \frac{4}{7}\left(\frac{21}{4}\right) = 3$

y-coordinate of $B = \frac{4}{7}\left(8\frac{3}{4}\right) = \frac{4}{7}\left(\frac{35}{4}\right) = 5$

The coordinates of B are $(3, 5)$. For R, the corresponding vertex is C.

x-coordinate of $R = \frac{7}{4}(1) = \frac{7}{4} = 1\frac{3}{4}$

y-coordinate of $R = \frac{7}{4}(4) = 7$

The coordinates of R are $\left(1\frac{3}{4}, 7\right)$.

Because $\triangle PQR$ is a dilation of $\triangle ABC$ by a scale factor of $\frac{7}{4}$, the ratio of the lengths of the corresponding sides is $\frac{7}{4}$. Therefore, by the Proportional Parts Conjecture, the corresponding altitudes will have the same ratio: $\frac{k}{h} = \frac{7}{4}$.

15. $\frac{\sqrt{2}}{1}$. Draw an isosceles right triangle in which each leg has length is 1. (Any side length will result in the same ratio of areas.) Then by the Isosceles Right Triangle Conjecture, the length of the hypotenuse is $\sqrt{2}$.

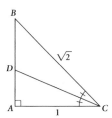

The areas of the two triangles can be calculated with the same height, AC.

Therefore, the ratio of areas is the same as the ratio of the bases:

$$\frac{\text{Area of } \triangle BCD}{\text{Area of } \triangle ACD} = \frac{\frac{1}{2}(AC)(BD)}{\frac{1}{2}(AC)(AD)} = \frac{BD}{AD}.$$

By the Angle Bisector/Opposite Side Conjecture, this ratio is $\frac{\sqrt{2}}{1}$.

16.

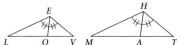

Possible proof: Consider similar triangles LVE and MTH with corresponding angle bisectors $\overline{EO}$ and $\overline{HA}$. Look at $\triangle EOL$ and $\triangle HAM$. $\angle L \cong \angle M$ because they are corresponding angles of $\triangle LVE$ and $\triangle MTH$. $m\angle LEO = \frac{1}{2}m\angle LEV$ and $m\angle MHA = \frac{1}{2}m\angle MHT$. $m\angle LEV = m\angle MHT$ from corresponding angles of the similar triangles, so $\frac{1}{2}m\angle LEV = \frac{1}{2}m\angle MHT$, and therefore $m\angle LEO = m\angle MHA$ by substitution. Thus, $\triangle EOL \sim \triangle HAM$ by the AA Similarity Conjecture. Corresponding sides of similar triangles are proportional, so $\frac{EO}{HA} = \frac{EL}{HM}$; that is, corresponding angle bisectors are proportional to corresponding sides.

17. If $\frac{a}{b} = \frac{c}{d}$, then

$$\frac{a}{b} + 1 = \frac{c}{d} + 1$$
$$\frac{a}{b} + \frac{b}{b} = \frac{c}{d} + \frac{d}{d}$$
$$\frac{a + b}{b} = \frac{c + d}{d}$$

18. The ratio will be the same as the ratio for the original rectangle. It will be $\frac{1}{2}$ if the rectangle is divided like this:

It might be any ratio if the rectangle is divided like this:

19. Yes, by the SSS Similarity Conjecture or the SAS Similarity Conjecture. The sides of the inner small triangle are midsegments of the original triangle, so each is half as long as the opposite side. The figure below shows sides that are congruent by the Triangle Midsegment Conjecture. From the figure, you can see that each of the four smaller congruent triangles is similar to the original triangle by the SSS Similarity Conjecture.

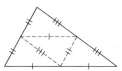

You can also use the SAS Similarity Conjecture by using opposite angles of parallelograms (Parallelogram Opposite Angles Conjecture) as the included congruent angles to show that the four small triangles are congruent and common angles to show that any of the three outer small triangles is similar to the original. Therefore, all four small triangles must be similar to the original.

20. a. $2a = b$. If the rectangles are congruent, they must have the same dimensions.

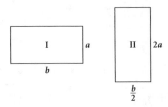

From this figure, you can see that the rectangles will be congruent if $2a = b$, or $a = \frac{b}{2}$.

b. $2a = b$. Perimeter of rectangle I $= 2a + 2b$ and perimeter of rectangle II $= 2(2a) + 2\left(\frac{b}{2}\right) = 4a + b$. The perimeter of the new rectangle will be equal to the perimeter of the original if $4a + b = 2a + 2b$, or $2a = b$, the same relationship as in 20a.

c. All values of a and b. Area of rectangle I $= ab$ and area of rectangle II $= (2a)\left(\frac{b}{2}\right) = ab$. Thus, the area of the new rectangle is equal to the area of the original for all values of a and b.

d. No values of a and b. If the rectangles are similar but not congruent, they cannot have the same area. In 20c, you found that the rectangles always have the same area, so there are no values of a and b for which the new rectangle is similar, but not congruent, to the original.

21. $AB = 3$ cm, $BC = 7.5$ cm. Let $p = AB$; then $BC = 10.5 - p$.

$$\frac{AB}{XY} = \frac{BC}{YZ}$$

$$\frac{p}{2} = \frac{10.5 - p}{5}$$

$$10\left(\frac{p}{2}\right) = 10\left(\frac{10.5 - p}{5}\right)$$

$$5p = 2(10.5 - p)$$

$$5p = 21 - 2p$$

$$7p = 21$$

$$p = 3 \text{ and } 10.5 - p = 7.5$$

Therefore, $AB = 3$ cm and $BC = 7.5$ cm.

IMPROVING YOUR ALGEBRA SKILLS

Write equations from two rows or columns in which the coefficients of x are different. In the second and third rows, for example, the coefficients of x are both 2, so the equations would be $2x + 20 = 2x + 20$, not yielding a way to solve for x. Many other pairs of equations lead to the solution, $x = 7$.

EXTENSIONS

A. True. The ratio of the lengths of corresponding medians and the ratio of the lengths of corresponding altitudes both equal the ratio of the lengths of corresponding sides, so they equal each other.

B. If the sides of the larger triangle are a, b, and c, then the sides of the smaller triangle are $\frac{2}{3}a$, $\frac{2}{3}b$, and $\frac{2}{3}c$. Therefore, the ratio of the perimeters is

$$\frac{\frac{2}{3}a + \frac{2}{3}b + \frac{2}{3}c}{a + b + c} = \frac{2}{3}$$

If the altitude of the larger triangle (from, say, side a) is h, then the corresponding altitude (from side $\frac{2}{3}a$) is $\frac{2}{3}h$. Therefore, the ratio of areas is

$$\frac{\frac{1}{2}\left(\frac{2}{3}a\right)\left(\frac{2}{3}h\right)}{\frac{1}{2}ah} = \frac{4}{9} = \left(\frac{2}{3}\right)^2$$

The ratio of the areas is less than the ratios of the length if the scale factor is less than one; it is greater if the scale factor is greater than one.

C. See the solution to Take Another Look activity 3 on page 254.

LESSON 11.5

EXERCISES

1. 18 cm². The ratio of the lengths of corresponding sides of the similar triangles (smaller triangle to larger triangle) is $\frac{ME}{CT} = \frac{6}{12} = \frac{1}{2}$. Then, by the Proportional Areas Conjecture, $\frac{\text{Area of } \triangle MSE}{\text{Area of } \triangle CAT} = \left(\frac{1}{2}\right)^2$, so $\frac{\text{Area of } \triangle MSE}{72} = \frac{1}{4}$. Therefore, area of $\triangle MSE = \frac{1}{4}(72) = 18$ cm².

2. 18. $\frac{\text{Area of } RECT}{\text{Area of } ANGL} = \frac{9}{16} = \left(\frac{TR}{LA}\right)^2$, so $\frac{TR}{LA} = \frac{3}{4}$. Then $\frac{TR}{24} = \frac{3}{4}$, so $TR = 6(3) = 18$.

3. $a = 5$, $b = 10$. $\frac{\text{Area of } ZOID}{\text{Area of } TRAP} = \frac{16}{25} = \left(\frac{4}{5}\right)^2$, so the ratio of the lengths of corresponding sides of the rectangles (smaller to larger) is $\frac{4}{5}$. Use proportions involving corresponding sides to find a and b. $\frac{4}{5} = \frac{4}{a}$, so $a = 5$, and $\frac{4}{5} = \frac{8}{b}$, so $b = 10$.

4. 27π cm². $\frac{r}{s} = \frac{3}{5}$, so the ratio of the areas of the semicircles (smaller to larger) is $\left(\frac{3}{5}\right)^2 = \frac{9}{25}$. Let A represent the area of semicircle R. Then $\frac{\text{Area of semicircle } R}{\text{Area of semicircle } S} = \frac{A}{75\pi} = \frac{9}{25}$. Solve the proportion to find A.

$$\frac{A}{75\pi} = \frac{9}{25}$$

$$75\pi \cdot \frac{A}{75\pi} = 75\pi \cdot \frac{9}{25}$$

$$A = 27\pi$$

The area of semicircle R is 27π cm².

5. $\frac{1}{49}$. The ratio of the lengths of corresponding diagonals is the same as the ratio of the lengths of corresponding sides, so by the Proportional Areas Conjecture, the ratio of the areas of the kites (smaller to larger) is $\left(\frac{1}{7}\right)^2 = \frac{1}{49}$.

6. 1:3. If the ratio of the areas is 1:9, or $\frac{1}{9}$, by the Proportional Areas Conjecture, the ratio of the lengths of corresponding sides will be $\sqrt{\frac{1}{9}} = \frac{1}{3}$. By the Proportional Parts Conjecture, the ratio of the lengths of altitudes is equal to the ratio of the lengths of corresponding sides, so the ratio of the lengths of corresponding altitudes is also $\frac{1}{3}$, or 1:3.

7. $\frac{m^2}{n^2}$, or $\left(\frac{m}{n}\right)^2$. Draw cubes with sides of lengths m and n and find their surface areas.

Area $= 6m^2$ Area $= 6n^2$

Ratio of areas $= \dfrac{6m^2}{6n^2} = \dfrac{m^2}{n^2} = \left(\dfrac{m}{n}\right)^2$

8. Possible answer: Assuming the ad is sold by area, Annie should charge \$6,000. If the length and width are both doubled, the area will be multiplied by 4, so the bill will also be multiplied by 4. 4(\$1,500) $=$ \$6,000.

9. 5000 tiles. The rectangular wall and the rectangle on which the design was created are similar because each angle of every rectangle is 90° and corresponding sides are proportional: $\frac{10}{2} = \frac{15}{3}$. The ratio of the lengths of corresponding sides is $\frac{5}{1}$, so, by the Proportional Areas Conjecture, the ratio of the areas is $\left(\frac{5}{1}\right)^2 = \frac{25}{1}$. Therefore, to cover the entire wall, $25 \cdot 200 = 5000$ tiles will be needed.

10. $\frac{9}{1}$. Because the Proportional Areas Conjecture is true for surface areas, the ratio of the surface area of the father's skin to that of his son's is $\left(\frac{3}{1}\right)^2 = \frac{9}{1}$.

11.

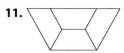

12. a. $a(x) = 2x$

x	Area in cm²
1	2
2	4
3	6
4	8
5	10
6	12

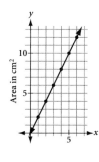

b. $A(x) = 2x^2$

x	Area in cm²
1	2
2	8
3	18
4	32
5	50
6	72

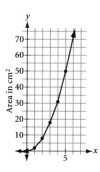

c. The equation for $a(x)$ is linear, so the graph is a line. The equation for $A(x)$ is quadratic, so the graph is a parabola.

13. Answers will vary. Possible proof: The area of the first rectangle is bh. The area of the dilated rectangle is $rh \cdot rb$, or r^2bh. The ratio of the area of the dilation to the area of the original rectangle is $\frac{r^2bh}{hh}$, or r^2.

14. $x = \frac{16}{3}$, $y = \frac{20}{3}$. The larger triangle is cut into two smaller triangles by the altitude from the right angle vertex, each of which is similar to the larger one by the AA Similarity Conjecture. Therefore, the two smaller triangles are similar to each other. First look at the small right triangle on the left.
The hypotenuse of this triangle has length 5, and the shorter leg has length 3, so this is a 3-4-5 triangle, and the longer leg has length 4. Because the small left triangle is similar to the right triangle, their corresponding sides are proportional. Therefore, $\frac{4}{3} = \frac{x}{4}$ and $\frac{5}{3} = \frac{y}{4}$. Solve the first equation to get $x = \frac{16}{3}$ and the second to get $y = \frac{20}{3}$.

15. 8. By the Trapezoid Midsegment Conjecture, $EF = \frac{1}{2}(20 + 36) = \frac{1}{2}(56) = 28$. Now apply the Triangle Midsegment Conjecture to $\triangle BCD$ to find $YF = \frac{1}{2}(CD) = \frac{1}{2}(20) = 10$ and to $\triangle ACD$ to find $EX = \frac{1}{2}(CD) = 10$. From the figure, $EX + XY + YF = EF$, so $XY = 28 - 10 - 10 = 8$.

16. a. i. $a = 90° - 50° = 40°$; $b = 90° - a = 50°$; $c = 90° - b = 40°$

ii. $a = 90° - 30° = 60°$; $b = 90° - a = 30°$; $c = 90° - b = 60°$

iii. $a = 90° - 68° = 22°$; $b = 90° - a = 68°$; $c = 90° - b = 22°$

Conjecture: The altitude to the hypotenuse of a right triangle divides the triangle into two right triangles that are similar to each other and to the original right triangle.

b. i. $\frac{h}{r} = \frac{s}{h}$. By the AA Similarity Conjecture, the two smaller right triangles are similar to each other and to the large right triangle. (See Lesson 11.2, Exercise 8.) To keep corresponding sides straight, think in terms of shorter leg, longer leg, and hypotenuse. The proportion $\frac{h}{r} = \frac{s}{h}$ says that the ratio of the length of the shorter leg to the length of the longer leg is the same in the two smaller right triangles.

ii. $\frac{y}{h} = \frac{h}{x}$. This proportion says that the ratio of the length of the longer leg to the length of the shorter leg is the same in the two smaller triangles.

iii. $\frac{n}{h} = \frac{h}{m}$. This proportion says that the ratio of the length of the longer leg to the length of the shorter leg is the same in the two smaller right triangles.

Conjecture: The altitude (length h) to the hypotenuse of a right triangle divides the hypotenuse into two segments (lengths p and q) such that $\frac{p}{h} = \frac{h}{q}$.

c.
$$h = \sqrt{pq}$$

$\frac{p}{h} = \frac{h}{q}$	Proportion from conjecture.
$hq\left(\frac{p}{h}\right) = hq\left(\frac{h}{q}\right)$	Multiply both sides by hq.
$pq = h^2$	Simplify.
$h = \sqrt{pq}$	Take the positive square root of both sides.

Notice that only the positive square root makes sense in the situation because p, q, and h all represent lengths.

d. $x = 9$, $y = 16$, $\frac{9}{12} = \frac{12}{16}$, $h = \sqrt{(9)(16)} = \sqrt{144} = 12$. Applying the Pythagorean Theorem to the right triangle with hypotenuse of length 15 gives $x^2 + 12^2 = 15^2$, so $x = \sqrt{15^2 - 12^2} = \sqrt{81} = 9$. Notice that this length can also be found by using the 3-4-5 Pythagorean triple: $12 = 3 \cdot 4$ and $15 = 3 \cdot 5$, so $x = 3 \cdot 3 = 9$. Now apply the Pythagorean Theorem to the right triangle with hypotenuse of length 20. Then $y^2 + 12^2 = 20^2$, so $y = \sqrt{20^2 - 12^2} = \sqrt{256} = 16$. This length can also be found by using the 3-4-5 Pythagorean triple: $12 = 3 \cdot 4$ and $20 = 5 \cdot 4$, so $y = 4 \cdot 4 = 16$. In the figure, $\frac{9}{12} = \frac{12}{16}$. If $p = 9$, $q = 16$, and $h = 12$, this is equivalent to the proportion $\frac{p}{h} = \frac{h}{q}$ and the equation $h = \sqrt{pq}$.

17.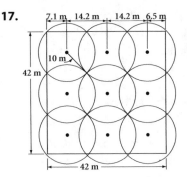

18.

Possible proof: Consider similar triangles $\triangle LVE$ and $\triangle MTH$ with corresponding altitudes $\overline{EO}$ and $\overline{HA}$. You need to show that the corresponding altitudes are proportional to corresponding sides, for example, $\frac{EO}{HA} = \frac{EL}{HM}$. If you show that $\triangle LOE \sim \triangle MAH$, then you can show that $\frac{EO}{HA} = \frac{EL}{HM}$. You know that $\angle L \cong \angle M$. Because $\overline{EO}$ and $\overline{HA}$ are altitudes, $\angle LOE$ and $\angle MAH$ are right angles, so $\angle LOE \cong \angle MAH$, and $\triangle LOE \sim \triangle MAH$ by AA. You can then write the proportion $\frac{EO}{HA} = \frac{EL}{HM}$, which shows that the corresponding altitudes are proportional to corresponding sides.

19. $x = 92°$. In the left isosceles triangle, one base angle forms a linear pair with the 112° angle, so each base angle measures $180° - 112° = 68°$, and the vertex angle measures $180° - 2(68°) = 44°$. Now look at the middle isosceles triangle. The base angle that has one side along the top parallel line has measure 68° by the AIA Theorem. Therefore, this is also a 68°-68°-44° triangle. Finally, look at the isosceles triangle on the right. The base angle in the lower left of this triangle has measure $180° - 68° - 68° = 44°$. The measure of the other base angle must also be 44°, so $x = 180° - 2(44°) = 92°$.

20. $\approx 105.5 \text{ cm}^2$. Use the Regular Polygon Area Conjecture.
$$A = \frac{1}{2}aP \approx \frac{1}{2}(5.7)(37) = 105.45 \text{ cm}^2$$

21. 60 ft². This is an isosceles triangle. Draw the altitude to the base.

The altitude to the base of an isosceles triangle divides the triangle into two congruent right triangles. Each of these triangles has a hypotenuse of length 12 ft and a shorter leg of length 5 ft, so these are 5-12-13 triangles, and each of the longer legs has length 12 ft. This is the length of the altitude to the base, so $A = \frac{1}{2}bh = \frac{1}{2}(10)(12) = 60$ ft².

22. True

23. Two pairs of angles are congruent, so the triangles are similar by the AA Similarity Conjecture. However, the two sets of corresponding sides are not proportional $\left(\frac{60}{80} \neq \frac{105}{135}\right)$, so the triangles are not similar.

24.

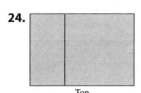

Top

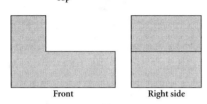

Front   Right side

Areas of orthographic views:

Top: $2 + 4 = 6$ square units; Front: $1 + 3 = 4$ square units; Right side: $2 + 2 = 4$ square units

The sum of these areas is $6 + 4 + 4 = 14$ square units. From Step 4 of Investigation 2, the surface area of the solid is 28 square units, so the sum of the areas of the orthographic views is half the surface area. The volume of the original solid is 8 cubic units. One way to find the volume of the enlarged solid is to first notice that the front side is composed of four squares, each 4 units by 4 units. Therefore, there are $4 \cdot 4 \cdot 4 = 64$ square units on the front. There are 8 layers, so the total volume is $64 \cdot 8 = 512$ cubic units. The ratio of volume of the enlarged solid to the original is $\frac{512}{8} = \frac{64}{1}$.

PROJECT

Project should satisfy the following criteria:

- The table of measured objects and the graph of data with the line of best fit are complete. The graph may compare the shorter side to the longer side or compare the length-width ratio to one of the sides.

- In the graph (shorter side, longer side), the slope of the line of best fit represents the ratio of sides.

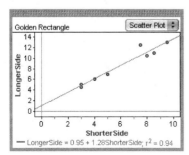

- In the graph (shorter side, ratio of longer side to shorter side), the slope may be nearly zero.

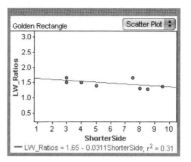

- Other representations of the data might include a distribution of the ratios along with the plotted mean value.

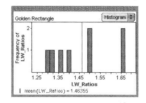

- The equation of the line of best fit is used to make predictions about other rectangles.

- It is unlikely that students will find the golden ratio, but their explanations might mention it.

Extra credit

- Predictions are checked with the measurements of other rectangles.

- Other representations of the data are included.

- Students gather more data or combine data.

Golden Rectangle Extensions

A. See the solution for Lesson 11.7, Exercise 27 on page 250.

B. The ratio of consecutive Fibonacci numbers approaches the golden ratio.

EXTENSIONS

A. These laws seem to be analogous to the Proportional Areas Conjecture.

B. If the base and height of one triangle are B and H, then $\frac{a}{b}B$ and $\frac{a}{b}H$ are the base and height of the other triangle. Its area, then, is $\frac{1}{2}\left(\frac{a}{b}B\right)\left(\frac{a}{b}H\right) = \left(\frac{a}{b}\right)^2\frac{1}{2}BH$, which is $\left(\frac{a}{b}\right)^2$ times the area of the first triangle.

LESSON 11.6

EXERCISES

1. 1715 cm^3. By the Proportional Parts Conjecture, the ratio of the volume of the small pyramid to the volume of the large one is $\left(\frac{4}{7}\right)^3 = \frac{64}{343}$. Let V represent the volume of the large pyramid.

$$\frac{64}{343} = \frac{320}{V}$$

$$343V \cdot \frac{64}{343} = 343V \cdot \frac{320}{V}$$

$$64V = 343 \cdot 320$$

$$V = \frac{343 \cdot 320}{64} = 343 \cdot 5 = 1715$$

The volume of the large pyramid is 1715 cm^3.

2. $H = 16$ cm, $h = 4$ cm. Volume of large cone $= 768\pi$ cm$^3 \approx 2412.7$ cm^3. Volume of small cone $= 12\pi$ cm$^3 \approx 37.7$ cm^3. $\frac{\text{Volume of large cone}}{\text{Volume of small cone}} = \frac{64}{1}$.

By the Pythagorean Theorem, $H = 16$ cm. Because the ratio of the radius of the large cone to the radius of the small cone is $\frac{12}{3} = \frac{4}{1}$, $h = \frac{1}{4}(16) = 4$ cm.

$$\text{Volume of large cone} = BH = \frac{1}{3}\pi r^2 H$$
$$= \frac{1}{3}\pi(12)^2 \cdot 16$$
$$= 768\pi \text{ cm}^3 \approx 2412.7 \text{ cm}^3$$

$$\text{Volume of small cone} = \frac{1}{3}\pi r^2 H = \frac{1}{3}\pi(3)^2 \cdot 4$$
$$= 12\pi \text{ cm}^3 \approx 37.7 \text{ cm}^3$$

$$\frac{\text{Volume of large cone}}{\text{Volume of small cone}} = \frac{768\pi \text{ cm}^3}{12\pi \text{ cm}^3} = \frac{768}{12} = \frac{64}{1}$$

3. $\frac{h}{H} = \frac{3}{5}$. $\frac{\text{Volume of large prism}}{\text{Volume of small prism}} = \frac{125}{27}$. Volume of large prism $= 1500$ cm^3. $\frac{\text{Area of base of small prism}}{\text{Area of base of large prism}} = \frac{9}{25} = \left(\frac{h}{H}\right)^2$, so $\frac{h}{H} = \sqrt{\frac{9}{25}} = \frac{3}{5}$. Then $\frac{\text{Volume of large prism}}{\text{Volume of small prism}} = \left(\frac{H}{h}\right)^3 = \left(\frac{5}{3}\right)^3 = \frac{125}{27}$.

Let V represent the volume of the large prism.

$$\frac{125}{27} = \frac{V}{324}$$

$$324 \cdot \frac{125}{27} = 324 \cdot \frac{V}{324}$$

$$V = \frac{324 \cdot 125}{27} = 1500$$

The volume of the large prism is 1500 cm^3.

4. Volume of small cylinder $= 1944\pi$ ft$^3 \approx 6107.3$ ft^3. $\frac{\text{Volume of large cylinder}}{\text{Volume of small cylinder}} = \frac{64}{27}$. $H = 32$ ft. Volume of small cylinder $= BH = \pi r^2 H = \pi(9)^2(24) = 1944\pi$ cm$^3 \approx 6107.3$ cm^3. $\frac{\text{Volume of large cylinder}}{\text{Volume of small cylinder}} = \frac{4608\pi}{1944\pi} = \frac{72 \cdot 64\pi}{72 \cdot 27\pi} = \frac{64}{27}$, so $\left(\frac{H}{24}\right)^3 = \frac{64}{27}$. Then $\frac{H^3}{24^3} = \frac{64}{27}$, or $\frac{H^3}{13{,}824} = \frac{64}{27}$. $13{,}824 = 512(27)$, so $H^3 = 512(64) = 32{,}768$. Then $H = \sqrt[3]{32{,}768} = 32$ ft.

5. $\frac{125}{27}$. By the Proportional Volumes Conjecture, the ratio of the volumes of the prisms (larger to smaller) is $\left(\frac{5}{3}\right)^3 = \frac{125}{27}$.

6. 2:5. The ratio of volumes is $8:125$, or $\frac{8}{125}$, so by the Proportional Volumes Conjecture, the ratio of corresponding heights is $\sqrt[3]{\frac{8}{125}} = \frac{2}{5}$.

7. $\frac{2}{3}$. For objects made of the same material (or any objects with the same density), weight is proportional to volume, so the ratio of volumes of the two balls (smaller to larger) is $\frac{8}{27}$, and the ratio of radii is $\sqrt[3]{\frac{8}{27}} = \frac{2}{3}$, so the ratio of diameters is also $\frac{2}{3}$.

8. $1,953.13. The two warehouses are similar rectangular prisms in which the ratio of the lengths of the corresponding edges is $\frac{2.5}{1}$, so the ratio of their volumes is $\left(\frac{2.5}{1}\right)^3$. Therefore, the volume of the large warehouse is $(2.5)^3 = 15.625$ times the volume of the small warehouse, and the daily cost of cooling the large warehouse is 15.625 times the cost of cooling the small warehouse: $15.625(\$125) = \$1,953.13$.

9. 2432 lb. The ratio of the weights of the two statues is equal to the ratio of their volumes, $\left(\frac{4}{1}\right)^3 = \frac{64}{1}$, so the weight of the large statue is 64 times the weight of the smaller statue: $64(38 \text{ lb}) = 2432$ lb.

10. Possible answer: No, $\left(\frac{14}{48}\right)^3 = \frac{7}{x}$, so a 4-foot chicken that is similar to a 14-inch 7-pound chicken would weigh approximately 282 lb. It is unlikely that the legs of the giant chicken would be able to support its weight.

11. Possible answer: Assuming the body types of the goliath frog and the gold frog are similar, the gold frog would weigh about 0.0001 kg, or 0.1 g. To find the scale factor, the lengths of both frogs must be given in the same units. Convert 9.8 mm to meters: 9.8 mm $=$ 0.0098 m. Now compare the lengths of the two frogs.

$$\frac{\text{Length of goliath frog}}{\text{Length of gold frog}} = \frac{0.3 \text{ m}}{0.0098 \text{ m}} \approx \frac{30.6}{1}$$

Now find the ratio of the weights, which is the same as the ratio of the volumes of the frogs.

$$\frac{\text{Weight of goliath frog}}{\text{Weight of gold frog}} = \left(\frac{30.6}{1}\right)^3 = \frac{(30.6)^3}{1}$$

Let w represent the weight of the gold frog.

$$\frac{(30.6)^3}{1} = \frac{3.2}{w}$$

$$w = \frac{3.2}{(30.6)^3} \approx 0.0001 \text{ kg, or } 0.1 \text{ g}$$

The Brazilian gold frog would weigh about 0.1 g.

12. Surface area ratio $= \frac{16}{1}$, volume ratio $= \frac{64}{1}$. The dolphin has the greater surface area to volume ratio. The ratio of corresponding lengths is $\frac{32}{8} = \frac{4}{1}$, so, by the Proportional Areas Conjecture, the ratio of the surface area of the orca to the surface area of the dolphin is $\left(\frac{4}{1}\right)^2 = \frac{16}{1}$, and by the Proportional

Volumes Conjecture, the ratio of the volume of the orca to the volume of the dolphin is $\left(\frac{4}{1}\right)^3 = \frac{64}{1}$. If the dolphin's surface area is A and volume is V, then the orca has surface area $16A$ and volume $64V$. Hence the orca's area-to-volume ratio is $\frac{16A}{64V} = \frac{1}{4} \cdot \frac{A}{V}$, which is one-fourth the dolphin's area-to-volume ratio.

13. The ratio of the volumes is $\frac{1}{27}$. The ratio of the surface areas is $\frac{1}{9}$. $\left(\frac{1}{3}\right)^3 = \frac{1}{27}$ and $\left(\frac{1}{3}\right)^2 = \frac{1}{9}$.

14.

x	1	2	3	4	5
Surface area in cm²	22	88	198	352	550
Volume in cm³	6	48	162	384	750

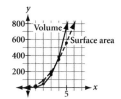

$S(x) = 22x^2$ and $V(x) = 6x^3$. Possible answer: The surface area equation is quadratic, so the graph is a parabola, and the volume equation is cubic, so the graph is a cubic graph.

15. Possible proof: The volume of the first rectangular prism is lwh. The volume of the second rectangular prism is $rl \cdot rw \cdot rh$, or r^3lwh. The ratio of the volumes is $\frac{r^3lwh}{lwh}$, or r^3.

16. $9{,}120\pi$ m³, or approximately 28,651 m³. The volume of the truncated cone is the difference between the volume of the large cone and the volume of the small cone. Recall that the volume of a cone is given by the formula $V = BH = \frac{1}{3}\pi r^2 H$.

$$
\begin{aligned}
V_{\text{truncated cone}} &= V_{\text{large cone}} - V_{\text{small cone}} \\
&= \frac{1}{3}\pi(36)^2(30) - \frac{1}{3}\pi(24)^2(20) \\
&= 9{,}120\pi \approx 28{,}651 \text{ m}^3
\end{aligned}
$$

17. $\frac{s}{2\sqrt{2}} - \frac{s}{4}$, or $\frac{s\sqrt{2}-s}{4}$. Connect the centers of two of the larger circles and the center of the small circle to form a 45°-45°-90° triangle. (This is a right triangle because two sides are parts of the diagonals of the square, and it is isosceles because the lengths of two sides are the sum of radii of the larger and smaller circles.)

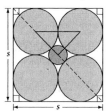

Each of the larger circles has diameter $\frac{s}{2}$ and therefore radius $\frac{s}{4}$. In the isosceles right triangle, the hypotenuse is formed from the radii of two larger circles, so the length of this hypotenuse is $2\left(\frac{s}{4}\right) = \frac{s}{2}$. Therefore, by the Isosceles Right Triangle Conjecture, the length of each leg is

$$
\frac{\frac{s}{2}}{\sqrt{2}} = \frac{\frac{s}{2}}{\frac{\sqrt{2}}{1}} = \frac{s}{2} \cdot \frac{1}{\sqrt{2}} = \frac{s}{2\sqrt{2}}
$$

The radius of the smaller circle is the difference between the length of a leg of the isosceles right triangle and the radius of a larger circle, so the radius of the smaller circle is $\frac{s}{2\sqrt{2}} - \frac{s}{4}$.

The expression for this radius can be written as a single fraction if you first rationalize the denominator of the first fraction and then subtract fractions with a common denominator.

$$
\begin{aligned}
\frac{s}{2\sqrt{2}} - \frac{s}{4} &= \frac{s}{2\sqrt{2}} \cdot \frac{\sqrt{2}}{\sqrt{2}} - \frac{s}{4} = \frac{s\sqrt{2}}{2 \cdot 2} - \frac{s}{4} \\
&= \frac{s\sqrt{2}}{4} - \frac{s}{4} = \frac{s\sqrt{2}-s}{4}
\end{aligned}
$$

18. Yes, because $18^2 + 24^2 = 30^2$ (Converse of the Pythagorean Theorem). The side lengths are a multiple of the 3-4-5 Pythagorean triple: $18 = 6(3)$, $24 = 6(4)$, $30 = 6(5)$.

19. a. Possible answer: Fold a pair of corresponding vertices (any vertex in the original figure and the corresponding vertex in the image) together and crease; repeat for another pair of corresponding vertices. The intersection of the two creases is the center of rotation, P.

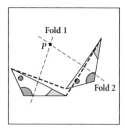

b. Possible answer: Draw a segment (a chord) between a pair of corresponding vertices and construct the perpendicular bisector; repeat for another pair of corresponding vertices; the intersection of the two perpendicular bisectors is the center of rotation, P.

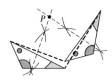

20. Bisect the angle between the sides of lengths $2x$ and $3x$. Let D be the point where the angle bisector intersects $\overline{AB}$.

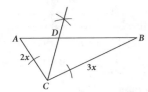

By the Angle Bisector/Opposite Side Conjecture, $\frac{AD}{DB} = \frac{2x}{3x} = \frac{2}{3}$, so this construction has divided $\overline{AB}$ into lengths with a ratio of 2:3.

IMPROVING YOUR VISUAL THINKING SKILLS

The only way to paint on all but exactly 60 small cubes is to paint three faces of a 5-by-5-by-5 cube.

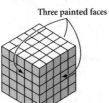

Three painted faces

EXTENSION

You can use the relationship (ratio of sizes of n-dimensional parts) $=$ (scale factor)^n with the understanding that the ratio of the fractal to the next-smaller similar piece (which must have the same dimension) is 3, whereas the corresponding scale factor is 2, so the equation becomes $3 = 2^n$. By approximations or logarithms, the dimension n can be found to be about 1.58.

LESSON 11.7

EXERCISES

1. 5 cm. The small triangle at the top of the figure is similar to $\triangle TWE$ by the AA Similarity Conjecture, so $\frac{4}{4 + 12} = \frac{a}{20}$, or $\frac{4}{16} = \frac{a}{20}$. Then $\frac{1}{4} = \frac{a}{20}$, so $a = 5$ cm.

2. $33\frac{1}{3}$ cm. Similar triangles are formed in the same way as in Exercise 1, so corresponding sides are proportional.

$$\frac{20}{b} = \frac{15}{15 + 10}$$

$$\frac{20}{b} = \frac{15}{25}$$

$$\frac{20}{b} = \frac{3}{5}$$

$$5b \cdot \frac{20}{b} = 5b \cdot \frac{3}{5}$$

$$100 = 3b$$

$$b = \frac{100}{3} = 33\frac{1}{3} \text{ cm}$$

3. 45 cm. Similar triangles are formed in the same way as in Exercises 1 and 2.

$$\frac{40}{70} = \frac{60}{c + 60}$$

$$\frac{4}{7} = \frac{60}{c + 60}$$

$$7(c + 60) \cdot \frac{4}{7} = 7(c + 60) \cdot \frac{60}{c + 60}$$

$$4(c + 60) = 420$$

$$4c + 240 = 420$$

$$4c = 180$$

$$c = \frac{180}{4} = 45 \text{ cm}$$

You can also find c by writing the proportion $\frac{60}{40} = \frac{c + 60}{70}$, which compares corresponding side lengths within each triangle. This will also lead to $c = 45$ cm.

4. 21 cm. Use the Parallel/Proportionality Conjecture.

$$\frac{24}{14} = \frac{36}{d}$$

$$\frac{12}{7} = \frac{36}{d}$$

$$36 = 3(12), \text{ so } d = 3(7) = 21 \text{ cm}.$$

5. 28 cm. Use the Parallel/Proportionality Conjecture.

$$\frac{36}{45} = \frac{e}{35}$$

$$\frac{4}{5} = \frac{e}{35}$$

$$35 = 7(5), \text{ so } e = 7(4) = 28 \text{ cm}.$$

6. No. By the converse part of the Parallel/Proportionality Conjecture, $r \parallel \overline{AN}$ if $\frac{15}{36} = \frac{25}{55}$. But $\frac{15}{36} = \frac{3 \cdot 5}{3 \cdot 12} = \frac{5}{12}$, and $\frac{25}{55} = \frac{5 \cdot 5}{5 \cdot 11} = \frac{5}{11}$, so the sides are not divided proportionally. Therefore, r is not parallel to $\overline{AN}$.

7. Jose's method is correct. Possible explanation: Alex's first ratio compares only part of a side of the larger triangle to the entire corresponding side of the smaller triangle, while the second ratio compares entire corresponding sides of the triangles.

8. Yes. $m \parallel \overline{FL}$ if $\frac{48}{56} = \frac{54}{63}$. To compare these two ratios, rewrite each of them in lowest terms.

$$\frac{48}{56} = \frac{8 \cdot 6}{8 \cdot 7} = \frac{6}{7}$$

$$\frac{54}{63} = \frac{9 \cdot 6}{9 \cdot 7} = \frac{6}{7}$$

The sides are divided proportionally, so $m \parallel \overline{FL}$.

9. $m = 6$ cm, $n = 4.5$ cm. Apply the Extended Parallel/Proportionality Conjecture. $\frac{2}{4} = \frac{3}{m}$, or $\frac{1}{2} = \frac{3}{m}$, so $m = 6$ cm. $\frac{2}{3} = \frac{3}{n}$, so $2n = 9$, and $n = \frac{9}{2}$ cm, or 4.5 cm.

10. $w = 13\frac{1}{3}$ cm, $x = 21.6$ cm. Use the Extended Parallel/Proportionality Conjecture.

$$\frac{12}{10} = \frac{x}{18} \qquad \qquad \frac{18}{24} = \frac{10}{w}$$

$$\frac{6}{5} = \frac{x}{18} \qquad \qquad \frac{3}{4} = \frac{10}{w}$$

$$18 \cdot \frac{6}{5} = 18 \cdot \frac{x}{18}$$

$$x = \frac{108}{5}$$

$$= 21.6 \text{ cm}$$

$$4w \cdot \frac{10}{w} = 4w \cdot \frac{3}{4}$$

$$40 = 3w$$

$$w = \frac{40}{3}$$

$$= 13\frac{1}{3} \text{ cm}$$

11. Yes, $m \parallel \overline{EA}$. No, n is not parallel to $\overline{EA}$. No, m is not parallel to n. $m \parallel \overline{EA}$ if $\frac{25}{40+35} = \frac{15}{25+20}$, or $\frac{25}{75} = \frac{15}{45}$. This is true because $\frac{25}{75} = \frac{1}{3}$ and $\frac{15}{45} = \frac{1}{3}$. $n \parallel \overline{EA}$ if $\frac{25+40}{35} = \frac{15+25}{20}$, or $\frac{65}{35} = \frac{40}{20}$. This is false because $\frac{65}{35} = \frac{13}{7}$ and $\frac{40}{20} = 2$.

Because m is parallel to $\overline{EA}$ but n is not parallel to $\overline{EA}$, m and n can't be parallel to each other.

12. Yes, $\overline{XY} \parallel \overline{GO}$. Yes, $\overline{XY} \parallel \overline{FR}$. Yes, $FROG$ is a trapezoid.

First look at $\triangle ZXY$. $\overline{XY} \parallel \overline{GO}$ if $\frac{24}{8} = \frac{36}{12}$, or $3 = 3$, which is true. Now look at $\triangle ZFR$. $\overline{XY} \parallel \overline{FR}$ if $\frac{24+8}{16} = \frac{36+12}{24}$, or $\frac{32}{16} = \frac{48}{24}$, or $2 = 2$, which is true. Because $\overline{XY} \parallel \overline{GO}$ and $\overline{XY} \parallel \overline{FR}$, $\overline{GO} \parallel \overline{FR}$, so $FROG$ is a trapezoid.

13. $a = 3\sqrt{2}$ cm, $b = 6\sqrt{2}$ cm. There are several ways to find a and b. Two approaches are shown here.

First solution: By the distance formula, $a + b = \sqrt{(12-3)^2 + (0-9)^2} = \sqrt{9^2 + 9^2} = \sqrt{2 \cdot 9^2} = 9\sqrt{2}$. Using corresponding angles formed when the parallel lines are cut by the transversals that are two sides of the large triangle, the small and large triangles are similar by the AA Similarity Conjecture. From the similar triangles,

$$\frac{4}{12} = \frac{a}{a+b} = \frac{a}{9\sqrt{2}}$$

$$\frac{1}{3} = \frac{a}{9\sqrt{2}}$$

$9\sqrt{2} = 3\sqrt{2}(3)$, so $a = 3\sqrt{2}(1) = 3\sqrt{2}$. Then $b = 9\sqrt{2} - a = 9\sqrt{2} - 3\sqrt{2} = 6\sqrt{2}$.

Second solution: First use the distance formula to find $a + b = 9\sqrt{2}$, as shown in the first solution. Then $b = 9\sqrt{2} - a$. Apply the Parallel/Proportionality Conjecture.

$$\frac{4}{8} = \frac{a}{9\sqrt{2} - a}$$

$$\frac{1}{2} = \frac{a}{9\sqrt{2} - a}$$

$$2(9\sqrt{2} - a) \cdot \frac{1}{2} = 2(9\sqrt{2} - a) \cdot \frac{a}{9\sqrt{2} - a}$$

$$9\sqrt{2} - a = 2a$$

$$9\sqrt{2} = 3a$$

$$a = 3\sqrt{2} \text{ cm}$$

$$b = 9\sqrt{2} - 3\sqrt{2} = 6\sqrt{2} \text{ cm}$$

14. This construction follows the method used in Example C on pages 626–627 of your book. The Extended Parallel/Proportionality Conjecture guarantees that the sides of the triangle are divided proportionally, and therefore $\overline{EF}$ is divided into five equal parts.

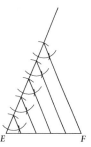

15.

First divide $\overline{IJ}$ into six equal parts using the method of Example C and Exercise 14. Then draw a circle with one of the equal parts of $\overline{IJ}$ as radius. Mark off six radii around the circle and connect the endpoints of the arcs to form a regular hexagon. The perimeter of the hexagon is six times the length of one of the equal parts of $\overline{IJ}$, so the perimeter is $\overline{IJ}$.

16. Extended Parallel/Proportionality Conjecture

17. You should connect the two 75-marks. By the Extended Parallel/Proportionality Conjecture, drawing a segment between the 75-marks will form a segment that has length $\frac{75}{100}$, or 75%, of the original.

18. 2064π cm³ ≈ 6484 cm³. Let x represent the height of the small missing cone. Use the similar triangles to write a proportion; then solve the proportion to find x.

$$\frac{x}{10} = \frac{x+12}{16}$$

$$80 \cdot \frac{x}{10} = 80 \cdot \frac{x+12}{16}$$

$$8x = 5(x+12)$$

$$8x = 5x + 60$$

$$3x = 60$$

$$x = 20$$

The height of the small cone is 20 cm.

$$V_{\text{large cone}} = BH = \frac{1}{3}\pi r^2 H = \frac{1}{3}\pi(16)^2(32)$$

$$= \frac{8192\pi}{3} \text{ cm}^3$$

$$V_{\text{small cone}} = BH = \frac{1}{3}\pi r^2 H = \frac{1}{3}\pi(10)^2(20)$$

$$= \frac{2000\pi}{3} \text{ cm}^3$$

$$V_{\text{truncated cone}} = \frac{8192\pi}{3} - \frac{2000\pi}{3} = \frac{6192\pi}{3}$$

$$= 2064\pi \text{ cm}^3 \approx 6484 \text{ cm}^3$$

19. Possible proof:

$$\frac{a}{c} = \frac{b}{d}$$

$$cd \cdot \frac{a}{c} = cd \cdot \frac{b}{d}$$

$$ad = cb$$

$$ad + ab = cb + ab$$

$$a(d + b) = b(c + a)$$

$$\frac{a(d + b)}{ab} = \frac{b(c + a)}{ab}$$

$$\frac{d + b}{b} = \frac{c + a}{a}$$

So, two pairs of corresponding sides of $\triangle XYZ$ and $\triangle XAB$ are proportional. $\angle X \cong \angle X$, so $\triangle XYZ \sim \triangle XAB$ by the SAS Similarity Conjecture. Because $\triangle XYZ \sim \triangle XAB$, $\angle XAB \cong \angle XYZ$. Hence, $\overleftrightarrow{AB} \parallel \overleftrightarrow{YZ}$ by the Converse of the Parallel Lines Conjecture.

20. Set the screw so that the shorter lengths of the styluses are three-fourths as long as the longer lengths. The two isosceles triangles will always be similar because their vertex angles are congruent vertical angles.

21. $x \approx 4.6$ cm, $y \approx 3.4$ cm. The two transversals to the parallel lines can be extended until they intersect, forming a triangle, so you can apply the Extended Parallel/Proportionality Conjecture.

$$\frac{3}{7} = \frac{y}{8} \qquad\qquad \frac{7}{4} = \frac{8}{x}$$

$$y = 8 \cdot \frac{3}{7} \qquad\qquad 7x = 32$$

$$y = \frac{24}{7} \approx 3.4 \text{ cm} \qquad x = \frac{32}{7} \approx 4.6 \text{ cm}$$

22. $x = 45$ ft, $y = 40$ ft, $z = 35$ ft. Apply the Extended Parallel/Proportionality Conjecture.

Road frontage $= 36 + 32 + 28 = 96$ ft

The ratio of road footage to river footage is $\frac{120}{96} = \frac{5}{4}$.

$$\frac{x}{36} = \frac{5}{4} \qquad \frac{y}{32} = \frac{5}{4} \qquad \frac{z}{28} = \frac{5}{4}$$

$$x = 36 \cdot \frac{5}{4} \qquad y = 32 \cdot \frac{5}{4} \qquad z = 28 \cdot \frac{5}{4}$$

$$x = 45 \text{ ft} \qquad y = 40 \text{ ft} \qquad z = 35 \text{ ft}$$

23. $\frac{343}{729}$. Let $\frac{m}{n}$ represent the ratio of side lengths of the two cubes (smaller to larger). Then $\frac{49}{81} = \left(\frac{m}{n}\right)^2$, so $\frac{m}{n} = \frac{7}{9}$ (Proportional Areas Conjecture), and therefore the ratio of the volumes of the two cubes is $\left(\frac{7}{9}\right)^3 = \frac{343}{729}$ (Proportional Volumes Conjecture).

24. She is incorrect. She can make only nine 8 cm diameter spheres.

Small cookies: $d = 4$ cm, $r = 2$ cm

Large cookies: $d = 8$ cm, $r = 4$ cm

$$\frac{\text{Radius of large cookie}}{\text{Radius of small cookie}} = \frac{4 \text{ cm}}{2 \text{ cm}} = \frac{2}{1}$$

By the Proportional Volumes Conjecture, the ratio of corresponding volumes is $\left(\frac{2}{1}\right)^3 = \frac{8}{1}$. Therefore, it will take 8 times as much dough to make 36 cannonballs with 8 cm diameter as with 4 cm diameter, but doubling the recipe gives only twice as much dough. Thus, she can make only $\frac{1}{4}$ as many large cannonballs as small ones: $\frac{1}{4}(36) = 9$.

25. $6x^2$; $24x^2$; $54x^2$. Each face of a cube is a square whose area is the square of the edge length, and every cube has six congruent square faces.

Edge x: Surface area $= 6x^2$

Edge $2x$: Surface area $= 6(2x)^2 = 6(4x^2) = 24x^2$

Edge $3x$: Surface area $= 6(3x)^2 = 6(9x^2) = 54x^2$

26. $\frac{1}{3}\pi r$. The chord and the two radii that meet the circle at the endpoints of the minor arc form an equilateral triangle, so the central angle is 60°.

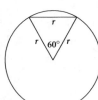

Let C represent the circumference of the circle.

Arc length $= \frac{60}{360}C = \frac{1}{6}(2\pi r) = \frac{1}{3}\pi r$

27. a. Possible construction method: Use the triangle-and-circle construction from Lesson 11.3, Exercise 18 to locate the golden cut, X, of $\overline{AB}$. Then use perpendicular lines and circles to create a rectangle with length AB and width AX.

b. Possible construction method: Construct golden rectangle $ABCD$ following the method from 27a. For square $AEFD$, locate $\overline{EF}$ by constructing circle A and circle D each with radius AD. Repeat the process of cutting off squares as often as desired. For the golden spiral from point D to point E, construct circle F with radius EF; select point D, point E, and circle F, and choose **Arc On Circle** from the Construct menu.

28. Possible proof:

Given: Circumscribed quadrilateral $ABCD$, with points of tangency P, Q, R, and S

Show: $AB + DC = AD + BC$

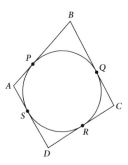

If you use segment addition, you can show that each sum of the lengths of opposite sides is composed of four lengths, $AB + CD = (AP + BP) + (DR + CR)$ and $AD + BC = (AS + DS) + (BQ + CQ)$. By the Tangent Segment Conjecture, you know that $AP = AS$, $BP = BQ$, $CR = CQ$, and $DR = DS$, and the four lengths in each sum are equivalent. Here are the algebraic steps to show that the whole sums are equivalent.

$AB + DC = (AP + BP)$ $+ (DR + CR)$	Segment addition.
$= (AS + BQ)$ $+ (DS + CQ)$	Substitute AS for AP, BQ for BP, DS for DR, and CQ for CR.
$= (AS + DS)$ $+ (BQ + CQ)$	Regroup the measurements by common points of tangency.
$AB + CD = AD + BC$	Use segment addition to rewrite the right side as the other sum of opposite sides.

29.

IMPROVING YOUR VISUAL THINKING SKILLS

A.   **B.** 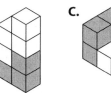 **C.**

D. This shape cannot be made.

EXTENSIONS

A. See the solutions to Take Another Look activities 6 and 7 on page 254.

B. If $\ell \parallel \overline{LU}$, then $\triangle LUV \sim \triangle MTV$ by the AA Similarity Conjecture.

If $\triangle LUV \sim \triangle MTV$, then $\frac{a + b}{a} = \frac{c + d}{c}$.

If $\frac{a + b}{a} = \frac{c + d}{c}$, then $\frac{a}{b} = \frac{c}{d}$.

Possible completion of proof:

$$\frac{a + b}{a} = \frac{c + d}{c}$$
$$\frac{a}{a} + \frac{b}{a} = \frac{c}{c} + \frac{d}{c}$$
$$1 + \frac{b}{a} = 1 + \frac{d}{c}$$
$$\frac{b}{a} = \frac{d}{c}, \text{ so } \frac{a}{b} = \frac{c}{d}$$

EXPLORATION · TWO MORE FORMS OF VALID REASONING

EXTENSION

Investigation results will vary.

CHAPTER 11 REVIEW

EXERCISES

1. $x = 24$. $15 = 3(5)$, so $x = 3(8) = 24$.

2. $x = 66$. Multiply both sides of the given proportion by the product of the denominators, $11x$.

$$11x \cdot \frac{4}{11} = 11x \cdot \frac{24}{x}$$
$$4x = 264$$
$$x = 66$$

3. $x = \pm 6$. Multiply both sides of the given proportion by the product of the denominators, $9x$.

$$9x \cdot \frac{4}{x} = 9x \cdot \frac{x}{9}$$
$$36 = x^2$$
$$x = \pm 6$$

4. $x = 17$. Writing $\frac{34}{40}$ in lowest terms as $\frac{17}{20}$ allows you to work with smaller numbers.

$$\frac{x}{x + 3} = \frac{17}{20}$$
$$20(x + 3) \cdot \frac{x}{x + 3} = 20(x + 3) \cdot \frac{17}{20}$$
$$20x = 17(x + 3)$$
$$20x = 17x + 51$$
$$3x = 51$$
$$x = 17$$

5. $w = 6$ cm, $x = 4.5$ cm, $y = 7.5$ cm, $z = 3$ cm. $ABCDE \sim FGHIJ$, so corresponding sides are proportional.

$$\frac{AB}{FG} = \frac{BC}{GH} = \frac{CD}{HI} = \frac{DE}{IJ} = \frac{AE}{FJ}$$
$$\frac{6}{9} = \frac{4}{w} = \frac{3}{x} = \frac{5}{y} = \frac{2}{z}$$
$$\frac{2}{3} = \frac{4}{w} = \frac{3}{x} = \frac{5}{y} = \frac{2}{z}$$

From $\frac{4}{w} = \frac{2}{3}$, $w = 6$ cm.

From $\frac{3}{x} = \frac{2}{3}$, $x = \frac{9}{2} = 4.5$ cm.

From $\frac{5}{y} = \frac{2}{3}$, $y = \frac{15}{2} = 7.5$ cm.

From $\frac{2}{z} = \frac{2}{3}$, $z = 3$ cm.

6. $x = 4\frac{1}{6}$ cm, $y = 7\frac{1}{2}$ cm. $\triangle ABC \sim \triangle DBA$, so corresponding sides are proportional.

$$\frac{AB}{DB} = \frac{BC}{BA} = \frac{AC}{DA}$$

$$\frac{5}{x} = \frac{6}{5} = \frac{9}{y}$$

From $\frac{5}{x} = \frac{6}{5}$, $6x = 25$, and $x = \frac{25}{6} = 4\frac{1}{6}$ cm.

From $\frac{6}{5} = \frac{9}{y}$, $6y = 45$, and $y = \frac{45}{6} = 7\frac{1}{2}$ cm.

7. 13 ft 2 in. First change 5 ft 8 in. to $5\frac{2}{3}$ ft, 11 ft 3 in. to $11\frac{1}{4}$ ft, and 8 ft 6 in. to $8\frac{1}{2}$ ft. Let h represent the height of the tree. Use the similar right triangles to write a proportion; then solve the proportion to find h.

$$\frac{h}{11\frac{1}{4} + 8\frac{1}{2}} = \frac{5\frac{2}{3}}{8\frac{1}{2}}$$

$$\frac{h}{19\frac{3}{4}} = \frac{5\frac{2}{3}}{8\frac{1}{2}}$$

$$\frac{h}{\frac{79}{4}} = \frac{\frac{17}{3}}{\frac{17}{2}} = \frac{17}{3} \cdot \frac{2}{17} = \frac{2}{3}$$

$$\frac{h}{\frac{79}{4}} = \frac{2}{3}$$

$$h = \frac{79}{4} \cdot \frac{2}{3} = \frac{158}{12} = 13\frac{1}{6} \text{ ft} = 13 \text{ ft 2 in.}$$

8. It would still be a 20° angle. A dilation doesn't change angle measures.

9. The method from Lesson 11.7, Example C can be used to divide $\overline{KL}$ into seven equal lengths. However, once you have constructed the segment that connects the point where the seventh arc intersects the ray to L, it is necessary only to connect the point where the third of the seven arcs intersects the ray with $\overline{KL}$ by constructing a parallel line. Let P be the point where this line intersects $\overline{KL}$. Then $KP = \frac{3}{7}(KL)$ and $PL = \frac{4}{7}(KL)$, so $\frac{KP}{KL} = \frac{3}{4}$.

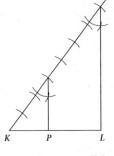

10. Yes. If two triangles are congruent, then corresponding angles are congruent and corresponding sides are proportional with a ratio of $\frac{1}{1}$, so the triangles are similar.

11. 15 m. Make a sketch.

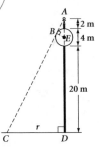

$\triangle ABE \sim \triangle ADC$ by the AA Similarity Conjecture. ($\angle A$ is a common angle, and each triangle has a right angle.)

$$\frac{AB}{BE} = \frac{AD}{CD}$$

$$\frac{2\sqrt{3}}{2} = \frac{26}{r}$$

$$\sqrt{3} = \frac{26}{r}$$

$$r\sqrt{3} = 26$$

$$r = \frac{26}{\sqrt{3}} \approx 15 \text{ m}$$

12. 4 gal; 8 times. The ratio of corresponding edges of the boxes (larger to smaller) is $\frac{2}{1}$, so the ratio of surface areas is $\left(\frac{2}{1}\right)^2 = \frac{4}{1}$ (Proportional Areas Conjecture), and the ratio of volumes is $\left(\frac{2}{1}\right)^3 = \frac{8}{1}$. Therefore, Lucy's box will have 4 times the surface area of Charlie's box, so she will need 4 gal of paint, and her box has 8 times the volume of his box.

13. Possible answer: You would measure the height and weight of the real clothespin and the height of the sculpture.

$$\frac{W_{\text{sculpture}}}{W_{\text{clothespin}}} = \left(\frac{H_{\text{sculpture}}}{H_{\text{clothespin}}}\right)^3$$

If you don't know the height of the sculpture, you could estimate it from this photo by setting up a ratio, for example,

$$\frac{H_{\text{person}}}{H_{\text{person's photo}}} = \frac{H_{\text{sculpture}}}{H_{\text{sculpture's photo}}}$$

14. 9:49. The ratio of the lengths of the corresponding sides is equal to the ratio of the perimeters because the perimeter is the sum of the lengths of the sides. Therefore, the ratio of the lengths of corresponding sides is, 3:7 or $\frac{3}{7}$, so, by the Proportional Areas Conjecture, the ratio of the areas of the two parallelograms (smaller to larger) is $\left(\frac{3}{7}\right)^2 = \frac{9}{49}$.

15. $\frac{5}{4}$, $\frac{125}{64}$. By the Proportional Areas Conjecture, the ratio of the radii is $\sqrt{\frac{25}{16}} = \frac{5}{4}$. By the Proportional Volumes Conjecture, the ratio of the volumes is $\left(\frac{5}{4}\right)^3 = \frac{125}{64}$.

16. $266.67. The ratio of corresponding sides of the Smith deck to the Jones deck is $\frac{16}{12} = \frac{20}{15} = \frac{4}{3}$. Therefore, the ratio of the areas of the decks is $\left(\frac{4}{3}\right)^2 = \frac{16}{9}$. Let S represent the cost of staining the Smith family's deck.

$$\frac{S}{150} = \frac{16}{9}$$

$$150 \cdot \frac{S}{150} = 150 \cdot \frac{16}{9}$$

$$S = \frac{800}{3} \approx 266.67$$

It will cost the Smith family $266.67 to have their deck stained.

17. 640π cm^3. Use the Proportional Volumes Conjecture. The ratio of the dimensions of the small cylinder to the large cylinder is $\frac{2}{3}$.

$$\frac{\text{Volume of small cylinder}}{\text{Volume of large cylinder}} = \left(\frac{2}{3}\right)^3 = \frac{8}{27}$$

Let V represent the volume of the small cylinder.

$$\frac{8}{27} = \frac{V}{2160\pi}$$

$2160\pi = 80\pi \cdot 27$, so $V = 80\pi \cdot 8 = 640\pi$ cm^2.

18. $w = 32$, $x = 24$, $y = 40$, $z = 126$. Apply the Extended Parallel/Proportionality Conjecture to find w, x, and y.

$$\frac{36}{24} = \frac{48}{w}$$

$$\frac{3}{2} = \frac{48}{w}$$

$48 = 16 \cdot 3$, so $w = 16 \cdot 2 = 32$.

$$\frac{36}{18} = \frac{48}{x}$$

$$\frac{2}{1} = \frac{48}{x}$$

$$x = 24$$

$$\frac{36}{30} = \frac{48}{y}$$

$$\frac{6}{5} = \frac{48}{y}$$

$48 = 8 \cdot 6$, so $y = 8 \cdot 5 = 40$.

The small triangle at the top of the figure (with base of length 42) is similar to the large triangle (with base of length z). Use a proportion based on this similarity to find z.

$$\frac{36 + 24 + 18 + 30}{z} = \frac{36}{42}$$

$$\frac{108}{z} = \frac{6}{7}$$

$108 = 18 \cdot 6$, so $z = 18 \cdot 7 = 126$.

19. 841 coconuts. Apply the Proportional Areas Conjecture.

$$\frac{\text{Height of statue}}{\text{Height of statuette}} = \frac{58}{2} = \frac{29}{1}$$

$$\frac{\text{Surface area of statue}}{\text{Surface area of statuette}} = \left(\frac{29}{1}\right)^2 = \frac{841}{1}$$

Because it will take the milk of one coconut to cover the surface of the statuette, it will take 841 coconuts to cover the surface of the full-size statue.

20. Because you are concerned with ratios in 20a and 20b, it doesn't make any difference what lengths you choose. For convenience, assign the square a side length of 2 before calculating areas and volumes. Then the radius of the circle is 1, and the base and height of the triangle are each 2.

a. 1 to $\frac{\pi}{4}$ to $\frac{1}{2}$, or 4 to π to 2. Find the areas of the square, the circle, and the triangle, using 2 as the side length of the square.

Area of square $= 2 \cdot 2 = 4$ square units

Area of circle $= \pi \cdot (1)^2 = \pi$ square units

Area of triangle $= \frac{1}{2}(2)(2) = 2$ square units

Area of square : Area of circle : Area of triangle is $4 : \pi : 2$, or $1 : \frac{\pi}{4} : \frac{1}{2}$.

b. 3 to 2 to 1. The cylinder has radius 1 and height 2, the sphere has radius 1, and the cone has radius 1 and height 2.

Volume of cylinder $= \pi r^2 H = \pi(1)^2(2)$
$$= 2\pi \text{ cubic units}$$

Volume of sphere $= \frac{4}{3}\pi r^3 = \frac{4}{3}\pi(1)^3$
$$= \frac{4}{3}\pi \text{ cubic units}$$

Volume of cone $= \frac{1}{3}\pi r^2 H = \frac{1}{3}\pi(1)^2(2)$
$$= \frac{2}{3}\pi \text{ cubic units}$$

Compare these volumes.

$$\frac{2\pi}{\frac{4}{3}\pi} = \frac{2}{\frac{4}{3}} = \frac{2}{1} \cdot \frac{3}{4} = \frac{3}{2}$$

$$\frac{2\pi}{\frac{2}{3}\pi} = \frac{2}{\frac{2}{3}} = \frac{2}{1} \cdot \frac{3}{2} = \frac{3}{1}$$

Therefore, the ratio of the volume of the cylinder to the volume of the sphere to the volume of the cone is $3 : 2 : 1$.

c. Possible answer: It represents the 3 : 2 : 1 ratio of the volumes of the cylinder, sphere, and cone.

21. Possible answer: If food is proportional to body volume, then $\frac{1}{8000}$ of the usual amount of food is required. If clothing is proportional to surface area, then $\frac{1}{400}$ of the usual amount of clothing is required. It would take 20 times longer to walk a given distance.

22. The ice cubes would melt faster because they have greater surface area.

TAKE ANOTHER LOOK

1. This rule describes a dilation by a factor of k followed by a translation by (b, c).

2. For each vertex, draw a ray from point A through the vertex. Mark off a point on the ray whose distance from point A is the scale factor times the distance of the vertex from point A. The coordinates of the vertices are not multiplied by the scale factor, but the lengths of the sides are.

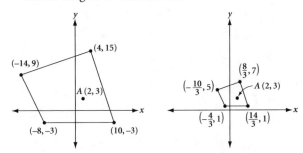

3. This is true by the Angle Bisector/Opposite Side Conjecture.

4. Figure A shows the positions of the Moon and the Sun during a total eclipse, relative to an observer at point A. The Moon blocks all of the Sun except the Sun's corona from Earth's view. $\triangle ABC \sim \triangle ADE$ by the AA Similarity Conjecture. AB is the approximate distance from Earth to the Moon. BC is the approximate diameter of the Moon. AD is the approximate distance from Earth to the Sun. DE is the approximate diameter of the Sun. (*Note:* The figures on the next page are not drawn to scale. Because the actual distances are so great, relative to the diameters, don't worry that $\overline{AB}$ and $\overline{AD}$ are not precisely tangent to the spheres of the Moon and the Sun; nor will we worry about what points on the Moon and the Sun we use in measuring the distance from Earth.)

By similar triangles, $\frac{AB}{BC} = \frac{AD}{DE}$. If the Moon were smaller (or farther away), these ratios wouldn't be equal—the Moon wouldn't block all of the Sun's

light (Figure B). If the Moon were larger (or closer), it would block an area larger than that of the Sun— we wouldn't be able to see the Sun's corona during an eclipse (Figure C).

The combination of the Moon's distance and diameter makes it fit "just right" in front of the Sun during a total eclipse.

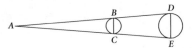

Figure A

Figure B

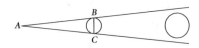

Figure C

5. Possible answers include any two triangles, one of whose sides have lengths a, b, and c, with the sides of the other having lengths b, c, and $\frac{c^2}{b}$. If one similar triangle has side lengths a, b, and c, then the other triangle has side lengths ar, br, and cr, where r is the scale factor. Because two sides must be congruent without the triangles being congruent, let $b = ar$ and $c = rb$. Then $c = ar \cdot r = ar^2$. To find values of r for which this relationship holds, use the Triangle Inequality Conjecture. $a + b > c$, $a + ar > ar^2$. (Similar equations that reduce to this occur for other pairs of sides.) Solve the inequality:

$$r < \frac{1 + \sqrt{5}}{2}$$

In other words, r must be less than the golden ratio.

6. The converse is not true. One counterexample:

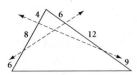

7. Conjecture: If three sides of one triangle are parallel to the three sides of another triangle, then the triangles are similar.

Proof: Extend all sides so that they intersect. Then for each angle, apply the Corresponding Angles Conjecture twice.

CHAPTER 12

LESSON 12.1

EXERCISES

1. 0.6018

2. 0.8746

3. 0.1405

4. 11.57. $\sin 40° = \frac{x}{18}$, so $x = 18\sin 40° \approx 11.57$.

5. 30.86. $\cos 52° = \frac{19}{x}$, so $x\cos 52° = 19$, and $x = \frac{19}{\cos 52°} \approx 30.86$.

6. 62.08. $\tan 29° = \frac{x}{112}$, so $x = 112\tan 29° \approx 62.08$.

7. $\sin A = \frac{s}{t}$; $\cos A = \frac{r}{t}$; $\tan A = \frac{s}{r}$. The length of the side opposite $\angle A$ is s, the length of the side adjacent to $\angle A$ is r, and the length of the hypotenuse is t.

8. $\sin \theta = \frac{4}{5}$; $\cos \theta = \frac{3}{5}$; $\tan \theta = \frac{4}{3}$. The right triangle has horizontal leg of length 6, vertical leg of length 8, and hypotenuse of length 10, so $\sin \theta = \frac{8}{10} = \frac{4}{5}$, $\cos \theta = \frac{6}{10} = \frac{3}{5}$, and $\tan \theta = \frac{8}{6} = \frac{4}{3}$.

9. $\sin A = \frac{7}{25}$; $\cos A = \frac{24}{25}$; $\tan A = \frac{7}{24}$; $\sin B = \frac{24}{25}$; $\cos B = \frac{7}{25}$; $\tan B = \frac{24}{7}$. To find that the length of the hypotenuse is 25, use the Pythagorean Theorem, or recall that 7-24-25 is a Pythagorean triple.

10. 30°. $A = \sin^{-1}(0.5) = 30°$.

11. 53°. $B = \cos^{-1}(0.6) \approx 53°$.

12. 30°. $C = \tan^{-1}(0.5773) \approx 30°$.

13. 24°. $x = \tan^{-1}\left(\frac{48}{106}\right) \approx 24°$.

14. $a \approx 35$ cm. $\tan 30° = \frac{20}{a}$, so $a\tan 30° = 20$, and $a = \frac{20}{\tan 30°} \approx 35$ cm.

15. $b \approx 15$ cm. $\sin 65° = \frac{b}{17}$, so $b = 17\sin 65° \approx 15$ cm.

16. $c \approx 105$ yd. $\cos 70° = \frac{36}{c}$, so $c\cos 70° = 36$, and $c = \frac{36}{\cos 70°} \approx 105$ yd.

17. $d \approx 40°$. $\tan d = \frac{107}{128}$, so $d = \tan^{-1}\left(\frac{107}{128}\right) \approx 40°$.

18. $e \approx 50$ cm. $\cos 15° = \frac{48}{e}$, so $e\cos 15° = 48$, and $e = \frac{48}{\cos 15°} \approx 50$ cm.

19. $f \approx 33°$. $\sin f = \frac{36}{66}$, so $f = \sin^{-1}\left(\frac{36}{66}\right) \approx 33°$.

20. $g \approx 18$ in. The radius of the circle is 21 in., so the diameter is 42 in. The angle opposite the diameter shown in the figure is a right angle because every angle inscribed in a semicircle is a right angle. Therefore, the triangle is a right triangle with hypotenuse of length 42 in. Then $\sin 25° = \frac{g}{42}$, so $g = 42\sin 25° \approx 18$ in.

21. Approximately 237 m. Let b represent the length of the base of the quadrilateral (which is a rectangle) and h represent the height. Find the length of the base and then the height: $\sin 35° = \frac{b}{85}$, so $b = 85(\sin 35°) \approx 48.75$ m, and $\cos 35° = \frac{h}{85}$, so $h = 85(\cos 35°) \approx 69.63$ cm. Then the perimeter of the rectangle is $2b + 2h \approx 2(48.75) + 2(69.63) \approx 237$ m.

22. $x \approx 121$ ft. x is not the length of a side of a right triangle, but you can find x by subtracting length a from length b in this figure.

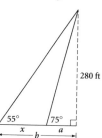

From the large right triangle, $\tan 55° = \frac{280}{b}$, so $b(\tan 55°) = 280$, and $b = \frac{280}{\tan 55°} \approx 196$ ft. From the small right triangle, $\tan 75° = \frac{280}{a}$, so $a(\tan 75°) = 280$, and $a = \frac{280}{\tan 75°} \approx 75$ ft. Therefore, $x \approx 196 - 75 = 121$ ft.

23. 6.375. To solve this proportion, multiply both sides by 3 to isolate x.

$$\frac{x}{3} = \frac{17}{8}$$
$$3 \cdot \frac{x}{3} = 3 \cdot \frac{17}{8}$$
$$x = \frac{51}{8} = 6.375$$

24. 2.2. To solve this proportion, multiply both sides by $11x$, the product of the two denominators.

$$\frac{5}{x} = \frac{25}{11}$$
$$11x \cdot \frac{5}{x} = 11x \cdot \frac{25}{11}$$
$$55 = 25x$$
$$x = \frac{55}{25} = \frac{11}{5} = 2.2$$

25. 16-inch pizza. The ratio of the diameters of the two pizzas is $\frac{20}{16} = \frac{5}{4}$, so the ratio of their radii is $\frac{5}{4}$. Therefore, by the Proportional Areas Conjecture, the ratio of their areas is $\left(\frac{5}{4}\right)^2 = \frac{25}{16}$. If the 20-inch pizza were exactly as good a buy as the 16-inch pizza, its price would be $\left(\frac{25}{16}\right)(\$12.50) = \$19.53$. But the price of the 20-inch pizza is \$20, so the 16-inch pizza is the better buy.

26. Box of ice cream. To find the better buy, you first need to find the volumes of the two containers. The radius of the cylinder is 3 in.

Volume of cylinder $= BH = \pi r^2 H = \pi(3)^2(8)$

$$= 72\pi \text{ in}^3$$

Volume of box (square prism) $= BH = (6 \cdot 6)(8)$

$$= 288 \text{ in}^3$$

$$\frac{\text{Volume of box}}{\text{Volume of cylinder}} = \frac{288}{72\pi}$$

If the box of ice cream were exactly as good a buy as the cylinder, the box would cost $\frac{288}{72\pi}(\$3.98) \approx$ $5.07. Because the actual cost of the box is only $4.98, the box of ice cream is the better buy.

27. $8\sqrt{3}$ cm ≈ 13.86 cm. Make a sketch. Draw radii to the endpoints of the chord and label the figure for reference.

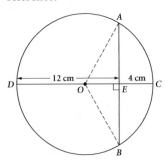

$DE + EC = 12 + 4 = 16$ cm. The diameter of the circle is 16 cm, so the radius is 8 cm. $\overline{OA}$ is a radius, so $OA = 8$ cm. Also, $\overline{OC}$ is a radius, so $OE = OC - EC = 8 - 4 = 4$ cm. Look at $\triangle OAE$. This is a right triangle with shorter leg of length 4 cm and hypotenuse of length 8 cm, so use the Pythagorean Theorem to find the length of the longer leg, AE. $4^2 + (AE)^2 = 8^2$, so $(AE)^2 = 64 - 16 = 48$, and $AE = \sqrt{48} = 4\sqrt{3}$ cm. By the same reasoning (or because $\triangle OAE \cong \triangle OBE$), $BE = 4\sqrt{3}$ cm. Therefore, $AB = 2(4\sqrt{3}) = 8\sqrt{3}$ cm ≈ 13.86 cm; that is, the length of the chord is about 13.86 cm.

28. $V = 288\pi$ ft$^3 \approx 904.8$ ft^3, $S = 144\pi$ ft$^2 \approx 452.4$ ft^2. Use the formulas for the volume and surface area of a sphere.

$$V = \frac{4}{3}\pi r^3 = \frac{4}{3}\pi(6)^3 = \frac{4}{3}\pi \cdot 216 = 288\pi \text{ ft}^3$$

$$S = 4\pi r^2 = 4\pi(6)^2 = 4\pi(36) = 144\pi \text{ ft}^2$$

IMPROVING YOUR VISUAL THINKING SKILLS

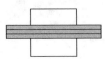

EXTENSIONS

A. Refer to the diagram at the top of page 642 in your book.

$$\text{cotangent of } \angle A = \frac{\text{length of side adjacent to } \angle A}{\text{length of side opposite } \angle A}$$

$$\text{or } \cot A = \frac{b}{a}$$

$$\text{secant of } \angle A = \frac{\text{length of hypotenuse}}{\text{length of side adjacent to } \angle A}$$

$$\text{or } \sec A = \frac{c}{b}$$

$$\text{cosecant of } \angle A = \frac{\text{length of hypotenuse}}{\text{length of side opposite } \angle A}$$

$$\text{or } \csc A = \frac{c}{a}$$

B. The completed table should show the sine, cosine, and tangent for angles measuring from 5° to 85° in 5° increments, with all values that are not exact rounded to the nearest thousandth. Here are the actual values: *(See table at bottom of page.)*

LESSON 12.2

EXERCISES

1. 9 cm. $\sin 32° = \frac{a}{17}$, so $a = 17(\sin 32°) \approx 9$ cm.

2. 64°. $\sin x = \frac{18}{20} = 0.9$, so $x = \sin^{-1}(0.9) \approx 64°$.

3. 7 cm. Every angle inscribed in a semicircle is a right angle, so the triangle in this figure is a right triangle whose hypotenuse is a diameter of the circle. The diameter of the circle is $2r$.

$$\cos 32° = \frac{12}{2r} = \frac{6}{r}$$

$$r(\cos 32°) = 6$$

$$r = \frac{6}{\cos 32°} \approx 7 \text{ cm}$$

Lesson 12.1, Extension B

Angle	5°	10°	15°	20°	25°	30°	35°	40°	45°	50°	55°	60°	65°	70°	75°	80°	85°
sin	0.087	0.174	0.259	0.342	0.423	0.500	0.574	0.643	0.707	0.766	0.819	0.866	0.906	0.940	0.966	0.985	0.996
cos	0.996	0.985	0.966	0.940	0.906	0.866	0.819	0.766	0.707	0.643	0.574	0.500	0.423	0.342	0.259	0.174	0.087
tan	0.087	0.176	0.268	0.364	0.466	0.577	0.700	0.839	1.00	1.19	1.43	1.73	2.14	2.75	3.73	5.67	11.4

4. 24 m. Draw a segment perpendicular to the two parallel lines, as shown below. Let d represent the length of this segment.

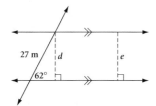

From the right triangle, $\sin 62° = \frac{d}{27}$, so $d = 27(\sin 62°) \approx 24$ m.

Look at the quadrilateral to the right of the triangle. One pair of opposite sides is marked as parallel. The other sides are also parallel by the Converse of the Parallel Lines Conjecture, using the right angles as congruent corresponding angles. Because of the right angles, this parallelogram is a rectangle. Opposite sides of a rectangle are congruent by the Parallelogram Opposite Sides Conjecture, so $e = d$. Thus, $e \approx 24$ m.

5. 22 in. The figure is a kite because it has exactly two distinct pairs of congruent consecutive sides. The Kite Diagonals Conjecture says that the diagonals of a kite are perpendicular, and the Kite Diagonal Bisector Conjecture says that the diagonal connecting the vertex angles of a kite is the perpendicular bisector of the other diagonal. Therefore, in this figure, the diagonals divide the kite into two pairs of congruent right triangles, and the shorter diagonal (of length d_1) is bisected by the longer one. Look at the triangle in the upper right. In this right triangle, the length of the hypotenuse is 20 in. and the length of the shorter leg is $\frac{1}{2}d_1$.

$$\cos 56° = \frac{\frac{1}{2}d_1}{20}$$

$$\frac{1}{2}d_1 = 20(\cos 56°)$$

$$d_1 = 40(\cos 56°) \approx 22 \text{ in.}$$

6. 49°. The large triangle is isosceles, and the segment of length 16 cm is the altitude to the base. The altitude to the base of any isosceles triangle bisects the base, so this altitude divides the isosceles triangle into two congruent right triangles each with legs of lengths 16 cm and 14 cm, and with the angle of measure f opposite the longer leg.

$$\tan f = \frac{16}{14} = \frac{8}{7}$$

$$f = \tan^{-1}\left(\frac{8}{7}\right) \approx 49°$$

7. 127°. Look at the right triangle inside the cone. Let α represent the measure of the larger acute angle of the right triangle (the angle opposite the 16-meter side). $\tan \alpha = \frac{16}{12} = \frac{4}{3}$, so $\alpha =$

$\tan^{-1}\left(\frac{4}{3}\right) \approx 53°$. The angles with measures α and θ form a linear pair, so $\alpha \approx 180° - 53° \approx 127°$.

Another way to find θ is to first find the measure of the smaller acute angle of the right triangle. Let β represent this angle measure. Then $\tan \beta = \frac{12}{16} = \frac{3}{4} = 0.75$, so $\beta = \tan^{-1}(0.75) \approx 37°$. The angle of measure θ is an exterior angle of the right triangle, so, by the Triangle Exterior Angle Conjecture, $\theta = \beta + 90° \approx 37° + 90° \approx 127°$.

8. 30°. First look at the base of the rectangular prism. The sides of this rectangular base have lengths 8 ft and 15 ft, so the length of the diagonal is 17 ft by the Pythagorean Theorem. (You may recall that 8-15-17 is a Pythagorean triple.) Now look at the right triangle inside the prism, with legs of lengths 10 ft and 17 ft. In this triangle, the angle of measure β is opposite the 10-foot side, so $\tan \beta = \frac{10}{17}$ and $\beta = \tan^{-1}\left(\frac{10}{17}\right) \approx 30°$.

9. 64 cm. $\tan 58° = \frac{h}{40}$, so $h = 40(\tan 58°) \approx 64$ cm.

10. Approximately 655 m. Let x represent the distance between General Han Xin's position and the palace. Make a sketch.

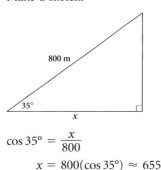

$$\cos 35° = \frac{x}{800}$$

$$x = 800(\cos 35°) \approx 655$$

The palace was approximately 655 m from General Han Xin's position.

11. Approximately 101 m. Let h represent the height of the kite. Make a sketch.

$$\tan 39° = \frac{h}{125}$$

$$h = 125(\tan 39°) \approx 101$$

The height of Benny's kite is approximately 101 m.

12. Approximately 65 m. Let y represent the distance between the ship and the shore.

$$\tan 33° = \frac{42}{y}$$

$$y(\tan 33°) = 42$$

$$y = \frac{42}{\tan 33°} \approx 65$$

The ship is approximately 65 m from the shore.

13. Approximately 188 m. Let d represent the distance that the diver needs to walk along the ocean floor to the wreckage. Make a sketch.

Because the angle of depression from the ship to the wreckage is 12°, the angle of elevation from the wreckage to the ship is also 12°. (The angle of depression is equal to the angle of elevation because these are alternate interior angles formed when two parallel lines are cut by a transversal. See the diagram at the top of page 647 in your book.)

$$\tan 12° = \frac{40}{d}$$

$$d(\tan 12°) = 40$$

$$d = \frac{40}{\tan 12°} \approx 188$$

The diver has to walk approximately 188 m along the ocean floor to the wreckage.

14. Approximately 1621 m. Let d represent the distance between the ship and the lighthouse at the second sighting.

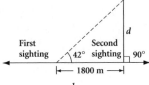

$$\tan 42° = \frac{d}{1800}$$

$$d = 1800(\tan 42°) \approx 1621 \text{ m}$$

15. Approximately 1570 m. Let h represent the height of the clouds. Make a sketch.

$$\tan 84° = \frac{h}{165}$$

$$h = 165(\tan 84°) \approx 1570 \text{ m}$$

The clouds are approximately 1570 m high.

16. Let h represent the height of the balloon *above* the level of the tripod (where the theodolite is placed) and d represent the horizontal distance along the ground from a point directly below the tripod to a point directly below the balloon. Make a sketch.

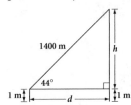

a. Approximately 974 m

$$\sin 44° = \frac{h}{1400}$$

$$h = 1400(\sin 44°) \approx 973$$

Because the tripod is 1 m tall, the balloon is $h + 1 \approx 974$ m high.

b. Approximately 1007 m

$$\cos 44° = \frac{d}{1400}$$

$$d = 1400(\cos 44°) \approx 1007$$

She is approximately 1007 m from a point directly below the balloon.

c. Yes, the height of the balloon would be 1 m less because you don't have to account for the tripod. The distance to a point under the balloon would not change.

17. 45°. $D = \sin^{-1}(0.7071) \approx 45°$

18. 60°. $E = \tan^{-1}(1.7321) \approx 60°$

19. 60°. $F = \cos^{-1}(0.5) = 60°$

20. a. 15.04. $4.7 = \frac{x}{3.2}$, so $x = 4.7(3.2) = 15.04$.

b. 2.05. $8 = \frac{16.4}{x}$, so $8x = 16.4$, and $x = \frac{16.4}{8} = 2.05$.

c. 5.2304. $0.3736 = \frac{x}{14}$, so $x = 14(0.3736) = 5.2304$.

d. ≈ 2.644. $0.9455 = \frac{2.5}{x}$, so $0.9455x = 2.5$, and $x = \frac{2.5}{0.9455} \approx 2.644$.

21. $x = 3.5$; $y = 9\frac{1}{7} \approx 9.14$. Label the points in the figure for reference.

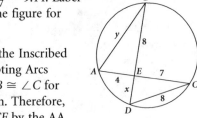

$\angle A \cong \angle D$ by the Inscribed Angles Intercepting Arcs Conjecture. $\angle B \cong \angle C$ for the same reason. Therefore, $\triangle ABE \sim \triangle DCE$ by the AA Similarity Conjecture. (You could also use the vertical angles as a pair of congruent angles.) Because the triangles are similar, corresponding sides are proportional.

$$\frac{AB}{DC} = \frac{BE}{CE} = \frac{AE}{DE}$$

$$\frac{y}{8} = \frac{8}{7} = \frac{4}{x}$$

From $\frac{8}{7} = \frac{4}{x}$, $8x = 28$, so $x = \frac{28}{8} = 3.5$.

From $\frac{y}{8} = \frac{8}{7}$, $y = \frac{64}{7} = 9\frac{1}{7} \approx 9.14$.

22. The block has a volume of 90 cm³, but it displaces only 62.8 cm³ of water. So not all of the block is under water, which means it floats.

Volume of block (rectangular prism) = $(3)(5)(6)$

$$= 90 \text{ cm}^3$$

Volume of displaced water = volume of cylinder with radius 5 cm and height 0.8 cm = $\pi r^2 H = \pi(5)^2(0.8) = 20\pi \approx 62.8 \text{ cm}^3$

23. $CZ < AX < BY$. $\overline{AX}$ is the altitude to $\overline{BC}$, $\overline{BY}$ is the altitude to $\overline{AC}$, and $\overline{CZ}$ is the altitude to $\overline{AB}$.

Discovering Geometry Solutions Manual
©2008 Key Curriculum Press

For any choice of base, the area of the triangle must be the same. Therefore, the area of $\triangle ABC$ is $\frac{1}{2}(AB)(CZ) = \frac{1}{2}(BC)(AX) = \frac{1}{2}(AC)(BY)$. Multiply by 2 to get $(AB)(CZ) = (BC)(AX) = (AC)(BY)$. Because the product of base and height must be the same for all three base-height pairs, the longest base must go with the shortest altitude, the middle-length base with the middle-length altitude, and the shortest base with the longest altitude. Because $AB > BC > AC$, the lengths of the altitudes are related by the inequality $CZ < AX < BY$.

24. **a.** decreases, approaching 0

b. decreases, approaching 0

c. remains 90°

d. increases, approaching $(AO)^2$

e. decreases, approaching 1

f. decreases, approaching 1

25. $R(8, 7)$ and $E(3, 9)$, or $R(4, -3)$ and $E(-1, -1)$. One way to find the two possible squares $SQRE$ is to make a careful drawing on graph paper. Draw $\overline{SQ}$ and then draw the two squares that have $\overline{SQ}$ as a side. (You can use a ruler and protractor to draw the squares, using the protractor to draw right angles and the ruler to copy $\overline{SQ}$. You can also construct the squares with compass and straightedge.)

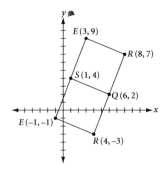

From this diagram, you can see that one of the possible squares with consecutive vertices $S(1, 4)$ and $Q(6, 2)$ has vertices $R(8, 7)$ and $E(3, 9)$, and the other has vertices $R(4, -3)$ and $E(-1, -1)$.

Another approach is to use the facts that the slopes of perpendicular lines are opposite reciprocals of each other and that all sides of a square have the same length to compute the possible coordinates for R and E.

To go from S to Q, move right 5 units and down 2 units.

Upper square: From $S(1, 4)$, move right 2 units and up 5 units to $E(3, 9)$. From $Q(6, 2)$, move right 2 units and up 5 units to $R(8, 7)$.

Lower square: From $S(1, 4)$, move left 2 units and down 5 units to $E(-1, -1)$. From $Q(6, 2)$, move left 2 units and down 5 units to $R(4, -3)$.

PROJECT

Project should satisfy the following criteria:

- Project includes research, narrative, drawings, and a model appropriate for the latitude.

- In climates with greater temperature extremes: The overhang should keep sunshine off the windows in the summer but allow it to hit the windows in the winter.

- In a tropical climate: Windows on the south and west sides of the model should be smaller and higher, or a covered patio could be attached to the house so that the sun's rays never hit the windows.

EXTENSION

Possible solution: Climb or fly to a point that's, say, 3 miles high, and measure the angle between the horizon and the vertical. Because your line of sight to the horizon is a tangent line perpendicular to a radius, the sine of that angle is $\frac{r}{r+3}$.

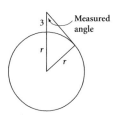

EXPLORATION · INDIRECT MEASUREMENT

IMPROVING YOUR VISUAL THINKING SKILLS

It takes four of the shapes to make a square.

LESSON 12.3

EXERCISES

1. 329 cm². Use the SAS Triangle Area Conjecture with $a = 29$ cm, $b = 25$ cm, and $C = 65°$.
$$A = \frac{1}{2}ab \sin C = \frac{1}{2}(29)(25)\sin 65° \approx 329 \text{ cm}^2$$

2. 4 cm². Use the SAS Triangle Area Conjecture with $a = 3.1$ cm, $b = 3.1$ cm, and $C = 50°$.
$$A = \frac{1}{2}ab \sin C = \frac{1}{2}(3.1)(3.1)\sin 50° \approx 4 \text{ cm}^2$$

3. 11,839 cm². Divide the quadrilateral into two triangles by drawing the diagonal connecting the two angles whose measures are not given. Use the SAS Triangle Area Conjecture to find the area of each triangle and then add the results.

Area of triangle with sides of lengths 124 cm and 115 cm and included angle of 78°:

$A = \frac{1}{2}ab \sin C = \frac{1}{2}(124)(115)\sin 78° \approx 6974$ cm^2

Area of triangle with sides of lengths 95 cm and 104 cm and included angle of 100°:

$A = \frac{1}{2}ab \sin C = \frac{1}{2}(95)(104)\sin 100° \approx 4865$ cm^2

Area of quadrilateral $\approx 6{,}974 + 4{,}865 = 11{,}839$ cm^2

4. 407 cm^2. The figure is a regular octagon inscribed in a circle. Draw radii from the center to each vertex of the octagon to form eight congruent isosceles triangles. Each of these triangles has vertex angle of $\frac{360°}{8} = 45°$ and legs of length 12 cm. The area of each triangle is $\frac{1}{2}(12)(12)\sin 45° = 72(\sin 45°)$, so the area of the octagon is $8 \cdot 72(\sin 45°) = 576(\sin 45°) \approx 407$ cm^2.

5. 35 cm. Use the Law of Sines with $a = 28$ cm, $b = w$, $A = 52°$, and $B = 79°$. Start with the Law of Sines and solve for b. (This was also done in Example B on page 656 in your book.)

$\frac{\sin A}{a} = \frac{\sin B}{b}$

$b \sin A = a \sin B$

$b = \frac{a \sin B}{\sin A}$

$w = \frac{28 \sin 79°}{\sin 52°} \approx 35$ cm

6. 17 cm. Use the Law of Sines with $a = 12$ cm, $b = x$, $A = 37°$, and $B = 58°$. Use the expression for b found in Exercise 5.

$b = \frac{a \sin B}{\sin A}$

$x = \frac{12 \sin 58°}{\sin 37°} \approx 17$ cm

7. 30 cm. By the Triangle Sum Conjecture, the missing angle measure is $180° - 46° - 87° = 47°$. Use the Law of Sines with $a = 41$ cm, $b = y$, $A = 87°$, and $B = 47°$. Use the expression for b found in Exercise 5.

$b = \frac{a \sin B}{\sin A}$

$x = \frac{41 \sin 47°}{\sin 87°} \approx 30$ cm

8. 56°. Use the Law of Sines with $a = 36$ cm, $c = 29$ cm, and $C = 42°$. Start with the Law of Sines and solve for $\sin A$; then find A.

$\frac{\sin A}{a} = \frac{\sin C}{c}$

$\sin A = \frac{a \sin C}{c}$

$\sin A = \frac{36 \sin 42°}{29}$

$A = \sin^{-1}\left(\frac{36 \sin 42°}{29}\right)$

$A \approx 56°$

The measure of $\angle A$ is approximately 56°.

9. 45°. Use the Law of Sines with $a = 445$ m, $b = 325$ m, and $A = 77°$.

$\frac{\sin A}{a} = \frac{\sin B}{b}$

$\sin B = \frac{b \sin A}{a}$

$\sin B = \frac{325 \sin 77°}{445}$

$B = \sin^{-1}\left(\frac{325 \sin 77°}{445}\right) \approx 45$

$B \approx 45°$

The measure of $\angle B$ is approximately 45°.

10. 66°. You can't find $m\angle C$ directly with the Law of Sines because the length of its opposite side, $\overline{AB}$, is not given. Instead, use the Law of Sines to find $m\angle A$, and then use the result to find $m\angle C$.

$\frac{\sin A}{a} = \frac{\sin B}{b}$

$\sin A = \frac{a \sin B}{b}$

$\sin A = \frac{362 \sin 63°}{415}$

$A = \sin^{-1}\left(\frac{362 \sin 63°}{415}\right)$

$A \approx 51°$

By the Triangle Sum Conjecture, $m\angle A + m\angle B + m\angle C = 180°$, so $m\angle C = 180° - m\angle A - m\angle B \approx 180° - 51° - 63° = 66°$.

11. a. Approximately 2200 m. The distance between Alphonse and Beatrice is AB. Because $\overline{AB}$ is the side of $\triangle ABC$ opposite $\angle C$, its length can also be represented by c. Similarly, $\overline{BC}$ is the side opposite $\angle A$, so its length can be represented by a. By the Triangle Sum Conjecture, $m\angle A = 180° - 39° - 62° = 79°$.

$\frac{\sin A}{a} = \frac{\sin C}{c}$

$c \sin A = a \sin C$

$c = \frac{a \sin C}{\sin A}$

$c = \frac{2500 \sin 62°}{\sin 79°} \approx 2200$ m

b. Approximately 1600 m. The distance between Alphonse and Collette is AC. Because $\overline{AC}$ is the side of $\triangle ABC$ opposite $\angle B$, its length can also be represented by b.

$b = \frac{a \sin B}{\sin A}$

$b = \frac{2500 \sin 39°}{\sin 79°} \approx 1600$ m

c. Approximately 1400 m. Draw the altitude from A to $\overline{DC}$ to form two right triangles. Let h represent the length of this altitude. You can use either of these two right triangles to find h, which represents Alphonse's height in the balloon. From the triangle on the left, $\sin 39° = \frac{h}{c}$, so $h = c \sin 39° \approx 2200 \sin 39° \approx 1400$ m.

12. The other two walls were 300 ft and approximately 413 ft. The area was approximately 45,000 ft².

First by the Triangle Sum Conjecture, $m\angle C = 180° - 87° - 46.5° = 46.5°$. $\angle C \cong \angle A$, so $\triangle ABC$ is isosceles with $\overline{BC} \cong \overline{AB}$ by the Converse of the Isosceles Triangle Conjecture. Thus, $BC = AB = 300$ ft. Now use the Law of Sines to find AC.

$$\frac{\sin B}{AC} = \frac{\sin C}{AB}$$

$$AC \sin C = AB \sin B$$

$$AC = \frac{AB \sin B}{\sin C} = \frac{300 \sin 87°}{\sin 46.5°} \approx 413 \text{ ft}$$

Now use the SAS Triangle Area Conjecture to find the area of the triangle.

$$A = \frac{1}{2}(AB)(BC)\sin 87° = \frac{1}{2}(300)(300)\sin 87°$$

$$\approx 45{,}000 \text{ ft}^2$$

13. Approximately 48 m. Label the figure for reference.

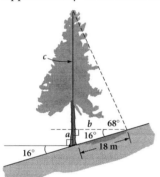

In this figure, the height of the tree is represented by $c + a$. Look at the small right triangle with legs of lengths a and b and hypotenuse of length 18 m. Because the two horizontal lines are parallel the smaller acute angle of this triangle (opposite the side of length a) measures 16° by the CA Conjecture. Use trigonometric ratios in this triangle to find a and b.

$\sin 16° = \frac{a}{18}$, so $a = 18 \sin 16°$.

$\cos 16° = \frac{b}{18}$, so $b = 18 \cos 16°$.

Now look at the large right triangle with legs of lengths b and c.

$\tan 68° = \frac{c}{b}$, so $c = b(\tan 68°) = 18(\cos 16°)(\tan 68°)$.

$c + a = 18(\cos 16°)(\tan 68°) + 18(\sin 16°) \approx 48$ m

14. 2366 cm; approximately 41°. Each side of the pyramid has 91 steps, each of height 26 cm, so the height of the pyramid is $91(26) = 2366$ cm (or 23.66 m). The depth of the pyramid from the

outer edge to the center is $91(30) = 2730$ cm (or 27.30 m). To find the angle of ascent, make a sketch.

In this figure, θ is the angle of ascent.

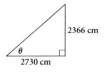

$$\tan \theta = \frac{2366}{2730}$$

$$\theta = \tan^{-1}\left(\frac{2366}{2730}\right) \approx 41°$$

15. Approximately 5°. Make a sketch.

$\sin \theta = \frac{4.8}{55}$, so $\theta = \sin^{-1}\left(\frac{4.8}{55}\right) \approx 5°$.

16. $\frac{9\pi\sqrt{3}}{8}$ cm³, or approximately 6 cm³. Look at the right triangle inside the cone. The angle of measure 120° is an exterior angle of the triangle. Its supplement is a 60° angle, so the triangle is a 30°-60°-90° right triangle, with hypotenuse of length 3 cm. By the 30°-60°-90° Triangle Conjecture, the length of the shorter leg is $\frac{1}{2}(3) = \frac{3}{2}$ cm, and the length of the longer leg is $\frac{3}{2}\sqrt{3}$ cm. The shorter leg of the triangle is a radius of the cone, and the longer leg is the height.

$$V = \frac{1}{3}BH = \frac{1}{3}\pi r^2 H = \frac{1}{3}\pi\left(\frac{3}{2}\right)^2\left(\frac{3}{2}\sqrt{3}\right)$$

$$= \frac{9\pi\sqrt{3}}{8} \text{ cm}^3 \approx 6 \text{ cm}^3$$

17. Because $\overline{AB} \parallel \overline{CD}$, $\angle A \cong \angle D$ by the AIA Conjecture. Because $\angle D$ and $\angle B$ intercept the same arc, $\angle D \cong \angle B$. Therefore, $\angle A \cong \angle B$ by the transitive property. So, $\triangle ABE$ is isosceles by the Converse of the Isosceles Triangle Conjecture.

18. Draw a line through the two points. Fold the paper so that the two points coincide. Draw another line along the fold. These two lines contain the diagonals of the square. Now fold the paper so that the two lines coincide. Mark the vertices on the other line.

19. $AC = 60$ cm, $AE = 93.75$ cm, $AF \approx 117$ cm. Apply the Extended Parallel/Proportionality Conjecture.

From $\triangle ABI \sim \triangle ACH$, $\frac{AB}{AC} = \frac{BI}{CH}$, so $\frac{20}{AC} = \frac{16}{48} = \frac{1}{3}$. $AC = 20(3) = 60$ cm.

From $\triangle ABI \sim \triangle AEF$, $\frac{AB}{AE} = \frac{BI}{EF}$, so $\frac{20}{AE} = \frac{16}{75}$. $16(AE) = 20(75) = 1500$, so $AF = \frac{1500}{16} = 93.75$ cm.

Also from $\triangle ABI \sim \triangle AEF$, $\frac{BI}{EF} = \frac{AI}{AF}$, so $\frac{16}{75} = \frac{25}{AF}$. Then $16(AF) = 75(25) = 1875$, so $AE = \frac{1875}{16} \approx 117$ cm.

20. The diagonal rod in Box 1 is about 1.2 in. longer. For each box, you need to find the length of the space diagonal, which can be found by extending the Pythagorean Theorem to three dimensions.

Box 1: Let d represent the length of the space diagonal.

$$d = \sqrt{5^2 + 9^2 + 4^2} = \sqrt{122} \approx 11.05 \text{ in.}$$

Box 2: Let e represent the length of the space diagonal.

$$e = \sqrt{5^2 + 6^2 + 6^2} = \sqrt{97} \approx 9.85 \text{ in.}$$

Therefore, the diagonal rod in Box 1 is longer. The difference in lengths is approximately $11.05 - 9.85 = 1.2$ in.

IMPROVING YOUR VISUAL THINKING SKILLS

Make a table or use recursive formulas to discover the patterns.

1. 151   **2.** 100

EXTENSION

See the solutions to Take Another Look activities 1 and 2 on page 278.

LESSON 12.4

EXERCISES

1. 32 cm. The lengths of two sides and the measure of the included angle are given. Use the Law of Cosines to find w.

$$c^2 = a^2 + b^2 - 2ab \cos C$$

$$w^2 = 41^2 + 36^2 - 2(41)(36)\cos 49°$$

$$w = \sqrt{41^2 + 36^2 - 2(41)(36)\cos 49°} \approx 32 \text{ cm}$$

2. 47 cm. Use the Law of Cosines to find y.

$$c^2 = a^2 + b^2 - 2ab \cos C$$

$$y^2 = 32^2 + 42^2 - 2(32)(42)\cos 78°$$

$$y = \sqrt{32^2 + 42^2 - 2(32)(42)\cos 78°} \approx 47 \text{ cm}$$

3. 341 cm. Use the Law of Cosines to find x.

$$x^2 = 235^2 + 282^2 - 2(235)(282)\cos 82°$$

$$x = \sqrt{235^2 + 282^2 - 2(235)(282)\cos 82°}$$

$$\approx 341 \text{ cm}$$

4. 74°. The lengths of all three sides of the triangle are given. Use the Law of Cosines to find $m\angle A$. Notice that $\angle A$ is opposite $\overline{KR}$ and $KR = 42$ cm.

$$42^2 = 34^2 + 36^2 - 2(34)(36)\cos A$$

$$42^2 - 34^2 - 36^2 = -2(34)(36)\cos A$$

$$\cos A = \frac{42^2 - 34^2 - 36^2}{-2 \cdot 34 \cdot 36}$$

$$A = \cos^{-1}\left(\frac{42^2 - 34^2 - 36^2}{-2 \cdot 34 \cdot 36}\right) \approx 74°$$

5. 64°. Use the Law of Cosines to find $m\angle B$. Notice that $\angle B$ is opposite $\overline{TE}$ and $TE = 390$ cm.

$$390^2 = 350^2 + 380^2 - 2(350)(380)\cos B$$

$$390^2 - 350^2 - 380^2 = -2(350)(380)\cos B$$

$$\cos B = \frac{390^2 - 350^2 - 380^2}{-2 \cdot 350 \cdot 380}$$

$$B = \cos^{-1}\left(\frac{390^2 - 350^2 - 380^2}{-2 \cdot 350 \cdot 380}\right)$$

$$\approx 64°$$

6. 85°. Use the Law of Cosines to find $m\angle C$. Notice that $\angle C$ is opposite $\overline{DL}$ and $DL = 508$ cm.

$$508^2 = 328^2 + 418^2 - 2(328)(418)\cos C$$

$$508^2 - 328^2 - 418^2 = -2(328)(418)\cos C$$

$$\cos C = \frac{508^2 - 328^2 - 418^2}{-2 \cdot 328 \cdot 418}$$

$$C = \cos^{-1}\left(\frac{508^2 - 328^2 - 418^2}{-2 \cdot 328 \cdot 418}\right)$$

$$\approx 85°$$

7. Approximately 43 cm. The two radii and the chord form an isosceles triangle with legs of length 24 cm and vertex angle of measure 126°. The vertex angle is the included angle between the two legs of an isosceles triangle, so you can use the Law of Cosines to find the base of the isosceles triangle, which is the chord of the circle. Let x represent the length of the chord.

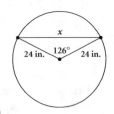

$$x^2 = 24^2 + 24^2 - 2(24)(24)\cos 126°$$

$$x = \sqrt{24^2 + 24^2 - 2(24)(24)\cos 126°} \approx 43 \text{ cm}$$

8. Approximately 30°. By the Side-Angle Inequality Conjecture, the smallest angle in the triangle is opposite the shortest side, so use the Law of Cosines to find the measure of the angle opposite the 4-meter side. Let $\angle A$ be the smallest angle of the triangle.

$$4^2 = 7^2 + 8^2 - 2(7)(8)\cos A$$

Discovering Geometry Solutions Manual
©2008 Key Curriculum Press

$$\cos A = \frac{4^2 - 7^2 - 8^2}{-2 \cdot 7 \cdot 8}$$

$$A = \cos^{-1}\left(\frac{4^2 - 7^2 - 8^2}{-2 \cdot 7 \cdot 8}\right) \approx 30°$$

9. Approximately 116° and 64°. Sketch parallelogram $ABCD$ with diagonal $\overline{BD}$.

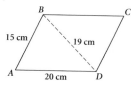

From the figure, you can see that the 19-centimeter diagonal must be the shorter one, $\overline{BD}$. (19 cm < 20 cm, so the angles opposite $\overline{BD}$, $\angle A$, and $\angle C$ must be acute.) Use the Law of Cosines to find $m\angle A$.

$$19^2 = 15^2 + 20^2 - 2(15)(20)\cos A$$

$$\cos A = \frac{19^2 - 15^2 - 20^2}{-2 \cdot 15 \cdot 20}$$

$$A = \cos^{-1}\left(\frac{19^2 - 15^2 - 20^2}{-2 \cdot 15 \cdot 20}\right) \approx 64°$$

By the Parallelogram Consecutive Angles Conjecture, $\angle A$ and $\angle B$ are supplementary, so $m\angle B = 180° - m\angle A \approx 180° - 64° = 116°$. By the Parallelogram Opposite Angles Conjecture, $\angle C \cong \angle A$ and $\angle D \cong \angle B$. Therefore, the measures of the angles of the parallelogram are approximately 64° and 116°.

10. Approximately 6 min. Make a sketch. Divide the large triangle into right triangles by drawing an altitude. Because distances and times are proportional, the lengths on the diagram can represent times as well as distances, so we can ignore distances entirely. First find the time that Captain Malloy actually flew (following the detour). He flew 60 min on the first leg (1 hr) and 80 min on the second leg. Therefore, he flew a total time of $60 + 80 = 140$ min.

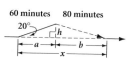

To find the straight-line time, x, find a and b from the two right triangles.

$\cos 20° = \dfrac{a}{60}$, so $a = 60\cos 20° \approx 56.4$ min.

$\sin 20° = \dfrac{h}{60}$, so $h = 60\sin 20°$.

By the Pythagorean Theorem, $b = \sqrt{80^2 - h^2} = \sqrt{80^2 - (60\sin 20°)^2} \approx 77.3$ min. Then $x = a + b \approx 56.4 + 77.3 = 133.7$ min.

Therefore, the extra time that the captain flew by taking the detour was approximately $140 - 133.7 = 6.3 \approx 6$ min.

11. Approximately 87.8 ft. Make a sketch.

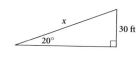

$$\sin 20° = \frac{30}{x}$$

$$x \sin 20° = 30$$

$$x = \frac{30}{\sin 20°} \approx 87.71$$

If the angle is 20°, the ramp will be approximately 87.71 ft long. If the angle is less than 20°, the ramp will be longer than 87.71 ft. Because 20° is the *maximum* angle permitted, round up to 87.8 ft.

12. Approximately 139 m. Let h represent the height of the original pyramid. Make a sketch.

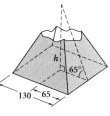

Look at the right triangle in the diagram. Notice that the length of the shorter leg is one-half the length of a side of the square, or $\frac{1}{2}(130) = 65$ cm.

$$\frac{h}{65} = \tan 65°$$

$$h = 65\tan 65° \approx 139 \text{ m}$$

13. Approximately 143 m. Let L represent the top of the lighthouse, B the base of the lighthouse, and S the position of the sailboat. Make a sketch.

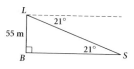

From the given information, $LB = 55$ m and the angle of depression is 21°. By the AIA Conjecture, $m\angle LSB = 21°$. Use $\triangle SLB$ to find SB, the distance between the sailboat and the base of the lighthouse.

$$\tan 21° = \frac{55}{SB}$$

$$SB \tan 21° = 55$$

$$SB = \frac{55}{\tan 21°} \approx 143 \text{ m}$$

14. The ladder is at approximately a 76° angle and is not safe. The ladder should be between approximately 6.5 ft and 14.3 ft from the base of the wall.

Make a sketch to show the position of Regina's ladder leaning against the wall.

$$\cos \theta = \frac{6}{25} = 0.24$$

$$\theta = \cos^{-1}(0.24) \approx 76°, \text{ so the ladder is not safe.}$$

To find the range of safe distances, let d represent the distance between the base of the ladder and the base of the wall. $\cos \theta = \frac{d}{25}$, so $d = 25\cos \theta$. If $\theta = 55°$, $d = 25\cos 55° \approx 14.3$ ft. If $\theta = 75°$, $d = 25\cos 75° \approx 6.5$ ft.

The ladder should be between approximately 6.5 ft and 14.3 ft from the base of the wall.

15. $\sin A = \dfrac{a}{c}$

$\cos A = \dfrac{b}{c}$

$\tan A = \dfrac{a}{b}$

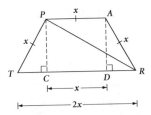

$\dfrac{\sin A}{\cos A} = \dfrac{\frac{a}{c}}{\frac{b}{c}} = \dfrac{a}{c} \cdot \dfrac{c}{b} = \dfrac{a}{b} = \tan A$

16. a. $PR = x\sqrt{3}$. Let C and D be the intersections of $\overline{TR}$ with altitudes from vertices P and A, respectively, so $CD = x$.

Then $\angle PTC \cong \angle ARD$ by the Isosceles Trapezoid Conjecture, so $\triangle PTC \cong \triangle ARD$ by SAA. Thus $\overline{CT} \cong \overline{DR}$ by CPCTC, so $CT = DR = \frac{1}{2}x$. Use the Pythagorean Theorem, or recognize $\triangle PCT$ as a 30-60-90 triangle because $CT = \frac{1}{2}PT$, to find that $CP = \dfrac{\sqrt{3}}{2}x$. Finally, use the Pythagorean Theorem in $\triangle CPR$ to find PR.

$(PR)^2 = \left(\dfrac{3}{2}x\right)^2 + \left(\dfrac{\sqrt{3}}{2}x\right)^2$

$(PR)^2 = \dfrac{9}{4}x^2 + \dfrac{3}{4}x^2$

$(PR)^2 = 3x^2$

$(PR) = \sqrt{3x^2} = x\sqrt{3}$

b. Because $x^2 + (x\sqrt{3})^2 = (2x)^2$, $\triangle TPR$ is a right triangle by the Converse of the Pythagorean Theorem. Therefore, $m\angle TPR = 90°$.

17. a. Increases. $\angle ABP$ will go from an acute angle to a right angle (when P is directly above B) to an obtuse angle, and then to larger and larger obtuse angles.

b. Decreases. $\angle PAB$ will go from an obtuse angle to a right angle to an acute angle, and then to smaller and smaller acute angles.

c. Increases, then decreases. It will increase until it reaches its maximum measure, when P is directly above the midpoint of $\overline{AB}$ so that $\triangle APB$ is isosceles with base $\overline{AB}$. After that, as P continues to move to the right, $\angle APB$ will continue to get smaller and smaller.

18. a. The base perimeters are equal. The base of the cone is a circle with diameter 10 cm. The base of the pyramid is a square with side length 2.5π cm.

The base perimeter of the cone is the circumference of a circle with $d = 10$ cm: $C = \pi d = \pi(10) = 10\pi$ cm.

The base perimeter of the pyramid is the perimeter of a square with side length 2.5π cm: $P = 4s = 4(2.5\pi) = 10\pi$ cm.

Both solids have the same base perimeter, 10π cm.

b. The cone has the greater volume. The cone has radius 5 cm and height 8 cm, and the pyramid also has height 8 cm.

Cone: $V = \frac{1}{3}BH = \frac{1}{3}\pi r^2 H = \frac{1}{3}\pi(5)^2 \cdot 8$

$\qquad = \dfrac{200\pi}{3}$ cm³

Pyramid: $V = \frac{1}{3}BH = \frac{1}{3}(2.5)^2 \cdot 8 = \dfrac{50\pi}{3}$ cm³

Thus, the volume of the cone is greater than the volume of the pyramid; in fact, the volume of the cone is four times the volume of the pyramid.

c. The cone has the greater surface area. In order to find their surface areas, you need to find the slant heights of the cone and the pyramid. Recall that l is used to represent slant height.

To find the slant height of the cone, look at the right triangle inside the cone. The shorter leg is a radius of the circular base, the longer leg is the height of the cone, and the slant height is the length of the hypotenuse. Use the Pythagorean Theorem to find the slant height: $l = \sqrt{5^2 + 8^2} = \sqrt{89}$. Use the formula for the surface area of a cone using slant height. (See page 465 of your book.) If S represents the surface area and l represents the slant height, $S = \pi r l + \pi r^2$.

$S = \pi r l + \pi r^2 = \pi(5)\left(\sqrt{89}\right) + \pi(5)^2$

$\quad = \left(5\sqrt{89}\right)\pi + 25\pi = \left(5\sqrt{89} + 25\right)\pi$

$\quad \approx 227$ cm²

To find the slant height of the pyramid, draw a right triangle inside the pyramid with right-angle vertex at the center of the square base, the shorter leg an apothem of the square, and the longer leg the height of the pyramid. Then the slant height will be the length of the hypotenuse. Use the Pythagorean Theorem to find the slant height: $l = \sqrt{(1.25\pi)^2 + 8^2} \approx 8.9$ cm.

To find the surface area, use one of the formulas for the surface area of a regular pyramid. (See page 464 of your book.) If S represents the surface area, a is the length of the apothem of the regular base, b is the base length, and n is the number of sides in the polygon, the surface area of a pyramid can be found from the formula $S = \frac{1}{2}nb(l + a)$.

$S = \frac{1}{2}nb(l + a) \approx \frac{1}{2} \cdot 4 \cdot 2.5\pi(8.9 + 1.25\pi)$

$\quad \approx 201$ cm²

Discovering Geometry Solutions Manual
©2008 Key Curriculum Press

The surface area of the cone is approximately 227 cm², while the surface area of the pyramid is approximately 201 cm², so the cone has the greater surface area.

19. a. A translation right 10 units; $(x, y) \rightarrow$ $(x + 10, y)$. The lines $x = -2$ and $x = 3$ are both vertical lines, so they are parallel, and you can apply the Reflections across Parallel Lines Conjecture. This conjecture tells you that the composition of these two reflections will be a translation and that the second image of each point will be twice the distance between the parallel lines. Because the lines are $3 - (-2) =$ 5 units apart, and because the second reflection is across the line farther to the right, the composition is equivalent to a translation to the right 10 units. Every point is moved 10 units to the right, but not moved up or down, so its x-coordinate increases by 10 while its y-coordinate does not change. Thus, the rule is $(x, y) \rightarrow (x + 10, y)$.

b. A rotation 180° about the origin; $(x, y) \rightarrow$ $(-x, -y)$. This is a composition of two reflections across intersecting lines, so you can apply the Reflections across Intersecting Lines Conjecture. The x-axis and y-axis are perpendicular, so the smaller angle between them is 90°. Therefore, the composition of the two reflections is a single rotation, and the angle of rotation is $2(90°) = 180°$.

20. Possible answer:

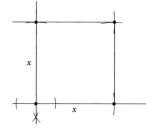

The first rectangle is a square, while the second rectangle has a length that is twice its width. The sides of these two rectangles are not proportional, so the rectangles are not similar.

21. Possible answer:

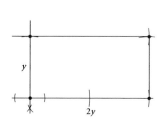 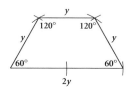

22. Results can vary from simple (circles, segments) to quite complex. Begin with the simplest case where all factors are equal. With circles of the same radius and with endpoints of the segment traveling in the

same direction and at the same speed, and starting from the same relative position, the midpoint will trace a circle equal in size to the constructed circles. Changing the size of both circles will change the size of the circle traced, as will changing the starting positions of the endpoints. The maximum radius of the traced circle is limited by the radius of the constructed circles; the smallest observable trace is a single point.

With all other factors equal and the endpoints of the segment traveling in opposite directions around the circles, the midpoint will trace a segment of length equal to the common diameter of the circles. Changing the relative speeds of the endpoints, or the relative radii of the circles, will yield traces that students might describe as flowers, stars, or "spirograph-like." Changing the distance between the centers has no effect on the shape of the trace, only its position.

You might encourage students to experiment with building their circles so the ratio of radii is exactly some fraction. For example, if one radius is 1.5 times the other and the points travel in opposite derections at equal speeds, the midpoint traces a 5-pointed star.

PROJECT

Project should satisfy the following criteria:

- The project problem is solved.

$$hyp = r_1 + r_2$$
$$leg = r_1 - r_2$$
$$AB = 2\sqrt{r_1 r_2}$$

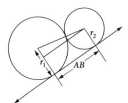

$$hyp = r_1 + r_3$$
$$leg = r_1 - r_3$$
$$x = 2\sqrt{r_1 r_3}$$

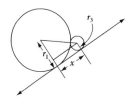

$$hyp = r_2 + r_3$$
$$leg = r_2 - r_3$$
$$y = 2\sqrt{r_2 r_3}$$

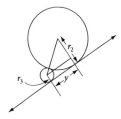

The three legs, AB, x, and y, are related by

$$AB = x + y, \text{ or } 2\sqrt{r_1 r_2} = 2\sqrt{r_1 r_3} + 2\sqrt{r_2 r_3}$$

- A *sangaku* tablet is replicated.

- At least two other *sangaku* are given, and their solutions are attempted.

Extra credit

- Additional cultural information is included (for example, that *sangaku* were hung in both Shinto shrines and Buddhist temples).

- The project includes some history of Japanese mathematics (*wasan*) or the origins of *sangaku*.

- The relationship $2\sqrt{r_1 r_2} = 2\sqrt{r_1 r_3} + 2\sqrt{r_2 r_3}$ is rewritten as $\frac{1}{\sqrt{r_3}} = \frac{1}{\sqrt{r_1}} + \frac{1}{\sqrt{r_2}}$ and is related to the Pythagorean Theorem.

EXTENSION

See the solutions to Take Another Look activities 3 and 4 on page 278.

LESSON 12.5

EXERCISES

1. Approximately 12.7 m. Make a sketch.

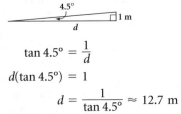

$$\tan 4.5° = \frac{1}{d}$$

$$d(\tan 4.5°) = 1$$

$$d = \frac{1}{\tan 4.5°} \approx 12.7 \text{ m}$$

The maximum permitted angle is 4.5°. If the angle is smaller than 4.5°, the distance between the building entrance and the bottom of the ramp will be *greater* than 12.7 m, so the *minimum* distance is approximately 12.7 m.

2. Approximately 142 mi/h. The resultant vector can be represented by the longer diagonal of the parallelogram. By the Parallelogram Consecutive Angles Conjecture, the measure of the obtuse angles in the parallelogram is $180° - 56° = 124°$. The longer diagonal is the third side of a triangle with sides of lengths 130 and 20 (representing speeds of 130 mi/h and 20 mi/h) and included angle of 124°.

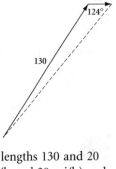

Let v represent the length of the resultant vector. Use the Law of Cosines to find v.

$$v^2 = 130^2 + 20^2 - 2(130)(20)(\cos 124°)$$

$$v = \sqrt{130^2 + 20^2 - 2(130)(20)(\cos 124°)} \approx 142$$

The resulting speed is approximately 142 mi/h.

3. Approximately 51 km. Let P represent the position of the patrol boat, L the position of the lighthouse, and S the position of the station.

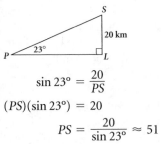

$$\sin 23° = \frac{20}{PS}$$

$$(PS)(\sin 23°) = 20$$

$$PS = \frac{20}{\sin 23°} \approx 51$$

The boat is approximately 51 km from the station.

4. Approximately 5.9 m. Let l represent the length of the cylinder.

$$\sin 25° = \frac{2.5}{l}$$

$$l(\sin 25°) = 2.5$$

$$l = \frac{2.5}{\sin 25°} \approx 5.9$$

The cylinder should be approximately 5.9 m long.

5. a. Approximately 9.1 km. Make a careful drawing.

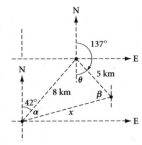

First find θ. From the diagram, $\theta = 180° - 137° = 43°$.

The north lines in the diagram are parallel, so the measure of the angle between the sides of lengths 8 km and 5 km is $42° + \theta = 85°$. In the diagram, x represents the distance between Annie and Sashi's position and the base camp. Use the Law of Cosines to find x.

$$x^2 = 8^2 + 5^2 - 2(8)(5)\cos 85°$$

$$x = \sqrt{8^2 + 5^2 - 2(8)(5)\cos 85°} \approx 9.1$$

They are approximately 9.1 km away from their base camp.

(*Note:* The value of x will be used in the calculation of the angle in 5b. In order to get a more accurate result, either store the actual value of x in your calculator or use a more accurate approximation, such as 9.057, in the calculation of β in 5b.)

b. Approximately 255°. The angle that you need to find is shown by the arrow in the figure. (Recall that bearing is measured clockwise from the north.)

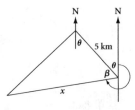

Use the Law of Sines to find β.

$$\frac{\sin \beta}{8} = \frac{\sin 85°}{x}$$

$$\sin \beta \approx \frac{8 \sin 85°}{9.057}$$

$$\beta \approx \sin^{-1}\left(\frac{8 \sin 85°}{9.057}\right) \approx 62°$$

By the AIA Conjecture, the angle adjacent to the angle with measure β has measure $\theta = 43°$. The bearing for the return trip is approximately $360° - 62° - 43°$, or approximately $255°$.

6. Approximately 240 m. Use the right triangle to find AC.

$$\tan 58° = \frac{AC}{150}$$

$$AC = 150 \tan 58° \approx 240$$

The distance between A and C is approximately 240 m.

7. Approximately 42 ft. Let x represent the height of the portion of the tree still standing and y represent the length of the bent-over portion. Then $x + y$ represents the original height of the tree. Change 20 ft 6 in. to 20.5 ft because this is an easier measurement to use in calculations.

$$\tan 38° = \frac{x}{20.5}$$

$$x = 20.5 \tan 38° \approx 16 \text{ ft}$$

$$\cos 38° = \frac{20.5}{y}$$

$$y = \frac{20.5}{\cos 38°} \approx 26 \text{ ft}$$

$$x + y \approx 16 + 26 = 42 \text{ ft}$$

The original height of the tree was approximately 42 ft.

8. They must dig at an angle of approximately $71.6°$ and dig for approximately 25.3 m. Draw $\overline{AB}$ to form right triangle ABC. Then $\angle B$ is the angle that you need to find.

$$\tan B = \frac{24}{8} = 3$$

$$B = \tan^{-1}(3) \approx 71.6°$$

Use the Pythagorean Theorem to find BC.

$$BC = \sqrt{(AC)^2 + (AB)^2} = \sqrt{24^2 + 8^2} \approx 25.3 \text{ m}$$

9. Approximately 168 km/h. Make a sketch.

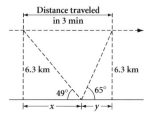

$$\tan 49° = \frac{6.3}{x}$$

$$x \tan 49° = 6.3$$

$$x = \frac{6.3}{\tan 49°} \approx 5.48 \text{ km}$$

$$\tan 65° = \frac{6.3}{y}$$

$$y \tan 65° = 6.3$$

$$y = \frac{6.3}{\tan 65°} \approx 2.94 \text{ km}$$

The distance that Olivia traveled is approximately $5.48 + 2.94 = 8.42$ km.

To find her flying speed, first change 3 minutes to hours: $3 \text{ min} = \frac{3}{60} \text{ h} = \frac{1}{20} \text{ h} = 0.05 \text{ h}$.

$d = rt$, so $r = \frac{d}{t} = \frac{8.42 \text{ km}}{0.05 \text{ h}} \approx 168 \text{ km/h}$.

10. a. Apothem ≈ 9.23 cm; area ≈ 277 cm². Look at one of the ten isosceles triangles. The measure of the vertex angle is $\frac{1}{10}(360°) = 36°$, so the measure of each base angle is $\frac{1}{2}(180° - 36°) = \frac{1}{2}(144°) = 72°$.

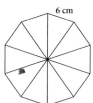

In this triangle, draw the altitude to the base, dividing the isosceles triangle into two congruent right triangles. Let h be the height of the isosceles triangle and x be the length of each of the legs. Each of the right triangles will have acute angles that measure 72° and 18°, legs of lengths 3 cm and h, and hypotenuse of length x.

Notice that h is also the length of the apothem of the decagon. Use the tangent ratio to find the value of h.

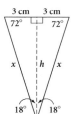

$\frac{h}{3} = \tan 72°$, so $h = 3 \tan 72° \approx 9.23$ cm.

Now use the Regular Polygon Area Conjecture to find the area of the decagon. The perimeter of the decagon is $10(6) = 60$ cm.

$$A = \frac{1}{2}aP \approx \frac{1}{2}(9.23)(60) \approx 277 \text{ cm}^2$$

b. Leg ≈ 9.7 cm; area of each isosceles triangle $\approx$ 27.7 cm²; area of decagon $\approx$ 277 cm². Look at one of the right triangles in the second diagram in part a. Use the cosine ratio to find the value of x, the length of a leg of the isosceles triangle.

$$\frac{3}{x} = \cos 72°, \text{ or } 3 = x \cos 72°, \text{ so } x = \frac{3}{\cos 72°} \approx 9.7 \text{ cm.}$$

Now use the SAS Triangle Area Conjecture to find the area of the isosceles triangle.

$$A = \tfrac{1}{2}ab \sin C = \tfrac{1}{2}(9.7)(9.7)\sin 36° \approx 27.7 \text{ cm}^2$$

The decagon is made up of ten congruent isosceles triangles, so the area of the decagon is approximately $10(27.7)$, or about 277 cm².

c. They are the same.

11. Approximately 108 cm³. In order to find the volume of the prism, first find the area of the pentagonal base. Divide the pentagon into five congruent isosceles triangles by drawing segments from the center of the pentagon to its vertices.

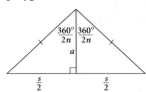

To find the area of the regular pentagon, you need to find the apothem, which is the height of one of the five triangles shown in the figure above. Look at one of these triangles. Let a represent the height of the triangle, which is the apothem of the pentagon.

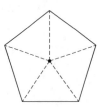

The vertex angle of this triangle is $\tfrac{1}{5}(360°) = 72°$ because this is one of five congruent angles around the center of the pentagon. Because the altitude from the vertex angle to the base of an isosceles triangle is also an angle bisector and a median, each of the congruent right triangles into which the altitude divides the isosceles triangle has a shorter leg of length 1.5 cm and a smallest angle of 36°.

$$\tan 36° = \frac{1.5}{a}$$
$$a(\tan 36°) = 1.5$$
$$a = \frac{1.5}{\tan 36°}$$

Recall that the formula $A = \tfrac{1}{2}asn$ gives the area of a regular polygon with n sides, apothem a, and side length s. In this case, use B to represent the area of the polygon because this is the base area of a prism.

$$B = \tfrac{1}{2}asn = \tfrac{1}{2}\left(\frac{1.5}{\tan 36°}\right) \cdot 3 \cdot 5 \approx 15.48 \text{ cm}^2$$

Finally, find the volume of the prism.

$$V = BH \approx (15.48)(7) \approx 108 \text{ cm}^3$$

12. Sample answer: Any regular polygon can be divided into n congruent isosceles triangles, each with a vertex angle of $\frac{360°}{n}$.

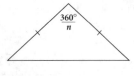

The altitude from the vertex angle of an isosceles triangle bisects the angle and the opposite side. This altitude is also an apothem of the regular polygon.

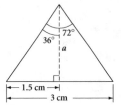

For simplicity, let $\theta = \frac{360°}{2n}$. Now use the tangent ratio to find the length of the apothem.

$$\tan \theta = \frac{\frac{s}{2}}{a}$$
$$a = \frac{s}{2\tan\theta}$$

Now use the area formula for a regular polygon.

$$A = \tfrac{1}{2}aP$$
$$A = \frac{1}{2} \cdot \frac{s}{2\tan\theta} \cdot ns$$
$$A = \frac{ns^2}{4\tan\theta}, \text{ where } \theta = \frac{360°}{2n}$$

13. Approximately 12.8 m at an angle of approximately 48°. Let l represent the length of pipe needed to go through the hill.

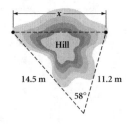

Use the Law of Cosines to find l.

$$l^2 = (14.5)^2 + (11.2)^2 - 2(14.5)(11.2)\cos 58°$$
$$l = \sqrt{14.5^2 + 11.2^2 - 2 \cdot 14.5 \cdot 11.2 \cos 58°}$$
$$\approx 12.8 \text{ m}$$

Let A be the vertex of the angle between the 14.5-meter side and the side of length l. Use the Law of Sines to find $m\angle A$.

$$\frac{\sin A}{11.2} = \frac{\sin 58°}{12.8}$$
$$\sin A = \frac{11.2\sin 58°}{12.8}$$
$$A = \sin^{-1}\left(\frac{11.2\sin 58°}{12.8}\right) \approx 48°$$

14. $1536\sqrt{3}$ cm³ ≈ 2660 cm³. A space diagonal of the cube will be a diameter of the sphere, and the diameter of the sphere is 24 cm. Let x represent the edge length of the cube. The diagonal of a square base of the cube is the hypotenuse of an isosceles right triangle with legs of length x, so, by the

Isosceles Right Triangle Conjecture, the length of this diagonal is $x\sqrt{2}$. Apply the Pythagorean Theorem to a right triangle with the diagonal of the base as the longer leg, an edge of the cube as the shorter leg, and the space diagonal as the hypotenuse.

$$x^2 + \left(x\sqrt{2}\right)^2 = 24^2$$
$$x^2 + 2x^2 = 576$$
$$3x^2 = 576$$
$$x^2 = 192$$
$$x = \sqrt{192} = \sqrt{64 \cdot 3} = 8\sqrt{3}$$

Now find the volume of the cube.

$$V = x^3 = \left(8\sqrt{3}\right)^3 = 512 \cdot 3\sqrt{3} = 1536\sqrt{3} \text{ cm}^3$$
$$\approx 2660 \text{ cm}^3$$

15. The area increases by a factor of 9. The ratio of the lengths of corresponding sides is $\frac{3}{1}$; by the Proportional Areas Conjecture, the ratio of corresponding areas is $\left(\frac{3}{1}\right)^2 = \frac{9}{1}$.

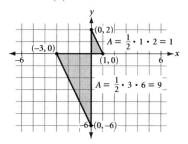

16. The large and small triangles are similar by the AA Similarity Conjecture because each triangle has a right angle and the triangles share an acute angle. Because the triangles are similar, corresponding sides must be proportional, which would give $\frac{5}{4} = \frac{15 + 5}{12}$, or $\frac{5}{4} = \frac{20}{12}$. But this situation is impossible because $\frac{20}{12} = \frac{5}{3}$ and $\frac{5}{4} \neq \frac{5}{3}$, so this is not true.

17. a. Decreases, then increases. PA decreases until P is directly above A so that $\overline{PA} \perp \overline{AB}$ and $\triangle PAB$ is a right angle; then PA increases as P moves farther to the right. (PA is at a minimum when $\overline{PA} \perp \overline{AB}$ because the shortest distance between two lines is the perpendicular distance.)

   b. Does not change. The area of $\triangle APB$ does not change because $\overline{AB}$ is always a base of the triangle, and the corresponding height is always the (perpendicular) distance between the two lines.

18. a. A reflection across the x-axis; $(x, y) \rightarrow (x, -y)$. Choose a point (x, y) in any quadrant. By the

Coordinate Transformations Conjecture or by understanding that this transformation reverses the two coordinates of any point, the image of (x, y) under this transformation is (y, x). Now rotate that first image point (y, x) counterclockwise by 270° about the origin to obtain the second image, which is the point $(x, -y)$. The result of the composition is to transform (x, y) to $(x, -y)$, so the rule for the composition is $(x, y) \rightarrow (x, -y)$. By the Coordinate Transformations Conjecture, this is a reflection across the x-axis.

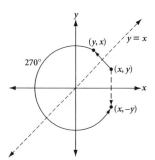

b. A reflection across the y-axis; $(x, y) \rightarrow (-x, y)$. Choose a point (x, y) in any quadrant. By the Coordinate Transformations Conjecture, the image of this point under a 180° rotation about the origin is the point $(-x, -y)$. Now reflect $(-x, -y)$ across the x-axis. This transformation reverses the sign of the y-coordinate but keeps the x-coordinate the same, so the second image is the point $(-x, y)$. The result of the composition is to transform (x, y) to $(-x, y)$, so the rule for the composition is $(x, y) \rightarrow (-x, y)$. By the Coordinate Transformations Conjecture, this is a reflection across the y-axis.

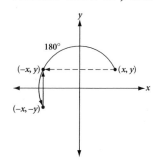

19. Software creations will vary.

IMPROVING YOUR ALGEBRA SKILLS

1. $x = \frac{50}{z}$. $2x = 3y$, so $x = \frac{3}{2}y = \frac{3}{2}(5w) = \frac{3}{2} \cdot 5 \cdot \frac{20}{3z} = \frac{50}{z}$.

2. $x = \frac{18}{z}$. $7x = 13y$, so $x = \frac{13}{7}y = \frac{13}{7}(28w) = \frac{13}{7} \cdot 28 \cdot \frac{9}{26z} = \frac{18}{z}$.

A. Make a sketch.

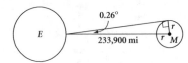

Use the tangent ratio to find the radius.

$$\tan 0.26° = \frac{r}{r + 233,900}$$

$$(r + 233,900)\tan 0.26° = r$$

$$r\tan 0.26° + 233,900\tan 0.26° = r$$

$$r\tan 0.26° + 233,900\tan 0.26° - r = 0$$

$$r\tan 0.26° - 1 = -233,900\tan 0.26°$$

$$r = \frac{-233,900\tan 0.26°}{\tan 0.26° - 1} \approx 1,070 \text{ mi}$$

B. The probability of an exact isosceles or equilateral triangle is theoretically 0. Because there are infinitely many points along the straw, the probability of choosing the same point more than once is $\frac{1}{\text{infinity}}$. The probability that one angle will measure exactly 90° is similarly 0. But, because measurements are rounded, you will occasionally get a special triangle. To sort the data for acute and obtuse triangles, use the inequality based on the Pythagorean Theorem.

EXPLORATION · TRIGONOMETRIC RATIOS AND THE UNIT CIRCLE

PROJECT

Project should satisfy the following criteria:

- Sketches and descriptions show important characteristics of each function. (Sample: The graph of $y = \sin(x)$ has a minimum y-value of -1 and a maximum y-value of $+1$. The period is 360°.)

- Descriptions show relationships between functions. (Sample: Sine and cosine have the same shape, but the cosine curve is translated left 90°. Both graphs have points in common when x equals $-315°$, $-135°$, $45°$, and 225°, or every 180° from 45°.)

Extra credit

- Symmetry in the graphs is recognized.

- Observations are generalized. (Sample: $\cos x = \sin(x + 90°)$ or $\sin x = \cos x$ for $x = 45° + 180n$, where n is any integer.)

- Characteristics are explained in terms of the trigonometric definitions. (Sample: As x approaches 90°, the tangent function approaches infinity, because as the measure of one of the acute angles in a right triangle approaches 90°, the opposite side gets longer and longer and the adjacent side gets shorter

and shorter, approaching 0; therefore, the ratio $\frac{\text{length of opposite side}}{\text{length of adjacent side}}$ gets infinitely large.)

USING YOUR ALGEBRA SKILLS 12

EXERCISES

1.

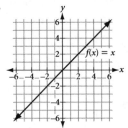

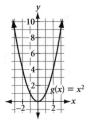
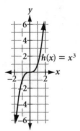

2.

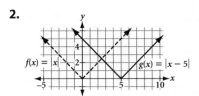

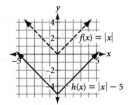

All three graphs are V-shaped, consisting of two half-lines that have slopes -1 and 1. The graph of g is a translation of the graph of f right 5 units, while the graph of h is a translation of the graph of f down 5 units.

3.

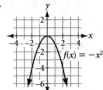
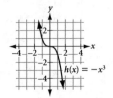

A vertical stretch by a factor of -1 reflects the graph across the x-axis.

4.

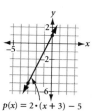

$p(x) = 2 \cdot (x + 3) - 5$

The graph of $y = 2x + 1$ is the same as the graph of $y = 2(x + 3) - 5$. The slope of a line is equal to the vertical stretch factor from the equation $y = x$. The y-intercept is equal to $-ah + k$.

5. A vertical stretch by a factor of 2 and a vertical translation down 5 units.

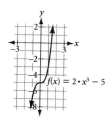

$f(x) = 2 \cdot x^3 - 5$

6. A horizontal translation right 5 units and a vertical translation up 2 units.

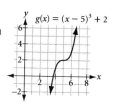

$g(x) = (x - 5)^3 + 2$

7. A vertical stretch by a factor of $\frac{1}{2}$ (a vertical shrink), a horizontal translation right 2 units, and a vertical translation down 5 units.

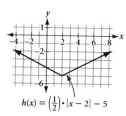

$h(x) = \left(\frac{1}{2}\right) \cdot |x - 2| - 5$

8. $f(x) = |x - 3| - 1$; A horizontal translation right 3 units and a vertical translation down 1 unit.

9. $f(x) = 3x^2$; A vertical stretch by a factor of 3.

10. $f(x) = -(x - 3)^2$; A vertical stretch by a factor of -1 (a reflection across the x-axis) and a horizontal translation right 3 units.

11. $f(x) = -2|x| + 3$; A vertical stretch by a factor of -2 and a vertical translation up 3 units.

12. $f(x) = 3(x + 1)^2 - 3$; A vertical stretch by a factor of 3, a horizontal translation left 1 unit, and a vertical translation down 3 units.

13. $f(x) = \frac{1}{2}(x - 3)^3 + 2$; A vertical stretch by a factor of $\frac{1}{2}$ (a vertical shrink), a horizontal translation right 3 units, and a vertical translation up 2 units.

14. Both graphs have the same "hills and valleys" shape, but one is a horizontal translation of the other.

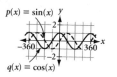

$p(x) = \sin(x)$

$q(x) = \cos(x)$

15. A horizontal translation. $a = 1$, $h = 90°$, $k = 0$.

16.

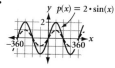 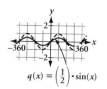

$p(x) = 2 \cdot \sin(x)$

$q(x) = \left(\frac{1}{2}\right) \cdot \sin(x)$

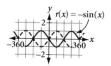

$r(x) = -\sin(x)$

Varying a in the equation of the sine function causes the same types of vertical stretches as with other functions.

17. Possible answer: $f(x) = 2 \sin(x - 90°) - 1$

A vertical stretch by a factor of 2, a horizontal translation right 90, and a vertical translation down 1 unit.

CHAPTER 12 REVIEW

EXERCISES

1. 0.8387

2. 0.9877

3. 28.6363

4. $\sin A = \frac{a}{b}$; $\cos A = \frac{c}{b}$; $\tan A = \frac{a}{c}$.

$$\sin A = \frac{\text{length of side opposite } \angle A}{\text{length of hypotenuse}} = \frac{a}{b}$$

$$\cos A = \frac{\text{length of side adjacent of } \angle A}{\text{length of hypotenuse}} = \frac{c}{b}$$

$$\tan A = \frac{\text{length of side opposite } \angle A}{\text{length of side adjacent to } \angle A} = \frac{a}{c}$$

5. $\sin B = \frac{8}{17}$; $\cos B = \frac{15}{17}$; $\tan B = \frac{8}{15}$. The side lengths in this triangle are a multiple of the 8-15-17 Pythagorean triple: $16 = 2(8)$, $30 = 2(15)$, so $OB = 2(17) = 34$. The trigonometric ratios are the same in this triangle as in an 8-15-17 triangle.

6. $\sin \phi = s$; $\cos \phi = t$; $\tan \phi = \frac{s}{t}$. Draw a perpendicular segment from the point (t, s) to the x-axis to form a right triangle. In this triangle, the length of the horizontal leg will be t, the length of the vertical length will be s, and the length of the hypotenuse will be 1, the radius of the circle. Then $\sin \phi = \frac{s}{1} = s$, $\cos \phi = \frac{t}{1} = t$, and $\tan \phi = \frac{s}{t}$.

7. 33°. $A = \sin^{-1}(0.5447) \approx 33°$.

8. 86°. $B = \cos^{-1}(0.0696) \approx 86°$.

9. 71°. $C = \tan^{-1}(2.9043) \approx 71°$.

10. 1823 cm². The shaded region is a semicircle; you need to know the radius of the circle to find its area. By the Angles Inscribed in a Semicircle Conjecture, the triangle in the figure is a right triangle whose hypotenuse is the diameter of the circle that is drawn in the figure. Let c equal the length of the hypotenuse.

$$\sin 37° = \frac{41}{c}$$
$$c(\sin 37°) = 41$$
$$c = \frac{41}{\sin 37°}$$

(Store this value in your calculator rather than rounding this intermediate result.)

Let r represent the radius of the circle. Then $r = \frac{1}{2}c$, and the area of the semicircle is given by $A = \frac{1}{2}\pi r^2 = \frac{1}{2}\pi\left(\frac{1}{2} \cdot \frac{41}{\sin 37°}\right)^2 \approx 1823$ cm².

11. 15,116 cm³. Look at the right triangle inside the cone. The shorter leg of this triangle is a radius of the circle, and the longer leg is the height of the cone. The angle with measure 112° is an exterior angle of the triangle. Its supplement, which is the larger acute angle in the triangle, measures $180° - 112° = 68°$. Use the triangle to find h.

$$\tan 68° = \frac{h}{18}$$
$$h = 18(\tan 68°)$$

(Store this value in your calculator rather than rounding this intermediate result.)

Now find the volume of the cone.

$$V = \frac{1}{3}BH = \frac{1}{3}\pi r^2 H = \frac{1}{3}\pi(18)^2(18 \tan 68°)$$
$$\approx 15{,}116 \text{ cm}^3$$

12. Yes, the plan meets the act's requirements. The angle of ascent is approximately 4.3°. Use the side view to find the slope of the ramp.

$$\text{slope} = \frac{\text{rise}}{\text{run}} = \frac{1.5}{20} = 0.075$$

The slope must be less than $\frac{1}{12} = 0.08\overline{3}$. Because $0.075 < 0.08\overline{3}$, the ramp is not too steep. By looking at the top and front views, you can see that there is a 5-by-5 ft landing for every 1.5 ft of rise, so

the landing requirement is exceeded. Thus, all requirements of the Americans with Disabilities Act are met.

The angle of ascent is $\tan^{-1}\left(\frac{1.5}{20}\right) \approx 4.3°$.

13. Approximately 52 km. Let d represent the distance between the sailboat and the dock. In the figure below, S represents the position of the sailboat, L represents the position of the lighthouse, and D represents the position of the dock.

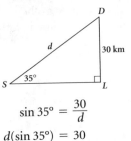

$$\sin 35° = \frac{30}{d}$$
$$d(\sin 35°) = 30$$
$$d = \frac{30}{\sin 35°} \approx 52$$

The distance between the lighthouse and the dock is approximately 52 km.

14. Approximately 7.3°. Let θ be the angle of descent. Recall that the angle of descent (or angle of depression) is measured with respect to the horizontal. Make a sketch.

By the AIA Conjecture, the smaller acute angle in the right triangle is congruent to the angle of descent. Use this triangle to find θ.

$$\tan \theta = \frac{5.6}{44}$$
$$\theta = \tan^{-1}\left(\frac{5.6}{44}\right) \approx 7.3°$$

The angle of descent is approximately 7.3°.

15. Approximately 22 ft. Let l represent the length of one rafter, not including the overhang. The center line of the house is the altitude from the vertex angle of the isosceles triangle, so it is also a median. Look at the right triangle on the left, which has longer leg of length $\frac{1}{2}(32) = 16$ ft and hypotenuse of length l.

$$\cos 36° = \frac{16}{l}$$
$$l(\cos 36°) = 16$$
$$l = \frac{16}{\cos 36°} \approx 20 \text{ ft}$$

Add 2 ft for the overhang. The carpenter should make each rafter approximately 22 ft long.

16. Approximately 6568 m. In the figure below, P represents the position of the patrol boat, H represents the position of the helicopter, and L represents the position of the landing spot.

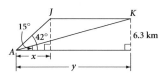

$$\cos 15° = \frac{PL}{6800}$$

$$PL = 6800(\cos 15°) \approx 6568$$

The patrol boat is approximately 6568 m from the point where the package will land.

17. Approximately 2973 km/h. Let A represent Amelia's position, J represent the jet's position the first time she sees it, and K represent the jet's position 20 seconds later.

To find the speed of the jet, you will need to find the distance JK that the jet flew in 20 seconds. There are two right triangles in the figure, but $\overline{JK}$ is not a side of either of them. However, notice that $JK = y - x$, and that x and y are lengths of legs of the right triangles, which can be found from the given information. (To get an accurate final answer, it is important not to round intermediate results.)

$$\tan 42° = \frac{6.3}{x}$$

$$x(\tan 42°) = 6.3$$

$$x = \frac{6.3}{\tan 42°}$$

$$\tan 15° = \frac{6.3}{y}$$

$$y(\tan 15°) = 6.3$$

$$y = \frac{6.3}{\tan 15°}$$

Then $JK = y - x = \left(\frac{6.3}{\tan 15°} - \frac{6.3}{\tan 42°} \right)$ km.

Convert 20 seconds to hours:

$$20 \text{ sec} \cdot \frac{1 \text{ min}}{60 \text{ sec}} \cdot \frac{1 \text{ h}}{60 \text{ min}} = \frac{1}{180} \text{ h}$$

To find the speed of the jet, use the formula $d = rt$, or $r = \frac{d}{t}$:

$$r = \frac{d}{t} = \frac{\left(\frac{6.3}{\tan 15°} - \frac{6.3}{\tan 42°} \right) \text{ km}}{\frac{1}{180} \text{ h}}$$

$$= \left(\frac{6.3}{\tan 15°} - \frac{6.3}{\tan 42°} \right) \cdot 180 \text{ km/h} \approx 2973 \text{ km/h}$$

18. 393 cm². Use the SAS Triangle Area Conjecture.

$$A = \frac{1}{2}ab \sin C = \frac{1}{2}(24)(40) \sin 55° \approx 393 \text{ cm}^2$$

19. 30 cm. Use the Law of Sines.

$$\frac{\sin A}{a} = \frac{\sin B}{b}$$

$$\frac{\sin 76°}{w} = \frac{\sin 53°}{25}$$

$$w \sin 53° = 25 \sin 76°$$

$$w = \frac{25 \sin 76°}{\sin 53°} \approx 30 \text{ cm}$$

20. 78°. Use the Law of Sines.

$$\frac{\sin A}{a} = \frac{\sin C}{c}$$

$$\frac{\sin A}{37} = \frac{\sin 50°}{29}$$

$$\sin A = \frac{37 \sin 50°}{29}$$

$$A = \sin^{-1}\left(\frac{37 \sin 50°}{29} \right) \approx 78°$$

21. 105 cm. Use the Law of Cosines.

$$c^2 = a^2 + b^2 - 2ab \cos C$$

$$x^2 = (101)^2 + (65)^2 - 2(101)(65) \cos 75°$$

$$x = \sqrt{101^2 + 65^2 - 2 \cdot 101 \cdot 65 \cos 75°}$$

$$\approx 105 \text{ cm}$$

22. 51°. Use the Law of Cosines. The length of the side opposite $\angle B$ is 27 cm, so $b = 27$ cm. Let $a = 27$ cm and $c = 34$ cm to identify the other two sides.

$$b^2 = a^2 + c^2 - 2ac \cos B$$

$$27^2 = 27^2 + 34^2 - 2(27)(34)\cos B$$

$$27^2 - 27^2 - 34^2 = -2(27)(34)\cos B$$

$$\cos B = \frac{-34^2}{-2(27)(34)} = \frac{34}{2 \cdot 27} = \frac{17}{27}$$

$$B = \cos^{-1}\left(\frac{17}{27} \right) \approx 51°$$

23. 759 cm². The figure is a rhombus, and the diagonal divides the rhombus into two congruent isosceles triangles. Let x represent the side length of the rhombus. Apply the Law of Cosines.

$$26^2 = x^2 + x^2 - 2 \cdot x \cdot x \cdot \cos 48°$$

$$676 = 2x^2 - 2x^2 \cdot \cos 48°$$

$$2x^2 = \frac{676}{1 - \cos 48°}$$

$$x^2 = \frac{1}{2} \cdot \frac{676}{1 - \cos 48°} = \frac{338}{1 - \cos 48°}$$

Although you can solve for x at this point, it is not necessary, because the next formula you'll use involves x^2 rather than x.

Apply the SAS Triangle Angle Conjecture.

$$A_{\text{triangle}} = \frac{1}{2}ab\sin C = \frac{1}{2} \cdot x \cdot x \cdot \sin 48°$$

$$= \frac{1}{2}x^2 \cdot \sin 48° = \frac{1}{2}\left(\frac{338}{1 - \cos 48°}\right)\sin 48°$$

$$A_{\text{rhombus}} = 2 \cdot A_{\text{triangle}} = 2 \cdot \frac{1}{2}\left(\frac{338}{1 - \cos 48°}\right)\sin 48°$$

$$= \frac{338}{1 - \cos 48°} \cdot \sin 48° \approx 759 \text{ cm}^2$$

24. Approximately 25 cm. Draw segments from the center of the pentagon to its five vertices to form five congruent isosceles triangles. The apothem of the pentagon is the height of each of these five triangles and divides each of them into two congruent right triangles.

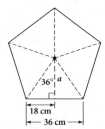

Use one of the small right triangles to find a, the apothem of the pentagon. Each of the five central angles in the figure has measure $\frac{360°}{5} = 72°$. Because the altitude from the vertex angle to the base of an isosceles triangle is also an angle bisector, the smaller acute angle in the right triangle has measure 36°. Because this altitude is also a median, the length of the shorter leg (opposite the 36° angle) is 18 cm.

$$\tan 36° = \frac{18}{a}$$

$$a(\tan 36°) = 18$$

$$a = \frac{18}{\tan 36°} \approx 25 \text{ cm}$$

25. 72 cm². There are several possible approaches to this problem. Three different possible solutions are shown here.

First solution: Make a sketch. Draw the triangle and the altitude from the vertex angle to the base of this isosceles triangle.

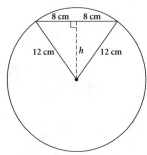

Let h represent the height of the isosceles triangle (the length of the altitude). This altitude divides the

isosceles triangle into two congruent right triangles. Use the Pythagorean Theorem to find h.

$$h = \sqrt{12^2 - 8^2} = \sqrt{80} = \sqrt{16 \cdot 5}$$

$$= \sqrt{16} \cdot \sqrt{5} = 4\sqrt{5} \text{ cm}$$

Now find the area of the triangle.

$$A = \frac{1}{2}bh = \frac{1}{2} \cdot 16 \cdot 4\sqrt{5} = 32\sqrt{5} \text{ cm}^2 \approx 72 \text{ cm}^2$$

Second solution: Use Hero's formula, $A = \sqrt{s(s - a)(s - b)(s - c)}$, where s is the semiperimeter of the triangle. (See pages 469–470 in your book.)

For this triangle, let $a = 12$ cm, $b = 12$ cm, and $c = 16$ cm.

$$s = \frac{1}{2}(a + b + c) = \frac{1}{2}(12 + 12 + 16) = \frac{1}{2}(40) = 20$$

$$A = \sqrt{s(s - a)(s - b)(s - c)}$$

$$= \sqrt{20(20 - 12)(20 - 12)(20 - 16)}$$

$$= \sqrt{20(8)(8)(4)} = \sqrt{5120} \approx 72 \text{ cm}^2$$

Note that $\sqrt{5120}$ can be simplified: $\sqrt{5120} = \sqrt{1024 \cdot 5} = \sqrt{1024} \cdot \sqrt{5} = 32\sqrt{5}$. This shows that the answers obtained in the first two solutions are equal. It is not necessary to simplify the radicals if you use your calculator to obtain a decimal approximation rather than giving an exact answer.

Third solution: Notice that the first two solutions do not involve trigonometry. It is also possible to solve this problem by using a combination of the Law of Cosines and the SAS Triangle Area Conjecture. Look at the sketch for the first solution above, but ignore the altitude and look at the whole isosceles triangle. Let θ be the central angle in the circle, which is the vertex angle of the isosceles triangle. Use the Law of Cosines to find an expression for the measure of this angle.

$$16^2 = 12^2 + 12^2 - 2 \cdot 12 \cdot 12 \cdot \cos\theta$$

$$16^2 - 12^2 - 12^2 = -2 \cdot 12 \cdot 12 \cdot \cos\theta$$

$$\cos\theta = \frac{16^2 - 12^2 - 12^2}{-2 \cdot 12 \cdot 12} = \frac{-32}{-288} = \frac{1}{9}$$

$$\theta = \cos^{-1}\left(\frac{1}{9}\right)$$

You can now find the area of the triangle by using the SAS Triangle Area Conjecture. Because this area formula involves $\sin\theta$, it is better to substitute the exact value of θ obtained above rather than a decimal approximation.

$$A = \frac{1}{2}ab\sin C = \frac{1}{2}(12)(12)\sin\left[\cos^{-1}\left(\frac{1}{9}\right)\right]$$

$$\approx 72 \text{ cm}^2$$

Discovering Geometry Solutions Manual
©2008 Key Curriculum Press

26. Approximately 15.7 cm. Make a sketch.

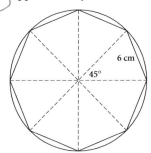

Draw radii to the eight vertices of the octagon, forming eight congruent isosceles triangles. The vertex angle of each of these triangles measures $\frac{360°}{8} = 45°$. In one of the isosceles triangles, draw the altitude to the base, which is an apothem of the octagon. Let r represent the radius of the circle, which is the length of a leg of the triangle.

The altitude divides the isosceles triangle into two congruent right triangles, each with shorter leg of length 3 cm and smallest angle of measure $\frac{45°}{2} = 22.5°$. Use this triangle to find r.

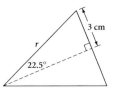

$$\sin 22.5° = \frac{3}{r}$$

$$r(\sin 22.5°) = 3$$

$$r = \frac{3}{\sin 22.5°} \approx 7.84$$

$$d = 2r = 2\left(\frac{3}{\sin 22.5°}\right) \approx 15.7 \text{ cm}$$

The diameter of the circle is approximately 15.7 cm.

27. Approximately 33.5 cm². The diameter of the circle is 24 cm, so the radius is 12 cm. Thus, you can use the same basic diagram as in Exercise 25. The shaded region in the figure below is the segment of the circle whose area you need to find.

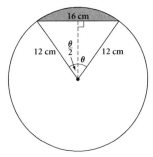

$$A_{\text{segment}} = A_{\text{sector}} - A_{\text{triangle}}$$

If you solved Exercise 25, you already have found the area of the triangle in this diagram. (If not, refer to the solution for Exercise 25, which shows three methods for finding this area.) Therefore, you only need to find the area of the sector and then subtract the area of the triangle.

$\sin \frac{\theta}{2} = \frac{8}{12} = \frac{2}{3}$, so $\frac{\theta}{2} = \sin^{-1}\left(\frac{2}{3}\right)$, and $\theta = 2\sin^{-1}\left(\frac{2}{3}\right)$. Find the area of the sector.

$$\frac{\theta}{360°} \cdot \pi r^2 = \left(\frac{2\sin^{-1}\left(\frac{2}{3}\right)}{360°} \cdot \pi \cdot 12^2\right) \text{cm}^2$$

From the first or second method of solution for Exercise 25, the area of the triangle is $32\sqrt{5}$ cm².

$$A_{\text{segment}} = A_{\text{sector}} - A_{\text{triangle}}$$

$$= \left(\frac{2\sin^{-1}\left(\frac{2}{3}\right)}{360°} \cdot \pi \cdot 12^2\right) - 32\sqrt{5}$$

$$\approx 33.5 \text{ cm}^2$$

28. Approximately 10.1 km/h at an approximate bearing of 24.5°. Place the figure in your book with respect to the north and east lines.

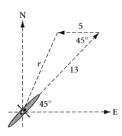

Recall that bearing is always measured clockwise from the north line. Because $90° - 45° = 45°$, the angle between the east line and the vector representing the velocity in still water is also 45°. The vector representing the current is parallel to the east line, so, by the AIA Conjecture, the angle of the triangle opposite the side of length r is also 45°. Use the Law of Cosines to find r.

$$r^2 = 5^2 + 13^2 - 2(5)(13)\cos 45°$$

$$r = \sqrt{5^2 + 13^2 - 2(5)(13)\cos 45°} \approx 10.1$$

The speed of Leslie's kayak is approximately 10.1 km/h. Now find the direction (bearing) of Leslie's kayak. Let θ be the angle of the triangle opposite the side of length 5. Use the Law of Sines to find θ.

$$\frac{\sin \theta}{5} = \frac{\sin 45°}{r}$$

$$\sin \theta = \frac{5 \sin 45°}{r}$$

$$\theta = \sin^{-1}\left(\frac{5 \sin 45°}{r}\right) \approx 20.5°$$

The bearing is $45° - \theta \approx 24.5°$.

29. False. An octahedron is a polyhedron with eight faces.

30. False

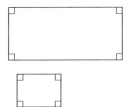

31. True

32. True

33. False. The ratio of their areas is $\frac{m^2}{n^2}$.

34. True

35. False. Tangent of $\angle T = \frac{\text{length of side opposite } \angle T}{\text{length of side adjacent to } \angle T}$.

36. True

37. True

38. True

39. True. The area of this triangle is $\frac{1}{2} \cdot 6 \cdot 8 \cdot \sin 60° = \frac{1}{2} \cdot 6 \cdot 8 \cdot \frac{\sqrt{3}}{2} = 12\sqrt{3}$ cm³. (You can find $\sin 60° = \frac{\sqrt{3}}{2}$ from the relationship between the sides of a 30°-60°-90° triangle.)

40. False. The slope of line ℓ_2 is $-\frac{1}{m}$.

41. False

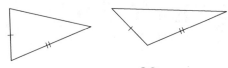

42. B

43. C

44. A. Use the Law of Sines to find $m\angle L$.

$\dfrac{\sin L}{JK} = \dfrac{\sin K}{JL}$ The Law of Sines.

$\sin L = \dfrac{(JK)\sin K}{JL}$ Solve for sin L.

$\sin L = \dfrac{(11)(\sin 42°)}{13}$ Substitute known values.

$L = \sin^{-1}\left[\dfrac{(11)(\sin 42°)}{13}\right]$ Take the inverse sine of both sides.

$L \approx 34.48°$ Use a calculator to evaluate.

45. D

46. B

47. B

48. A

49. B

50. C. Apply the Extended Parallel/Proportionality Conjecture.

$\dfrac{6}{9 + 6 + 3} = \dfrac{4}{m}$

$\dfrac{6}{18} = \dfrac{4}{m}$

$m = 12$

51. D. The displaced volume is $(4)(8)(9) = 288$ cm³.

52. C

53. A. Use proportional sides of similar triangles. Let h equal the height of the boy.

$\dfrac{h}{1.75} = \dfrac{32}{12} = \dfrac{8}{3}$

$h = 1.75 \cdot \dfrac{8}{3}$

$h = \dfrac{14}{3}$ ft $= 4\dfrac{2}{3}$ ft $= 4$ ft 8 in.

54. $\frac{100\pi}{3}$ cm³ ≈ 104.7 cm³. The central angle of the base of the remaining portion of the cone is $360° - 240° = 120°$, so the solid is $\frac{120}{360} = \frac{1}{3}$ of the cone.

$V_{\text{cone}} = \dfrac{1}{3}BH = \dfrac{1}{3}\pi r^2 H$

$V_{\text{portion of cone}} = \dfrac{1}{3}\left(V_{\text{cone}}\right) = \dfrac{1}{3}\left(\dfrac{1}{3}\pi r^2 H\right) = \dfrac{1}{9}\pi r^2 H$

$\qquad = \dfrac{1}{9}\pi(5)^2(12) = \dfrac{300\pi}{9} = \dfrac{100\pi}{3}$ cm³

$\qquad \approx 104.7$ cm³

55. 28π cm³ ≈ 87.96 cm³. The solid is a truncated cone. To find its volume, subtract the volume of the missing cone (portion removed) from the volume of the complete cone. The height of the missing cone is $6 - 3 = 3$ cm. The radius of the missing cone is not shown, but can be found using proportional sides of similar right triangles. Let x represent the radius of the missing cone.

$\dfrac{3}{6} = \dfrac{x}{4}$

$x = 2$ cm

$V_{\text{complete cone}} = \dfrac{1}{3}\pi r^2 H = \dfrac{1}{3}\pi(4)^2 \cdot 6 = 32\pi$ cm³

$V_{\text{missing cone}} = \dfrac{1}{3}\pi r^2 H = \dfrac{1}{3}\pi(2)^2 \cdot 3 = 4\pi$ cm³

$V_{\text{truncated cone}} = 32\pi - 4\pi = 28\pi$ cm³ ≈ 87.96 cm³

56. 30.5π cm³ ≈ 95.82 cm³. The volume of the solid, which is a shell of a cone, is the difference between the volume of the complete cone and the volume of the missing cone (the portion of the original cone that has been removed).

$V_{\text{complete cone}} = \dfrac{1}{3}\pi r^2 H = \dfrac{1}{3}\pi(5)^2(7.5) = 62.5\pi$ cm³

$V_{\text{missing cone}} = \dfrac{1}{3}\pi r^2 H = \dfrac{1}{3}\pi(4)^2(6) = 32\pi$ cm³

$V_{\text{shell}} = 62.5\pi - 32\pi = 30.5\pi$ cm³ ≈ 95.82 cm³

57. 33. Use inductive reasoning.

Number of people	2	3	4	5
Number of hugs	1	3	6	10

From the table, you can find a rule: If there are n people, there will be $\dfrac{n(n-1)}{2}$ hugs. You can also find this pattern by the following reasoning: Each person hugs each other person exactly once. If there are n people, each of them must hug each of the other people exactly once, and there are $(n-1)$ other people. However, if you count $n(n-1)$ hugs, you would be counting each hug twice, once for each of the two people hugging. Therefore, if there are n people, there will be $\dfrac{n(n-1)}{2}$ hugs. Use algebra to

Discovering Geometry Solutions Manual
©2008 Key Curriculum Press

find the value of n for which $\frac{n(n-1)}{2} = 528$.

$$\frac{n(n-1)}{2} = 528$$

$$n(n-1) = 1056$$

$$n^2 - n = 1056$$

$$n^2 - n - 1056 = 0$$

$$(n+32)(n-33) = 0$$

$$n + 32 = 0 \text{ or } n - 33 = 0$$

$$n = -32 \quad \text{ or } n = 33$$

Reject -32 as a possible solution because the number of people must be a positive integer. There were 33 people at the reunion.

58. $(x, y) \rightarrow (x + 1, y - 3)$. The first translation moves each point of the triangle right 2 units and down 1 unit, while the second translation moves each point of the image triangle left 1 unit and down 2 units. Thus, the composition moves each point of the original triangle right 1 unit and down 3 units; the rule for the single translation is $(x, y) \rightarrow (x + 1, y - 3)$. (Notice that you don't need to know the coordinates of the vertices to find the rule.)

59. $w = 48$ cm, $x = 24$ cm, $y = 28.5$ cm. First use the similar triangles to find w. Because $\triangle LMN \sim \triangle PQR$, corresponding sides are proportional.

$$\frac{LM}{PQ} = \frac{MN}{QR}$$

$$\frac{28}{21} = \frac{w}{36}$$

$$\frac{4}{3} = \frac{w}{36}$$

$36 = 12(3)$, so $w = 12(4) = 48$ cm.

Now recall the Angle Bisector/Opposite Side Conjecture: A bisector of an angle of a triangle divides the opposite side into two segments whose lengths are in the same ratio as the lengths of the two sides forming the angle. This conjecture can be used to find x.

$$\frac{14}{x} = \frac{28}{w}$$

$$\frac{14}{x} = \frac{28}{48} = \frac{7}{12}$$

$14 = 2(7)$, so $x = 2(12) = 24$ cm.

Then $LN = 14 + x = 14 + 24 = 38$ cm.

Go back to the similar triangles to find y.

$$\frac{ML}{QP} = \frac{LN}{PR}$$

$$\frac{28}{21} = \frac{38}{y}$$

$$\frac{4}{3} = \frac{38}{y}$$

$$4y = 114$$

$$y = 28.5 \text{ cm}$$

60. Approximately 18 cm. By the Triangle Sum Conjecture, the measure of the third angle of the triangle is $180° - 48° - 26° = 106°$. Use the Law of Sines to find x.

$$\frac{\sin 26°}{x} = \frac{\sin 106°}{39}$$

$$x(\sin 106°) = 39(\sin 26°)$$

$$x = \frac{39 \sin 26°}{\sin 106°} \approx 18 \text{ cm}$$

61. $(x - 5)^2 + (y - 1)^2 = 9$. To write the equation of the circle, you need to find its center and radius. The center of the circle is the midpoint of any diameter. Let C represent the center of the circle.

$$C = \left(\frac{5+5}{2}, \frac{-2+4}{2}\right) = (5, 1)$$

The radius is the distance between the center and any point on the circle. The distance between $(5, 1)$ and $(5, 4)$ is 3 units. (You can use the distance formula to find this distance, but because both points have x-coordinate 5, it is easier to just find the difference of their y-coordinates: $4 - 1 = 3$.) Substitute $h = 5$, $k = 1$, and $r = 3$ in the equation of a circle.

$$(x - h)^2 + (y - k)^2 = r^2$$

$$(x - 5)^2 + (y - 1)^2 = 3^2$$

$$(x - 5)^2 + (y - 1)^2 = 9$$

62. Possible answer: Each interior angle in a regular pentagon is $108°$. Three angles would have a sum of $324°$, $36°$ short of $360°$, which would leave a gap. Four angles would have a sum exceeding $360°$ and hence create an overlap.

63. Approximately 99.46 m. Let h represent the height of the temple and x represent the height of the temple above Ertha's eye level. Make a sketch.

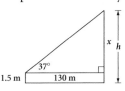

$$\tan 37° = \frac{x}{130}$$

$$h = x + 1.5 = 130 \tan 37° + 1.5 \approx 99.46 \text{ m}$$

64. 30 ft. By the Parallel Lines Intercepted Arcs Conjecture, $m\widehat{HK} = m\widehat{SJ}$. Therefore, $m\widehat{HK} = \frac{1}{2}(360° - 80° - 40°) = \frac{1}{2}(240°) = 120°$. Now use the Arc Length Conjecture to find the circumference, and then use the circumference to find the radius. Here r represents the radius of the circle and C represents the circumference.

Length of $\overparen{HK} = \dfrac{120°}{360°} \cdot C = \dfrac{1}{3}C$

$$20\pi = \dfrac{1}{3}C$$

$$3(20\pi) = 3\left(\dfrac{1}{3}C\right)$$

$$C = 60\pi \text{ ft}$$

$C = 2\pi r$, so $60\pi = 2\pi r$, and $r = \dfrac{60\pi}{2\pi} = 30$ ft.

65. 4 cm. The shaded region is a sector of the circle with central angle of measure $360° - 135° = 225°$. Use the given area of the sector to find the radius.

$$A_{\text{sector}} = \left(\dfrac{225°}{360°}\right)\pi r^2 = \dfrac{5}{8}\pi r^2$$

$$10\pi = \dfrac{5}{8}\pi r^2$$

$$\dfrac{8}{5}(10\pi) = \dfrac{8}{5}\left(\dfrac{5}{8}\pi r^2\right)$$

$$r^2 = 16$$

$$r = \sqrt{16} = 4$$

(Because r represents the radius of a circle, only the positive square root makes sense in this situation.) The radius of the circle is 4 cm.

66.

a. $m\angle ABC = 2 \cdot m\angle ABD$. Look at the two right triangles in the figure. $\overline{AB} \cong \overline{CB}$ and $\overline{BD} \cong \overline{BD}$. Then, by the Pythagorean Theorem, $\overline{AD} \cong \overline{CD}$. Thus, $\triangle ABD \cong \triangle CBD$ by the SSS Congruence Conjecture, and thus $\angle ABD \cong \angle CBD$ by CPCTC. This is equivalent to saying that $m\angle ABC = 2 \cdot m\angle ABD$. (This proves that the altitude from the vertex angle of *any* isosceles triangle is also the angle bisector.)

b. Possible answers: $\overline{BD}$ is the perpendicular bisector of $\overline{AC}$. It is the angle bisector of $\angle ABC$, it is the median to $\overline{AC}$ and it divides $\triangle ABC$ into two congruent right triangles. The other possible answers follow from using more corresponding parts of the right triangles or by applying the Vertex Angle Bisector Conjecture: In an isosceles triangle, the bisector of the vertex angle is also the altitude and the median.

TAKE ANOTHER LOOK

1. Several approaches are possible. Here is one of the simplest.

$$\dfrac{a}{\sin A} = \dfrac{1}{\dfrac{\sin A}{a}} = \dfrac{1}{\dfrac{\sin B}{b}} = \dfrac{b}{\sin B}$$

A similar argument can be used for $\dfrac{c}{\sin C}$.

2. Students might want to use geometry software to help them see patterns. Measurements indicate that $\angle CB_2A$ and $\angle CB_1A$ are supplementary; for example, $m\angle CB_2A = 57.7°$ and $m\angle CB_1A = 123.3°$. The Law of Sines, then, says that $\sin \theta = \sin(180° - \theta)$.

3. $a^2 = b^2 + c^2 - 2bc \cos A$; $b^2 = a^2 + c^2 - 2ac \cos B$

4. Possible answer:

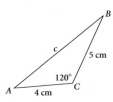

In this triangle, $a = 5$ cm, $b = 4$ cm, and $m\angle C = 120°$.

Use the Law of Cosines to find c.

$$c^2 = a^2 + b^2 - 2ab \cos C$$

$$= 5^2 + 4^2 - 2(5)(4) \cos 120°$$

$$= 25 + 16 - 40(-0.5)$$

$$= 61$$

$$c = \sqrt{61} \approx 7.8 \text{ cm}$$

Measuring c with a ruler also gives $c \approx 7.8$ cm.

Drawing and measuring other obtuse triangles will confirm that the Law of Cosines gives the correct length for the side opposite the obtuse angle.

The Law of Cosines works for obtuse triangles. When $\angle C$ is obtuse, $\cos C$ is negative, so $-2ab \cos C$ is positive.

5. Possible proof: From the diagram, $DB = x - a$. Apply the Pythagorean Theorem to right triangle ADB.

$$c^2 = (x - a)^2 + h^2$$

Now apply the Pythagorean Theorem to right triangle ADC.

$$b^2 = h^2 + x^2 \text{, or } h^2 = b^2 - x^2$$

Substitute $b^2 - x^2$ for h^2 in the first equation.

$$c^2 = (x - a)^2 + b^2 - x^2$$

Use algebra to expand $(x - a)^2$ and simplify.

$$c^2 = x^2 - 2ax + a^2 + b^2 - x^2$$

$$c^2 = a^2 + b^2 - 2ax$$

In $\triangle ADC$, $\cos C = \dfrac{x}{b}$, so $x = b \cos C$.

Substitute $b \cos C$ for x in the equation $c^2 = a^2 + b^2 - 2ax$ to obtain the Law of Cosines.

$$c^2 = a^2 + b^2 - 2ab \cos C$$

6. Both x and y can be related to the circumference of the cone's base, which is the length of the sector's arc. Label the radius of the arc L, the slant height of the cone, so the arc's length is $\frac{x}{360°} \cdot 2\pi L = \pi L\left(\frac{x}{180°}\right)$. The radius of the cone, then, is this circumference divided by 2π, or $L\left(\frac{x}{360°}\right)$. The sine of $\frac{y}{2}$ is this radius over L, or $\frac{x}{360°}$, so $y = 2\sin^{-1}\left(\frac{x}{360°}\right)$. Or use the Law of Cosines with $c = L \cdot \frac{x}{180°}$, $a = L$, and $b = L$ to arrive at the equivalent answer: $y = \cos^{-1}\left(1 - \frac{x^2}{64{,}800}\right)$.

7. Possible answer:

If $m\angle A = 20°$, $(\sin A)^2 + (\cos A)^2 \approx (0.3420)^2 + (0.9397)^2 \approx 0.1170 + 0.8830 = 1$.

If $m\angle A = 40°$, $(\sin A)^2 + (\cos A)^2 \approx (0.6428)^2 + (0.7660)^2 \approx 0.4132 + 0.5868 = 1$.

If $m\angle A = 75°$, $(\sin A)^2 + (\cos A)^2 \approx (0.9659)^2 + (0.2588)^2 \approx 0.9330 + 0.0670 = 1$.

Conjecture: For any angle A, $(\sin A)^2 + (\cos A)^2 = 1$.

From the diagram, $\sin A = \frac{a}{c}$ and $\cos A = \frac{b}{c}$.

Paragraph Proof: Because $\sin A = \frac{a}{c}$ and $\cos A = \frac{b}{c}$, $(\sin A)^2 + (\cos A)^2 = \frac{a^2 + b^2}{c^2}$, and, by the Pythagorean Theorem, $a^2 + b^2 = c^2$. Therefore, $(\sin A)^2 + (\cos A)^2 = \frac{a^2 + b^2}{c^2} = \frac{c^2}{c^2} = 1$.

CHAPTER 13

LESSON 13.1

EXERCISES

1. A postulate is a statement accepted as true without proof. A theorem is deduced from other theorems or postulates.

2. Subtraction: Equals minus equals are equal. Multiplication: Equals times equals are equal. Division: Equals divided by nonzero equals are equal.

3. Reflexive: Any figure is congruent to itself.

$\triangle ABC \cong \triangle ABC$

Transitive: If Figure A is congruent to Figure B and Figure B is congruent to Figure C, then Figure A is congruent to Figure C.

If $\overline{PQ} \cong \overline{RS}$ and $\overline{RS} \cong \overline{XY}$, then $\overline{PQ} \cong \overline{XY}$.

Symmetric: If Figure A is congruent to Figure B, then Figure B is congruent to Figure A.

If $\angle XYZ \cong \angle LMN$, then $\angle LMN \cong \angle XYZ$.

4. Reflexive property of equality; reflexive property of congruence

5. Transitive property of congruence

6. Subtraction property of equality

7. Division property of equality

8. Distributive; Subtraction; Addition; Division

9. Given; Addition property of equality; Multiplication property of equality; Commutative property of addition

10. True; definition of midpoint

11. True; Midpoint Postulate

12. True; definition of angle bisector

13. True; Angle Bisector Postulate

14. False; Line Intersection Postulate

15. False; Line Postulate

16. True; Angle Addition Postulate

17. True; Segment Addition Postulate

18. • That all men are created equal.

• That they are endowed by their creator with certain inalienable rights, that among these are life, liberty, and the pursuit of happiness.

• That to secure these rights, governments are instituted among men, deriving their just powers from the consent of the governed.

• That whenever any form of government becomes destructive to these ends, it is the right of the people to alter or to abolish it, and to institute new government, laying its foundations on such principles and organizing its powers in such form as to them shall seem most likely to effect their safety and happiness.

19. 1. $\overline{AO}$ and $\overline{BO}$ are radii; 3. $\triangle AOB$ is isosceles, Definition of isosceles

20. 1. $\angle 1 \cong \angle 2$, Given; 2. $m \parallel n$; 3. $\angle 3 \cong \angle 4$, Corresponding Angles Postulate

21. 1. Given; 2. $\overline{AD} \cong \overline{BC}$, Given; 4. $\triangle ABC \cong \triangle BAD$, SSS Congruence Postulate; 5. $\angle D \cong \angle C$

22. 2. $\overline{AB} \cong \overline{CB}$; 3. $\angle ABD \cong \angle CBD$, Definition of angle bisector; 4. Reflexive property of congruence; 5. $\triangle BAD \cong \triangle BCD$, SAS Congruence Postulate; 6. $\angle A \cong \angle C$, CPCTC

23. Add the two integers: $(2n - 1) + (2m - 1) = 2n + 2m - 2 = 2(n + m - 1)$, which is always even.

24. Multiply the two integers: $(2n - 1)(2m - 1) = 4nm - 2n - 2m + 1 = 4nm - 2n - 2m + 2 - 1 = 2(2nm - n - m + 1) - 1$, which is always odd.

25. Let n be any integer. Then the next two consecutive integers are $n + 1$ and $n + 2$. The sum of these three integers is $(n) + (n + 1) + (n + 2) = n + n + 1 + n + 2$. Combining like terms gives $3n + 3 = 3(n + 1)$, which is divisible by 3.

26. ≈ 299 m. Draw the perpendicular segment from the top of the mountain to the ground. Labels have been added to the resulting figure for reference below. In this figure, x represents the distance from B to the mountain peak, D.

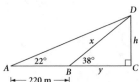

Notice that the figure contains two right triangles.

From $\triangle ACD$, $\tan 22° = \dfrac{h}{220 + y}$. From $\triangle BCD$, $\tan 38° = \dfrac{h}{y}$.

From the first equation, $h = (220 + y)(\tan 22°)$, and from the second equation, $h = y(\tan 38°)$. Therefore, $(220 + y)(\tan 22°) = y(\tan 38°)$. Solve this equation.

$$(220 + y)(\tan 22°) = y(\tan 38°)$$

$$220(\tan 22°) + y(\tan 22°) = y(\tan 38°)$$

$$220(\tan 22°) = y(\tan 38°) - y(\tan 22°)$$

$$220(\tan 22°) = y(\tan 38° - \tan 22°)$$

$$y = \frac{220 \tan 22°}{\tan 38° - \tan 22°}$$

$$h = y(\tan 38°) = \left(\frac{220 \tan 22°}{\tan 38° - \tan 22°}\right)(\tan 38°)$$

By the Pythagorean Theorem, $x^2 = h^2 + y^2$, so $x = \sqrt{h^2 + y^2} \approx 299$ m.

27. Volume: sphere, cylinder, cone

Cone: $V = \frac{1}{3}\pi r^2 H = \frac{1}{3}\pi(6)^2(12) = 144\pi \approx 452.4$ cm³

Sphere: $V = \frac{4}{3}\pi r^3 = \frac{4}{3}\pi(5)^3 = \frac{500}{3}\pi \approx 523.6$ cm³

Cylinder: $V = \pi r^2 H = \pi(5.5)^2(5.5) \approx 522.7$ cm³

Surface area: cylinder, cone, sphere

Cone: l (slant height) $= \sqrt{12^2 + 6^2} = \sqrt{180} = \sqrt{36 \cdot 5} = 6\sqrt{5}$ cm

$S = \pi r^2 + \pi r l = \pi(6)^2 + \pi(6)(6\sqrt{5}) = 36\pi + 36\sqrt{5}\pi \approx 366.0$ cm²

Sphere: $S = 4\pi r^2 = 4\pi(5)^2 = 100\pi \approx 314.2$ cm²

Cylinder: $S = 2\pi r^2 + 2\pi r H = 2\pi(5.5)^2 + 2\pi(5.5)(5.5) = 121\pi \approx 380.1$ cm²

Length of longest rod that will fit inside: cone, cylinder, sphere

Cone: length of longest rod = slant height = $6\sqrt{5}$ cm ≈ 13.4 cm

Sphere: length of longest rod = diameter = 10 cm

Cylinder: length of longest rod = hypotenuse of right triangle with one leg of length 11 cm (diameter of base) and other leg of length 5.5 cm (height of cylinder) = $\sqrt{11^2 + 5.5^2} = \sqrt{151.25} \approx 12.3$ cm

28. 30 ft. Let h represent the height at which the guy wires cross. Add labels to the figure for reference.

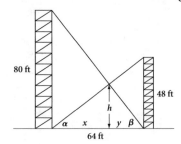

Use similar triangles. From the two right triangles that share the angle with measure α, $\dfrac{h}{x} = \dfrac{48}{64} = 0.75$, so $h = 0.75x$. From the two triangles that share the angle with measure β, $\dfrac{h}{64 - x} = \dfrac{80}{64} = 1.25$, so $h = 1.25(64 - x)$. Therefore, $0.75x = 1.25(64 - x)$. Solve this equation for x.

$$0.75x = 1.25(64 - x)$$

$$0.75x = 80 - 1.25x$$

$$2x = 80$$

$$x = 40$$

$$h = x(\tan \alpha) = 40(0.75) = 30 \text{ ft}$$

You may want to challenge students to do this problem without knowing the distance between the two towers (the height of the crossing is independent of this distance). Here is a possible solution.

Add a vertical segment 80 ft tall, going through the point of intersection. Also add a horizontal segment from the top of the 80-ft tower to the top of the new vertical segment, and another from the base of the 48-ft tower to the base of the new vertical segment. Mark all congruent angles, by the Corresponding Angles Conjecture.

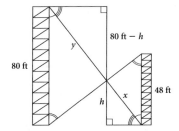

By the AA Similarity Conjecture, the two triangles having a tower as one side are similar, so $\frac{x}{y} = \frac{48}{80} = \frac{3}{5}$. Similarly, the two right triangles are similar, so $\frac{h}{80 - h} = \frac{x}{y} = \frac{3}{5}$. Solve this equation for h.

$$\frac{h}{80 - h} = \frac{3}{5}$$

$$5h = 3(80 - h)$$

$$5h = 240 - 3h$$

$$8h = 240$$

$$h = 30$$

Note that we never once referred to the distance between the two towers. This same argument can be used to show that if the two towers have heights a and b, then the height of the intersection of the guy wires is $h = \frac{ab}{a + b}$, which in our case is $h = \frac{80 \cdot 48}{80 + 48} = \frac{3840}{128} = 30$.

29. $FG = 2\sqrt{6}$ and $DG = 2\sqrt{3}$ because $ABGF$ and $BCDG$ are parallelograms. Triangle FGD is right ($m\angle FGD = 90°$) by the Converse of the Pythagorean Theorem because $(2\sqrt{6})^2 + (2\sqrt{3})^2 = 6^2$. But $m\angle FGB = 128°$ by the Parallelogram Consecutive Angles Conjecture and $m\angle DGB = 140°$ by the Parallelogram Opposite Angles Conjecture. So, $m\angle FGD = 92°$ because the sum of the angles around G is 360°. So, $m\angle FGD$ is both 90° and 92°.

30. $x = 54°$, $y = 126°$, $a = 7.3$ m. First look at the right triangle that contains the 27° angle. The measure of the third angle in this triangle is $90° - 27° = 63°$. This angle and the angle marked as congruent to it form a linear pair with the angle of measure x. Thus, $x + 2(63°) = 180°$, so $x = 54°$. Now look at the right triangle in which the hypotenuse has length 7.3. In this triangle, the measure of the unmarked angle is $90° - 54° = 36°$. Next look at the triangle that contains the side of length 6.8. By the AIA Conjecture, the angle opposite this side is a right angle. The angle whose measure is the sum of this right angle and the adjacent 36° angle forms a vertical angle with the angle of measure y, so $y = 90° + 36° = 126°$. Now look at the triangle in the center of the figure that contains a 63° angle and an angle that forms a linear pair with the angle of measure y. The

measure of that angle is $180° - y = 180° - 126° = 54°$. (You can also find this angle measure by AIA using $x = 54°$.) The measure of the third angle of this triangle is $180° - 63° - 54° = 63°$, so the triangle is isosceles. The side opposite one of the 63° angles is 7.3, so the side opposite the other 63° angle is also 7.3 (Converse of the Isosceles Triangle Conjecture). Finally, look at the obtuse triangle with angles of measure y and 27°. Because $y = 126°$, the measure of the third angle in this triangle is $180° - 126° - 27° = 27°$, so this triangle is also isosceles. From the 63°-63°-54° triangle, you know that the length of the side opposite the 27° angle on the far right is 7.3, so the length of the side opposite the other 27° angle must also be 7.3, that is, $a = 7.3$.

31. a. $\frac{\pi}{4}$. The shaded region is a quarter-circle with radius 1, so $A = \frac{1}{4}\pi r^2 = \frac{1}{4}\pi(1)^2 = \frac{\pi}{4}$.

   b. $1 - \frac{\pi}{4}$. The area of the shaded region is the difference between the area of the square of side length 1 and the area of the shaded region in 31a, so $A = 1^2 - \frac{\pi}{4} = 1 - \frac{\pi}{4}$.

   c. $\frac{\pi}{2} - 1$. By looking at the figures from 31a and 31b and using the symmetry of these figures, you can see that the area of the shaded region is the difference between the area you found in 31a and the area you found in 31b. Therefore,

   $$A = \frac{\pi}{4} - \left(1 - \frac{\pi}{4}\right) = \frac{\pi}{4} - 1 + \frac{\pi}{4} = \frac{\pi}{2} - 1.$$

IMPROVING YOUR REASONING SKILLS

Because only four moves are allowed and the letter in each place changes, each letter must change only once. There are several possibilities for each string and for original creations. Here's one of many possible sets:

1. MATH ⇒ MATE ⇒ RATE ⇒ ROTE ⇒ ROSE

2. MATH ⇒ MATE ⇒ MARE ⇒ MORE ⇒ CORE

3. MATH ⇒ MASH ⇒ MAST ⇒ MOST ⇒ HOST

4. MATH ⇒ MASH ⇒ MASS ⇒ MESS ⇒ LESS

5. MATH ⇒ LATH ⇒ LATE ⇒ LAVE ⇒ LIVE

Sample answer for original creation: MATH ⇒ PATH ⇒ PITH ⇒ PITA ⇒ PICA

LESSON 13.2

EXERCISES

1. Linear Pair Postulate

2. Parallel Postulate, Angle Addition Postulate, Linear Pair Postulate, CA Postulate (through the AIA Theorem)

3. Parallel Postulate

4. Perpendicular Postulate

5. Given: Two angles are both congruent and supplementary

Show: Each angle is a right angle

(These angles may form a linear pair, as in the figure below, but they do not have to for the proof to work.)

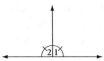

Given: $\angle 1 \cong \angle 2$ and $\angle 1$ and $\angle 2$ are supplementary

Show: $\angle 1$ and $\angle 2$ are right angles

Paragraph Proof: By the definition of supplementary angles, $m\angle 1 + m\angle 2 = 180°$. By the definition of congruence, $m\angle 1 = m\angle 2$. Therefore, by substitution, $m\angle 1 + m\angle 1 = 180°$, or $2m\angle 1 = 180°$. By the division property, $m\angle 1 = 90°$. Then, by the transitive property, $m\angle 2 = 90°$. Thus, by the definition of a right angle, $\angle 1$ and $\angle 2$ are both right angles.

6. Given: Two angles are congruent

Show: The supplements of the two angles are congruent

(The figure below shows supplementary angles as linear pairs, but they do not have to be for the proof to work.)

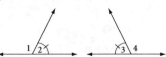

Given: $\angle 2 \cong \angle 3$, $\angle 1$ and $\angle 2$ are supplementary, $\angle 4$ and $\angle 3$ are supplementary

Show: $\angle 1 \cong \angle 4$

Paragraph Proof: By the definition of supplementary angles, $m\angle 1 + m\angle 2 = 180°$ and $m\angle 4 + m\angle 3 = 180°$. Then, by the transitive property, $m\angle 1 + m\angle 2 = m\angle 4 + m\angle 3$. By the definition of congruence, $m\angle 2 = m\angle 3$, so, by substitution, $m\angle 1 + m\angle 2 = m\angle 4 + m\angle 2$. By the subtraction property, $m\angle 1 = m\angle 4$. Therefore, by the definition of congruence, $\angle 1 \cong \angle 4$.

7. Given: Two angles are right angles

Show: The two angles are congruent

Given: $\angle 1$ and $\angle 2$ are right angles

Show: $\angle 1 \cong \angle 2$

Paragraph Proof: By the definition of a right angle, $m\angle 1 = 90°$ and $m\angle 2 = 90°$. Then, by the transitive property, $m\angle 1 = m\angle 2$. Therefore, by the definition of congruence, $\angle 1 \cong \angle 2$.

8. Given: Two lines cut by a transversal to form congruent alternate interior angles

Show: The two lines are parallel

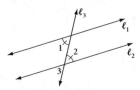

Given: Lines ℓ_1 and ℓ_2 cut by transversal ℓ_3; $\angle 1 \cong \angle 2$

Show: $\ell_1 \parallel \ell_2$

Flowchart Proof

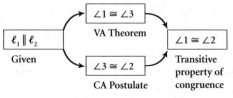

9. Given: Two parallel lines cut by a transversal to form alternate exterior angles

Show: The alternate exterior angles are congruent

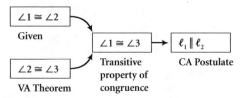

Given: Lines ℓ_1 and ℓ_2 cut by transversal ℓ_3; $\ell_1 \parallel \ell_2$

Show: $\angle 1 \cong \angle 2$

Flowchart Proof

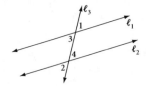

10. Given: Two lines cut by a transversal to form congruent alternate exterior angles

Show: The lines are parallel

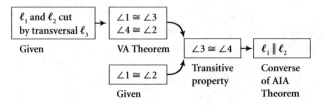

Given: Lines ℓ_1 and ℓ_2 cut by transversal ℓ_3; $\angle 1 \cong \angle 2$

Show: $\ell_1 \parallel \ell_2$

Flowchart Proof

11. Given: Two parallel lines cut by a transversal to form interior angles on the same side of the transversal

Show: The two angles are supplementary

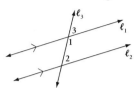

Given: Lines ℓ_1 and ℓ_2 cut by transversal ℓ_3; $\ell_1 \parallel \ell_2$

Show: $\angle 1$ and $\angle 2$ are supplementary

Flowchart Proof *(See proof at bottom of page)*

12. Given: Two lines cut by a transversal to form supplementary interior angles on the same side of the transversal

Show: The two lines are parallel

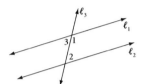

Given: Lines ℓ_1 and ℓ_2 cut by transversal ℓ_3; $\angle 1$ and $\angle 2$ are supplementary

Show: $\ell_1 \parallel \ell_2$

Paragraph Proof: By the definition of supplementary angles, $m\angle 1 + m\angle 2 = 180°$. By the Linear Pair Postulate, $\angle 1$ and $\angle 3$ are supplementary. Then, by the definition of supplementary angles, $m\angle 1 + m\angle 3 = 180°$. Therefore, by the substitution property, $m\angle 1 + m\angle 3 = m\angle 1 + m\angle 2$. By the subtraction property, $m\angle 3 = m\angle 2$. Angles 3 and 2 are alternate interior angles, so, by the Converse of the AIA Theorem, $\ell_1 \parallel \ell_2$.

13. Given: Two lines in the same plane, each parallel to a third line

Show: The two lines are parallel to each other

Given: Coplanar lines ℓ_1, ℓ_2, and ℓ_3 with $\ell_1 \parallel \ell_2$ and $\ell_3 \parallel \ell_2$

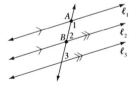

Show: $\ell_1 \parallel \ell_3$

Paragraph Proof: By the Line Postulate, construct $\overleftrightarrow{AB}$ with A on ℓ_1 and B on ℓ_2. This transversal will intersect ℓ_3 by the Parallel Postulate (otherwise there would be 2 lines through point B parallel to ℓ_3). By the Interior Supplements Theorem, $\angle 1$ and $\angle 2$ are supplementary, so, by the definition of supplementary angles, $m\angle 1 + m\angle 2 = 180°$. By the CA Postulate, $\angle 2 \cong \angle 3$, so, by the definition of congruence, $m\angle 2 = m\angle 3$. Then, by the substitution property, $m\angle 1 + m\angle 3 = 180°$ and $\angle 1$ and $\angle 3$ are supplementary by definition. Therefore, $\ell_1 \parallel \ell_3$ by the Converse of the Interior Supplements Theorem.

14. Given: Two lines in the same plane are each perpendicular to a third line

Show: The two lines are parallel to each other

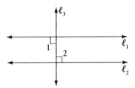

Given: Coplanar lines ℓ_1, ℓ_2, and ℓ_3 with $\ell_1 \perp \ell_3$ and $\ell_2 \perp \ell_3$

Show: $\ell_1 \parallel \ell_2$

Flowchart Proof

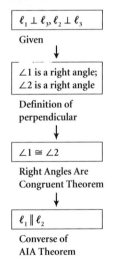

Lesson 13.2, Exercise 11.

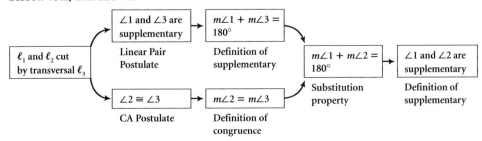

15. Given: Right triangle with ∠1 as the right angle and ∠2 and ∠3 as the acute angles

Show: ∠2 and ∠3 are complementary

Paragraph Proof: By the Triangle Sum Theorem, $m\angle1 + m\angle2 + m\angle3 = 180°$. By the definition of right angle, $m\angle1 = 90°$. Using the subtraction property, $m\angle2 + m\angle3 = 90°$, so by the definition of complementary angles, ∠2 and ∠3 are complementary.

16.

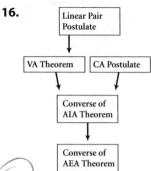

17. 1066 cm³. The volume of the truncated pyramid is the difference between the volume of the complete pyramid (before the top was sliced off) and the volume of the top that was sliced off, which is a smaller pyramid. These two pyramids will be referred to as *large pyramid* and *small pyramid* in this solution.

The cut is two-thirds of the distance from the base to the vertex, or one-third of the distance from the vertex to the base. This means that the height of the small pyramid is one-third the height of the large one. The two pyramids are similar, so each side of the base of the small triangle is one-third the length of the corresponding side of the large triangle. By the Proportional Volumes Conjecture,

$$\frac{V_{\text{small pyramid}}}{V_{\text{large pyramid}}} = \left(\frac{1}{3}\right)^3 = \frac{1}{27}$$

Then the volume of the truncated pyramid is $1 - \frac{1}{27} = \frac{26}{27}$ of the volume of the large pyramid, or $\frac{26}{27}(1107) = 1066$ cm³.

18. No, assuming the bottom is included. (If the bottom is *not* included and the gables can be cut separately from the rectangular parts of the back and front, then yes.) Make a table showing the pieces needed.

	Area (ft)²
Bottom (2-by-3 rectangle)	6
2 sides $\left(3\text{-by-}1\frac{1}{2}\text{ rectangle}\right)$	9
Back and front $\left(2\text{-by-}1\frac{1}{2}\text{ rectangle}\right)$	6
2 rooftops $\left(3\text{-by-}\sqrt{2}\text{ rectangle}\right)$	$\approx 8\frac{1}{2}$
2 gable ends (2-by-1 triangle)	2
Total	$31\frac{1}{2}$
Plywood (4-by-8 rectangle)	32

The area is less than that of one sheet of plywood. However, it is impossible to cut the correct size pieces from one piece, because so many of the dimensions add to 3 ft, leaving a one-foot strip that is too small for any pieces but the gables. Two sheets would be enough.

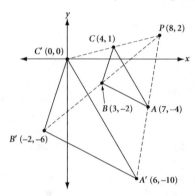

19. $A'(6, -10)$, $B'(-2, -6)$, $C'(0, 0)$; mapping rule: $(x, y) \rightarrow (2x - 8, 2y - 2)$. Draw △ABC on graph paper and locate the center of the dilation, (8, 2). Label (8, 2) as P. To find the vertices of the image triangle, △A'B'C', draw $\overline{PA}$, $\overline{PB}$, and $\overline{PC}$. Extend each of these segments to locate A', B', and C' such that $A'A = PA$, $B'B = PB$, and $C'C = PC$.

Use the figure to find the coordinates of the image triangle: $A'(6, -10)$, $B'(-2, -6)$, and $C'(0, 0)$. Because the center of dilation is (8, 2) rather than (0, 0) and the scale factor is 2, the mapping rule is $(x, y) \rightarrow (8 + 2(x - 8), 2 + 2(y - 2)) = (2x - 8, 2y - 2)$. You can verify that this rule gives the same results as the graph for the image of each point of △ABC.

IMPROVING YOUR VISUAL THINKING SKILLS

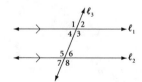

EXTENSION

Given: $\ell_1 \parallel \ell_2$, ℓ_1 and ℓ_2 cut by transversal ℓ_3

Show: $\angle2 \cong \angle6$

Paragraph Proof: $\angle 2 \cong \angle 7$ by AEA. $\angle 7 \cong \angle 6$ by the VA Theorem, so $\angle 2 \cong \angle 6$ by the transitive property of congruence.

LESSON 13.3

EXERCISES

1. Given: A point on the perpendicular bisector of a segment

Show: The point is equidistant from the endpoints of the segment

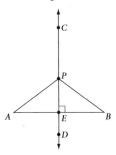

Given: $\overline{AB}$ with perpendicular bisector $\overleftrightarrow{CD}$; $\overleftrightarrow{CD}$ intersects $\overline{AB}$ at E; P is a point on $\overleftrightarrow{CD}$

Show: $AP = BP$

Case 1: A, B, and P are collinear.

Paragraph Proof: P is on $\overline{AB}$ and $\overleftrightarrow{CD}$ (given), so $P = E$ by the Line Intersection Postulate. P is the midpoint of $\overline{AB}$ by the definition of perpendicular bisector, so $AP = BP$ by the definition of midpoint.

Case 2: A, B, and P are not collinear.

Plan: Use the SAS Congruence Postulate to get $\triangle AEP \cong \triangle BEP$. Then use CPCTC to get $\overline{AP} \cong \overline{BP}$.

Proof:

Statement	Reason
1. $\overleftrightarrow{CD}$ is the perpendicular bisector of $\overline{AB}$	1. Given
2. E is the midpoint of $\overline{AB}$	2. Definition of perpendicular bisector
3. $\overline{AE} \cong \overline{BE}$	3. Definition of midpoint
4. $\overline{PE} \perp \overline{AB}$	4. Definition of perpendicular bisector
5. $\angle PEA$ and $\angle PEB$ are right angles	5. Definition of perpendicular
6. $\angle PEA \cong \angle PEB$	6. Right Angles Are Congruent Theorem
7. $\overline{PE} \cong \overline{PE}$	7. Reflexive property of congruence
8. $\triangle AEP \cong \triangle BEP$	8. SAS Congruence Postulate
9. $\overline{AP} \cong \overline{BP}$	9. CPCTC
10. $AP = BP$	10. Definition of congruence

2. Given: A segment and a point that is equidistant from the endpoints of the segment

Show: The point is on the perpendicular bisector of the segment

Let $\overline{AB}$ be the segment and P be the point. In order to prove the theorem, two cases need to be considered.

Case 1: A, P, and B are collinear. (P is on $\overline{AB}$ between A and B.)

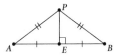

Given: A, P, and B are collinear; $PA = PB$

Show: P is on the perpendicular bisector of $\overline{AB}$

Paragraph Proof: $PA = PB$ is given, so $\overline{PA} \cong \overline{PB}$ by the definition of congruence. Because P is on $\overline{AB}$, this means that P is the midpoint of $\overline{AB}$ by the definition of midpoint. Then P is on the perpendicular bisector of $\overline{AB}$ by the definition of perpendicular bisector.

Case 2: A, P, and B are not collinear. (P is not on $\overline{AB}$.)

Given: A, P, and B are not collinear; $PA = PB$

Show: P is on the perpendicular bisector of $\overline{AB}$

Paragraph Proof: Let E be the midpoint of $\overline{AB}$ (Midpoint Postulate). Use the Line Postulate to draw $\overline{PE}$. $PA = PB$ is given, so $\overline{PA} \cong \overline{PB}$ by the definition of congruence. $\overline{EA} \cong \overline{EB}$ by the definition of midpoint. $\overline{PE} \cong \overline{PE}$ by the reflexive property of congruence. Therefore, $\triangle AEP \cong \triangle BEP$ by the SSS Congruence Postulate. Then $\angle AEP \cong \angle BEP$ by CPCTC and $\angle AEP$ and $\angle BEP$ are a linear pair by construction and are thus supplementary by the Linear Pair Postulate. So, $\angle AEP$ and $\angle BEP$ are both right angles by the Congruent and Supplementary Theorem. Therefore, $\overline{PE}$ is the perpendicular bisector of $\overline{AB}$ by the definition of perpendicular bisector.

3. Given: Isosceles triangle

Show: The base angles of the triangle are congruent

Given: Isosceles triangle ABC

Show: $\angle A \cong \angle B$

Plan: Use the reflexive property and the SSS Congruence Postulate to get $\triangle ABC \cong \triangle BAC$. Therefore, $\angle A \cong \angle B$ by CPCTC.

Proof:

Statement	Reason
1. $\overline{AC} \cong \overline{BC}$	1. Definition of isosceles
2. $\overline{BC} \cong \overline{AC}$	2. Symmetric property of congruence
3. $\overline{AB} \cong \overline{AB}$	3. Reflexive property of congruence
4. $\triangle ABC \cong \triangle BAC$	4. SSS Congruence Postulate
5. $\angle A \cong \angle B$	5. CPCTC

4. Given: Triangle with two congruent angles

Show: The triangle is isosceles

Given: $\triangle ABC$ with $\angle A \cong \angle B$

Show: $\triangle ABC$ is isosceles

Plan: Use the reflexive property and the ASA Congruence Postulate to get $\triangle ABC \cong \triangle BAC$. Then use CPCTC and the definition of isosceles triangle.

Proof:

Statement	Reason
1. $\angle A \cong \angle B$	1. Given
2. $\angle B \cong \angle A$	2. Symmetric property of congruence
3. $\overline{AB} \cong \overline{BA}$	3. Reflexive property of congruence
4. $\triangle ABC \cong \triangle BAC$	4. ASA Congruence Postulate
5. $\overline{AC} \cong \overline{BC}$	5. CPCTC
6. $\triangle ABC$ is isosceles	6. Definition of isosceles triangle

5. Given: An angle with a point that is equidistant from the sides of the angle

Show: The point is on the bisector of the angle

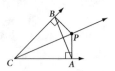

Given: $\angle BCA$ with P in the interior of the angle; P is equidistant from $\overrightarrow{CA}$ and $\overrightarrow{CB}$.

Show: P is on the angle bisector of $\angle BCA$

Paragraph Proof: Use the Line Postulate and Perpendicular Postulate to draw perpendicular segments $\overline{PB}$ and $\overline{PA}$ from P to the sides of the angle and also to draw $\overline{BA}$. By the definition of distance from a point to a line and the given equidistance, $PB = PA$, so $\overline{PB} \cong \overline{PA}$ by the definition of congruence. Thus, $\triangle PAB$ is isosceles with legs $\overline{PB}$ and $\overline{PA}$. Therefore, by the Isosceles Triangle Theorem, $\angle PAB \cong \angle PBA$. By the Angle Addition Postulate, $m\angle CAP = m\angle BAC + m\angle PAB$, and

$m\angle CBP = m\angle CBA + m\angle PBA$. $m\angle CAP = m\angle CBP = 90°$ by the definition of perpendicular. Thus, by the subtraction property, $\angle BAC \cong \angle ABC$. Then, by the Converse of the Isosceles Triangle Theorem, $\overline{CB} \cong \overline{CA}$. By the reflexive property of congruence, $\overline{CP} \cong \overline{CP}$. Therefore, $\triangle ACP \cong \triangle BCP$ by the SSS Congruence Postulate, and thus $\angle ACP \cong \angle BCP$ by CPCTC. Therefore, $\overrightarrow{CP}$ is the angle bisector of $\angle BCA$ by the definition of angle bisector, and P is on the angle bisector.

6. Given: A triangle with the three perpendicular bisectors of the sides

Show: The three perpendicular bisectors are concurrent

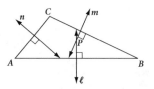

Given: $\triangle ABC$ with lines ℓ, m, and n as perpendicular bisectors of sides $\overline{AB}$, $\overline{BC}$, and $\overline{AC}$, respectively

Show: ℓ, m, and n are concurrent

Paragraph Proof: By the Line Intersection Postulate, lines ℓ and m intersect in exactly one point; call that point P. Because P is on the perpendicular bisectors of both $\overline{AB}$ and $\overline{BC}$, by the Perpendicular Bisector Theorem, $AP = BP$ and $BP = CP$. Then, by the transitive property, $AP = CP$. Then, by the Converse of the Perpendicular Bisector Theorem, point P is on line n, the perpendicular bisector of $\overline{AC}$. Therefore ℓ, m, and n are concurrent by the definition of concurrent.

7. Given: A triangle with the three angle bisectors

Show: The three angle bisectors are concurrent

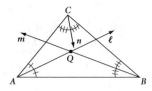

Given: $\triangle ABC$ with lines ℓ, m, and n as the angle bisectors of $\angle A$, $\angle B$, and $\angle C$, respectively

Show: ℓ, m, and n are concurrent

Paragraph Proof: By the Line Intersection Postulate, lines ℓ and m intersect in exactly one point; call that point Q. Because Q is on the angle bisectors of both $\angle A$ and $\angle B$, by the Angle Bisector Theorem, Q is equally distant from $\overrightarrow{AB}$ and $\overrightarrow{AC}$ and also from $\overrightarrow{AB}$ and $\overrightarrow{BC}$. Then, by the transitive property, Q is equally distant from $\overrightarrow{AC}$ and $\overrightarrow{BC}$. Then, by the Converse of the Angle Bisector Theorem, point Q is on n. Therefore ℓ, m, and n are concurrent by the definition of concurrent.

8. Given: A triangle with one exterior angle drawn

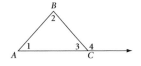

Show: The measure of the exterior angle is equal to the sum of the measures of its two remote interior angles

Given: $\triangle ABC$ with interior angles $\angle 1$, $\angle 2$, and $\angle 3$ at vertices A, B, and C, respectively; $\angle 4$ an exterior angle at vertex C

Show: $m\angle 4 = m\angle 1 + m\angle 2$

Plan: Use the Linear Pair Postulate and the definition of supplementary angles to get $m\angle 3 + m\angle 4 = 180°$. Then use the Triangle Sum Theorem and the transitive property to get $m\angle 1 + m\angle 2 + m\angle 3 = m\angle 3 + m\angle 4$. Therefore, $m\angle 1 + m\angle 2 = m\angle 4$ by the subtraction property.

Proof:

Statement	Reason
1. $\angle 4$ is an exterior angle at vertex C	1. Given
2. $\angle 3$ and $\angle 4$ are supplementary	2. Linear Pair Postulate
3. $m\angle 3 + m\angle 4 = 180°$	3. Definition of supplementary
4. $m\angle 1 + m\angle 2 + m\angle 3 = 180°$	4. Triangle Sum Theorem
5. $m\angle 1 + m\angle 2 + m\angle 3 = m\angle 3 + m\angle 4$	5. Transitive property
6. $m\angle 1 + m\angle 2 = m\angle 4$	6. Subtraction property

9. Given: Any quadrilateral

Show: The sum of the measures of the four angles is 360°

Given: Quadrilateral $ABCD$

Show: $m\angle A + m\angle ABC + m\angle C + m\angle CDA = 360°$

Plan: Use the Triangle Sum Theorem and the addition property to get $m\angle A + m\angle 1 + m\angle 3 + m\angle C + m\angle 4 + m\angle 2 = 360°$. Then use the Angle Addition Postulate and the substitution property to get $m\angle A + m\angle ABC + m\angle C + m\angle CDA = 360°$.

Proof:

Statement	Reason
1. Construct $\overline{DB}$	1. Line Postulate
2. $m\angle A + m\angle 1 + m\angle 3 = 180°$	2. Triangle Sum Theorem
3. $m\angle C + m\angle 4 + m\angle 2 = 180°$	3. Triangle Sum Theorem
4. $m\angle A + m\angle 1 + m\angle 3 + m\angle C + m\angle 4 + m\angle 2 = 360°$	4. Addition property
5. $m\angle A + (m\angle 1 + m\angle 2) + m\angle C + (m\angle 3 + m\angle 4) = 360°$	5. Commutative and associative properties of addition
6. $m\angle 1 + m\angle 2 = m\angle ABC$	6. Angle Addition Postulate
7. $m\angle 3 + m\angle 4 = m\angle ADC$	7. Angle Addition Postulate
8. $m\angle A + m\angle ABC + m\angle C + m\angle ADC = 360°$	8. Substitution property

10. Given: Isosceles triangle

Show: The medians to the congruent sides are congruent

Given: Isosceles triangle ABC with $\overline{AC} \cong \overline{BC}$; $\overline{BN}$ is the median to $\overline{AC}$ and $\overline{AM}$ is the median to $\overline{BC}$

Show: $\overline{BN} \cong \overline{AM}$

Plan: Use the definitions of median and midpoint to get $BM = \frac{1}{2}BC$ and $AN = \frac{1}{2}AC$. Then use the multiplication property and the substitution property to get $\overline{AN} \cong \overline{BM}$. By the reflexive property, the Isosceles Triangle Theorem, and the SAS Congruence Postulate, $\triangle ABN \cong \triangle BAM$. Therefore, $\overline{BN} \cong \overline{AM}$ by CPCTC.

Proof:	**Statement**	**Reason**
	1. $\overline{BN}$ is the median to $\overline{AC}$; $\overline{AM}$ is the median to $\overline{BC}$	1. Given
	2. N is the midpoint of $\overline{AC}$; M is the midpoint of $\overline{BC}$	2. Definition of median
	3. $\overline{AC} \cong \overline{BC}$	3. Given
	4. $AC = BC$	4. Definition of congruence
	5. $\frac{1}{2}AC = \frac{1}{2}BC$	5. Multiplication property
	6. $AN = \frac{1}{2}AC$; $BM = \frac{1}{2}BC$	6. Definition of midpoint
	7. $AN = BM$	7. Substitution property
	8. $\overline{AN} \cong \overline{BM}$	8. Definition of congruence
	9. $\overline{AB} \cong \overline{BA}$	9. Reflexive property of congruence
	10. $\angle CAB \cong \angle CBA$	10. Isosceles Triangle Theorem
	11. $\triangle ABN \cong \triangle BAM$	11. SAS Congruence Postulate
	12. $\overline{BN} \cong \overline{AM}$	12. CPCTC

11. Given: Isosceles triangle

Show: The angle bisectors to congruent sides are congruent

Given: Isosceles triangle ABC with $\overline{AC} \cong \overline{BC}$; $\overline{BQ}$ is the angle bisector to $\overline{AC}$ and $\overline{AP}$ is the angle bisector to $\overline{BC}$

Show: $\overline{AP} \cong \overline{BQ}$

Plan: Use the definition of angle bisector to get $m\angle PAB = \frac{1}{2}m\angle CAB$ and $m\angle QBA = \frac{1}{2}m\angle CBA$. Then use the Isosceles Triangle Theorem, the multiplication property, and the substitution property to get $\angle PAB \cong \angle QBA$. By the reflexive property and the ASA Congruence Postulate, $\triangle ABP \cong \triangle BAQ$. Therefore, $\overline{AP} \cong \overline{BQ}$ by CPCTC.

Proof:	**Statement**	**Reason**
	1. $\overline{BQ}$ is the angle bisector to $\overline{AC}$; $\overline{AP}$ is the angle bisector to $\overline{BC}$	1. Given
	2. $\overline{BQ}$ is the angle bisector of $\angle CBA$; $\overline{AP}$ is the angle bisector of $\angle CAB$	2. $\overline{AC}$ is opposite $\angle ABC$; $\overline{BC}$ is opposite $\angle CAB$
	3. $m\angle PAB = \frac{1}{2}m\angle CAB$; $m\angle QBA = \frac{1}{2}m\angle CBA$	3. Definition of angle bisector
	4. $\overline{AC} \cong \overline{BC}$	4. Given
	5. $\angle CAB \cong \angle CBA$	5. Isosceles Triangle Theorem
	6. $m\angle CAB = m\angle CBA$	6. Definition of congruence
	7. $\frac{1}{2}m\angle CAB = \frac{1}{2}m\angle CBA$	7. Multiplication property
	8. $m\angle PAB = m\angle QBA$	8. Substitution
	9. $\angle PAB \cong \angle QBA$	9. Definition of congruence
	10. $\overline{AB} \cong \overline{BA}$	10. Reflexive property of congruence
	11. $\triangle ABP \cong \triangle BAQ$	11. ASA Congruence Postulate
	12. $\overline{AP} \cong \overline{BQ}$	12. CPCTC

12. Given: Isosceles triangle

Show: The altitudes to congruent sides are congruent

Given: Isosceles triangle ABC with $\overline{AC} \cong \overline{BC}$; $\overline{AS}$ is the altitude to $\overline{BC}$, and $\overline{BT}$ is the altitude to $\overline{AC}$

Show: $\overline{AS} \cong \overline{BT}$

Discovering Geometry Solutions Manual
©2008 Key Curriculum Press

Plan: Use the Isosceles Triangle Theorem, the Right Angles Are Congruent Theorem, and the SAA Theorem to get $\triangle ASB \cong \triangle BTA$. Then $\overline{AS} \cong \overline{BT}$ by CPCTC.

Proof: Statement	Reason
1. $\overline{AS}$ is the altitude to $\overline{BC}$; $\overline{BT}$ is the altitude to $\overline{AC}$	1. Given
2. $\overline{AS} \perp \overline{BC}$; $\overline{BT} \perp \overline{AC}$	2. Definition of altitude
3. $\angle ASB$ is a right angle; $\angle BTA$ is a right angle	3. Definition of perpendicular
4. $\angle ASB \cong \angle BTA$	4. Right Angles Are Congruent Theorem
5. $\overline{AC} \cong \overline{BC}$	5. Given
6. $\angle ABC \cong \angle CAB$	6. Isosceles Triangle Theorem
7. $\overline{AB} \cong \overline{BA}$	7. Reflexive property of congruence
8. $\triangle ASB \cong \triangle BTA$	8. SAA Theorem
9. $\overline{AS} \cong \overline{BT}$	9. CPCTC

---

13. Theorem A: median → angle bisector

Given: Isosceles triangle ACB with $\overline{AC} \cong \overline{BC}$; $\overline{CD}$ is the median to $\overline{AB}$

Show: $\overline{CD}$ is the angle bisector of $\angle ACB$

Paragraph Proof: By the definition of median, $\overline{AD} \cong \overline{BD}$. $\overline{AC} \cong \overline{BC}$ is given. $\overline{CD} \cong \overline{CD}$ by the reflexive property of congruence. Therefore, $\triangle ADC \cong \triangle BDC$ by the SSS Congruence Postulate. $\angle ACD \cong \angle BCD$ by CPCTC, and $\overline{CD}$ is the angle bisector of $\angle ACB$ by the definition of angle bisector.

Theorem B: angle bisector → altitude

Given: Isosceles triangle ACB with $\overline{AC} \cong \overline{BC}$; $\overline{CD}$ is the angle bisector of $\angle ACB$

Show: $\overline{CD}$ is the altitude from C to $\overline{AB}$

Paragraph Proof: By the definition of angle bisector, $\angle ACD \cong \angle BCD$. $\overline{AC} \cong \overline{BC}$ is given. $\overline{CD} \cong \overline{CD}$ by the reflexive property of congruence. Therefore, $\triangle ADC \cong \triangle BDC$ by the SAS Congruence Postulate. $\angle CDA \cong \angle CDB$ by CPCTC. By the Linear Pair Postulate and the Congruent and Supplementary Theorem, $\angle ADC$ and $\angle BDC$ are both right angles. Therefore, $\overline{CD}$ is the altitude by the definitions of perpendicular and altitude.

Theorem C: altitude → median

Given: Isosceles triangle ACB with $\overline{AC} \cong \overline{BC}$; $\overline{CD}$ is the altitude from C to $\overline{AB}$

Show: $\overline{CD}$ is the median to $\overline{AB}$

Paragraph Proof: By the definitions of altitude and perpendicular, $\angle CDA$ and $\angle CDB$ are right angles. Then $\angle CDA \cong \angle CDB$ by the Right Angles Are Congruent Theorem. $\overline{AC} \cong \overline{BC}$ is given, and therefore $\angle A \cong \angle B$ by the Isosceles Triangle Theorem. Thus, $\triangle ADC \cong \triangle BDC$ by the SAA Theorem, and $\overline{AD} \cong \overline{BD}$ by CPCTC. Therefore, $\overline{CD}$ is the median to $\overline{AB}$ by the definition of median.

14. $x = 6$, $y = 3$. Label points in the figure for reference.

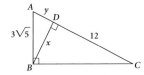

$\triangle ABD \sim \triangle ACB$ by the AA Similarity Conjecture. ($\angle A$ is common to both triangles; $\angle ADB$ and $\angle ABC$ are both right angles.) Corresponding sides of similar triangles are proportional, so $\frac{AB}{AC} = \frac{AD}{AB}$. Use this proportion to find y.

$$\frac{3\sqrt{5}}{y + 12} = \frac{y}{3\sqrt{5}}$$
$$y(y + 12) = \left(3\sqrt{5}\right)^2$$
$$y^2 + 12y = 45$$

$$y^2 + 12y - 45 = 0$$

$$(y + 15)(y - 3) = 0$$

$$y + 15 = 0 \text{ or } y - 3 = 0$$

$$y = -15 \text{ or } y = 3$$

Reject -15 because y represents a side length and therefore must be positive, so $y = 3$.

Now apply the Pythagorean Theorem to $\triangle ABD$ to find x:

$$x^2 + y^2 = \left(3\sqrt{5}\right)^2$$

$$x^2 + 9 = 45$$

$$x^2 = 36$$

$$x = 6$$

15. ≈ 21.9 m. Let S be the location of the nest on the top of the shorter tree and T be the location of the nest on the taller tree.

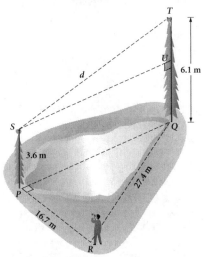

Triangle PQR is a right triangle with hypotenuse $\overline{RQ}$. Apply the Pythagorean Theorem to this triangle to find PQ.

$$16.7^2 + (PQ)^2 = 27.4^2$$

$$PQ = \sqrt{27.4^2 - 16.7^2} = \sqrt{471.87}$$

(This length is approximately 21.72 m, but do not round this intermediate result.)

Because both trees are vertical, $\overline{SP} \parallel \overline{TQ}$. $\overline{ST}$ and $\overline{PQ}$ are not parallel. Thus, $PSTQ$ is a trapezoid. Draw $\overline{SU}$, the perpendicular segment from S to $\overline{TQ}$, to form parallelogram $PSUQ$ (which is also a rectangle). Opposite sides of a parallelogram are congruent, so $SU = PQ = \sqrt{471.87}$. Now look at $\triangle STU$. Because $\overline{SU} \perp \overline{TU}$, this is a right triangle with hypotenuse $\overline{ST}$. Because $\overline{SP}$ and $\overline{UQ}$ are opposite sides of a parallelogram, $UQ = SP = 3.6$, so

$TU = TQ - UQ = 6.1 - 3.6 = 2.5$. Apply the Pythagorean Theorem to $\triangle STU$ to find $d = ST$.

$$d^2 = \left(\sqrt{471.87}\right)^2 + (2.5)^2$$

$$d = \sqrt{\left(\sqrt{471.87}\right)^2 + (2.5)^2} = \sqrt{478.12} \approx 21.9$$

The distance between the two nests is about 21.9 m.

16. First image: $(0, 3)$; second image: $(6, 1)$. Let B represent the first image of A under the glide reflection and let C represent the second image. Use a graph to find the images.

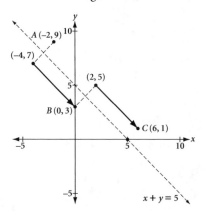

To find the images of A and B under the reflection, draw the line $x + y = 5$, or $y = 5 - x$.

First glide reflection: The image of $A(-2, 9)$ under the reflection across the line $x + y = 5$ is $(-4, 7)$; the image of $(-4, 7)$ under the translation $(x, y) \rightarrow (x + 4, y - 4)$ is $(0, 3)$, so the coordinates of B are $(0, 3)$.

Second glide reflection: Start with $(0, 3)$, the image of A under the first glide reflection. The image of $(0, 3)$ under the reflection is $(2, 5)$; the image of $(2, 5)$ under the translation is $(6, 1)$, so the coordinates of C are $(6, 1)$.

17. $BC = FC$ makes $ABCF$ a rhombus, so the diagonals, $\overline{AC}$ and $\overline{BF}$, are perpendicular. $m\angle FGC = 90°$, so $m\angle CFG + m\angle FCG = 90°$. $\overline{FD} \perp \overline{GE}$, so $m\angle 2 + m\angle CFG = 90°$. By subtraction and transitivity, $m\angle 2 = m\angle FCG$. $\angle 1 \cong \angle FCG$ by AIA, so $\angle 1 \cong \angle 2$ by transitivity.

18. a. $\frac{\sqrt{3}}{4}$. The arcs show that the shaded region is an equilateral triangle with side length 1. Any altitude of this triangle divides the triangle into two congruent 30°-60°-90° triangles with shorter leg of length $\frac{1}{2}$, so the length of the longer leg, which is the height of the triangle, is $\frac{1}{2}(\sqrt{3}) = \frac{\sqrt{3}}{2}$.

Therefore, $A = \frac{1}{2}bh = \frac{1}{2}(1)\left(\frac{\sqrt{3}}{2}\right) = \frac{\sqrt{3}}{4}$.

b. $\frac{\pi}{6}$. The shaded region is a sector of a circle with radius 1. The central angle of this sector is the same angle as the angle in the lower left of the shaded triangle in 18a. Because that triangle is equilateral, the measure of each of its angles is $60°$, so the sector has a $60°$ central angle. Therefore, $A = \frac{60°}{360°}\pi r^2 = \frac{1}{6}\pi(1)^2 = \frac{\pi}{6}$.

c. $\frac{\pi}{3} - \frac{\sqrt{3}}{4}$. The difference between the areas of the shaded regions in 18b and 18a is $\frac{\pi}{6} - \frac{\sqrt{3}}{4}$. To find the area of the shaded region, add twice this difference to the area of the triangle from 18a:

$$A = \frac{\sqrt{3}}{4} + 2\left(\frac{\pi}{6} - \frac{\sqrt{3}}{4}\right) = \frac{\sqrt{3}}{4} + \frac{\pi}{3} - \frac{\sqrt{3}}{2}$$
$$= \frac{\pi}{3} - \frac{\sqrt{3}}{4}$$

19. One possible sequence:

1. Fold A onto B and crease. Label the crease ℓ_1. Label the midpoint of the arc M.

2. Fold line ℓ_1 onto itself so that M is on the crease. Label this crease ℓ_2.

M is the midpoint of $\overset{\frown}{AB}$, and ℓ_2 is the desired tangent.

20. $m\angle BAC \approx 13°$. $\overline{AB} \perp \overline{BC}$, so $\triangle ABC$ is a right triangle with hypotenuse $\overline{AC}$. By the Pythagorean Theorem, $AB = \sqrt{5^2 + 12^2} = 13$. Thus, $\tan\angle BAC = \frac{BC}{AB} = \frac{3}{13}$, and $m\angle BAC = \tan^{-1}\left(\frac{3}{13}\right) \approx 13°$.

21. In each figure, draw $\overline{YW}$ and $\overline{WX}$ to form $\triangle WXY$, $\triangle XOW$, and $\triangle YOW$.

a. B. In each figure, $\overline{OW}$ is a radius and $\overline{YX}$ is a diameter.

In Figure A, $OW = 10$ cm, so $YX = 20$ cm. Because $m\angle WOX = 40°$ and $\angle WOX$ is a central angle of the circle, $m\overset{\frown}{WX} = 40°$. Because $\angle WYX$ is an inscribed angle that intercepts $\overset{\frown}{WX}$, $m\angle WYX = \frac{1}{2}(40°) = 20°$. Because it is inscribed in a semicircle, $\angle YWX$ is a right angle and $\triangle WYX$ is a right triangle with hypotenuse $\overline{YX}$.

Therefore, $\sin 20° = \frac{WX}{YX} = \frac{WX}{20}$, so $WX = 20\sin 20°$, and $\cos 20° = \frac{YW}{YX} = \frac{YW}{20}$, so

$YW = 20\cos 20°$. Thus, perimeter of $\triangle WXY = YX + YW + WX = 20 + 20\sin 20° + 20\cos 20° \approx 45.6$ cm.

In Figure B, $OW = 20$ cm, so $YX = 40$ cm. Use the same reasoning as above to find the other two side lengths in $\triangle WXY$. First $m\angle WOX = 10°$, so $m\overset{\frown}{WX} = 10°$, and $m\angle WYX = \frac{1}{2}(10°) = 5°$. Then $WX = 40\sin 5°$ and $YW = 40\cos 5°$. Thus, perimeter of $\triangle WXY = YX + YW + WX = 40 + 40\sin 5° + 40\cos 5° \approx 83.3$ cm.

Therefore, the perimeter of $\triangle WXY$ is greater in Figure B.

b. B. In both figures, $\triangle XOW$ is an isosceles triangle whose legs are radii of the circle. Apply the SAS Triangle Area Conjecture to $\triangle XOW$ in both figures.

Figure A: $A = \frac{1}{2}(OW)(OX)\sin\angle WOX$
$$= \frac{1}{2}(10)(10)\sin 40° \approx 32.1 \text{ cm}^2$$

Figure B: $A = \frac{1}{2}(OW)(OX)\sin\angle WOX$
$$= \frac{1}{2}(20)(20)\sin 10° \approx 34.7 \text{ cm}^2$$

Therefore, the area of $\triangle XOW$ is greater in Figure B.

22. a. $x = \frac{1}{2}(a + c)$; $y = \frac{1}{2}(a + b)$; $z = \frac{1}{2}(b + c)$

b. $w = \frac{1}{2}(a + b)$; $x = \frac{1}{2}(b + e)$; $y = \frac{1}{2}(e + d)$; $z = \frac{1}{2}(d + a)$

IMPROVING YOUR REASONING SKILLS

The reasoning used for solving these puzzles will vary. Here is a possible approach to solving the first puzzle. Focus on the three squares of nine boxes at the top. The upper left square has 1 and 9 in the middle row, and the upper middle square has 9 and 1 in the bottom row. The top right square also needs a 1 and a 9, and both digits must fall in the top row to avoid repetition. Because the right column contains a 1, the 9 must go in the top right box, leaving the 1 in the adjacent box.

The upper right square is now missing 3, 6, and 7. The 3 must go in the middle row because there is already a 3 in the bottom row of the upper left square. Because there is a 6 in the second column from the right, the 6 must go in the lower right square of the upper right box, and the 7 must be adjacent to it. *Note:* In the completed puzzles below, the bold numbers are the ones that are given in puzzles in the textbook.

7	6	4	8	3	5	2	1	9
1	9	2	6	4	7	3	5	8
5	8	3	9	2	1	4	7	6
8	2	1	4	7	9	5	6	3
6	3	5	2	1	8	7	9	4
9	4	7	3	5	6	1	8	2
4	5	6	1	8	3	9	2	7
2	7	9	5	6	4	8	3	1
3	1	8	7	9	2	6	4	5

4	1	6	8	3	2	5	7	9
7	8	9	5	1	4	3	6	2
5	2	3	7	9	6	1	4	8
8	7	2	3	6	1	9	5	4
3	6	4	2	5	9	8	1	7
9	5	1	4	8	7	2	3	6
6	9	5	1	4	8	7	2	3
2	3	8	6	7	5	4	9	1
1	4	7	9	2	3	6	8	5

LESSON 13.4

EXERCISES

1. Given: A quadrilateral with two pairs of congruent opposite angles

Show: The quadrilateral is a parallelogram

Given: Quadrilateral $ABCD$ with $\angle A \cong \angle C$ and $\angle B \cong \angle D$

Show: $ABCD$ is a parallelogram

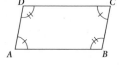

Plan: Use x to represent the measures of one pair of congruent angles and y to represent the other pair. Use the Quadrilateral Sum Theorem and the division property to get $x + y = 180°$. Therefore, the opposite sides are parallel by the Converse of the Interior Supplements Theorem.

Proof:	**Statement**	**Reason**
	1. $\angle A \cong \angle C$; $\angle B \cong \angle D$	1. Given
	2. $m\angle A = m\angle C = x$; $m\angle B = m\angle D = y$	2. Definition of congruence
	3. $x + x + y + y = 360°$	3. Quadrilateral Sum Theorem
	4. $2x + 2y = 360°$	4. Combine like terms
	5. $2(x + y) = 360°$	5. Distributive property
	6. $x + y = 180°$	6. Division property
	7. $\angle A$ and $\angle D$ are supplementary	7. Definition of supplementary
	8. $\overline{DC} \parallel \overline{AB}$	8. Converse of the Interior Supplements Theorem
	9. $\angle A$ and $\angle B$ are supplementary	9. Definition of supplementary
	10. $\overline{AD} \parallel \overline{BC}$	10. Converse of the Interior Supplements Theorem
	11. $ABCD$ is a parallelogram	11. Definition of parallelogram

2. Given: A quadrilateral with one pair of opposite sides that are both parallel and congruent

Show: The quadrilateral is a parallelogram

Given: Quadrilateral $ABCD$ with $\overline{AD} \parallel \overline{BC}$ and $\overline{AD} \cong \overline{BC}$

Show: $ABCD$ is a parallelogram

Plan: Use the AIA Theorem, the reflexive property, and the SAS Congruence Postulate to get $\triangle ADC \cong \triangle CBA$. Then use CPCTC and the Converse of the AIA Theorem to get $\overline{AB} \parallel \overline{DC}$.

Discovering Geometry Solutions Manual
©2008 Key Curriculum Press

Proof:

Statement	Reason
1. Construct $\overline{AC}$	1. Line Postulate
2. $\overline{AD} \parallel \overline{BC}$	2. Given
3. $\angle 1 \cong \angle 2$	3. AIA Theorem
4. $\overline{AD} \cong \overline{BC}$	4. Given
5. $\overline{AC} \cong \overline{CA}$	5. Reflexive property of congruence
6. $\triangle ADC \cong \triangle CBA$	6. SAS Congruence Postulate
7. $\angle 3 \cong \angle 4$	7. CPCTC
8. $\overline{DC} \parallel \overline{AB}$	8. Converse of the AIA Theorem
9. $ABCD$ is a parallelogram	9. Definition of parallelogram

3. Given: Rhombus

Show: Each diagonal of the rhombus bisects two opposite angles

Given: Rhombus $ABCD$ with diagonals $\overline{AC}$ and $\overline{BD}$

Show: $\overline{AC}$ bisects $\angle DAB$ and $\angle BCD$; $\overline{BD}$ bisects $\angle ADC$ and $\angle CBA$

Plan: Use the definition of rhombus, the reflexive property, and the SSS Congruence Postulate to get $\triangle ABC \cong \triangle ADC$. Then use CPCTC and the definition of angle bisector to prove that $\overline{AC}$ bisects $\angle DAB$ and $\angle BCD$. Repeat using diagonal $\overline{BD}$.

Proof:

Statement	Reason
1. $ABCD$ is a rhombus	1. Given
2. $\overline{AB} \cong \overline{AD}$	2. Definition of rhombus
3. $\overline{BC} \cong \overline{DC}$	3. Definition of rhombus
4. $\overline{AC} \cong \overline{AC}$	4. Reflexive property of congruence
5. $\triangle ABC \cong \triangle ADC$	5. SSS Congruence Postulate
6. $\angle 1 \cong \angle 2$; $\angle 6 \cong \angle 5$	6. CPCTC
7. $\overline{AC}$ bisects $\angle DAB$ and $\angle BCD$	7. Definition of angle bisector
8. $\overline{AD} \cong \overline{CD}$	8. Definition of rhombus
9. $\overline{AB} \cong \overline{CB}$	9. Definition of rhombus
10. $\overline{BD} \cong \overline{BD}$	10. Reflexive property of congruence
11. $\triangle ADB \cong \triangle CDB$	11. SSS Congruence Postulate
12. $\angle 3 \cong \angle 4$; $\angle 8 \cong \angle 7$	12. CPCTC
13. $\overline{BD}$ bisects $\angle ABC$ and $\angle ADC$	13. Definition of angle bisector

4. Given: Parallelogram

Show: The consecutive angles are supplementary

Given: Parallelogram $ABCD$

Show: $\angle A$ and $\angle B$ are supplementary; $\angle B$ and $\angle C$ are supplementary; $\angle C$ and $\angle D$ are supplementary; $\angle D$ and $\angle A$ are supplementary

Plan: Use the definition of a parallelogram to get $\overline{AD} \parallel \overline{BC}$ and $\overline{AB} \parallel \overline{DC}$. Then use the Interior Supplements Theorem.

Flowchart Proof

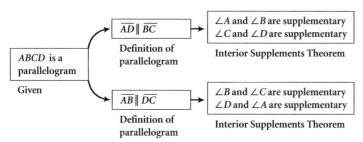

5. Given: A quadrilateral with four congruent sides

   Show: The quadrilateral is a rhombus

   Given: Quadrilateral $ABCD$ with $\overline{AB} \cong \overline{BC} \cong \overline{CD} \cong \overline{DA}$

Show: $ABCD$ is a rhombus

Plan: Use the reflexive property and the SSS Congruence Postulate to get $\triangle ABD \cong \triangle CDB$. Then use CPCTC and the Converse of the AIA Theorem to get $\overline{AB} \parallel \overline{CD}$ and $\overline{AD} \parallel \overline{CB}$. Therefore, $ABCD$ is a rhombus by the definitions of parallelogram and rhombus.

Proof:

Statement	Reason
1. Construct $\overline{BD}$	1. Line Postulate
2. $\overline{AB} \cong \overline{CD}$	2. Given
3. $\overline{AD} \cong \overline{CB}$	3. Given
4. $\overline{BD} \cong \overline{DB}$	4. Reflexive property of congruence
5. $\triangle ABD \cong \triangle CDB$	5. SSS Congruence Postulate
6. $\angle 1 \cong \angle 2$	6. CPCTC
7. $\overline{AB} \parallel \overline{CD}$	7. Converse of the AIA Theorem
8. $\angle 3 \cong \angle 4$	8. CPCTC
9. $\overline{AD} \parallel \overline{CB}$	9. Converse of the AIA Theorem
10. $ABCD$ is a parallelogram	10. Definition of parallelogram
11. $ABCD$ is a rhombus	11. Definition of rhombus

6. Given: A quadrilateral with four congruent angles

   Show: The quadrilateral is a rectangle

   Given: Quadrilateral $ABCD$ with $\angle A \cong \angle B \cong \angle C \cong \angle D$

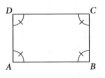

Show: $ABCD$ is a rectangle

Plan: Use the Converse of the Opposites Angles Theorem to prove that $ABCD$ is a parallelogram. Then use the definition of rectangle.

Proof:

Statement	Reason
1. $\angle A \cong \angle C$; $\angle B \cong \angle D$	1. Given
2. $ABCD$ is a parallelogram	2. Converse of Opposite Angles Theorem
3. $\angle A \cong \angle B \cong \angle C \cong \angle D$	3. Given
4. $m\angle A = m\angle B = m\angle C = m\angle D$	4. Definition of congruence
5. $m\angle A + m\angle B + m\angle C + m\angle D = 360°$	5. Quadrilateral Sum Theorem
6. $4m\angle A = 360°$	6. Substitution property
7. $m\angle A = 90°$	7. Division property
8. $m\angle A = m\angle B = m\angle C = m\angle D = 90°$	8. Substitution property
9. $ABCD$ has four right angles	9. Definition of right angle
10. $ABCD$ is a rectangle	10. Definition of rectangle

7. Given: Rectangle

   Show: The diagonals of the rectangle are congruent

   Given: Rectangle $ABCD$ with diagonals $\overline{BD}$ and $\overline{AC}$

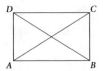

Show: $\overline{BD} \cong \overline{AC}$

Plan: Use the definition of a rectangle to prove that $ABCD$ is a parallelogram and $\angle DAB \cong \angle CBA$. Then use the Opposite Sides Theorem, the reflexive property, and the SAS Congruence Postulate to get $\triangle DAB \cong \triangle CBA$. Finish with CPCTC.

Proof:

Statement	Reason
1. *ABCD* is a rectangle	1. Given
2. *ABCD* is a parallelogram	2. Definition of rectangle
3. $\overline{DA} \cong \overline{CB}$	3. Opposite Sides Theorem
4. $\angle DAB$ and $\angle CBA$ are right angles	4. Definition of rectangle
5. $\angle DAB \cong \angle CBA$	5. Right Angles Are Congruent Theorem
6. $\overline{AB} \cong \overline{BA}$	6. Reflexive property of congruence
7. $\triangle DAB \cong \triangle CBA$	7. SAS Congruence Postulate
8. $\overline{BD} \cong \overline{AC}$	8. CPCTC

8. Given: A parallelogram with congruent diagonals

Show: The parallelogram is a rectangle

Given: Parallelogram *ABCD* with $\overline{DB} \cong \overline{AC}$

Show: *ABCD* is a rectangle

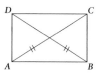

Plan: Use the Opposite Sides Theorem, the reflexive property of congruence, and the SSS Congruence Postulate to get $\triangle DAB \cong \triangle CBA$. Repeat the above steps to get $\triangle ADC \cong \triangle CBA$ and $\triangle DAB \cong \triangle BCD$. Then use CPCTC and the transitive property to get $\angle DAB \cong \angle CBA \cong \angle BCD \cong \angle ADC$. Finish with the Four Congruent Angles Rectangle Theorem.

Flowchart Proof

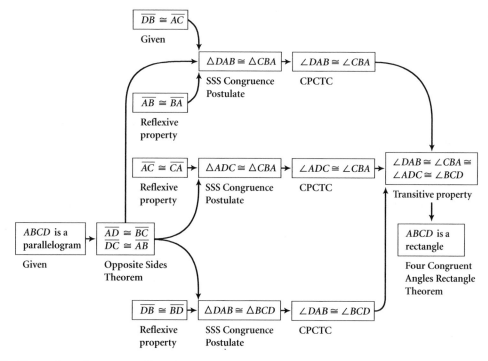

9. Given: Isosceles trapezoid

Show: The base angles are congruent

Given: Isosceles trapezoid *ABCD* with $\overline{DC} \parallel \overline{AB}$, $\overline{AD} \cong \overline{BC}$

Show: $\angle A \cong \angle B$

Plan: Use the Parallel Postulate to construct $\overline{DE} \parallel \overline{CB}$. Then use the Opposite Sides Theorem and the transitive property to prove that $\triangle AED$ is isosceles. Therefore, $\angle A \cong \angle B$ by the Isosceles Triangle Theorem and the CA Postulate.

Proof:	Statement	Reason
	1. $\overline{DC} \parallel \overline{AB}$	1. Given
	2. Construct $\overline{DE} \parallel \overline{CB}$	2. Parallel Postulate
	3. $DCBE$ is a parallelogram	3. Definition of parallelogram
	4. $\overline{DE} \cong \overline{BC}$	4. Opposite Sides Theorem
	5. $\overline{AD} \cong \overline{BC}$	5. Given
	6. $\overline{AD} \cong \overline{DE}$	6. Transitive property of congruence
	7. $\triangle ADE$ is isosceles	7. Definition of isosceles triangle
	8. $\angle A \cong \angle DEA$	8. Isosceles Triangle Theorem
	9. $\angle DEA \cong \angle B$	9. CA Postulate
	10. $\angle A \cong \angle B$	10. Transitive property of congruence

10. **Given:** Isosceles trapezoid

Show: The diagonals are congruent

Given: Isosceles trapezoid $ABCD$ with $\overline{DC} \parallel \overline{AB}$, $\overline{AD} \cong \overline{BC}$

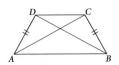

Show: $\overline{AC} \cong \overline{BD}$

Plan: Use the Isosceles Trapezoid Theorem, the reflexive property, and the SAS Congruence Postulate to get $\triangle DAB \cong \triangle CBA$. Then $\overline{AC} \cong \overline{BD}$ by CPCTC.

Flowchart Proof

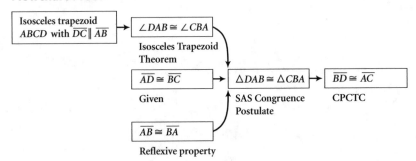

11. **Given:** Parallelogram with a diagonal that bisects two opposite angles

Show: The parallelogram is a rhombus

Given: Parallelogram $ABCD$; $\overline{AC}$ bisects $\angle DAB$ and $\angle BCD$

Show: $ABCD$ is a rhombus

Plan: Use the Opposite Angles Theorem, the multiplication property, and the definition of angle bisector to get $\angle 1 \cong \angle 3$. Then use the Converse of the Isosceles Triangle Theorem, the definition of isosceles triangle, and the Opposite Sides Theorem to get $\overline{AB} \cong \overline{BC} \cong \overline{DC} \cong \overline{AD}$.

Proof:	Statement	Reason
	1. $\overline{AC}$ bisects $\angle DAB$ and $\angle BCD$	1. Given
	2. $\angle 1 \cong \angle 2$; $\angle 3 \cong \angle 4$	2. Definition of angle bisector
	3. $m\angle 1 = m\angle 2$; $m\angle 3 = m\angle 4$	3. Definition of congruence
	4. $m\angle 1 + m\angle 2 = m\angle DAB$; $m\angle 3 + m\angle 4 = m\angle BCD$	4. Angle Addition Postulate
	5. $2m\angle 1 = m\angle DAB$; $2m\angle 3 = m\angle BCD$	5. Substitution property
	6. $m\angle 1 = \frac{1}{2}(m\angle DAB)$; $m\angle 3 = \frac{1}{2}(m\angle BCD)$	6. Multiplication property
	7. $ABCD$ is a parallelogram	7. Given
	8. $\angle DAB \cong \angle BCD$	8. Opposite Angles Theorem
	9. $m\angle DAB = m\angle BCD$	9. Definition of congruence

(Proof continued)

(Exercise 11 Proof continued)

Statement	Reason
10. $\frac{1}{2}(m\angle DAB) = \frac{1}{2}(m\angle BCD)$	10. Multiplication property
11. $m\angle 1 = m\angle 3$	11. Substitution property
12. $\overline{AB} \cong \overline{BC}$	12. Converse of the Isosceles Triangle Theorem
13. $\overline{AB} \cong \overline{DC}$; $\overline{AD} \cong \overline{BC}$	13. Opposite Sides Theorem
14. $\overline{AB} \cong \overline{BC} \cong \overline{DC} \cong \overline{AD}$	14. Transitive property of congruence
15. $ABCD$ is a rhombus	15. Definition of rhombus

12. **Given:** A pair of parallel lines intersected by a second pair of parallel lines; the distance between each pair of lines is the same

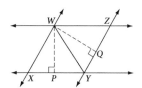

Show: The parallelogram formed is a rhombus

Given: $\overleftrightarrow{WZ} \parallel \overleftrightarrow{XY}$, $\overleftrightarrow{XW} \parallel \overleftrightarrow{YZ}$, distance between $\overleftrightarrow{WZ}$ and $\overleftrightarrow{XY}$ equals distance between $\overleftrightarrow{XW}$ and $\overleftrightarrow{YZ}$

Show: $XWZY$ is a rhombus

Plan: Use the Converse of the Angle Bisector Theorem to prove that $\overline{WY}$ is the angle bisector of $\angle Y$ and of $\angle W$. Therefore, $WXYZ$ is a rhombus by the Converse of the Rhombus Angles Theorem.

Proof: Statement	Reason
1. $\overleftrightarrow{WZ} \parallel \overleftrightarrow{XY}$, $\overleftrightarrow{XW} \parallel \overleftrightarrow{YZ}$	1. Given
2. $WXYZ$ is a parallelogram	2. Definition of parallelogram
3. Distance from W to $\overleftrightarrow{XY}$ = distance from W to $\overleftrightarrow{YZ}$	3. Given
4. $\overline{WY}$ is the angle bisector of $\angle Y$	4. Converse of the Angle Bisector Theorem
5. Distance from Y to $\overleftrightarrow{XW}$ = distance from Y to $\overleftrightarrow{WZ}$	5. Given
6. $\overline{WY}$ is the angle bisector of $\angle W$	6. Converse of the Angle Bisector Theorem
7. $XWZY$ is a rhombus	7. Converse of the Rhombus Angles Theorem

13.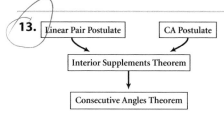

14.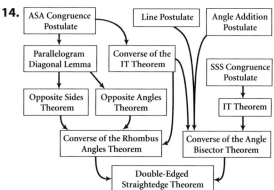

15. **a.** Always. Because its diagonals bisect each other, $ABCD$ is a parallelogram (converse of Parallelogram Diagonals Conjecture). Then $\angle BAD$ and $\angle ADC$ are supplementary because consecutive angles of a parallelogram are supple-

mentary (Parallelogram Consecutive Angles Conjecture).

b. Sometimes. $\angle ADM$ and $\angle MAD$ are complementary if $m\angle AMD = 90°$, that is, if $\overline{AC} \perp \overline{BD}$. But the diagonals of a parallelogram are perpendicular only if the parallelogram is a rhombus. This parallelogram may or may not be a rhombus; you don't have enough information to tell.

c. Sometimes. A diagonal of a parallelogram could be longer than the sum of the lengths of two opposite sides, or it could be shorter or the same length. There is not enough information to tell.

d. Never. By the Triangle Inequality Conjecture, $AD + CD > AC$.

16. 2386 ft^2. Divide the grazing area into five sections and find the area of each.

Notice that each section is a sector of a circle, but the radii

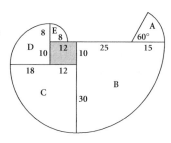

of the circles differ depending on the positions of the sectors in the diagram.

Sector A: $r = 15$ ft; central angle $= 60°$, so sector is $\frac{1}{6}$ of circle.

$A_{\text{sector A}} = \frac{1}{6}\pi r^2 = \frac{1}{6}\pi(15)^2 = \frac{1}{6}\pi \cdot 225 = 37.5\pi$ ft^2

Sector B: $r = 40$ ft; central angle $= 90°$, so sector is $\frac{1}{4}$ of circle.

$A_{\text{sector B}} = \frac{1}{4}\pi r^2 = \frac{1}{4}\pi(40)^2 = \frac{1}{4}\pi \cdot 1600 = 400\pi$ ft^2

Sector C: $r = 30$ ft; central angle $= 90°$, so sector is $\frac{1}{4}$ of circle.

$A_{\text{sector C}} = \frac{1}{4}\pi r^2 = \frac{1}{4}\pi(30)^2 = \frac{1}{4}\pi \cdot 900 = 225\pi$ ft^2

Sector D: $r = 18$ ft; central angle $= 90°$, so sector is $\frac{1}{4}$ of circle.

$A_{\text{sector D}} = \frac{1}{4}\pi r^2 = \frac{1}{4}\pi(18)^2 = \frac{1}{4}\pi \cdot 324 = 81\pi$ ft^2

Sector E: $r = 8$ ft; central angle $= 90°$, so sector is $\frac{1}{4}$ of circle.

$A_{\text{sector E}} = \frac{1}{4}\pi r^2 = \frac{1}{4}\pi(8)^2 = \frac{1}{4}\pi \cdot 64 = 16\pi$ ft^2

To find the total grazing area, add the areas of the five sectors:

$37.5\pi + 400\pi + 225\pi + 81\pi + 16\pi = 759.5\pi \approx 2386$ ft^2

17.

Name	Lines of symmetry	Rotational symmetry
parallelogram	none	**2-fold**
trapezoid	**none**	none
kite	1 diagonal	none
square	**2 diagonals** **2 ⊥ bisectors of sides**	4-fold
rectangle	2 ⊥ bisectors of sides	**2-fold**
rhombus	**2 diagonals**	**2-fold**
isosceles trapezoid	**1 ⊥ bisector of sides**	none

18. $\overrightarrow{V_1 + V_2}$ has length 12.8 and bearing 72.6°. Label the vertices in the figure, and use the given bearings and vector lengths to find angle measures and side lengths in parallelogram $ABCD$ and $\triangle ACD$.

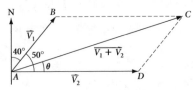

Because the bearing of $\overrightarrow{V_1}$ is 40° and the bearing of $\overrightarrow{V_2}$ is 90°, $m\angle BAD = 90° - 40° = 50°$. Because consecutive angles of a parallelogram are

supplementary, $m\angle ADC = 180° - 50° = 130°$. Because opposite sides of a parallelogram are congruent, $CD = 5$. Use the Law of Cosines to find AC, the length of the resultant vector, $\overrightarrow{V_1 + V_2}$.

$(AC)^2 = (AD)^2 + (CD)^2 - 2(AD)(CD)(\cos 130°)$

$(AC)^2 = 9^2 + 5^2 - 2(9)(5)(\cos 130°)$

$AC = \sqrt{9^2 + 5^2 - 2(9)(5)(\cos 130°)} \approx 12.8$

(Keep all digits of the value of AC in your calculator for use in the next calculation.)

Let $\theta = m\angle CAD$. Use the Law of Sines to find θ.

$\dfrac{\sin\theta}{5} = \dfrac{\sin 130°}{AC}$

$\sin\theta = \dfrac{5\sin 130°}{AC}$

$\theta = \sin^{-1}\left(\dfrac{5\sin 130°}{AC}\right) \approx 17.4°$

The bearing of the resultant vector, $\overrightarrow{V_1 + V_2}$, is $90° - 17.4° = 72.6°$.

19. a. B. Look at $\triangle XYZ$ in both figures and find the unknown side lengths in each of these triangles. In both figures, let $\theta = m\angle XYZ$.

Figure A: Apply the Pythagorean Theorem to obtain $XZ = \sqrt{4^2 + 5^2} = \sqrt{41}$. $\triangle XYZ$ is a right triangle, with right angle Z. Use the tangent ratio to find θ.

$\tan\theta = \dfrac{XZ}{YZ} = \dfrac{\sqrt{41}}{9}$

$\theta = \tan^{-1}\dfrac{\sqrt{41}}{9} \approx 35.4°$

Figure B: Follow the steps applied to Figure A.

$XZ = \sqrt{6^2 + 5^2} = \sqrt{61}$

$\tan\theta = \dfrac{XZ}{YZ} = \dfrac{\sqrt{61}}{6}$

$\theta = \tan^{-1}\dfrac{\sqrt{61}}{6} \approx 52.5°$

Thus, $m\angle XYZ$ is greater in Figure B.

b. A. Remember that the shortest distance between two points is a straight line. To find the straight line from X to Y on the surface of Figure A, draw a net of the prism. The path has to cross two faces, and there are six ways to do so, so there are six paths to consider. But each path is the mirror image of the path opposite it, so there are only three different paths.

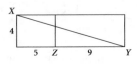

$\sqrt{4^2 + (5 + 9)^2} = \sqrt{212} \approx 14.6$

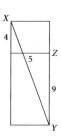

$$\sqrt{(4+9)^2 + 5^2} = \sqrt{194} \approx 13.9$$

$$\sqrt{(5+4)^2 + 9^2} = \sqrt{162} \approx 12.7$$

Notice that the expressions for Figure A are the three possible ways to group the three dimensions into a pair and a "singleton," so you can find the corresponding distances for Figure B without drawing.

$$\sqrt{5^2 + (6+6)^2} = \sqrt{169} = 13$$

$$\sqrt{6^2 + (5+6)^2} = \sqrt{157} \approx 12.5$$

$$\sqrt{6^2 + (6+5)^2} = \sqrt{157} \approx 12.5$$

The shortest distance is $\sqrt{162} \approx 12.7$ for Figure A and $\sqrt{157} \approx 12.5$ for Figure B. So the value is greater in Figure A.

20. a. 19°. $\angle EOD$ is a central angle of circle O, so $m\widehat{ED} = 38°$. $\angle EAD$ is an inscribed angle that also intercepts $\widehat{ED}$, so $m\angle A = \frac{1}{2}(38°) = 19°$. $\overline{OA}$ and $\overline{OE}$ are both radii of the circle, so $\triangle AOE$ is an isosceles triangle with $OA = OE$. Therefore, by the Isosceles Triangle Theorem, $m\angle AEO = m\angle A = 19°$.

b. 52°. Look at $\triangle DGO$. Because $\overleftrightarrow{GF}$ is tangent to circle O at D, $\overline{OD} \perp \overleftrightarrow{GF}$ by the Tangent Conjecture. Thus, $m\angle ODG = 90°$. $\angle GOD$ and $\angle EOD$ are the same angle, so $m\angle GOD = 38°$. Therefore, $m\angle DGO = 180° - 90° - 38° = 52°$.

c. 52°. Because $\overleftrightarrow{GF} \parallel \overleftrightarrow{EC}$, $\angle HEO \cong \angle DGO$ by the CA Postulate. $\angle OEC$ and $\angle OEH$ are the same angle, so $m\angle OEC = 52°$. $\triangle OEC$ is isosceles because $\overline{OE}$ and $\overline{OC}$ are both radii of the circle. Therefore, $\angle OCE \cong \angle OEC$ by the Isosceles Triangle Theorem, so $m\angle OCE = 52°$. Finally, because $\overline{OB} \parallel \overleftrightarrow{EC}$, $\angle BOC \cong \angle OCE$ by AIA, so $m\angle BOC = 52°$.

d. 232°. $m\widehat{EAB} = 360° - m\widehat{ED} - m\widehat{DC} - m\widehat{CB}$. In 20a, you found that $m\widehat{ED} = 38°$. Look at the central angles for $\widehat{ED}$, $\widehat{DC}$, and $\widehat{CB}$. Because $\overline{OH}$ is the altitude to the base of isosceles triangle EOC, it is also the angle bisector, so $m\angle COH = 38°$. Then, because $\angle COH$ and $\angle COD$ are the

same angle and $\angle COD$ intercepts $\widehat{DC}$, $m\widehat{DC} = 38°$. From 20c, $m\angle BOC = 52°$, so $m\widehat{CB} = 52°$. Therefore, $m\widehat{EAB} = 360° - 38° - 38° - 52° = 232°$.

e. 19°. Notice that $\angle HED$ is the same angle as $\angle CED$, which is an inscribed angle that intercepts $\widehat{DC}$. From 20d, $m\widehat{DC} = 38°$, so $m\angle HED = m\angle CED = \frac{1}{2}m\widehat{DC} = \frac{1}{2}(38°) = 19°$.

IMPROVING YOUR VISUAL THINKING SKILLS

Look at each net and see if adjacent faces are related as they are in the cube. A good problem-solving technique here is to eliminate choices. For example, the net in 1A can be eliminated because the base of the green face is touching the red face, unlike in the cube.

1. D

2. C

EXTENSION

Answers will vary.

EXPLORATION · PROOF AS CHALLENGE AND DISCOVERY

IMPROVING YOUR ALGEBRA SKILLS

There is a flaw in the proof. If $h = n - p$, then $h - n + p = 0$. The step from $h(h - n + p) = n(h - n + p)$ to $h = n$ is not valid, because when you divide both sides by $h - n + p$, you are dividing by zero.

LESSON 13.5

EXERCISES

1. D. Paris is in France; Tucson is in the United States; London is in England. Therefore, Bamako must be the capital of Mali.

2. C. The "Sir" in 2A shows that Halley was English; Julius Caesar was an emperor, not a scientist; Madonna is a singer. Therefore, Galileo Galilei must be the answer.

3. No, the proof is claiming only that if two particular angles are not congruent, then the two particular sides opposite them are not congruent. A different pair of sides might still be congruent.

4. Yes, this statement is the contrapositive of the conjecture proved in Example B, so they are logically equivalent.

5. 1. Assume the opposite of the conclusion; 2. Triangle Sum Theorem; 3. Substitution property of equality; 4. $m\angle C = 0$, Subtraction property of equality.

6. Paragraph Proof: Assume $ZOID$ is equiangular. Then, by the definition of equiangular, $\angle Z \cong \angle O \cong \angle I \cong \angle D$. Then, by the Four Congruent

Angles Rectangle Theorem, ZOID is a rectangle. Therefore, ZOID is a parallelogram, which creates a contradiction because, by definition, a trapezoid has exactly one pair of parallel sides and thus cannot be a parallelogram. Therefore, the assumption that ZOID is equiangular is false and the conjecture is true.

7. Paragraph Proof: Assume $\overline{CD}$ is the altitude to $\overline{AB}$. Then, by the definition of altitude, $\overline{CD} \perp \overline{AB}$, and by the definition of perpendicular, $\angle CDA$ and $\angle CDB$ are right angles. Thus, $\angle CDA \cong \angle CDB$ by the Right Angles Are Congruent Theorem. $\overline{CD} \cong \overline{CD}$ by the reflexive property of congruence. It is given that $\overline{CD}$ is a median, so D is the midpoint of $\overline{AB}$, and $\overline{AD} \cong \overline{BD}$ by the definition of midpoint. Then $\triangle ADC \cong \triangle BDC$ by the SAS Congruence Postulate. Therefore, $\overline{AC} \cong \overline{BC}$ by CPCTC, so $\triangle ABC$ is isosceles. It is given that $\triangle ABC$ is scalene. Therefore, the assumption that $\overline{CD}$ is the altitude to $\overline{AB}$ is false and the conjecture is true.

8. Paragraph Proof: Assume $ZO = ID$. Then $\overline{ZO} \cong \overline{ID}$ by the definition of congruence. $\overline{ZO} \parallel \overline{ID}$ is given. Therefore, by the Opposite Sides Parallel and Congruent Theorem, ZOID is a parallelogram. This creates a contradiction because ZOID is a trapezoid, and a trapezoid cannot be a parallelogram. Thus, the assumption that $ZO \neq ID$ is false, and the conjecture is true.

9. Given: A chord of a circle

Show: The perpendicular bisector of the chord passes through the center of the circle

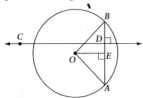

Given: Circle O with chord $\overline{AB}$ and perpendicular bisector $\overleftrightarrow{CD}$

Show: $\overleftrightarrow{CD}$ passes through O

Paragraph Proof: It is given that $\overleftrightarrow{CD}$ is the perpendicular bisector of $\overline{AB}$. Then, by the definition of perpendicular bisector, D is the midpoint of $\overline{AB}$. Assume $\overleftrightarrow{CD}$ does *not* pass through O. Use the Line Postulate to construct $\overline{OB}$ and $\overline{OA}$ and the Perpendicular Postulate to construct $\overline{OE}$, where $\overline{OE}$ is the perpendicular segment from O to $\overline{AB}$. Because $\overline{OE} \perp \overline{AB}$, $\angle OEB$ and $\angle OEA$ are right angles, so $\angle OEB \cong \angle OEA$ by the Right Angles Are Congruent Theorem. $\overline{OB} \cong \overline{OA}$ because they are radii of the same circle, so $\angle B \cong \angle A$ by the Isosceles Triangle Theorem. $\overline{OE} \cong \overline{OE}$ by the reflexive property of congruence. Therefore, $\triangle OEB \cong \triangle OEA$ by the SAA Congruence Theorem,

and $\overline{EB} \cong \overline{EA}$ by CPCTC. Then E is the midpoint of $\overline{AB}$, and $\overleftrightarrow{OE}$ is the perpendicular bisector of $\overline{AB}$. This contradicts the assumption that the perpendicular bisector of $\overline{AB}$ does not pass through O. (A segment can have only one midpoint and one perpendicular bisector.) Thus, the assumption is false and the conjecture is true.

10. $a = 75°$, $b = 47°$, $c = 58°$. By the Interior Supplements Theorem, $a = 180° - 105° = 75°$. $b + a + 58° = 180°$, or $b + 75° + 58° = 180°$, so $b = 180° - 75° - 58° = 47°$. By the CA Postulate, $c = 58°$.

11. 42π ft³ ≈ 132 ft³. The volume of the container is the sum of the volumes of a cylinder with radius 3 ft and height 3 ft and a cone with radius 3 ft and height 5 ft.

$$V_{cylinder} = \pi r^2 H = \pi(3)^2(3) = 27\pi \text{ ft}^3$$
$$V_{cone} = \frac{1}{3}\pi r^2 H = \frac{1}{3}\pi(3)^2(5) = 15\pi \text{ ft}^3$$
$$V_{container} = 27\pi + 15\pi = 42\pi \text{ ft}^3 \approx 132 \text{ ft}^3$$

12. a. $\frac{\sqrt{3}}{4} - \frac{\pi}{12}$. The shaded region is the difference between the shaded area in Lesson 13.1, Exercise 31a and the shaded area in Lesson 13.3, Exercise 18c, so subtract the areas you found in those exercises:

$$A = \frac{\pi}{4} - \left(\frac{\pi}{3} - \frac{\sqrt{3}}{4}\right) = \frac{\pi}{4} - \frac{\pi}{3} + \frac{\sqrt{3}}{4}$$
$$= \frac{\sqrt{3}}{4} - \frac{\pi}{12}$$

b. $1 - \sqrt{3} + \frac{\pi}{3}$. To find the area of the shaded region, subtract four times the shaded area from 12a from the area of the square.

$$A = 1 - 4\left(\frac{\sqrt{3}}{4} - \frac{\pi}{12}\right) = 1 - \sqrt{3} + \frac{\pi}{3}$$

13. a. Always. This is the Angles Inscribed in a Semicircle Conjecture.

b. Never. An angle inscribed in a major arc intercepts a minor arc, where the sum of the major arc and the minor arc is the complete circle. By the Inscribed Angle Conjecture, the measure of an angle that intercepts a minor arc will be half of an arc measure that is greater than 0° and less than 180°, so the angle measure will be greater than 0° and less than 90°. Thus, the angle will always be acute.

c. Sometimes. Because your book defines angles to have measures that are greater than 0° and less than 180°, this statement is true only for minor arcs. If the arc is a semicircle, its measure is 180°. The measure of a major arc is found by subtracting the measure of the corresponding minor arc from 360°.

d. Sometimes. The measure of an angle formed by two intersecting chords equals the *average* of the

Discovering Geometry Solutions Manual
©2008 Key Curriculum Press

measures of the two intercepted arcs, so this statement is true only when the two intercepted arcs are congruent. That happens when the chords are diameters.

e. Always. Make a sketch. Draw radii to the two points of tangency.

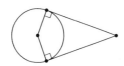

Because the two radii are congruent and the two tangent segments are congruent (Tangent Segments Conjecture), the quadrilateral is a kite. By the Tangent Conjecture, the two nonvertex angles are right angles. Therefore, the two vertex angles must be supplementary. These two angles are the angle formed by the tangents and the central angle of the minor intercepted arc.

IMPROVING YOUR REASONING SKILLS

Possible derivation:

$$V = \frac{1}{3}BH = \frac{1}{3}\left[\frac{1}{2}h(a + b)\right]H = \frac{1}{3}\left[\frac{1}{2}(2x)(2b + b)\right]H$$
$$= \frac{1}{3}[x(3b)]H = bxH = x^2H = x^2 \cdot \frac{12}{x} = 12x$$

EXTENSIONS

A. Conjecture: The largest angle of a triangle must have a measure of at least 60°.

Given: Triangle ABC with $\angle A$ the largest angle

Show: $m\angle A \geq 60°$

Paragraph Proof: Assume $m\angle A < 60°$. Because $\angle A$ is the largest angle of the triangle, $m\angle B < m\angle A$ and $m\angle C < m\angle A$. Therefore, $m\angle B < 60°$ and $m\angle C < 60°$. Then $m\angle A + m\angle B + m\angle C < 60° + 60° + 60° = 180°$, or $m\angle A + m\angle B + m\angle C < 180°$. This creates a contradiction because, by the Triangle Sum Theorem, $m\angle A + m\angle B + m\angle C = 180°$. Thus the assumption that $m\angle A < 60°$ is false, and the conjecture is true. (If the triangle is isosceles or equilateral so that $m\angle B = m\angle A$ and/or $m\angle C = m\angle A$, the proof is still valid.)

B. Conjecture: The largest side of a triangle must be opposite an angle with a measure greater than or equal to 60°.

Given: $\triangle ABC$ with $\overline{BC}$ the longest side

Show: $m\angle A > 60°$

Paragraph Proof: Because $\angle A$ is opposite $\overline{BC}$, and $\overline{BC}$ is the longest side of $\triangle ABC$, $\angle A$ is the largest angle of the triangle by the Side-Angle Inequality Conjecture. By the theorem that was proved in Extension A, $m\angle A > 60°$.

LESSON 13.6

EXERCISES

1. Given: Two inscribed angles in a circle that intercept the same or congruent arcs

Show: The inscribed angles are congruent

Case 1: Two angles intercepting the same arc

Given: Circle with inscribed angles XAW and XBW intercepting $\overarc{XW}$

Show: $\angle XAW \cong \angle XBW$

Paragraph Proof: By the Inscribed Angle Theorem, $m\angle XAW = \frac{1}{2}(m\overarc{XW})$ and $m\angle XBW = \frac{1}{2}(m\overarc{XW})$. Therefore, by the transitive property, $m\angle XAW = m\angle XBW$, so $\angle XAW \cong \angle XBW$ by the definition of congruence.

Case 2: Two angles intercepting congruent arcs

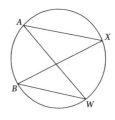

Given: Circle with inscribed angle ZAY intercepting $\overarc{ZY}$ and inscribed angle XBW intercepting $\overarc{XW}$; $\overarc{ZY} \cong \overarc{XW}$

Show: $\angle ZAY \cong \angle XBW$

Paragraph Proof: By the Inscribed Angle Theorem, $m\angle ZAY = \frac{1}{2}(m\overarc{ZY})$ and $m\angle XBW = \frac{1}{2}(m\overarc{XW})$. Because $\overarc{ZY} \cong \overarc{XW}$ is given, $\frac{1}{2}(m\overarc{ZY}) = \frac{1}{2}(m\overarc{XW})$ by the definition of congruence and the multiplication property. Therefore, $m\angle ZAY = m\angle XBW$ by the transitive property, so $\angle ZAY \cong \angle XBW$ by the definition of congruence.

2. Given: Quadrilateral inscribed in a circle

Show: The opposite angles of the quadrilateral are supplementary

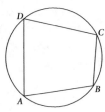

Given: Circle with inscribed quadrilateral $ABCD$

Show: $\angle A$ and $\angle C$ are supplementary; $\angle B$ and $\angle D$ are supplementary

Plan: Use the Inscribed Angle Theorem, the addition property, and the distributive property to get $m\angle A + m\angle C = \frac{1}{2}(m\widehat{BCD} + m\widehat{DAB})$. Then use the definition of degrees in a circle, the substitution property, and the definition of supplementary to get $\angle A$ and $\angle C$ are supplementary. Repeat the above steps, using different angles and arcs, to get $\angle B$ and $\angle D$ are supplementary.

Proof:

Statement	Reason
1. $ABCD$ is inscribed in the circle	1. Given
2. $m\angle A = \frac{1}{2}(m\widehat{BCD})$; $m\angle C = \frac{1}{2}(m\widehat{DAB})$ $m\angle B = \frac{1}{2}(m\widehat{ACD})$; $m\angle D = \frac{1}{2}(m\widehat{ABC})$	2. Inscribed Angle Theorem
3. $m\angle A + m\angle C = \frac{1}{2}(m\widehat{BCD}) + \frac{1}{2}(m\widehat{DAB})$ $m\angle B + m\angle D = \frac{1}{2}(m\widehat{ACD}) + \frac{1}{2}(m\widehat{ABC})$	3. Addition property
4. $m\angle A + m\angle C = \frac{1}{2}(m\widehat{BCD} + m\widehat{DAB})$ $m\angle B + m\angle D = \frac{1}{2}(m\widehat{ACD} + m\widehat{ABC})$	4. Distributive property
5. $m\angle A + m\angle C = \frac{1}{2}$(arc measure of circle) $m\angle B + m\angle D = \frac{1}{2}$(arc measure of circle)	5. Arc Addition Postulate
6. $m\angle A + m\angle C = \frac{1}{2}(360°)$ $m\angle B + m\angle D = \frac{1}{2}(360°)$	6. Arc measure of full circle $= 360°$
7. $m\angle A + m\angle C = 180°$ $m\angle B + m\angle D = 180°$	7. Multiplication property
8. $\angle A$ and $\angle C$ are supplementary $\angle B$ and $\angle D$ are supplementary	8. Definition of supplementary

3. Given: Circle with parallel secants

Show: The secants intercept congruent arcs

Given: Circle with secants $\overleftrightarrow{AB}$ and $\overleftrightarrow{CD}$; $\overleftrightarrow{AB} \parallel \overleftrightarrow{CD}$

Show: $\widehat{AC} \cong \widehat{BD}$

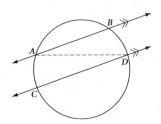

Plan: Use the Line Postulate to construct $\overline{AD}$. Then use the AIA Theorem and the Inscribed Angle Theorem to get $\widehat{AC} \cong \widehat{BD}$.

Proof:

Statement	Reason
1. Construct $\overline{AD}$	1. Line Postulate
2. $\angle CDA \cong \angle BAD$	2. AIA Theorem
3. $m\angle CDA = m\angle BAD$	3. Definition of congruence
4. $m\angle CDA = \frac{1}{2}(m\widehat{AC})$; $m\angle BAD = \frac{1}{2}(m\widehat{BD})$	4. Inscribed Angle Theorem
5. $\frac{1}{2}(m\widehat{AC}) = \frac{1}{2}(m\widehat{BD})$	5. Transitive property
6. $m\widehat{AC} = m\widehat{BD}$	6. Multiplication property
7. $\widehat{AC} \cong \widehat{BD}$	7. Definition of congruence

4. Given: Parallelogram inscribed in a circle

Show: The parallelogram is a rectangle

Given: Parallelogram *ACER* inscribed in a circle

Show: *ACER* is a rectangle

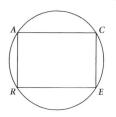

Plan: Use the Cyclic Quadrilateral Theorem, the Opposite Angles Theorem, and the Congruent and Supplementary Theorem to show that all four angles are right angles.

Proof:

Statement	Reason
1. *ACER* is inscribed in a circle	1. Given
2. ∠*A* and ∠*E* are supplementary; ∠*C* and ∠*R* are supplementary	2. Cyclic Quadrilateral Theorem
3. *ACER* is a parallelogram	3. Given
4. ∠*A* ≅ ∠*E*; ∠*C* ≅ ∠*R*	4. Opposite Angles Theorem
5. ∠*A* and ∠*E* are right angles; ∠*C* and ∠*R* are right angles	5. Congruent and Supplementary Theorem
6. *ACER* is a rectangle	6. Definition of rectangle

5. Given: A circle and a point outside the circle; two segments tangent to the circle with the point as one endpoint and the point of tangency as the other endpoint

Show: The segments are congruent

Given: Circle *O* with point *P* outside the circle; $\overrightarrow{PS}$ and $\overrightarrow{PT}$ tangent to the circle at *S* and *T*, respectively

Show: $\overline{PS} \cong \overline{PT}$

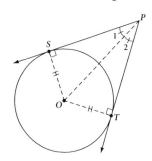

Plan: Use the Line Postulate to construct $\overline{OS}$, $\overline{OT}$, and $\overline{OP}$. Then use the Tangent Theorem, the Converse of the Angle Bisector Theorem, and the SAA Congruence Postulate to get △*OSP* ≅ △*OTP*. Use CPCTC to show $\overline{PS} \cong \overline{PT}$.

Proof:

Statement	Reason
1. Construct $\overline{OS}$, $\overline{OT}$, and $\overline{OP}$	1. Line Postulate
2. $\overline{OS} \cong \overline{OT}$	2. Definition of circle
3. $\overline{OS} \perp \overline{PS}$; $\overline{OT} \perp \overline{PT}$	3. Tangent Theorem
4. ∠*OSP* is a right angle; ∠*OTP* is a right angle	4. Definition of perpendicular
5. ∠*OSP* ≅ ∠*OTP*	5. Right Angles Are Congruent Theorem
6. *O* is on the angle bisector of ∠*SPT*	6. Converse of the Angle Bisector Theorem
7. ∠1 ≅ ∠2	7. Definition of angle bisector
8. △*OSP* ≅ △*OTP*	8. SAA Theorem
9. $\overline{PS} \cong \overline{PT}$	9. CPCTC

6. Given: Circle with two intersecting chords

Show: The measure of the angle formed by the chords is half the sum of the measures of the two intercepted arcs

Given: Circle with chords $\overline{AB}$ and $\overline{CD}$ intersecting at *E*

Show: $m\angle 1 = \frac{1}{2}(m\widehat{AC} + m\widehat{BD})$

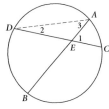

Paragraph Proof: Use the Line Postulate to construct $\overline{AD}$, forming ∠2 and ∠3. By the Inscribed Angle Theorem, $m\angle 2 = \frac{1}{2}(m\widehat{AC})$ and $m\angle 3 = \frac{1}{2}(m\widehat{BD})$. Then, by the addition and distributive properties, $m\angle 2 + m\angle 3 = \frac{1}{2}(m\widehat{AC}) + \frac{1}{2}(m\widehat{BD}) = \frac{1}{2}(m\widehat{AC} + m\widehat{BD})$. By the Triangle Exterior Angle Theorem, $m\angle 1 = m\angle 2 + m\angle 3$, so, by the transitive property, $m\angle 1 = \frac{1}{2}(m\widehat{AC} + m\widehat{BD})$.

7. Intersecting Secants Theorem: The measure of an angle formed by two secants intersecting outside a circle is half the difference between the measure of the larger intercepted arc and the measure of the smaller intercepted arc.

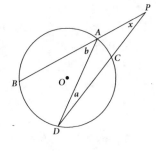

Given: Circle O with point P outside the circle; secant $\overleftrightarrow{PB}$ intersects the circle at A and B; secant $\overleftrightarrow{PD}$ intersects the circle at C and D

Show: $x = \frac{1}{2}(m\overset{\frown}{BD} - m\overset{\frown}{AC})$

Paragraph Proof: Using the Line Postulate, construct $\overline{AD}$. By the Triangle Exterior Angle Theorem, $b = a + x$, so, by the subtraction property, $x = b - a$. By the Inscribed Angle Theorem, $b = \frac{1}{2}(m\overset{\frown}{BD})$ and $a = \frac{1}{2}(m\overset{\frown}{AC})$. Then, by the substitution and distributive properties, $x = \frac{1}{2}(m\overset{\frown}{BD}) - \frac{1}{2}(m\overset{\frown}{AC}) = \frac{1}{2}(m\overset{\frown}{BD} - m\overset{\frown}{AC})$.

8. Given: Circle with an angle inscribed in a semicircle

Show: The inscribed angle is a right angle

Given: Circle A with $\angle BDC$ inscribed in semicircle BDC

Show: $\angle BDC$ is a right angle

Paragraph Proof: By the Inscribed Angle Theorem, $m\angle BDC = \frac{1}{2}m\overset{\frown}{BEC}$. By the definition of semicircle, $m\overset{\frown}{BEC} = 180°$, so by the division property, $m\angle BDC = 90°$. By the definition of right angle, $\angle BDC$ is a right angle. Because only definitions, properties, and the Inscribed Angle Theorem are needed to prove this conjecture, it is a corollary of the Inscribed Angle Theorem.

9.

Angle Addition Postulate

Line Postulate — ASA Congruence Postulate — SSS Congruence Postulate

Converse of the IT Theorem — SAA Theorem — IT Theorem

SAS Congruence Postulate

Right Angles Are Congruent Theorem

Midpoint Postulate

Converse of the Angle Bisector Theorem — Tangent Theorem

Perpendicular Postulate

Tangent Segments Theorem

10.

Linear Pair Postulate — CA Postulate — Parallel Postulate — Angle Addition Postulate — Arc Addition Postulate

SSS Congruence Postulate — VA Theorem

IT Theorem — AIA Theorem

Triangle Sum Theorem

ASA Congruence Postulate

Exterior Angle Sum Theorem

Inscribed Angle Theorem — Parallelogram Diagonal Lemma — Congruent and Supplementary Theorem

Cyclic Quadrilateral Theorem — Opposite Angles Theorem — Right Angles Are Congruent Theorem

Parallelogram Inscribed in a Circle Theorem

11. $A(4.0, 2.9)$, $P(-1.1, -2.8)$. To find the coordinates of A, draw the perpendicular segment from A to the x-axis, forming a right triangle with horizontal leg of length a and vertical leg of length b.

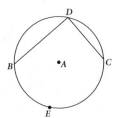

$\frac{a}{5} = \cos 36°$, so $a = 5 \cos 36° \approx 4.0$.

$\frac{b}{5} = \sin 36°$, so $b = 5 \sin 36° \approx 2.9$.

To find the coordinates of P, draw a perpendicular segment from P to the y-axis, forming a right triangle with horizontal leg of length $|p|$ and vertical leg of length $|q|$. (Absolute-value bars are used here because the side lengths of the triangle are positive, but p and q, the coordinates of P, are negative because P is in Quadrant III.)

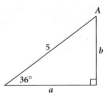

$\frac{|p|}{3} = \sin 22°$, so $|p| = 3 \sin 22°$, $|p| \approx 1.1$, and $p \approx -1.1$.

$\frac{|q|}{3} = \cos 22°$, so $|q| = 3 \cos 22°$, $|q| \approx 2.8$, and $q \approx -2.8$.

12. $BY = 3$, $YC = 1$, $AZ = 9$. First look at $\triangle ABC$ with $\overleftrightarrow{XZ} \parallel \overline{BC}$. By the Parallel/Proportionality Conjecture, $\frac{AX}{XB} = \frac{AZ}{ZC}$. Then $\frac{6}{2} = \frac{AZ}{3}$, so $3 \cdot \frac{6}{2} = 3 \cdot \frac{AZ}{3}$ and $AZ = 9$. Now look at $\triangle ABC$ again, this time with $\overleftrightarrow{ZY} \parallel \overline{AB}$. Apply the Parallel/Proportionality

Discovering Geometry Solutions Manual
©2008 Key Curriculum Press

Conjecture again to get the proportion $\frac{YC}{BY} = \frac{ZC}{AZ}$.
$BC = 4$, $BY = 4 - YC$, so $\frac{YC}{4 - YC} = \frac{3}{9}$. Then $9(YC)$
$= 3(4 - YC)$, or $9(YC) = 12 - 3(YC)$, so $12(YC) =$
12, and $YC = 1$. Therefore, $BY = 4 - YC = 3$.

13. $\overline{BC}$, $\overline{AB}$, $\overline{AC}$, $\overline{CD}$, $\overline{AD}$. First use the Triangle Sum
Theorem to find the angle measures that are not
given. In $\triangle ABC$, $m\angle ABC = 180° - 60° - 59° =$
61°. In $\triangle ADC$, $m\angle ACD = 180° - 57° - 61° = 62°$.
Now apply the Side-Angle Inequality Conjecture to
each triangle to find the relative lengths of the sides.

In $\triangle ABC$, $\overline{BC}$ is opposite the smallest angle, $\overline{AB}$ is
opposite the middle-size angle, and $\overline{AC}$ is opposite
the largest angle, so $BC < AB < AC$.

In $\triangle ADC$, $\overline{AC}$ is opposite the smallest angle, $\overline{CD}$ is
opposite the middle-size angle, and $\overline{AD}$ is opposite
the largest angle, so $AC < CD < AD$.

Because $\overline{CD}$ is common to both triangles and is the
longest side of one triangle but the shortest side of
the other, you can arrange all five segments in order
from shortest to longest: $\overline{BC}$, $\overline{AB}$, $\overline{AC}$, $\overline{CD}$, $\overline{AD}$.

14. 32.5. Let P and Q be the centers of the smaller and
larger circles, respectively. Draw radii $\overline{PA}$ and $\overline{QB}$.
Also draw a segment $\overline{AR}$ so that $\overline{AR} \parallel \overline{PQ}$ and R is
on $\overline{QB}$.

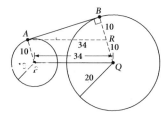

By the Tangent Theorem, $\overline{PA} \perp \overline{AB}$ and $\overline{QB} \perp \overline{AB}$,
so $\overline{PA} \parallel \overline{QB}$. $\overline{AR} \parallel \overline{PQ}$ by construction. Therefore,
$PARQ$ is a parallelogram. Because opposite sides of
a rectangle are congruent, $QR = PA$, so $QR = 10$, so
$BR = 20 - 10 = 10$, and $AR = PQ$, so $AR = 34$.
Apply the Pythagorean Theorem to right triangle
ABR to find AB: $(AB)^2 + (BR)^2 = (AR)^2$, so $AB =$
$\sqrt{(AR)^2 - (BR)^2} = \sqrt{34^2 - 10^2} = \sqrt{1056} \approx 32.5$.

15. As long as P is inside the triangle, $a + b + c = h$.

Proof: Let x be the length of a side. The areas of
the three small triangles are $\frac{1}{2}xa$, $\frac{1}{2}xb$, and $\frac{1}{2}xc$.
The area of the large triangle is $\frac{1}{2}xh$. So, $\frac{1}{2}xa +$
$\frac{1}{2}xb + \frac{1}{2}xc = \frac{1}{2}xh$. Divide by $\frac{1}{2}x$ on both sides to
get $a + b + c = h$.

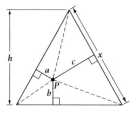

16. a. 27°. $\angle P$ is formed by two secants intersecting
outside the circle, so apply the Intersecting
Secants Theorem: $m\angle P = \frac{1}{2}(m\widehat{NQ} - m\widehat{OM}) =$
$\frac{1}{2}(94° - 40°) = \frac{1}{2}(54°) = 27°$.

b. 47°. $\angle QON$ is an inscribed angle that intercepts
$\widehat{NQ}$, so, by the Inscribed Angle Theorem,
$m\angle QON = \frac{1}{2}(94°) = 47°$.

c. 67°. $\angle QRN$ is formed by two intersecting chords,
$\overline{QM}$ and $\overline{ON}$, so, by the Intersecting Chords
Theorem, $m\angle QRN = \frac{1}{2}(m\widehat{NQ} + m\widehat{OM}) =$
$\frac{1}{2}(94° + 40°) = \frac{1}{2}(134°) = 67°$.

d. 133°. Look at $\triangle QMP$. From 16a, $m\angle P = 27°$.
$\angle PQM$ is the same angle as $\angle OQM$, which is an
inscribed angle that intercepts $\widehat{MO}$, so, by the
Inscribed Angle Theorem, the measure of this
angle is $\frac{1}{2}(40°) = 20°$. Therefore, by the Triangle
Sum Theorem, $m\angle QMP = 180° - 27° - 20° =$
133°. Another way to find $m\angle QMP$ is to notice
that $\angle QMN$ is an inscribed angle that intercepts
$\widehat{NQ}$, so $m\angle QMN = 47°$. Then, because $\angle QMN$
and $\angle QMP$ form a linear pair, $m\angle QMP =$
$180° - 47° = 133°$.

e. Cannot be determined. $m\angle ONF$ depends on
$m\widehat{OMN}$, or $m\widehat{MO} + m\widehat{MN}$. You know that
$m\widehat{OQ} + m\widehat{MN} = 360° - 94° - 40° = 226°$,
but there is not enough information to
determine $m\widehat{OQ}$ and $m\widehat{MN}$ individually.

f. Cannot be determined. As in 16e, there is not
enough information to determine $m\widehat{MN}$.

17. First construct $\overline{OP}$, then bisect it. Label the
midpoint M. Then construct a circle with center M
and radius $\overline{PM}$. Label the intersection of the two
circles A and B. Finally, construct $\overline{PA}$ and $\overline{PB}$, which
are the required tangents.

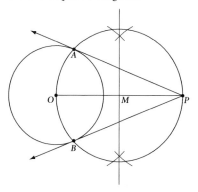

$\angle OAP$ and $\angle OBP$ are right angles; since they are
inscribed in semicircles.

IMPROVING YOUR REASONING SKILLS

The color of a spot is determined by the colors of the
two spots above it. If they are the same, the spot is
yellow; otherwise, the spot is green. (The last spot in a
row is always green because there can't be two same-
colored spots above it.) A row could never be all yellow

because the last spot is always green. Because there are only $2^5 = 32$ possible ways to color a row (two choices for each of the first five spots), some row must be repeated after at most 32 rows, and then the whole cycle will repeat. For example, the first row is repeated as the ninth row, so the cycle is eight rows long. The cycle based on this starting pattern does not include an all-green row. However, some other starting pattern can lead to an all-green row. In fact, starting with an all-green row gives an eight-row cycle, which after the ninth row is all green, and any row in the cycle would lead to all green. The figure below shows rows 7 through 11. The shaded spots represent yellow.

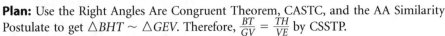

LESSON 13.7

EXERCISES

1. Given: Two similar triangles with corresponding altitudes

Show: The altitudes are proportional to the corresponding sides

Given: $\triangle BTA \sim \triangle GVL$; $\overline{TH}$ is the altitude to $\overline{BA}$; $\overline{VE}$ is the altitude to $\overline{GL}$

Show: $\dfrac{BT}{GV} = \dfrac{TH}{VE}$

Plan: Use the Right Angles Are Congruent Theorem, CASTC, and the AA Similarity Postulate to get $\triangle BHT \sim \triangle GEV$. Therefore, $\dfrac{BT}{GV} = \dfrac{TH}{VE}$ by CSSTP.

Proof:

Statement	Reason
1. $\triangle BTA \sim \triangle GVL$	1. Given
2. $\angle B \cong \angle G$	2. CASTC
3. $\overline{TH}$ is the altitude to $\overline{BA}$; $\overline{VE}$ is the altitude to $\overline{GL}$	3. Given
4. $\overline{TH} \perp \overline{BA}$; $\overline{VE} \perp \overline{GL}$	4. Definition of altitude
5. $\angle THB$ is a right angle; $\angle VEG$ is a right angle	5. Definition of perpendicular
6. $\angle THB \cong \angle VEG$	6. Right Angles Are Congruent Theorem
7. $\triangle BHT \sim \triangle GEV$	7. AA Similarity Postulate
8. $\dfrac{BT}{GV} = \dfrac{TH}{VE}$	8. CSSTP

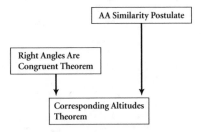

2. Given: Two similar triangles with corresponding medians

Show: The medians are proportional to the corresponding sides

Given: $\triangle BGI \sim \triangle SAM$; $\overline{GY}$ is the median to $\overline{BI}$; $\overline{AL}$ is the median to $\overline{SM}$

Show: $\dfrac{BG}{SA} = \dfrac{GY}{AL}$

Paragraph Proof: By the definitions of median and midpoint, $BY = YI$ and $SL = LM$. Then, by the Segment Addition Postulate and the substitution property, $BI = 2BY$ and $SM = 2SL$, or $BY = \frac{1}{2}BI$ and $SL = \frac{1}{2}SM$. $\triangle BGI \sim \triangle SAM$ is given, so, by CSSTP,

$$\frac{BG}{SA} = \frac{BI}{SM} = \frac{\frac{1}{2}BI}{\frac{1}{2}SM} = \frac{BY}{SL}$$

Also, $\angle B \cong \angle S$ by CASTC. Therefore, $\triangle BYG \sim \triangle SLA$ by the SAS Similarity Theorem. Therefore, $\frac{BG}{SA} = \frac{GY}{AL}$ by CSSTP.

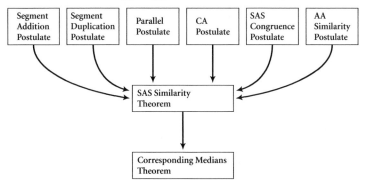

3. **Given:** Two similar triangles with corresponding angle bisectors

   Show: The angle bisectors are proportional to the corresponding sides

   Given: $\triangle ACB \sim \triangle DFE$; $\overline{CP}$ is the angle bisector of $\angle ACB$; $\overline{FQ}$ is the angle bisector of $\angle DFE$

   Show: $\dfrac{AC}{DF} = \dfrac{CP}{FQ}$

   Plan: Use the definition of angle bisector, the Angle Addition Postulate, and the substitution property to get $m\angle ACB = 2m\angle 1$ and $m\angle DFE = 2m\angle 2$. Then use CASTC and the AA Similarity Postulate to get $\triangle APC \sim \triangle DQF$. Therefore, $\frac{AC}{DF} = \frac{CP}{FQ}$ by CSSTP.

Proof:	**Statement**	**Reason**
	1. $\overline{CP}$ is the angle bisector of $\angle ACB$; $\overline{FQ}$ is the angle bisector of $\angle DFE$	1. Given
	2. $\angle 1 \cong \angle 3$; $\angle 2 \cong \angle 4$	2. Definition of angle bisector
	3. $m\angle 1 = m\angle 3$; $m\angle 2 = m\angle 4$	3. Definition of congruence
	4. $m\angle ACB = m\angle 1 + m\angle 3$; $m\angle DFB = m\angle 2 + m\angle 4$	4. Angle Addition Postulate
	5. $m\angle ACB = 2m\angle 1$; $m\angle DFB = 2m\angle 2$	5. Substitution property
	6. $\triangle ACB \sim \triangle DFE$	6. Given
	7. $\angle A \cong \angle D$	7. CASTC
	8. $\angle ACB \cong \angle DFE$	8. CASTC
	9. $m\angle ACB = m\angle DFE$	9. Definition of congruence
	10. $2m\angle 1 = 2m\angle 2$	10. Transitive property
	11. $m\angle 1 = m\angle 2$	11. Division property
	12. $\angle 1 \cong \angle 2$	12. Definition of congruence
	13. $\triangle APC \sim \triangle DQF$	13. AA Similarity Postulate
	14. $\dfrac{AC}{DF} = \dfrac{CP}{FQ}$	14. CSSTP

4. Given: Triangle cut by a line passing through two sides and parallel to the third side

Show: The line divides the two sides proportionally

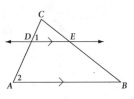

Given: $\triangle ACB$ with $\overset{\leftrightarrow}{DE} \parallel \overline{AB}$

Show: $\dfrac{DA}{CD} = \dfrac{EB}{CE}$

Plan: Use the CA Postulate and the AA Similarity Postulate to get $\triangle CDE \sim \triangle CAB$. Then use CSSTP and the Segment Addition Postulate to get $\dfrac{CD + DA}{CD} = \dfrac{CE + EB}{CE}$. Therefore, $\dfrac{DA}{CD} = \dfrac{EB}{CE}$ by algebra and the subtraction property.

Proof:

Statement	Reason
1. $\overset{\leftrightarrow}{DE} \parallel \overline{AB}$	1. Given
2. $\angle 1 \cong \angle 2$	2. CA Postulate
3. $\angle DCE \cong \angle ACB$	3. Reflexive property
4. $\triangle CDE \sim \triangle CAB$	4. AA Similarity Postulate
5. $\dfrac{CA}{CD} = \dfrac{CB}{CE}$	5. CSSTP
6. $CA = CD + DA;\ CB = CE + EB$	6. Segment Addition Postulate
7. $\dfrac{CD + DA}{CD} = \dfrac{CE + EB}{CE}$	7. Substitution property
8. $\dfrac{CD}{CD} + \dfrac{DA}{CD} = \dfrac{CE}{CE} + \dfrac{EB}{CE}$	8. Algebra
9. $1 + \dfrac{DA}{CD} = 1 + \dfrac{EB}{CE}$	9. Algebra
10. $\dfrac{DA}{CD} = \dfrac{EB}{CE}$	10. Subtraction property

5. Given: Triangle cut by a line passing through two sides, dividing them proportionally

Show: The line is parallel to the third side

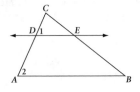

Given: $\triangle ACB$ with $\overset{\leftrightarrow}{DE}$ intersecting $\overline{CA}$ and $\overline{CB}$ such that $\dfrac{DA}{CD} = \dfrac{EB}{CE}$

Show: $\overset{\leftrightarrow}{DE} \parallel \overline{AB}$

Plan: Use the addition property to get $\dfrac{DA}{CD} + 1 = \dfrac{EB}{CE} + 1$. Then use algebra and the Segment Addition Postulate to get $\dfrac{CA}{CD} = \dfrac{CB}{CE}$. Therefore, $\triangle ABC \sim \triangle DEC$ by the SAS Similarity Theorem, $\angle 1 \cong \angle 2$ by CASTC, and $\overset{\leftrightarrow}{DE} \parallel \overline{AB}$ by the CA Postulate.

Proof:

Statement	Reason
1. $\dfrac{DA}{CD} = \dfrac{EB}{CE}$	1. Given
2. $1 + \dfrac{DA}{CD} = 1 + \dfrac{EB}{CE}$	2. Addition property
3. $\dfrac{CD}{CD} + \dfrac{DA}{CD} = \dfrac{CE}{CE} + \dfrac{EB}{CE}$	3. Algebra
4. $\dfrac{CD + DA}{CD} = \dfrac{CE + EB}{CE}$	4. Algebra
5. $CA = CD + DA;\ CB = CE + EB$	5. Addition property
6. $\dfrac{CA}{CD} = \dfrac{CB}{CE}$	6. Substitution property
7. $\angle ACB \cong \angle DCE$	7. Reflexive property
8. $\triangle ABC \sim \triangle DEC$	8. SAS Similarity Theorem
9. $\angle 1 \cong \angle 2$	9. CASTC
10. $\overset{\leftrightarrow}{DE} \parallel \overline{AB}$	10. CA Postulate

6. Given: Right triangle with altitude to the hypotenuse

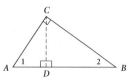

Show: The two smaller triangles formed are similar to each other and to the original triangle

Given: Right triangle ABC with right angle ACB; $\overline{CD}$ is the altitude to hypotenuse $\overline{AB}$

Show: $\triangle ADC \sim \triangle ACB \sim \triangle CDB$

Plan: Use the Right Angles Are Congruent Theorem, the reflexive property, and the AA Similarity Postulate to get $\triangle ADC \sim \triangle ACB$ and $\triangle ACB \sim \triangle CDB$. Therefore, $\triangle ADC \sim \triangle ACB \sim \triangle CDB$ by the transitive property of similarity.

Proof:

Statement	Reason
1. $\angle ACB$ is a right angle	1. Given
2. $\overline{CD}$ is the altitude to hypotenuse $\overline{AB}$	2. Given
3. $\overline{CD} \perp \overline{AB}$	3. Definition of altitude
4. $\angle CDA$ is a right angle	4. Definition of perpendicular
5. $\angle CDA \cong \angle ACB$	5. Right Angles Are Congruent Theorem
6. $\angle 1 \cong \angle 1$	6. Reflexive property
7. $\triangle ADC \sim \triangle ACB$	7. AA Similarity Postulate
8. $\angle CDB$ is a right angle	8. Definition of perpendicular
9. $\angle ACB \cong \angle CDB$	9. Right Angles Are Congruent Theorem
10. $\angle 2 \cong \angle 2$	10. Reflexive property
11. $\triangle ACB \sim \triangle CDB$	11. AA Similarity Postulate
12. $\triangle ADC \sim \triangle ACB \sim \triangle CDB$	12. Transitive property of similarity

7. Given: Right triangle with altitude to the hypotenuse

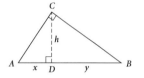

Show: The length of the altitude is the geometric mean of the lengths of the two segments on the hypotenuse

Given: Right triangle ABC with right angle ACB; $\overline{CD}$ is the altitude to hypotenuse $\overline{AB}$

Show: CD is the geometric mean of AD and DB

Paragraph Proof: By the Three Similar Right Triangles, $\triangle ADC \sim \triangle CDB$. Then, by CSSTP, $\frac{AD}{CD} = \frac{CD}{DB}$, or $\frac{x}{h} = \frac{h}{y}$. This is equivalent to $h^2 = xy$, or $h = \sqrt{xy}$ (h must be positive). Thus, by the definition of geometric mean, h is the geometric mean of x and y, or CD is the geometric mean of AD and DB.

8. Given: Right triangle

Show: The square of the length of the hypotenuse is equal to the sum of the squares of the lengths of the two legs

Given: Right triangle with legs of lengths a and b and hypotenuse of length c

Show: $a^2 + b^2 = c^2$

Paragraph Proof: Use the Perpendicular Postulate to draw the altitude to the hypotenuse. By the Three Similar Right Triangles Theorem, each of the small right triangles is similar to the large right triangle. Because the small triangle on the right is similar to the large triangle, $\frac{a}{c} = \frac{c-d}{a}$ by CSSTP. This proportion is equivalent to $\frac{a}{c-d} = \frac{c}{a}$. (The ratio of the length of the shorter leg to the length of the hypotenuse is the same in both triangles.) By algebra, either of these proportions is equivalent to $a^2 = c(c - d)$. By the distributive property, $a^2 = c^2 - cd$. Now look at the other small triangle, which is also similar to the large triangle by the Three Similar Right

Triangles Theorem, so $\frac{b}{c} = \frac{d}{b}$ by CSSTP. This proportion is equivalent to $\frac{b}{d} = \frac{c}{b}$. (The ratio of the length of the hypotenuse to the length of the longer leg is the same in both triangles.) By algebra, either of these proportions is equivalent to $b^2 = cd$. Substitute b^2 for cd in the equation $a^2 = c^2 - cd$ to obtain $a^2 = c^2 - b^2$. Then, by the addition property, $a^2 + b^2 = c^2$.

9. **Given:** Triangle with the square of one side equal to the sum of the squares of the other two sides

 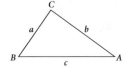

Show: The triangle is a right triangle

Given: $\triangle ABC$ with side lengths a, b, and c such that $a^2 + b^2 = c^2$

Show: $\triangle ABC$ is a right triangle with right angle C

Paragraph Proof: Construct right triangle DEF with $\angle E$ a right angle, and with legs of lengths a and b. Let x represent the length of the hypotenuse of this triangle. By the Pythagorean Theorem, $a^2 + b^2 = x^2$. Because $a^2 + b^2 = c^2$ is given, $x^2 = c^2$ by the transitive property of equality. Because x and c both represent side lengths and therefore must be positive numbers, $x = \sqrt{c^2} = c$. Therefore, $\triangle DEF \cong \triangle ABC$ by the SSS Congruence Postulate. Then $\angle E \cong \angle C$ by CPCTC. $\angle E$ is a right angle by construction and $\angle E \cong \angle C$, so $\angle C$ must also be a right angle. Therefore, $\triangle ABC$ is a right triangle with right angle C.

10. **Given:** Two right triangles with the hypotenuse and one leg of one triangle congruent to the hypotenuse and one leg of the other triangle

Show: The triangles are congruent

Given: Right triangles HYP and LEG with right angles Y and E; $\overline{HP} \cong \overline{LG}$; $\overline{YP} \cong \overline{EG}$

Show: $\triangle HYP \cong \triangle LEG$

Plan: Use the Pythagorean Theorem to write expressions for the lengths of the unknown legs. Show that the expressions are equivalent. The triangles are congruent by SSS or SAS.

Proof:

Statement	Reason
1. $\triangle HYP$ is a right triangle with right angle Y; $\triangle LEG$ is a right triangle with right angle E	1. Given
2. $\overline{HP} \cong \overline{LG}$; $\overline{YP} \cong \overline{EG}$	2. Given
3. $HP = LG$; $YP = EG$	3. Definition of congruence
4. $(HY)^2 + (YP)^2 = (HP)^2$; $(LE)^2 + (EG)^2 = (LG)^2$	4. Pythagorean Theorem
5. $HY = \sqrt{(HP)^2 - (YP)^2}$; $LE = \sqrt{(LG)^2 - (EG)^2}$	5. Algebra
6. $HY = LE$	6. Substitution and transitive properties
7. $\overline{HY} \cong \overline{LE}$	7. Definition of congruence
8. $\triangle HYP \cong \triangle LEG$	8. SSS Congruence Postulate

Discovering Geometry Solutions Manual
©2008 Key Curriculum Press

11.

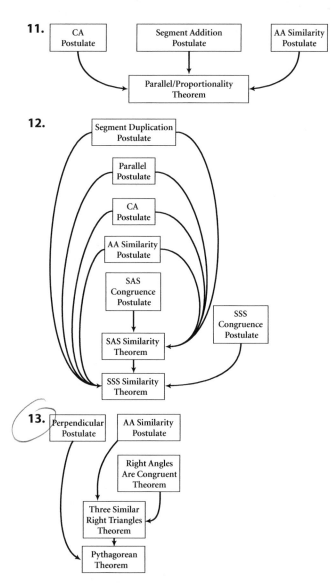

12.

13.

triangles into two congruent right triangles in which the length of one leg is half the length of the chord, and the hypotenuse is a radius of the circle.

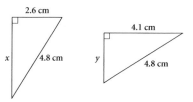

Apply the Pythagorean Theorem to each of the right triangles shown to find x and y.

$$x = \sqrt{(4.8)^2 - (2.6)^2}$$
$$y = \sqrt{(4.8)^2 - (4.1)^2}$$

The distance between the two chords is $x - y = \sqrt{(4.8)^2 - (2.6)^2} - \sqrt{(4.8)^2 - (4.1)^2} \approx 1.5$ cm.

Now look at the case where the chords are on opposite sides of the diameter.

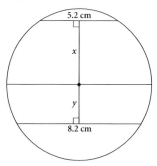

Notice that the distances of the two chords from the center, x and y, are the same as before, but now the distance between the chords is $x + y = \sqrt{(4.8)^2 - (2.6)^2} + \sqrt{(4.8)^2 - (4.1)^2} \approx 6.5$ cm.

14. Approximately 1.5 cm or 6.5 cm. There are two possible answers because the chords can be either on the same side or on opposite sides of the diameter they are parallel to. First look at the case where the chords are on the same side of the diameter. The longer chord will be closer to the center of the circle.

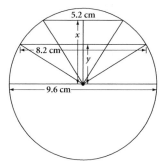

In each case, the distance from the center to the chord is the altitude of an isosceles triangle whose legs are radii and therefore have length $\frac{1}{2}(9.6) = 4.8$ cm. These altitudes divide each of the isosceles

15. a. C. The perimeter of the hexagon is $6(10) = 60$ cm, and the perimeter of the pentagon is $5(12) = 60$ cm, so the perimeters are equal.

b. A. Divide each polygon into congruent isosceles triangles by drawing congruent segments from the centers of the polygons to each of their vertices. In each case, the apothem is an altitude of one of these triangles, so this segment divides the isosceles triangle into two congruent right triangles.

Regular hexagon:

$m\angle RST = \frac{1}{6}(360°) = 60°$, so $\triangle RST$ is an equilateral triangle and $\triangle RSU$ is a 30°-60°-90° triangle. In this triangle, $\overline{RU}$ is the shorter leg and $\overline{SU}$ is the longer leg. Because $RU = \frac{1}{2}(10) = 5$ cm, $a = SU = 5\sqrt{3}$ cm ≈ 8.66 cm.

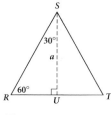

Regular pentagon:

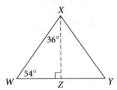

$m\angle WXY = \frac{1}{5}(360°) = 72°$. Because $\triangle WXY$ is isosceles, $m\angle XWY = \frac{1}{2}(180° - 72°) = 54°$. Now look at right triangle WXZ. Here $WZ = \frac{1}{2}(WY) = 6$ cm. Because $\angle XWZ$ and $\angle XWY$ are the same angle, $m\angle XWZ = 54°$. Then $\frac{a}{6} = \tan 54°$, so $a = 6 \tan 54° \approx 8.26$ cm.

Thus, the apothem is greater in the hexagon.

c. A. Recall that you can find the area of a regular polygon by using the formula $A = \frac{1}{2}aP$, where a is the length of the apothem and P is the perimeter (Regular Polygon Area Conjecture). Because both of the regular polygons have the same perimeter (from 15a), the polygon with the greater apothem will have the greater area. From 15b, you know that this is the hexagon.

d. A. Recall that the Polygon Sum Conjecture states that the sum of the measures of the n interior angles of an n-gon is $180°(n - 2)$. It follows that as the number of sides of an n-gon increases, the sum of the measures of the interior angles will increase. Therefore, because the hexagon has more sides than the pentagon, the sum of the measures of the interior angles will be greater in the hexagon.

e. C. Recall that the Exterior Angle Sum Conjecture states that for any polygon, the sum of the measures of a set of exterior angles (one exterior angle at each vertex) is 360°. Therefore, the sum is the same for both polygons.

16. a. The vectors are diagonals of your quadrilateral.

b. A 180° rotation about the midpoint of the common side; the entire tessellation maps onto itself.

17. a. A 180° rotation about the midpoint of any side

b. Possible answer: A vector running from each vertex of the quadrilateral to the opposite vertex (or any multiple of that vector)

18. a. 33°. Label the intersection point of $\overline{PQ}$ and $\overline{ST}$ as R and the intersection points of the two circles with $\overline{PQ}$ as Z and W, as shown in the figure below. Also construct $\overline{GT}$.

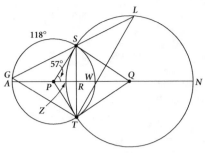

Look at $\triangle PSQ$. Because $\overline{PS}$ is tangent to circle Q, $\overline{PS} \perp \overline{SQ}$ by the Tangent Conjecture, so $m\angle PSQ = 90°$. Therefore, $m\angle SQP = 180° - 57° - 90° = 33°$. Because $\angle SQZ$ is a central angle in circle Q and $\angle SQZ$ and $\angle SQP$ are the same angle, $m\overarc{SZ} = 33°$. Because $\triangle PSQ \cong \triangle PTQ$ by the SSS Congruence Postulate (using the two pairs of congruent radii and the common side), $m\angle TQZ = m\angle SQZ = 33°$, so $m\angle SQT = 66°$. In circle Q, $\angle SLT$ is an inscribed angle that intercepts $\overline{SZT}$, so $m\angle SLT = \frac{1}{2}(m\overarc{SZT}) = \frac{1}{2}(66°) = 33°$. $\angle GLT$ is the same angle as $\angle SLT$, so $m\angle GLT = m\angle SLT = 33°$.

b. 66°. $m\angle SQT$ was found in the solution for 18a.

c. 57°. $\overline{PS} \cong \overline{PT}$ because they are both radii of circle P, and $\overline{QS} \cong \overline{QT}$ because they are both radii of circle Q. Therefore, $PSQT$ is a kite. Then $\overline{PQ} \perp \overline{ST}$ because the diagonals of a kite are perpendicular, so $\triangle SRQ$ is a right triangle. Look at the angles in this triangle. From 18a, $m\angle SQR = 33°$, so $m\angle RSQ = 90° - 33° = 57°$. $\angle RSQ$ is the same angle as $\angle TSQ$, so $m\angle TSQ = 57°$.

d. 62°. Look at $\triangle GTL$. $\angle SGT$ is an inscribed angle in circle P, so $m\angle SGT = \frac{1}{2}(m\overarc{SWT})$. $m\overarc{SWT} = m\angle SPT$ by the definition of arc measure, and $m\angle SPT = 2(57°) = 114°$ by the Kite Diagonal Conjecture. So, $m\angle SGT = \frac{1}{2}(114°) = 57°$. This gives one angle measure in $\triangle GTL$ because $\angle SGT$ and $\angle LGT$ are the same angle. From 18a, $m\angle GLT = 33°$ ($\angle GLT$ is the same angle as $\angle SLT$). Then, by the Triangle Sum Conjecture, $m\angle GTL = 180° - 57° - 33° = 90°$. By the Angle Addition Postulate, $m\angle GTS + m\angle STL = m\angle GTL$. Because $\angle GTS$ is an inscribed angle in circle P, $m\angle GTS = \frac{1}{2}m\overarc{GS} = \frac{1}{2}(118°) = 59°$. Then $m\angle STL = m\angle GTL - m\angle GTS = 90° - 59° = 31°$. Because $\angle STL$ is an inscribed angle in circle Q, $m\angle STL = \frac{1}{2}(m\overarc{SL})$, or $m\overarc{SL} = 2(m\angle STL) = 2(31°) = 62°$.

e. $\angle PSQ$ and $\angle PTQ$ are both right angles by the Tangent Theorem and thus are supplementary. Therefore, $\angle SPT$ and $\angle SQT$ must also be supplementary by the Quadrilateral Sum Theorem. Therefore, $PSQT$ is cyclic by the Converse of the Cyclic Quadrilateral Theorem.

f. Because $\overline{PS}$ is tangent to circle Q, $m\angle PSQ = 90°$ (Tangent Theorem). Because $m\angle PSQ = 90°$, $\overline{SQ}$ must be tangent to circle P (Converse of Tangent Theorem).

19. a. $\dfrac{\pi}{2} + \dfrac{\sqrt{3}}{2} - 1$

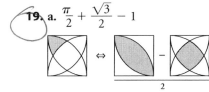

Substitute the area expressions you found in Lesson 13.1, Exercise 31c and in Lesson 13.5, Exercise 12b.

$$A = \frac{\left(\dfrac{\pi}{2} - 1\right) - \left(1 - \sqrt{3} + \dfrac{\pi}{3}\right)}{2}$$

$$= \frac{\dfrac{\pi}{2} - 1 - 1 + \sqrt{3} - \dfrac{\pi}{3}}{2}$$

$$= \frac{\dfrac{\pi}{6} + \sqrt{3} - 2}{2} = \frac{\pi}{12} + \frac{\sqrt{3}}{2} - 1$$

b. $-\dfrac{\pi}{6} - \dfrac{\sqrt{3}}{4} + 1$

Substitute the area expressions you found in Lesson 13.5, Exercise 12a and in 19a above.

$$A = \left(\frac{\sqrt{3}}{4} - \frac{\pi}{12}\right) - \left(\frac{\pi}{12} + \frac{\sqrt{3}}{2} - 1\right)$$

$$= \frac{\sqrt{3}}{4} - \frac{\pi}{12} - \frac{\pi}{12} - \frac{\sqrt{3}}{2} + 1 = -\frac{\pi}{6} - \frac{\sqrt{3}}{4} + 1$$

20. a. $\triangle CDG \cong \triangle CFG$ by SAA; $\triangle GEA \cong \triangle GEB$ by SAS; $\triangle DGA \cong \triangle FGB$ by the Hypotenuse Leg Theorem.

b. $\overline{CD} \cong \overline{CF}$ and $\overline{DA} \cong \overline{FB}$ by CPCTC; $CD + DA = CF + FB$ (addition property). Therefore, $\overline{CA} \cong \overline{CB}$, and $\triangle ABC$ is isosceles.

c. The figure is inaccurate.

d. The angle bisector does not intersect the perpendicular bisector inside the triangle as shown, except in the special case of an isosceles triangle, when they coincide.

21. 173 cm, 345 cm, 20 stones. Draw the trapezoid, and extend the legs until they meet to form a triangle. Let r represent the rise. Use proportional sides in similar triangles to find x.

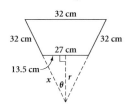

$$\frac{x}{x + 32} = \frac{27}{32}$$

$$32x = 27(x + 32)$$

$$32x = 27x + 864$$

$$5x = 864$$

$$x = 172.8$$

Then, by the Pythagorean Theorem, $r = \sqrt{(172.8)^2 - (13.5)^2} \approx 172.3 \approx 172$. The rise, which is the radius of the semicircular arch, is approximately 172 cm. The span is the diameter of the arch, so it is twice the rise. Therefore, the span is approximately $344.6 \approx 345$ cm. Use the inverse sine to find the central angle measure: $\theta = \sin^{-1}\left(\frac{13.5}{172.8}\right) \cong 4.5°$, so the central angle is approximately $2(4.5°) = 9°$. Divide into $180°$ to find the number of voussoirs: $\frac{180°}{9°} = 20$.

IMPROVING YOUR ALGEBRA SKILLS

1. Add; $5x - y = 29$

2. Add; $10x + 2y = 50$

3. Subtract; $x + y = 4$

EXTENSIONS

A.

Given: $\triangle ABC \sim \triangle DEF$ with $\dfrac{AB}{DE} = \dfrac{BC}{EF} = \dfrac{AC}{DF} = s$; $\overline{BD}$ is the altitude to $\overline{AC}$; $\overline{EQ}$ is the altitude to $\overline{DF}$

Show: $\dfrac{\text{Area of } \triangle ABC}{\text{Area of } \triangle DEF} = s^2$

Paragraph Proof: Choose $\overline{AC}$ as the base of $\triangle ABC$ and $\overline{DF}$ as the base of $\triangle DEF$. Let $b = DF$ and $h = EQ$. $\frac{AC}{DF} = s$, so $\frac{AC}{b} = s$, and $AC = sb$. $\overline{BD}$ is the altitude to $\overline{AC}$ and $\overline{EQ}$ is the altitude to $\overline{DF}$, so, by the Corresponding Altitudes Theorem, $\frac{BD}{EQ} = \frac{AB}{DE}$. Thus, by the transitive property, $\frac{BD}{EQ} = s$, or $\frac{BD}{h} = s$, so $BD = hs$. Now find the area of each triangle:

Area of $\triangle DEF = \frac{1}{2}(DF)(EQ) = \frac{1}{2}bh$

Area of $\triangle ABC = \frac{1}{2}(AC)(BD) = \frac{1}{2}(sb)(sh)$

$$= \frac{1}{2}s^2 bh = s^2\left(\frac{1}{2}bh\right)$$

$$\frac{\text{Area of } \triangle ABC}{\text{Area of } \triangle DEF} = \frac{s^2\left(\dfrac{1}{2}bh\right)}{\dfrac{1}{2}bh} = s^2$$

B.

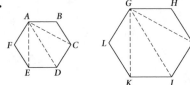

Given: Two similar polygons with scale factor s

Show: The area of one polygon is s^2 times the area of the other polygon

Paragraph Proof: Divide each polygon into $(n - 2)$ triangles by drawing the diagonals from one vertex. (The process is shown for hexagons.) Show that $\triangle AFE \sim \triangle GLK$ and $\triangle ABC \sim \triangle GHI$ by the SAS Similarity Theorem. Then use CSSTP and CASTC and the subtraction property to show that $\triangle AED \sim \triangle GKJ$ and $\triangle ACD \sim \triangle GIJ$.

(Although this process is shown only for hexagons, it can be generalized to any polygons.) Then, because the polygons are made up of similar triangles, you can use the result from Extension A to show that their areas are similar, with ratio s^2.

USING YOUR ALGEBRA SKILLS 13

EXERCISES

1. $B(a, 0)$. The y-axis passes through the midpoint of $\overline{AB}$, the base of the isosceles triangle. B lies on the x-axis. Because $(0, 0)$ is the midpoint of $\overline{AB}$, B must be the same distance from the origin as A, so the coordinates of B are $(a, 0)$.

2. $C(a + b, c)$. Because $ABCD$ is a parallelogram, $\overline{DC} \parallel \overline{AB}$. $\overline{AB}$ lies along the x-axis, so $\overline{DC}$ must also be a horizontal segment. Therefore, the y-coordinate of C must be the same as the y-coordinate of D, which is c. Because opposite sides of a parallelogram are congruent, $DC = AB$. Because $AB = a - 0 = a$, the x-coordinate of C must be $a + b$ to get $CD = (a + b) - b = a$.

3. $C\left(a + b, \sqrt{a^2 - b^2}\right)$, $D\left(b, \sqrt{a^2 - b^2}\right)$. The length of $\overline{AB}$ is $a - 0 = a$. All sides of a rhombus are congruent, so the length of each of the other three sides must also be a. A rhombus is a parallelogram, so $\overline{DC} \parallel \overline{AB}$. Therefore, $\overline{DC}$ must be a horizontal segment, and C and D will have the same y-coordinate. The x-coordinate of C must be $a + b$ to get $CD = (a + b) - b = a$. Draw a perpendicular segment from D to the x-axis to form a right triangle.

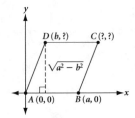

The shorter leg of the right triangle has length b. Because $\overline{AD}$, the hypotenuse of this triangle, is a side of the rhombus, its length is a. Therefore, by the Pythagorean Theorem, the length of the longer leg is $\sqrt{a^2 - b^2}$. This is the y-coordinate of D and therefore also the y-coordinate of C. Thus, the coordinates of C are $\left(a + b, \sqrt{a^2 - b^2}\right)$ and the coordinates of D are $\left(b, \sqrt{a^2 - b^2}\right)$.

4. Possible answer:

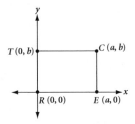

Slope $\overline{RE} = \dfrac{0 - 0}{a - 0} = \dfrac{0}{a} = 0$

Slope $\overline{CE} = \dfrac{b - 0}{a - a} = \dfrac{b}{0}$ (undefined)

Slope $\overline{TC} = \dfrac{b - b}{a - 0} = \dfrac{0}{a} = 0$

Slope $\overline{TR} = \dfrac{b - 0}{0 - 0} = \dfrac{b}{0}$ (undefined)

Opposite sides have the same slope and are therefore parallel by the parallel slope property. (In this case, two sides have undefined slope.) Two sides are horizontal and two sides are vertical, so the angles are all right angles. Because $RECT$ is a parallelogram with four right angles, it is a rectangle.

5. Possible answer:

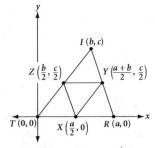

Coordinates of $X = \left(\dfrac{a + 0}{2}, \dfrac{0 + 0}{2}\right) = \left(\dfrac{a}{2}, 0\right)$

Coordinates of $Y = \left(\dfrac{a + b}{2}, \dfrac{0 + c}{2}\right) = \left(\dfrac{a + b}{2}, \dfrac{c}{2}\right)$

Coordinates of $Z = \left(\dfrac{b + 0}{2}, \dfrac{c + 0}{2}\right) = \left(\dfrac{b}{2}, \dfrac{c}{2}\right)$

X, Y, and Z are the midpoints of $\overline{TR}$, $\overline{RI}$, and $\overline{TI}$, respectively, by the coordinate midpoint property. Therefore $\overline{XY}$, $\overline{YZ}$, and $\overline{ZX}$ are midsegments by definition.

Discovering Geometry Solutions Manual
©2008 Key Curriculum Press

6.

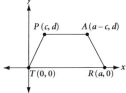

Slope $\overline{TR} = \dfrac{0-0}{a-0} = \dfrac{0}{a} = 0$

Slope $\overline{RA} = \dfrac{d-0}{a-c-a} = -\dfrac{d}{c}$

Slope $\overline{AP} = \dfrac{d-d}{a-c-c} = \dfrac{0}{a-2c} = 0$

Slope $\overline{PT} = \dfrac{d-0}{c-0} = \dfrac{d}{c}$

$\overline{TR}$ and $\overline{AP}$ have the same slope and are parallel by the parallel slope property. $\overline{PT}$ and $\overline{RA}$ have unequal slopes, so they are not parallel. Thus, *TRAP* has only one pair of parallel sides and is a trapezoid by definition.

Use the distance formula to find the lengths of the nonparallel sides.

$PT = \sqrt{(c-0)^2 + (d-0)^2} = \sqrt{c^2 + d^2}$

$RA = \sqrt{(a-c-a)^2 + (d-0)^2}$

$\quad = \sqrt{(-c)^2 + d^2} = \sqrt{c^2 + d^2}$

The nonparallel sides of the trapezoid have the same length, so trapezoid *TRAP* is isosceles by definition.

7.

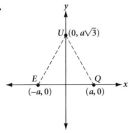

The *y*-axis splits $\triangle EQU$ into two 30°-60°-90° triangles, and the altitude of the equilateral triangle is the longer leg of each of the 30°-60°-90° triangles, so the *y*-coordinate of *U* will be $a\sqrt{3}$.

$EQ = 2a$

$EU = \sqrt{(-a-0)^2 + \left(0 - a\sqrt{3}\right)^2} = \sqrt{a^2 + 3a^2}$

$\quad = \sqrt{4a^2} = 2a$

$UQ = \sqrt{(a-0)^2 + \left(0 - a\sqrt{3}\right)^2} = \sqrt{a^2 + 3a^2}$

$\quad = \sqrt{4a^2} = 2a$

Therefore, $EQ = EU = UQ$, so $\overline{EQ} \cong \overline{EU} \cong \overline{UQ}$, and $\triangle EQU$ is equilateral by definition.

8. Given: A rectangle with both diagonals

Show: The diagonals are congruent

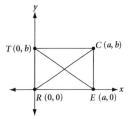

Given: Rectangle *RECT* with diagonals $\overline{RC}$ and $\overline{TE}$

Show: $\overline{RC} \cong \overline{TE}$

Proof: To show that two segments are congruent, use the distance formula to show that they have the same length.

$TE = \sqrt{(a-0)^2 + (0-b)^2} = \sqrt{a^2 + b^2}$

$RC = \sqrt{(0-a)^2 + (0-b)^2} = \sqrt{a^2 + b^2}$

$\overline{RC} \cong \overline{TE}$ because both segments have the same length. Therefore, the diagonals of a rectangle are congruent.

9. Given: A triangle with one midsegment

Show: The midsegment is parallel to the third side and half the length of the third side

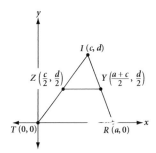

Given: $\triangle TRI$ and midsegment $\overline{ZY}$

Show: $\overline{ZY} \parallel \overline{TR}$ and $ZY = \dfrac{1}{2}TR$

Proof: To show that two segments are parallel, use the parallel slope property. To compare lengths, use the distance formula.

Slope $\overline{TR} = \dfrac{0-0}{a-0} = \dfrac{0}{a} = 0$

Slope $\overline{ZY} = \dfrac{\frac{d}{2} - \frac{d}{2}}{\frac{a+c}{2} - \frac{c}{2}} = \dfrac{0}{\frac{a}{2}} = 0$

The slopes are the same, so the segments are parallel by the parallel slope property. $\overline{TR}$ and $\overline{ZY}$ are horizontal lines, so to find their lengths, subtract their *x*-coordinates.

$TR = a - 0 = a$

$ZY = \dfrac{a+c}{2} - \dfrac{c}{2} = \dfrac{a}{2} = \dfrac{1}{2}a = \dfrac{1}{2}TR$

Thus, the midsegment is half the length of the third side. Therefore, the midsegment of a triangle is parallel to the third side and half the length of the third side.

10. Given: Trapezoid

Show: The midsegment is parallel to the bases

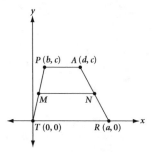

Given: Trapezoid *TRAP* with midsegment $\overline{MN}$

Show: $\overline{MN} \parallel \overline{TR}$

Proof: By the coordinate midpoint property, the coordinates of *M* are $\left(\frac{b}{2}, \frac{c}{2}\right)$ and the coordinates of *N* are $\left(\frac{a+d}{2}, \frac{c}{2}\right)$. To show that the midsegment and bases are parallel, find their slopes.

$$\text{Slope } \overline{MN} = \frac{\frac{c}{2} - \frac{c}{2}}{\frac{a+d}{2} - \frac{b}{2}} = \frac{0}{\frac{a+d-b}{2}} = 0$$

$$\text{Slope } \overline{TR} = \frac{0-0}{a-0} = \frac{0}{a} = 0$$

$$\text{Slope } \overline{PA} = \frac{c-c}{d-b} = \frac{0}{d-b} = 0$$

The slopes are equal. Therefore, the lines are parallel.

11. Given: A quadrilateral in which only one diagonal is the perpendicular bisector of the other

Show: The quadrilateral is a kite

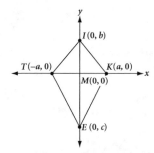

Given: Quadrilateral *KITE* with diagonals $\overline{IE}$ and $\overline{TK}$. $\overline{IE}$ is the perpendicular bisector of $\overline{TK}$, but $\overline{TK}$ is not the perpendicular bisector of $\overline{IE}$ $\left(|b| \neq |c|\right)$

Show: *KITE* is a kite

Proof: To show that a quadrilateral is a kite, use the distance formula to show that only two pairs of adjacent sides have the same length.

$$KI = \sqrt{(0-a)^2 + (b-0)^2} = \sqrt{a^2 + b^2}$$

$$IT = \sqrt{(0-(-a))^2 + (b-0)^2} = \sqrt{a^2 + b^2}$$

$$TE = \sqrt{(0-(-a))^2 + (c-0)^2} = \sqrt{a^2 + c^2}$$

$$EK = \sqrt{(a-0)^2 + (0-c)^2} = \sqrt{a^2 + c^2}$$

Adjacent sides $\overline{KI}$ and $\overline{IT}$ have the same length and adjacent sides $\overline{TE}$ and $\overline{EK}$ have the same length, and because $|b| \neq |c|$, the pairs are not equal in

length to each other. Therefore, *KITE* is a kite by definition. Therefore, if only one diagonal of a quadrilateral is the perpendicular bisector of the other diagonal, then the quadrilateral is a kite.

12. Given: A quadrilateral with midpoints connected to form a second quadrilateral

Show: The second quadrilateral is a parallelogram

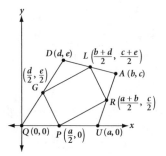

Given: Quadrilateral *QUAD* with midpoints *P*, *R*, *L*, and *G*

Show: *PRLG* is a parallelogram

Proof: To show that a quadrilateral is a parallelogram, show that opposite sides have the same slope.

$$\text{Slope } \overline{PR} = \frac{\frac{c}{2} - 0}{\frac{a+b}{2} - \frac{a}{2}} = \frac{\frac{c}{2}}{\frac{b}{2}} = \frac{c}{b}$$

$$\text{Slope } \overline{RL} = \frac{\frac{c+e}{2} - \frac{c}{2}}{\frac{b+d}{2} - \frac{a+b}{2}} = \frac{\frac{e}{2}}{\frac{d-a}{2}} = \frac{e}{d-a}$$

$$\text{Slope } \overline{LG} = \frac{\frac{e}{2} - \frac{c+e}{2}}{\frac{d}{2} - \frac{b+d}{2}} = \frac{\frac{-c}{2}}{\frac{-b}{2}} = \frac{c}{b}$$

$$\text{Slope } \overline{GP} = \frac{\frac{e}{2} - 0}{\frac{d}{2} - \frac{a}{2}} = \frac{\frac{e}{2}}{\frac{d-a}{2}} = \frac{e}{d-a}$$

$\overline{PR}$ and $\overline{LG}$ have the same slope, and $\overline{RL}$ and $\overline{GP}$ have the same slope, so the opposite sides are parallel by the parallel slope property, and *PRLG* is a parallelogram by definition. Therefore, the figure formed by connecting the midpoints of the sides of a quadrilateral is a parallelogram.

13. Given: An isosceles triangle with the midpoint of the base connected to the midpoint of each leg to form a quadrilateral

Show: The quadrilateral is a rhombus

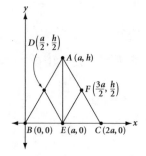

Given: Isosceles triangle *ABC* with midpoint of base, *E*, and midpoints of legs, *D* and *F*, connected to form quadrilateral *ADEF*

Show: *ADEF* is a rhombus

Proof: Use the distance formula to show that all the sides of *ADEF* have the same length.

$$AD = \sqrt{\left(a - \frac{a}{2}\right)^2 + \left(h - \frac{h}{2}\right)^2} = \sqrt{\left(\frac{a}{2}\right)^2 + \left(\frac{h}{2}\right)^2}$$
$$= \frac{\sqrt{a^2 + h^2}}{2}$$

$$AF = \sqrt{\left(\frac{3a}{2} - a\right)^2 + \left(\frac{h}{2} - h\right)^2} = \sqrt{\left(\frac{a}{2}\right)^2 + \left(-\frac{h}{2}\right)^2}$$
$$= \frac{\sqrt{a^2 + h^2}}{2}$$

$$DE = \sqrt{\left(a - \frac{a}{2}\right)^2 + \left(0 - \frac{h}{2}\right)^2} = \sqrt{\left(\frac{a}{2}\right)^2 + \left(-\frac{h}{2}\right)^2}$$
$$= \frac{\sqrt{a^2 + h^2}}{2}$$

$$EF = \sqrt{\left(\frac{3a}{2} - a\right)^2 + \left(\frac{h}{2} - 0\right)^2} = \sqrt{\left(\frac{a}{2}\right)^2 + \left(\frac{h}{2}\right)^2}$$
$$= \frac{\sqrt{a^2 + h^2}}{2}$$

$AD = AF = DE = EF$ by the transitive property. Therefore, *ADEF* is a rhombus by the definition of a rhombus.

PROJECT

Project should satisfy the following criteria:

- Proofs, which might not match the sample proofs, are logically valid and clearly written. Students need not create the proofs themselves; they might research the proofs and write them up to demonstrate under-standing.

- Students use the Triangle Sum Theorem for proof 3. To prove it formally for any *n*-gon requires mathematical induction.

- To illustrate proof 4, students draw rays that start at the point of intersection of the two intersecting lines and that pass through corresponding points on the original figure, and then draw its first and second images.

- In proof 5, students find the ordered pairs of the three midpoints and the equations of the three medians. Then they solve the equations simultaneously.

Sample proofs:

1. Three, four, or five triangles fitted about a point leave a gap that can be closed by folding the triangles to start a tetrahedron, an octahedron, or an icosahedron, respectively. Likewise, three squares or three pentagons leave a gap and can be folded to start a cube or a dodecahedron. Three hexagons leave no gap, and three of any polygon with more than six sides overlap. (See the *Platonic Solids* video.)

2. If each vertex is an endpoint of an even number of edges, then whenever a traveler enters that vertex on one edge, at least one unused edge is available for departure. (The vertex at which the traveler begins will have one edge left for ending there.) If all but two vertices have an even number of edges, then the same argument applies to the nonspecial vertices; moreover, one of those special vertices can be used as a beginning and the other as an ending, so the network can be traveled. If more than two vertices have an odd number of edges, the network cannot be traveled, because one edge of one of those vertices can be used as a beginning and one edge of another of those vertices can be used as an ending, but the third vertex will have a leftover edge which can be neither a beginning nor an ending.

3. The *n*-gon can be divided into *n* triangles with a common vertex by drawing a segment from an interior point to each of the *n* vertices. (Each segment drawn to one of the *n* vertices is the side of two triangles, and each side of the *n*-gon is the side of one triangle; this gives $2n + n = 3n$ sides and therefore *n* triangles.) Each triangle has interior angles whose measures sum to 180°. Because the sum of the measures of the interior angles of the *n*-gon is the sum of the measures of the triangles minus the 360° around the central point, it equals $n \cdot 180° - 360° = (n - 2)180°$.

4. To consider $\overline{PQ}$ reflected across two lines, $\overleftrightarrow{OM}$ and $\overleftrightarrow{OL}$, you must consider three cases: $\overline{PQ}$ is outside the angle and is reflected across the nearer line first; $\overline{PQ}$ is inside $\angle MOL$; and $\overline{PQ}$ is outside the angle and is reflected across the farther line first. Consider the second case:

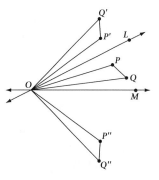

Because reflection is an isometry, $\overline{PO} \cong \overline{P'O}$ and $\overline{P'O} \cong \overline{P''O}$, so $\overline{PO} \cong \overline{P''O}$. Likewise, $\overline{QO} \cong \overline{Q'O}$ and $\overline{Q'O} \cong \overline{Q''O}$, so $\overline{QO} \cong \overline{Q''O}$. By angle addition, $m\angle POP'' = (m\angle P''OM + m\angle MOP') - (m\angle P'OL + m\angle LOP)$. Also, because reflection is an isometry, $\angle P''OM \cong \angle MOP'$ and $\angle P'OL \cong \angle LOP$. So, by substitution, $m\angle POP'' = 2(m\angle MOP' - m\angle P'OL)$. But $m\angle MOP' - m\angle P'OL = m\angle MOL$.

Therefore, $m\angle POP'' = 2m\angle MOL$. The same procedure applies to $\angle QOQ''$. Because $\overline{PQ}$ is the same distance from point O as is $\overline{P''Q''}$ and because both images move the same number of degrees, therefore, by the definition of rotation, the image $\overline{P''Q''}$ is a rotation of $\overline{PQ}$ about point O a distance of $2m\angle MOL$. Similar proofs can be given for the other cases.

5. The coordinates of the midpoints are
$D\left(\dfrac{c+e}{2}, \dfrac{d+f}{2}\right)$, $E\left(\dfrac{a+e}{2}, \dfrac{b+f}{2}\right)$, and $F\left(\dfrac{a+c}{2}, \dfrac{b+d}{2}\right)$.

The equations of the medians are

$\overleftrightarrow{AD}: y = \dfrac{d+f-2b}{c+e-2a}x + \dfrac{b(c+e)-a(d+f)}{c+e-2a}$

$\overleftrightarrow{BE}: y = \dfrac{b+f-2d}{a+e-2c}x + \dfrac{d(a+e)-c(b+f)}{a+e-2c}$

$\overleftrightarrow{CF}: y = \dfrac{b+d-2f}{a+c-2e}x + \dfrac{f(a+c)-e(b+d)}{a+c-2e}$

Solving any two of these equations simultaneously yields the coordinates of the centroid, $(x, y) = \left(\dfrac{a+c+e}{3}, \dfrac{b+d+f}{3}\right)$.

6. Here is one of many proofs that $\sqrt{2}$ is irrational: Assume that $\sqrt{2}$ is rational and then arrive at a contradiction. If $\sqrt{2}$ is rational, then it can be written as a fraction, $\frac{a}{b}$, in reduced form. Because $\frac{a}{b} = \sqrt{2}$, $\frac{a^2}{b^2} = 2$. Therefore $a^2 = 2b^2$, which shows that 2 is a factor of a^2. The only way that 2 can be a factor of the square of a is if 2 is a factor of a, so $a = 2c$ for some integer c. Substitute this into the equation $a^2 = 2b^2$ to get $4c^2 = 2b^2$, so $2c^2 = b^2$. This shows that 2 is a factor of b^2, so it must also be a factor of b. This is a contradiction because we assumed that a and b had no common factors, yet we showed that they have a common factor of 2. This contradiction arose from the assumption that $\sqrt{2}$ is rational, so $\sqrt{2}$ is irrational.

7. An Archimedean tiling is a distinct edge-to-edge tiling of regular polygons with all vertices of the same type. For these shapes to fill the plane from edge to edge without gaps or overlaps, their angles, when arranged around a point, must have measures that add exactly to 360°. An Archimedean tiling can be constructed using only equilateral triangles, squares, or regular hexagons. Any other regular polygon would create either a gap or an overlap in the single shape tiling. Hence, there are three *monohedral* tessellations, which are Archimedean tilings.

To find other possible edge-to-edge tilings, use the fact that the measure of an interior angle of a regular n-gon is $\dfrac{180°(n-2)}{n}$ degrees. If the n_1-gon, n_2-gon, $\ldots$, and n_k-gon meet at a vertex, you know that

$\dfrac{180°(n_1-2)}{n_1} + \dfrac{180°(n_2-2)}{n_2} + \cdots + \dfrac{180°(n_k-2)}{n_k}$
$= 360°$

$\dfrac{n_1-2}{n_1} + \dfrac{n_2-2}{n_2} + \cdots + \dfrac{n_k-2}{n_k} = 2$

There are 17 groups of positive integers that satisfy this equation. Therefore, there are 17 choices of polygons that can be fitted around a vertex without gaps or overlaps. In four cases, these polygons can be arranged in two ways (such as $3^2.4.12$ and $3.4.3.12$). Thus, there are 21 possible types of vertices: 3^6, $3^4.6$, $3^3.4^2$, $3^2.4.3.4$, $3^2.4.12$, $3.4.3.12$, $3.6.3.6$, $3^2.6^2$, $3.4.2.6$, $3.4.6.4$, $3.7.42$, $3.8.24$, $3.9.18$, $3.10.15$, 3.12^2, 4^4, $4.5.20$, $4.6.12$, 4.8^2, $5^2.10$, and 6^3. After checking each of these types, you will find 11 that are edge-to-edge tilings by regular polygons with all vertices of the same type: 3^6, $3^4.6$, $3^3.4^2$, $3^2.4.3.4$, $3.6.3.6$, $3.4.6.4$, 3.12^2, 4^4, $4.6.12$, 4.8^2, and 6^3. (See *Tilings and Patterns* by Gruenbaum and Shephard.)

EXTENSION

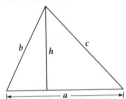

Given: Triangle with side lengths a, b, and c; altitude with length h to side of length a

Show: Area of triangle $= \sqrt{s(s-a)(s-b)(s-c)}$, where $s = \dfrac{a+b+c}{2}$

Paragraph Proof: The altitude divides the triangle into two right triangles and divides the side of length a into two parts. By the Pythagorean Theorem, the lengths of these parts are $\sqrt{b^2-h^2}$ and $\sqrt{c^2-h^2}$. Therefore, $a = \sqrt{b^2-h^2} + \sqrt{c^2-h^2}$. To eliminate radicals from this equation, square both sides twice.

$a = \sqrt{b^2-h^2} + \sqrt{c^2-h^2}$

$a^2 = \left(\sqrt{b^2-h^2} + \sqrt{c^2-h^2}\right)^2$

$a^2 = b^2 - h^2 + 2\sqrt{b^2-h^2}\sqrt{c^2-h^2} + c^2 - h^2$

$a^2 - b^2 - c^2 + 2h^2 = 2\sqrt{b^2-h^2}\sqrt{c^2-h^2}$

$(a^2 - b^2 - c^2 + 2h^2)^2 = \left(2\sqrt{b^2-h^2}\sqrt{c^2-h^2}\right)^2$

$[(a^2 - b^2 - c^2) + 2h^2]^2 = \left(2\sqrt{b^2-h^2}\sqrt{c^2-h^2}\right)^2$

$(a^2 - b^2 - c^2)^2 + 4h^2(a^2 - b^2 - c^2) + 4h^4$
$\quad = 4(b^2 - h^2)(c^2 - h^2)$

$(a^2 - b^2 - c^2)^2 + 4h^2a^2 - 4h^2b^2 - 4h^2c^2 + 4h^4$
$\quad = 4(b^2c^2 - b^2h^2 - c^2h^2 + h^4)$

$(a^2 - b^2 - c^2)^2 + 4h^2a^2 - 4h^2b^2 - 4h^2c^2 + 4h^4$
$\quad = 4b^2c^2 - 4b^2h^2 - 4c^2h^2 + 4h^4$

$(a^2 - b^2 - c^2)^2 + 4h^2a^2 = 4b^2c^2$

$4h^2a^2 = 4b^2c^2 - (a^2 - b^2 - c^2)^2$

Let A represent the area of the triangle. Using a as the length of the base, the standard formula for the area of a triangle gives $A = \frac{1}{2}ah$. The last equation above contains $4h^2a^2$ on one side, so rewrite $A = \frac{1}{2}ah$ to get an expression for $4h^2a^2$.

$$A = \frac{1}{2}ah$$

$$2A = ah$$

$$4A^2 = a^2h^2$$

$$16A^2 = 4a^2h^2 = 4h^2a^2$$

Because $16A^2 = 4h^2a^2$ and $4h^2a^2 = 4b^2c^2 - (a^2 - b^2 - c^2)^2$, by the transitive property $16A^2 = 4b^2c^2 - (a^2 - b^2 - c^2)^2$. Rearrange terms in this equation to write A^2 as a product of four fractions. Some of the steps below involve factoring the difference of two squares using the factoring pattern $x^2 - y^2 = (x + y)(x - y)$.

$$16A^2 = 4b^2c^2 - (a^2 - b^2 - c^2)^2$$

$$16A^2 = (2bc)^2 - (a^2 - b^2 - c^2)^2$$

$$16A^2 = [(2bc) + (a^2 - b^2 - c^2)]$$
$$\cdot\, [(2bc) - (a^2 - b^2 - c^2)]$$

$$16A^2 = (2bc + a^2 - b^2 - c^2)(2bc - a^2 + b^2 + c^2)$$

$$16A^2 = [a^2 - (b^2 - 2bc + c^2)]$$
$$\cdot\, [(b^2 + 2bc + c^2) - a^2]$$

$$16A^2 = [a^2 - (b - c)^2][(b + c)^2 - a^2]$$

$$16A^2 = [a - (b - c)][a + (b - c)]$$
$$\cdot\, [(b + c) - a][(b + c) + a]$$

$$16A^2 = (a - b + c)(a + b - c)$$
$$\cdot\, (b + c - a)(b + a + c)$$

$$A^2 = \frac{(a - b + c)(a + b - c)(b + c - a)(b + a + c)}{16}$$

$$A^2 = \left(\frac{a - b + c}{2}\right)\left(\frac{a + b - c}{2}\right)\left(\frac{b + c - a}{2}\right)$$
$$\cdot\, \left(\frac{b + a + c}{2}\right)$$

In Hero's formula, s represents the semiperimeter of the triangle: $s = \frac{a + b + c}{2}$. Then $s - a = \frac{a + b + c}{2} - \frac{2a}{2} = \frac{b + c - a}{2}$, $s - b = \frac{a + b + c}{2} - \frac{2b}{2} = \frac{a - b + c}{2}$, and $s - c = \frac{a + b + c}{2} - \frac{2c}{2} = \frac{a + b - c}{2}$.

Because $A^2 = \left(\frac{a - b + c}{2}\right)\left(\frac{a + b - c}{2}\right)\left(\frac{b + c - a}{2}\right)$
$\cdot\, \left(\frac{b + a + c}{2}\right) = \left(\frac{a + b + c}{2}\right)\left(\frac{b + c - a}{2}\right)\left(\frac{a - b + c}{2}\right)$
$\cdot\, \left(\frac{a + b - c}{2}\right)$, $A^2 = s(s - a)(s - b)(s - c)$.
Therefore, $A = \sqrt{s(s - a)(s - b)(s - c)}$.

CHAPTER 13 REVIEW

EXERCISES

1. False. The quadrilateral could be an isosceles trapezoid.

2. True

3. False. The figure could be an isosceles trapezoid or a kite.

4. True

5. False. The angles are supplementary but not necessarily congruent.

6. False. See Lesson 13.5, Example B.

7. True

8. Perpendicular

9. Congruent

10. The center of the circle

11. Four congruent triangles that are similar to the original triangle

12. An auxiliary theorem proven specifically to help prove other theorems

13. If a segment joins the midpoints of the diagonals of a trapezoid, then it is parallel to the bases.

14. Angle Bisector Postulate

15. Perpendicular Postulate

16. Assume the opposite of what you want to prove, then use valid reasoning to derive a contradiction.

17. a. That smoking is *not* glamorous

    b. If smoking were glamorous, then this smoker would look glamorous. This smoker does not look glamorous, therefore smoking is not glamorous.

18. False. The parallelogram is a rhombus. (It could be a square, but it might not be.)

19. False. In fact, the measure of the angle between them equals the measure of one of the other base angles. The figure below shows a possible counterexample.

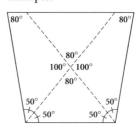

20. False. The sum of the measures of the interior angles of the pentagon formed by the perpendicular bisectors is $(5 - 2)(180°) = 540°$, so $x = 540° - (180° + 2b) = 360° - 2b$. The perpendicular bisectors of the sides of congruent sides of the isosceles trapezoid will be perpendicular if $360° - 2b = 90°$. Solving this equation gives $b = 135°$. Therefore, the statement is true only if the measures of one pair of base angles of the trapezoid are 135°.

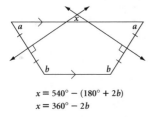

$$x = 540° - (180° + 2b)$$
$$x = 360° - 2b$$

21. True (except in the special case of an isosceles right triangle, in which the segment is not defined because the feet coincide).

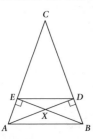

Given: Isosceles $\triangle ABC$ with $\overline{AC} \cong \overline{BC}$; altitudes $\overline{AD}$ and $\overline{BE}$; $\overline{ED}$

Show: $\overline{ED} \parallel \overline{AB}$

Paragraph Proof: $\overline{AC} \cong \overline{BC}$ is given, so $\angle EAB \cong \angle DBA$ by the Isosceles Triangle Theorem. $\angle AEB \cong \angle BDA$ by the definition of altitude and the Right Angles Are Congruent Theorem. $\overline{AB} \cong \overline{AB}$ by the reflexive property of congruence. $\triangle AEB \cong \triangle BDA$ by SAA. Therefore $\overline{AE} \cong \overline{BD}$ by CPCTC. By the definition of congruence, $AE = BD$ and $AC = BC$, so $AC - AE = BC - BD$ by the substitution and subtraction properties. But, by the Segment Addition Postulate, $AC - AE = EC$ and $BC - BD = DC$, so $EC = DC$ by the transitive property. Then $\frac{EC}{AC} = \frac{DC}{BC}$ by substitution and the division property. Thus $\overline{ED}$ divides $\overline{AC}$ and $\overline{BC}$ proportionately. Therefore $\overline{ED} \parallel \overline{AB}$ by the Converse of the Parallel/Proportionality Theorem.

22. True

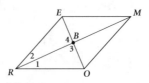

Given: Rhombus *ROME* with diagonals $\overline{RM}$ and $\overline{EO}$ intersecting at B

Show: $\overline{RM} \perp \overline{EO}$

Proof:

Statement	Reason
1. $\angle 1 \cong \angle 2$	1. Rhombus Angles Theorem
2. $RO = RE$	2. Definition of rhombus
3. $\overline{RO} \cong \overline{RE}$	3. Definition of congruence
4. $\overline{RB} \cong \overline{RB}$	4. Reflexive property of congruence
5. $\triangle ROB \cong \triangle REB$	5. SAS Congruence Postulate
6. $\angle 3 \cong \angle 4$	6. CPCTC
7. $\angle 3$ and $\angle 4$ are supplementary	7. Linear Pair Postulate
8. $\angle 3$ and $\angle 4$ are right angles	8. Congruent and Supplementary Theorem
9. $\overline{RM} \perp \overline{EO}$	9. Definition of perpendicular

23. True

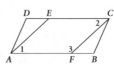

Given: Parallelogram *ABCD* with $\overline{AE}$ bisecting $\angle DAB$ and $\overline{CF}$ bisecting $\angle DCB$

Show: $\overline{AE} \parallel \overline{CF}$

Paragraph Proof: $m\angle 1 = \frac{1}{2}m\angle BAD$ and $m\angle 2 = \frac{1}{2}m\angle DCB$ by the definition of angle bisector. $\angle BAD \cong \angle DCB$ by the Opposite Angles Theorem. Therefore, $\frac{1}{2}m\angle BAD = \frac{1}{2}m\angle DCB$ by the multiplication property, so $m\angle 1 = m\angle 2$ by the transitive property. $\overline{AB} \parallel \overline{DC}$ by the definition of parallelogram, so $\angle 2$ and $\angle 3$ are supplementary by the Interior Supplements Theorem, that is, $m\angle 2 + m\angle 3 = 180°$. Then, by substitution, $m\angle 1 + m\angle 3 = 180°$, so, by definition and the substitution property, $\angle 2$ and $\angle 3$ are supplementary. Therefore, $\overline{AE} \parallel \overline{CF}$ by the Converse of the Interior Supplements Theorem.

Discovering Geometry Solutions Manual
©2008 Key Curriculum Press

24. Plan: Use the Inscribed Angle Theorem, the addition property, and the distributive property to get $m\angle P + m\angle E + m\angle N + m\angle T + m\angle A = \frac{1}{2}(m\widehat{TN} + m\widehat{AT} + m\widehat{PA} + m\widehat{EP} + m\widehat{NE})$. Because there are 360° in a circle, $m\angle P + m\angle E + m\angle N + m\angle T + m\angle A = 180°$.

Proof:

Statement	Reason
1. $m\angle P = \frac{1}{2}m\widehat{TN}$; $m\angle E = \frac{1}{2}m\widehat{AT}$; $m\angle N = \frac{1}{2}m\widehat{PA}$; $m\angle T = \frac{1}{2}m\widehat{EP}$; $m\angle A = \frac{1}{2}m\widehat{NE}$	**1.** Inscribed Angle Theorem
2. $m\angle P + m\angle E + m\angle N + m\angle T + m\angle A = \frac{1}{2}m\widehat{TN} + \frac{1}{2}m\widehat{AT} + \frac{1}{2}m\widehat{PA} + \frac{1}{2}m\widehat{EP} + \frac{1}{2}m\widehat{NE}$	**2.** Addition property
3. $m\angle P + m\angle E + m\angle N + m\angle T + m\angle A = \frac{1}{2}(m\widehat{TN} + m\widehat{AT} + m\widehat{PA} + m\widehat{EP} + m\widehat{NE})$	**3.** Distributive property
4. $m\angle P + m\angle E + m\angle N + m\angle T + m\angle A = \frac{1}{2}(360°) = 180°$	**4.** There are 360° in a circle, substitution property

25. Given: Right triangle *RTH*

Show: At least one nonright angle ($\angle H$ or $\angle T$) has measure less than or equal to 45°

Indirect Paragraph Proof: Assume $m\angle H > 45°$ and $m\angle T > 45°$. Then $m\angle H + m\angle T > 45° + 45°$, so $m\angle H + m\angle T > 90°$. Because $m\angle R = 90°$, this would give $m\angle H + m\angle T + m\angle R > 90° + 90°$, or $m\angle H + m\angle T + m\angle R > 180°$. But this creates a contradiction because $m\angle H + m\angle T + m\angle R = 180°$ by the Triangle Sum Theorem. Therefore, the assumption that $m\angle H > 45°$ and $m\angle T > 45°$ is false, and the conclusion that either $m\angle H \leq 45°$ or $m\angle T \leq 45°$ (or possibly both) is true.

26. Given: $\triangle TYR$ with midsegment $\overline{MS}$

Show: $\overline{MS} \parallel \overline{TR}$ and $MS = \frac{1}{2}(TR)$

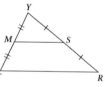

Plan: Use the definition of midpoint, the Segment Addition Postulate, the substitution property, and the division property to get $\frac{MY}{TY} = \frac{1}{2}$ and $\frac{SY}{RY} = \frac{1}{2}$. Then use the reflexive property and the SAS Similarity Theorem to get $\triangle MSY \sim \triangle TRY$. Therefore, $MS = \frac{1}{2}(TR)$ by CSSTP and the multiplication property, and $\overline{MS} \parallel \overline{TR}$ by CASTC and the CA Postulate.

Proof:

Statement	Reason
1. $\overline{MS}$ is a midsegment of $\triangle TYR$	**1.** Given
2. M is the midpoint of $\overline{YT}$; S is the midpoint of $\overline{YR}$	**2.** Definition of midsegment
3. $MY = MT$; $YS = SR$	**3.** Definition of midpoint
4. $TY = MY + MT$; $RY = SY + SR$	**4.** Segment Addition Postulate
5. $TY = 2(MY)$; $RY = 2(SY)$	**5.** Substitution
6. $\frac{MY}{TY} = \frac{1}{2}$; $\frac{SY}{RY} = \frac{1}{2}$	**6.** Division property
7. $\frac{MY}{TY} = \frac{SY}{RY}$	**7.** Transitive property
8. $\angle MYS \cong \angle TYR$	**8.** Reflexive property
9. $\triangle MSY \sim \triangle TRY$	**9.** SAS Similarity Theorem

(Proof continued)

Statement	Reason
10. $\dfrac{MS}{TR} = \dfrac{MY}{TY}$	10. CSSTP
11. $\dfrac{MS}{TR} = \dfrac{1}{2}$	11. Transitive property
12. $MS = \dfrac{1}{2}(TR)$	12. Multiplication property
13. $\angle YMS \cong \angle YTR$	13. CASTC
14. $\overline{MS} \parallel \overline{TR}$	14. CA Postulate

27. Given: Trapezoid *ZDYO* with midsegment $\overline{TR}$

Show: $\overline{TR} \parallel \overline{ZO}$; $TR = \dfrac{1}{2}(ZO + DY)$

Plan: Use the Line Postulate to extend $\overline{ZO}$ and $\overline{DR}$. Then use the Line Intersection Postulate to label *P* as the intersection of $\overleftrightarrow{ZO}$ and $\overleftrightarrow{DR}$. $\triangle DYR \cong \triangle POR$ by the SAA Congruence Theorem; thus, $\overline{DY} \cong \overline{OP}$ by CPCTC. Use the Triangle Midsegment Theorem and the substitution property to get $TR = \dfrac{1}{2}(ZO + DY)$. Also, apply the Triangle Midsegment Theorem to get $\overline{TR} \parallel \overline{ZO}$.

Proof: Statement	Reason
1. Extend $\overline{ZO}$ and $\overline{DR}$	1. Line Postulate
2. $\overleftrightarrow{ZO}$ and $\overrightarrow{DR}$ intersect at point *P*	2. Line Intersection Postulate
3. $\overline{TR}$ is the midsegment of trapezoid *ZDYO*	3. Given
4. *R* is the midpoint of $\overline{YO}$	4. Definition of midsegment
5. $YR = OR$	5. Definition of midpoint
6. $\overline{YR} \cong \overline{OR}$	6. Definition of congruence
7. $\angle DRY \cong \angle PRO$ ($\angle 3 \cong \angle 4$)	7. VA Theorem
8. $\overline{DY} \parallel \overline{ZO}$	8. Definition of trapezoid
9. $\overline{DY} \parallel \overline{ZP}$	9. *Z*, *O*, and *P* are collinear
10. $\angle YDR \cong \angle OPR$	10. AIA Theorem
11. $\triangle DYR \cong \triangle POR$	11. SAA Theorem
12. $\overline{DY} \cong \overline{PO}$	12. CPCTC
13. $DY = OP$	13. Definition of congruence
14. $TR = \dfrac{1}{2}(ZP)$	14. Triangle Midsegment Theorem ($\triangle ZDP$)
15. $ZO + OP = ZP$	15. Segment Addition Postulate
16. $TR = \dfrac{1}{2}(ZO + OP)$	16. Transitive property
17. $TR = \dfrac{1}{2}(ZO + DY)$	17. Substitution property
18. $\overline{TR} \parallel \overline{ZP}$	18. Triangle Midsegment Theorem ($\triangle ZDP$)
19. $\overline{TR} \parallel \overline{ZO}$	19. *Z*, *O*, and *P* are collinear

28. a. Conjecture: The quadrilateral formed when the midpoints of the sides of a rectangle are connected is a rhombus.

b.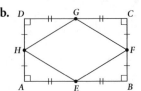

Given: Rectangle $ABCD$ with E, F, G, and H the midpoints of $\overline{AB}$, $\overline{BC}$, $\overline{CD}$, and $\overline{DA}$, respectively

Show: $EFGH$ is a rhombus

Plan: Use the Right Angles Are Congruent Theorem and the SAS Congruence Postulate to get $\triangle AEH \cong \triangle BEF \cong \triangle DGH \cong \triangle CGF$. Then use CPCTC.

Proof:

Statement	**Reason**
1. $ABCD$ is a rectangle	1. Given
2. $ABCD$ is a parallelogram	2. Definition of rectangle
3. $\overline{BC} \cong \overline{DA}$; $\overline{AB} \cong \overline{CD}$	3. Opposite Sides Theorem
4. $BC = DA$; $AB = CD$	4. Definition of congruence
5. F is the midpoint of $\overline{BC}$; H is the midpoint of $\overline{DA}$; E is the midpoint of $\overline{AB}$; G is the midpoint of $\overline{CD}$	5. Given
6. $BF = FC$; $DH = HA$; $AE = EB$; $CG = GD$	6. Definition of midpoint
7. $BF + FC = BC$; $DH + HA = DA$; $AE + EB = AB$; $CG + DG = CD$	7. Segment Addition Postulate
8. $2(BF) = 2(FC) = BC$; $2(DH) = 2(HA) = DA$; $2(AE) = 2(EB) = AB$; $2(GC) = 2(GD) = CD$	8. Substitution property
9. $BF = FC = \frac{1}{2}(BC)$; $DH = HA = \frac{1}{2}(DA)$; $AE = BE = \frac{1}{2}(AB)$; $CG = DG = \frac{1}{2}(CD)$	9. Multiplication property
10. $BF = CF = DH = AH$; $AE = BE = CG = DG$	10. Transitive property
11. $\overline{BF} \cong \overline{CF} \cong \overline{DH} \cong \overline{AH}$; $\overline{AE} \cong \overline{BE} \cong \overline{CG} \cong \overline{DG}$	11. Definition of congruence
12. $\angle A$, $\angle B$, $\angle C$, and $\angle D$ are right angles	12. Definition of rectangle
13. $\angle A \cong \angle B \cong \angle C \cong \angle D$	13. Right Triangles Are Congruent Theorem
14. $\triangle AEH \cong \triangle BEF \cong \triangle DGH \cong \triangle CGF$	14. SAS Congruence Postulate
15. $\overline{EH} \cong \overline{EF} \cong \overline{GH} \cong \overline{GF}$	15. CPCTC
16. $EFGH$ is a rhombus	16. Four Congruent Sides Rhombus Theorem

29. a. Conjecture: The quadrilateral formed when the midpoints of the sides of a rhombus are connected is a rectangle.

b.

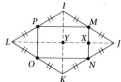

Given: Rhombus $IJKL$ with M, N, O, and P the midpoints of $\overline{IJ}$, $\overline{JK}$, $\overline{KL}$, and $\overline{LI}$, respectively

Show: $MNOP$ is a rectangle

Paragraph Proof: Apply the Triangle Midsegment Theorem to $\triangle LIJ$ to get $\overline{PM} \parallel \overline{LJ}$ and to $\triangle LKJ$ to get $\overline{ON} \parallel \overline{LJ}$. Then, by the Parallel Transitivity Theorem, $\overline{PM} \parallel \overline{ON}$. Similarly, apply the Triangle Midsegment Theorem to $\triangle ILK$ to get $\overline{PO} \parallel \overline{IK}$ and to $\triangle IJK$ to get $\overline{MN} \parallel \overline{IK}$. Then, by the Parallel Transitivity Theorem, $\overline{PO} \parallel \overline{MN}$. Thus, $MNOP$ has two pairs of opposite parallel sides and is by definition a parallelogram. Because $IJKL$ is a rhombus, $\overline{LJ} \perp \overline{IK}$ by the Rhombus Diagonals Conjecture. Then $\angle IYL$, $\angle KYL$, $\angle IYJ$, and $\angle KYJ$ are right angles by the definition of perpendicular.

Using the parallel sides found earlier from the Triangle Midsegment Theorem, $MNOP$ is made up of four small parallelograms, so $\angle IYL \cong \angle MPO$, $\angle KYL \cong \angle PON$, $\angle IYJ \cong \angle PMN$, and $\angle KYJ \cong \angle MNO$ by the Opposite Angles Theorem. Thus, the four angles of $MNOP$ are all right angles. Thus, $MNOP$ is a parallelogram with four right angles, so, by definition, it is a rectangle.

30. a. Conjecture: The quadrilateral formed when the midpoints of the sides of a kite are connected is a rectangle.

b.

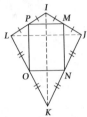

Given: Kite $IJKL$ with M, N, O, and P the midpoints of $\overline{IJ}$, $\overline{JK}$, $\overline{KL}$, and $\overline{LI}$, respectively

Show: $MNOP$ is a rectangle

Paragraph Proof: Apply the Triangle Midsegment Theorem to $\triangle LIJ$ to get $\overline{PM} \parallel \overline{LJ}$ and to $\triangle LKJ$ to get $\overline{ON} \parallel \overline{LJ}$. Then, by the Parallel Transitivity Theorem, $\overline{PM} \parallel \overline{ON}$. Also, by the Triangle Midsegment Theorem, $PM = \frac{1}{2}(LJ)$ and $ON = \frac{1}{2}(LJ)$, so $PM = ON$ by the transitive property. Then $\overline{PM} \cong \overline{ON}$ by the definition of congruence. Therefore, $MNOP$ is a parallelogram by the Opposite Sides Parallel and Congruent Theorem. Because $IJKL$ is a kite, $\overline{LJ} \perp \overline{IK}$ by the Kite Diagonals Conjecture. Then, by the CA Postulate and Interior Supplements Theorem, the four angles of $MNOP$ are all right angles. Thus, $MNOP$ is a parallelogram with four right angles, so it is a rectangle by definition.

31. Given: Circle O with chords $\overline{AB}$ and $\overline{CD}$ intersecting at P

Show: $AP \cdot PB = DP \cdot PC$

Plan: Use the Line Postulate to construct chords $\overline{DB}$ and $\overline{AC}$. Then use the Inscribed Angles Intercepting Arcs Theorem and the AA Similarity Postulate to get $\triangle APC \sim \triangle DPB$. Therefore, by CSSTP and the multiplication property, $AP \cdot PB = DP \cdot PC$.

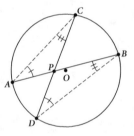

Proof:

Statement	Reason
1. Construct $\overline{DB}$ and $\overline{AC}$	1. Line Postulate
2. $\angle CAB \cong \angle CDB$; $\angle ACD \cong \angle DBA$	2. Inscribed Angles Intercepting Arcs Theorem
3. $\triangle APC \sim \triangle DPB$	3. AA Similarity Postulate
4. $\dfrac{AP}{DP} = \dfrac{PC}{PB}$	4. CSSTP
5. $(DP)(PB) \cdot \dfrac{AP}{DP} = (DP)(PB) \cdot \dfrac{PC}{PB}$	5. Multiplication property
6. $AP \cdot PB = DP \cdot PC$	6. Algebra

Key Curriculum Press
Innovators in Mathematics Education

Comment Form

Please take a moment to provide us with feedback about this book. We are eager to read any comments or suggestions you may have. Once you've filled out this form, simply fold it along the dotted lines and drop it in the mail. We'll pay the postage. Thank you!

Your Name _____

School _____

School Address _____

City/State/Zip _____

Phone _____ Email _____

Book Title _____

Please list any comments you have about this book.

_____
_____
_____
_____
_____
_____
_____
_____
_____
_____
_____

Do you have any suggestions for improving the student or teacher material?

_____
_____
_____
_____
_____
_____

To request a catalog or place an order, call us toll free at 800-995-MATH or send a fax to 800-541-2242. For more information, visit Key's website at www.keypress.com.

Fold carefully along this line.

NO POSTAGE
NECESSARY
IF MAILED
IN THE
UNITED STATES

BUSINESS REPLY MAIL
FIRST CLASS   PERMIT NO. 338   EMERYVILLE, CA

POSTAGE WILL BE PAID BY ADDRESSEE

Key Curriculum Press
Innovators in Mathematics Education

Attn: Editorial Department
1150 65th Street
Emeryville, CA 94608-9740

Fold carefully along this line.

Key Curriculum Press
Innovators in Mathematics Education

Comment Form

Please take a moment to provide us with feedback about this book. We are eager to read any comments or suggestions you may have. Once you've filled out this form, simply fold it along the dotted lines and drop it in the mail. We'll pay the postage. Thank you!

Your Name _____

School _____

School Address _____

City/State/Zip _____

Phone _____ Email _____

Book Title _____

Please list any comments you have about this book.

_____
_____
_____
_____
_____
_____
_____
_____
_____
_____

Do you have any suggestions for improving the student or teacher material?

_____
_____
_____
_____
_____
_____
_____

To request a catalog or place an order, call us toll free at 800-995-MATH or send a fax to 800-541-2242. For more information, visit Key's website at www.keypress.com.

Fold carefully along this line.

- -

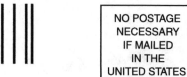

BUSINESS REPLY MAIL
FIRST CLASS   PERMIT NO. 338   EMERYVILLE, CA

POSTAGE WILL BE PAID BY ADDRESSEE

Key Curriculum Press
Innovators in Mathematics Education

Attn: Editorial Department
1150 65th Street
Emeryville, CA 94608-9740

Fold carefully along this line.

- -